HEART IN STRESS

ANNALS OF THE NEW YORK ACADEMY OF SCIENCES
Volume 874

HEART IN STRESS

Edited by Dipak K. Das

The New York Academy of Sciences
New York, New York
1999

♾*The paper used in this publication meets the minimum requirements of the American National Standard for Information Sciences—Permanence of Paper for Printed Library Materials, ANSI Z39.48-1984.*

Cover: The art on the softcover version of this volume was provided by Hiroaki Sasaki, M.D.

GYAT / PCP

Printed in the United States of America

ISBN 1-57331-164-2 (cloth)

ISBN 1-57331-165-0 (paper)

ISSN 0077-8923

ANNALS OF THE NEW YORK ACADEMY OF SCIENCES

Volume 874
June 30, 1999

HEART IN STRESS[a]

Editor and Conference Organizer
DIPAK K. DAS

CONTENTS

[a]The papers of this volume resulted from a conference entitled **Heart in Stress–Jubilee Symposium in Conjunction with the 3rd International Congress of Pathophysiology**, held June 28–July 3, 1998 in Helsinki, Finland.

Part X. Apoptosis and Molecular Signaling

Financial assistance was received from:

***Major Contributor*:**

- UNESCO GLOBAL NETWORK FOR MOLECULAR AND CELL BIOLOGY

***Contributors*:**

- DAINIPPON PHARMACEUTICAL COMPANY LIMITED, JAPAN
- INTER-HEALTH NEUTRACEUTICALS, USA
- JOEL LIMITED, JAPAN
- LINC PEN & PLASTICS LTD., INDIA
- OXYGEN CLUB OF CALIFORNIA, USA
- SANWELL CO., LTD., JAPAN
- SENJU PHARMACEUTICAL COMPANY LIMITED, JAPAN
- SKY FOOD LIMITED COMPANY, JAPAN
- TAHEEBO CO., LTD., JAPAN
- TOXICOLOGY SECTION–INTERNATIONAL UNION OF PHARMACOLOGY

Preface

All animals including humans experience stress in daily life. Stress can be classified into many categories, including environmental stress and psychological stress. While high amounts of a stressor can cause cellular injury, at a fairly low concentrations, a stressor can promote the healing process. Thus, for beneficial effects, stress must be considered a "dose-dependent" phenomenon. Repeated stress can cause imbalance in biological and physiological systems, ultimately leading to adaptation. However, too much stress can upset the adaptive response by critically unbalancing the regulatory mechanisms. Such failed adaptation plays a crucial role in the pathogenesis of a variety of degenerative diseases such as cancer, brain and cardiovascular diseases. However, not everyone becomes a victim of failed adaptation because of tremendous individual differences in coping with stress. The same is true for individual cells and tissues.

The heart is probably the best example of a tissue that is exposed to repeated stress responses, because it is subjected frequently to either pressure or volume overload. Fortunately, the heart possesses remarkable ability to protect itself from stressful situations by increasing resistance to the adverse consequences. Failed adaptation leads to cardiovascular disease including atherosclerosis, hypertension, spasm, diabetes, cardiomyopathy, and congestive heart failure.

A growing body of evidence suggests that a normal heart can be adapted to ischemia by subjecting it to a minimal stress challenge. A variety of stresses including repeated short-term ischemia/reperfusion, heat shock and oxidative stress have been found to adapt the heart to withstand more severe ischemic insult compared to the heart that has not been subjected to previous stress adaptation. This phenomenon has been termed "preconditioning." The hibernating heart is probably the best example of a naturally adapted myocardium where a chronic but small amount of ischemia over a prolonged period induces an energy-sparing adaptation of the myocardium. Patients with coronary artery stenosis exhibit the preconditioning phenomenon.

While a normal heart can certainly be adapted to ischemia by repeated low-grade stress challenge, it remains controversial whether an adapted heart can be further adapted to ischemia. For example, an atherosclerotic, cardiomyopathic or failing heart is the manifestation of failed adaptation. A limited number of studies have been conducted to determine whether a heart with failed adaptation can be further adapted to stress.

An enormous number of scientific papers have been published in recent years on the subject of ischemic preconditioning. While all of these papers support the cardioprotective aspects of ischemic preconditioning, significant controversies exist about the mechanism(s) of adaptation. A wealth of evidence supports that preconditioning is induced by one or more intracellular mediators, such as catecholamines, adenosine and bradykinin, which trigger a signal-transduction pathway through the activation of both G-proteins and protein tyrosine kinase receptors. These receptors trigger one or more signal transduction pathway(s) involving phospholipases C and D, diacyl glycerol, phosphatidic acid and multiple kinases including protein kinase C and several MAP kinases. The recently identified tyrosine kinase-phospholipase D-MAPKAP kinase 2 pathway seems to play a crucial role in preconditioning. It appears that preconditioning occurs through both protein kinase C–dependent and protein kinase C–independent pathways. Oxygen free radicals appear to function as a second messenger during stress response.

The nuclear transcription factors, NFκB and AP-1, play a significant role in myocardial adaptation to ischemia. Nuclear translocation and activation of NFκB binding appear to be essential for preconditioning. Interestingly, in addition to decreasing necrosis, preconditioning also reduces apoptosis, the latter being regulated by both NFκB and AP-1.

The present volume of the *Annals of the New York Academy of Sciences* is the outcome of a recent symposium on *Heart in Stress* held in Lahti, Finland. Clinicians and basic scientists joined together to discuss the molecular and cellular mechanisms of preconditioning and its potential clinical application. The aim of this volume is to report the current status of preconditioning, which has been recognized as the state-of-the-art technique for myocardial protection.

The editor expresses his gratitude to the participants of the symposium *Heart in Stress*, and especially to those who contributed papers to this volume of the *Annals of the New York Academy of Sciences*. It is my hope that the readers will benefit immensely by reading the results of the cutting edge research of these scientists.

DIPAK K. DAS

Cardiac Hypertrophy: Signal Transduction, Transcriptional Adaptation, and Altered Growth Control

MICHAEL WAGNER, EDUARDO MASCARENO, AND M.A.Q. SIDDIQUI[a]

Department of Anatomy and Cell Biology, State University of New York Health Science Center at Brooklyn, Brooklyn, New York 11203, USA

ABSTRACT: Cardiac hypertrophy results from the enlargement of cardiac muscle and fibroblast cells. This abnormal pattern of growth can be elicited by a number of hypertrophic agents, such as cytokines and hormones that participate in normal cell-cell signaling events during development. Under conditions yet to be defined, these same signaling molecules can cause hypertrophy of the heart. Intracellular signal transduction pathways appear to be the prime means by which the hypertrophic signal is transduced in cardiomyocytes. There is no evidence that the signal transduction pathways in hypertrophic cardiomyocytes differ from those of normal cardiomyocytes. Perhaps the signal itself is aberrant, mistimed, misplaced, or occurring at non-physiological concentrations. Alternatively, as a quiescent cell, the cardiomyocyte may not be able to respond completely to a growth signal by turning on its proliferative machinery. Three avenues of research are described: (1) the study of the upregulation of the cardiac MLC-2 gene, (2) STAT proteins and activation of angiotensin II, and (3) hypertrophy as a perturbation of cell cycle controls.

INTRODUCTION

Cardiac hypertrophy is an increase in the size and mass of the heart that ultimately leads to cardiac dysfunction and heart failure. This increase in size can be attributed to a number of diverse factors including physiological, mechanical, hormonal, and genetic influences.[1] Despite the number and variety of factors contributing to cardiac hypertrophy, their effect on the heart is predictably the same: they all lead to an increase in the size and mass of cardiac cells. This uniform response of cardiac cells to a variety of hypertrophic stimuli implies that a common mechanism may be responsible for hypertrophic growth and suggests that an altered or misappropriated cellular mechanism of growth control may be at the root of cardiac hypertrophy. Given this possibility, the problem of cardiac hypertrophy can be reduced to two overriding questions: what are the normal processes in heart cells that respond to hypertrophic stimuli and how do they cause these cells to become enlarged?

Progress in answering these questions has been aided in large part by the ability to induce hypertrophy experimentally *in vivo* and *in vitro*, in heart and isolated cardiomyocytes in culture, respectively.[2] The ability to induce the hypertrophic pheno-

[a]Address correspondence to: Dr. M.A.Q. Siddiqui, Department of Anatomy and Cell Biology, State University of New York Health Science Center at Brooklyn, Box 5, 450 Clarkson Street, Brooklyn, New York 11203; Telephone: 718/270-1014; Fax: 718/270-3732.

type in cardiomyocytes *in vitro* has been particularly informative. This system has shown that a number of known extracellular signaling molecules can cause hypertrophy in cardiomyocytes under certain conditions. Equally important, the intracellular signal transduction pathways used by these signaling molecules are well characterized and thus can be implicated in the etiology of hypertrophy. Because of this, cardiac hypertrophy can be considered a molecular disease caused by perturbation of normal molecular pathways of signal transduction and treated by the restitution of the normal homeostatic balance between these various pathways.

Among the extracellular signaling molecules implicated in causing cardiac hypertrophy are cytokines, such as interleukin-1b (Il-1b) and cardiotrophin-1 (CT-1); growth factors, such as fibroblast growth factor (FGF), insulin growth factor (IGF-1), and transforming growth factor–beta (TGF-beta); catecholamines; and cardiovascular peptide hormones, such as angiotensin II.[3] These signaling molecules activate intracellular signal transduction pathways by first binding to a cell surface receptor that transmits its signal via a protein kinase cascade to the nucleus where nuclear transcription factors are activated and gene transcription is induced. When conditions are such that these signaling molecules lead to hypertrophy, the net effect of this signaling cascade is an increase in cardiomyocyte cell volume, protein content per cell, protein synthesis, and increased mRNA and rRNA levels.[3] In addition to a general increase in RNA and protein synthesis, the expression of specific genes is also induced. Among these genes are the early response genes, e.g., c-fos, c-jun, and c-myc, and interestingly, genes normally expressed during fetal development, such as beta-myosin heavy chain, alpha-skeletal muscle and alpha-smooth muscle actin, and atrial natriuretic factor. In addition to the re-expression of "fetal" type genes, the expression of the gene encoding the cardiac myosin light chain 2 protein,[4] which is found in embryonic, fetal, and adult heart, is upregulated four- to fivefold during hypertrophy. Together these observations suggest that the hypertrophic stimulus could be a mistimed or aberrant extracellular signaling molecule or combination of signaling molecules that signal the quiescent cardiomyocyte to undergo growth and replication. These signals may trigger a genetic program designed for growth and cell proliferation as evidenced by the re-expression of "fetal" gene markers. However, within the context of a post-mitotic, quiescent cell type, such as the cardiomyocyte, this "growth" program may not be fully realized. The cardiomyocyte may begin to synthesize the mRNAs and proteins needed for sustaining two daughter cells, but in the absence of cell division this increased synthesis ultimately leads to an increase in cell size rather than cell number.

Rather than provide an exhaustive review of cardiac hypertrophy research (many excellent reviews of which have recently been published[3,5]), we will focus on three avenues of research being conducted in our laboratory as well as other laboratories that adhere to the notion that hypertrophy results from normal signaling processes gone awry. We first consider the upregulation of the cardiac myosin light chain– 2 (MLC-2) gene and the transcription factors required for its expression during normal development and its increased expression during hypertrophy. We then consider signal transduction in hypertrophy by examining a class of signaling molecules called STAT proteins and their involvement in the activation of the angiotensinogen gene, which encodes the hypertrophic agent angiotensin II. Lastly, we will consider the processes that control the cell cycle and how their perturbation may be involved in hypertrophy.

MYOSIN LIGHT CHAIN-2 GENE EXPRESSION

One of the hallmarks of cardiac hypertrophy is an altered profile of protein expression characterized by the re-expression of fetal protein isoforms[6,7] and the upregulation of certain cardiac contractile proteins such as cardiac MLC-2.[4] While it is unclear whether this alteration is a cause of hypertrophy or an adaptational response of the cardiac muscle cell to hypertrophy, it nonetheless indicates that an important facet of hypertrophy is the reenlistment of the transcriptional apparatus that was active during development. To fully appreciate the molecular basis of the re-expression of fetal genes in cardiac hypertrophy, knowledge of the gene promoters driving cardiac gene expression and the transcription factors and associated proteins interacting with promoter elements to activate their transcription is required. In the case of the MLC-2 gene, our laboratory, as well as others, has delineated both the cis- and trans-acting elements responsible for MLC-2 gene expression and has conducted studies of MLC-2 gene expression in heart tissue during development and under hypertrophic conditions.[8–12]

The chicken MLC-2 gene promoter consists of both positive and negative regulatory elements that together control the expression of the gene. Among the positive elements are three sequence domains: the TATA-box, the MEF-2 binding site, and the CArG-box.[12] Further upstream is the negative regulatory element CSS, a cardiac muscle-specific sequence that represses cardiac MLC-2 transcription in skeletal muscle.[9,13] The elements that appear responsible for differential expression of the MLC-2 gene during development are the CArG-box and MEF-2 binding site. Our laboratory has shown that during early chicken development, the MEF-2 binding site is bound by a transcription factor called BBF-1.[12] BBF-1 appears to be immunologically distinct from the major MEF-2 protein isoforms and to bind the MEF-2 binding site *prior* to binding by cognate MEF-2 proteins. BBF-1 binding occurs as early as stage 5 of chicken development, a stage that coincides with specification of the pre-cardiac mesoderm as cardiogenic and well before the first overt signs of cardiac cell differentiation. Thus, BBF-1 may be an important regulator of chicken MLC-2 gene expression during development of the cardiovascular system.

The upregulation of the MLC-2 gene and re-expression of "fetal" genes during hypertrophy raises the possibility that all the trans-activating factors responsible for their expression during development are likewise upregulated and/or re-expressed in hypertrophic cardiac cells. To investigate this possibility for the MLC-2 gene, our laboratory compared the binding activity of nuclear proteins to both the MEF-2 binding site and the CArG-box of the MLC-2 promoter in normal (WKY) and genetically hypertensive (SHR) strains of rats.[14] The results of these studies indicated that for both the MEF-2 binding site and the CArG-box, nuclear extracts from SHR rat hearts exhibited significantly higher binding activity than extracts from WKY rats. For the MEF-2 binding site, this increase resulted from increased binding by BBF-1, BBF-3 (another binding protein of the MEF-2 binding site), and MEF-2 proteins as well. Interestingly, using age-matched nuclear extracts from WKY and SHR rats, binding by BBF-1 and MEF-2 appeared to coincide with the development of hypertrophy in the SHR rats. CArG-box binding activity also showed significant changes between normal and hypertensive rat nuclear extracts. The onset of BBF-1 binding activity for the MEF-2 binding site has been shown to occur as early as the formation of the cardiogenic mesoderm in chicken development.[12] This finding, together with the observed increase in BBF-1 binding activity in the myocardium of hypertrophic adult rats, suggest that the upregulation of MLC-2 gene expression during hypertrophy is dependent upon the assembly of the transcriptional apparatus responsible for MLC-2 gene expression during development. While the gel-mobility shift assays used in these studies indicate an increased binding activity for BBF-1 and MEF-2, it is presently unclear whether this increase indicates a similar upregulation, i.e., increased transcription, of the genes encoding these transcription factors. Thus, it is presently unknown if the transduction of the hypertrophic signal through the signaling cascade that terminates in the nucleus is responsible for activating the genes encoding BBF-1 or MEF-2. The molecular cloning of the mRNAs and genes encoding these transcription factors will facilitate the study of how cell signal transduction pathways activate the BBF-1 and MEF-2 genes and other aspects of their expression in both normal and hypertrophic states.

SIGNAL TRANSDUCTION THROUGH STAT PROTEINS AND ACTIVATION OF ANGIOTENSIN II

Many of the extracellular growth factors, cytokines, and hormones shown to induce the hypertrophic phenotype in cardiomyocytes transmit their signal through the activation of cell surface receptors and their associated intracellular signaling pathways. The characterization of many of these signal transduction pathways has facilitated the analysis of hypertrophic signal transduction in cardiomyocytes. Our laboratory has focused on one of these hypertrophic agents, angiotensin II, and has provided some insight into how angiotensin II activates a normal cellular signaling pathway to bring about activation of the angiotensinogen gene (angiotensinogen is the prohormone precursor to angiotensin II).

Angiotensin II promotes myocardial hypertrophy via activation of the renin-angiotensin system (RAS).[15] When angiotensin II binds to its cell surface receptors, it activates G-proteins, which trigger a cascade of multiple second messenger systems.[16] This second messenger cascade leads to the nucleus where it ultimately causes the activation of the angiotensinogen gene[17] and thus, presumably, more production of angiotensin II and activation of RAS. Recent studies have shown that angiotensin II activates the angiotensinogen gene through the Janus kinase (Jak)/STAT pathway of signal transduction and gene activation.[18]

The Jak/STAT signal transduction pathway leading from the cell membrane to the cell nucleus has a very interesting means of regulation.[19,20] In the absence of activating signal, STAT proteins reside in the cytoplasm. Upon activation by ligand, cell surface receptors activate Jak kinases which then phosphorylate the cytoplasmic STAT proteins. Upon phosphorylation, the STAT proteins migrate to the nucleus where they activate the transcription of target genes. The specificity of this signal transduction pathway resides in promoter elements of the target genes that specifically bind the STAT proteins.

In the case of angiotensin II, this hypertrophic agent promotes myocardial hypertrophy by activating the Jak/STAT signal transduction pathway to specifically induce expression of the angiotensinogen gene. Exactly how a general signal transduction pathway such as the Jak/STAT pathway specifically activates the angiotensinogen gene in cardiomyocytes has been a focus of our laboratory's research.[21] Sequence analysis of the angiotensinogen gene promoter has revealed the presence of a conserved sequence element (called the GAS domain for Gamma (interferon) activated sequence) originally found in the promoter of the gamma interferon gene and required for its activation by STAT proteins. By using the STAT binding domain (St-domain) of this element as a probe in electromobility shift assays (EMSA), this promoter element was shown to bind STAT proteins in cardiomyocytes treated with angiotensin II. Comparison with untreated cardiomyocytes indicated that STAT3 and STAT6 are selectively and functionally activated in response to angiotensin II. Further linking angiotensin II with activation of STAT3 and STAT6 is the finding that upstream components of the Jak/STAT pathway, specifically the Jak kinases required for STAT phosphorylation and activation, were also activated (as indicated by phosphorylation of their tyrosine residues).

These studies support the idea that normal cell signal transduction pathways, such as the Jak/STAT pathway, are used by hypertrophic agents to transmit their signal to the cell nucleus where they activate genes. The peptide hormone angiotensin II turns on the angiotensinogen gene through activation of the Jak/STAT pathway. Activation of the angiotensinogen gene by angiotensin II to produce more of the angiotensin II prohormone for processing could lead to the formation of an autocrine loop that positively reinforces production of angiotensin II in cardiomyocytes. A feedback loop of this kind may be one way in which a cardiac hypertrophic agent maintains the hypertrophic state.

Despite the importance of angiotensin II in the etiology of cardiac hypertrophy, further work needs to be done on this and the other signal transduction pathways used by other hypertrophic agents. For instance, we need to know if other genes are regulated by angiotensin II and if the Jak/STAT pathway is also involved in their regulation. It is well known that the other extracellular signaling molecules implicated in hypertrophy act through different receptor systems with different second messenger pathways.[3] Their complexity, however, has precluded working out a direct signal-to-gene pathway similar to what was done for angiotensin II and the angiotensinogen gene. In this regard, it should be noted that the linkage between the Jak/STAT pathway of signal transduction and the genes it activates was first elucidated using a "gene-to-signal" approach, that is, genes upregulated by external stimuli were first identified, their promoter elements defined, and the nuclear factors that interacted with these elements isolated.[22] These factors, for example, the STAT proteins, were themselves found to be cytoplasmic and linked to cell surface receptors via the Janus kinases. Thus, the link between signal, cytoplasm, nucleus, and gene could be drawn. In the case of hypertrophy, a number of genes are upregulated in response to the hypertrophic signal. These genes provide a starting point with which to work out a "gene-to-signal" approach for signaling pathways active in hypertrophy. At present, the best candidate genes for such an approach are the "fetal" genes (beta-myosin heavy chain, alpha-skeletal muscle actin, alpha-smooth muscle actin, and atrial natriuretic factor), which are re-expressed during hypertrophy, and the cardiac myosin light chain–2 gene, which is upregulated. Defining the promoter elements of these genes and the nuclear factors with which they interact would be the first step toward identifying the second messenger and signal transduction pathways regulating their expression under normal and hypertrophic conditions. Our laboratory has defined a number of promoter elements and trans-acting factors for one of these genes—the cardiac myosin light chain–2 gene—and is now in the process of defining the second messenger system(s) controlling its expression.

CELL CYCLE CONTROL AS THE COMMON TARGET OF HYPERTROPHIC AGENTS

As mentioned above, cardiac cells respond to a variety of hypertrophic stimuli in a very singular and predictable way—they enlarge. This enlargement is a form of aberrant growth and suggests that the cardiac cell's response to hypertrophic agents may involve mechanisms normally associated with growth control. In support of this notion is recent evidence suggesting that a contributing factor in cardiac as well as other types of hypertrophy may be aberrant effects on the cellular processes controlling growth and cell replication induced by growth factors or cytokines.[23,24] Specifically, factors known either to cause cardiac hypertrophy or be associated with the hypertrophic state may also be able to perturb or in some way alter the cell cycle of cardiomyocytes.

During normal development, signaling molecules such as growth factors and cell cycle control molecules, such as tumor suppressor proteins,[25,26] must act together to coordinate the growth and proliferation of cells and tissues. Under certain conditions, growth and proliferation can become unbalanced leading to abnormal cell growth, morphology, and function. This is most evident in cellular hypertrophy, which is characterized by cell growth in the absence of cell division. While the molecular basis of such aberrant growth control is not known, increasing knowledge of cell cycle regulation and the activity of growth factors has provided some insights. One growth factor in particular, transforming growth factor–beta (TGF-beta), has been found to have altered expression and biological activity in hypertrophic cardiac cells and has been shown to play a role in other forms of hypertrophy.[23,24]

TGF-beta is a prototypical member of a family of highly conserved polypeptides involved with cell growth, proliferation, immunosuppression, and extracellular matrix production.[27] All of the cell types within the cardiovascular system express TGF-beta1 receptors and secrete TGF-beta1. In genetically determined hypertrophy, TGF-beta1 mRNA levels are markedly elevated,[28] while agonists that promote cardiac hypertrophy, such as norepinephrine and angiotensin II, increase TGF-beta1 expression in cardiac myocytes.[29] One hallmark of hypertrophic cardiomyocytes is the re-expression of genes, such as alpha- and beta-MHC, smooth muscle alpha-actin, atrial natriuretic factor, and sarcoplasmic reticulum ATPase, in a pattern resembling that of early embryonic cardiac gene expression.[6] Interestingly, TGF-beta treatment of neonatal cardiac myocytes results in the expression of these same genes in the same pattern observed in cardiac hypertrophy.[30] Together, these observations raise the possibility that TGF-beta may mediate the effects of known hypertrophy-causing agents including angiotensin II.[31,32] How TGF-beta might accomplish this is not known, but recent studies of tubular renal cell hypertrophy may provide some insight.

In an *in vitro* cell culture model of proximal tubular renal cell hypertrophy, Franch and coworkers found that TGF-beta can convert EGF-induced hyperplastic renal cells to hypertrophic renal cells and that this activity was dependent on maintaining the retinoblastoma tumor suppressor protein (pRb) in an active, i.e., growth suppressing, state.[24] Cell cycle analysis showed that hypertrophic renal cells failed to progress from the G1 to S phase of the cell cycle. Importantly, these studies provide evidence linking the actions of a growth factor often associated with cardiac hypertrophy (TGF-beta) to perturbation of the mechanisms involved in controlling the cell cycle.

While similar studies have yet to be done on hypertrophic cardiomyocytes, some recent studies of the effects of growth factor cytokines on cardiomyocytes show some interesting parallels. In studies done on chicken heart ventricle cells in culture, EGF was shown to increase DNA synthesis while TGF-beta had an inhibitory effect.[33] As in the renal cell study, when both cytokines were added together, TGF-beta attenuated the stimulatory effect of EGF. While renal epithelial cells differ in many respects from cardiac muscle cells, these findings nonetheless provide some precedent for studying the effect of TGF-beta on cardiomyocyte cell cycle control and whether TGF-beta–dependent alterations in cell cycle dynamics are associated with angiotensin II–induced cardiac hypertrophy.

To begin studying the possibility that aberrant cell cycle control processes may play a role in hypertrophy, we have focused on the proteins normally involved in controlling the cell cycle. The best candidates for this are tumor suppressor proteins. We have begun to investigate the role of tumor suppressors in normal and hypertrophic heart by first focusing on isolating tumor suppressor genes from early stage chicken heart tissue and analyzing their expression pattern with respect to onset and type of differentiated tissue. From a 3-day chicken embryo heart cDNA library we have isolated a novel form of retinoblastoma (Rb) gene transcript that apparently represents an alternatively spliced form of the Rb mRNA. Analysis of the earliest stages of chicken development using RT-PCR procedures revealed the presence of other alternatively spliced forms of the Rb gene transcript with a significantly more complex pattern of alternatively spliced mRNA isoforms present in the embryonic heart tube. We have cloned these RT-PCR products and sequence analysis shows a complex pattern of splicing within the 3′ untranslated region of the Rb mRNA such that additional amino acids are added to the carboxy terminal of the encoded Rb protein. Two isoforms are seen in heart tube RNA that are not seen in total early embryo RNA. *In situ* hybridization analysis shows the earliest expression of the Rb mRNA detectable by this method to be in the heart tube and anterior central nervous system. The observation of alternatively spliced transcripts and apparent tissue specificity of Rb in general and its spliced isoforms in particular together suggest that Rb may play an important role in the early stages of tissue-specific differentiation. Moreover, it appears that tumor suppressor genes may not play a critical role in controlling early embryonic growth since they are not expressed at significant levels until primitive germ cells begin to differentiate into phenotypically distinct tissues. These observations raise the possibility that cell cycle control genes play a much more pivotal role at the transitional junction between growth and differentiation than was previously thought.

In addition to the retinoblastoma protein, we have also isolated from an embryonic chicken heart cDNA library cDNA clones for other tumor suppressor proteins such as p107[34] and p300,[35] a related gene that can also act as a transcriptional coactivator. The expression of the p107 gene is high in heart tissue and also appears to be regulated with respect to isoform production and tissue specificity.[36]

PERSPECTIVES

In summary, cardiac hypertrophy results from the enlargement of cardiac muscle and fibroblast cells. This abnormal pattern of growth can be elicited by a number of hypertrophic agents. For the most part, these agents are extracellular signaling molecules such as cytokines and hormones that participate in normal cell-cell signaling events during development. Under conditions yet to be defined, these same signaling molecules can cause hypertrophy of certain organs including the heart. The intracellular signal transduction pathways used by these signaling molecules appear to be the prime means by which the hypertrophic signal is transduced in cardiomyocytes. What is unclear at present and needs to be studied in the future is how this signal causes hypertrophy. There is no evidence to date that the signal transduction pathways in hypertrophic cardiomyocytes differ from those of normal cardiomyocytes. This raises two possibilities: (1) that the signal itself is aberrant, perhaps mistimed, misplaced, or occurring at non-physiological concentrations or (2) as a quiescent cell the cardiomyocyte may not be able to respond completely to a growth signal by turning on its proliferative machinery. Such an abortive response could lead to increased synthesis of mRNA and protein in anticipation of cell proliferation, but in the absence of cell division result instead in cell enlargement. Further defining the signal transduction pathways used by hypertrophic agents, the adaptational response on the part of certain genes to these agents, and how the normal mechanisms of growth and cell cycle control are perturbed in hypertrophic cardiomyocytes should provide greater insight into the molecular etiology of cardiac hypertrophy.

REFERENCES

1. KENT, R.L., D.L. MANN & G. COOPER. 1991. Signals for cardiac muscle hypertrophy in hypertension. J. Cardiovasc. Pharmacol. **17(S):** S7–S13.
2. GLENNON, P.E., P.H. SUDGEN & P.A. POOLE-WILSON. 1995. Cellular mechanisms of cardiac hypertrophy. Br. Heart J. **73:** 496–499.
3. SCHAUB, M.C. & M.A. HEFTI. 1997. Various hypertrophic stimuli induce distinct phenotypes in cardiomyocytes. J. Mol. Med. **75:** 901–920.
4. KUMAR, C., C. SAIDAPET, P. DELANEY, C. MENDOLA & M.A.Q. SIDDIQUI. 1988. Expression of ventricular type myosin light chain messenger RNA in spontaneously hypertensive rat atria. Circ. Res. **62:** 1093–1097.
5. MARIAN, A.J. & R. ROBERTS. 1995. Recent advances in the molecular genetics of hypertrophic cardiomyopathy. Circulation **92:** 1336–1347.
6. SIMPSON, P.C., C.S. LONG, L.E. WASPE, C.J. HENRICH & C.P. ORDAHL. 1989. Transcription of early developmental isogenes in cardiac myocyte hypertrophy. Mol. Cell. Cardiol. **21:** 79–89.
7. NADAL-GINARD, B. & V. MAHDAVI. 1989. Molecular basis of cardiac performance: plasticity of the myocardium generated through protein isoform switches. J. Clin. Invest. **84:** 1693–1700.
8. HENDERSON, S.A., M. SPENCER, A. SEN, C. KUMAR, M. A. Q. SIDDIQUI & K. CHIEN. 1989. Structure, organization and expression of the rat MLC-2 gene, identification of a 250 base pair fragment which confers cardiac specific expression. J. Biol. Chem. **264:** 18142–18148.

9. Shen, R., S.K. Goswami, E. Mascareno, A. Kumar & M. A. Q. Siddiqui. 1991. Tissue-specific transcription of the cardiac myosin light chain-2 gene is regulated by an upstream repressor element. Mol. Cell. Biol. **11:** 1676–1685.
10. Qasba, P., E. Lin, M.D. Zhou, A. Kumar & M.A.Q. Siddiqui. 1992. A single transcription factor binds two divergent sequence elements with a common function in myosin light chain-2 promoter. Mol. Cell. Biol. **12:** 1107–1116.
11. Zhou, M.D., S.K. Goswami, M.E. Martin & M.A.Q. Siddiqui. 1993. A new serum responsive, cardiac tissue-specific transcription factor recognizes the MEF-2 site in the myosin light chain-2 promoter. Mol. Cell. Biol. **13:** 1222–1231.
12. Goswami, S., P. Qasba, S. Ghatpande, A.K. Deshpande, M. Baig & M.A.Q. Siddiqui. 1994. Differential expression of myocyte enhancer factor 2 family of transcription factors in development: the cardiac factor BBF-1 is an early marker for cardiogenesis. Mol. Cell. Biol. **14:** 5130–5138.
13. Dhar, M., E.M. Mascareno & M.A.Q. Siddiqui. 1997. Two distinct factor-binding DNA elements in cardiac myosin light chain 2 gene are essential for repression of its expression in skeletal muscle. Isolation of a cDNA clone for repressor protein Nished. J. Biol. Chem. **272:** 18490–18497.
14. Doud, S.K., L-X. Pan, S. Carleton, S. Marmorstein & M.A.Q. Siddiqui. 1995. Adaptational response in transcription factors during development of myocardial hypertrophy. J. Mol. Cell. Cardiol. **27:** 2359–2372.
15. Raizada, M., M. Phillips & C. Summers. 1993. Cellular and Molecular Biology of the Renin-Angiotensin System. CRC Press. Boca Raton, FL.
16. Marrero, M.B., B. Schieffer, W.G. Paxton, J.L. Duff, B.C. Berk & K.E. Bernstein. 1995. The role of tyrosine phosphorylation in angiotensin II-mediated intracellular signalling. Cardiovas. Res. **30:** 530–536.
17. Sadoshima, J. & S. Izumo. 1993. Molecular characterization of angiotensin II-induced hypertrophy of cardiac myocytes and hyperplasia of cardiac fibroblasts. Circ. Res. **73:** 413–423.
18. Marrero, M.B., B. Schieffer, W.G. Paxton, L. Heerdt, B.C. Berk, P. Delafontaine & K.E. Bernstein. 1995. Direct stimulation of Jak/STAT pathway by the angiotensin II At1 receptor. Nature **375:** 247–250.
19. Ihle, J.N. 1996. STATs: Signal transducers and activators of transcription. Cell **84:** 331–334.
20. Horvath, C.M. & J.E. Darnell. 1997. The state of the STATs: recent developments in the study of signal transduction to the nucleus. Curr. Opin. Cell Biol. **9:** 233–239.
21. Mascareno, E., M. Dhar & M.A.Q. Siddiqui. 1998. Signal transduction and activator of transcription (STAT) protein-dependent activation of angiotensinogen promoter: A cellular signal for hypertrophy in cardiac muscle. Proc. Natl. Acad. Sci. USA **95:** 5590–5594.
22. Darnell, J.E. Jr., I.M. Kerr & G.R. Stark. 1994. Jak/STAT pathways and transcriptional activation in response to IFNs and other extracellular signaling proteins. Science **264:** 1415–1421.
23. Brand, T. & M.D. Schneider. 1995. The TGF-beta superfamily in myocardium: ligands, receptors, transduction, and function. J. Mol. Cell. Cardiol. **27:** 5–18.
24. Franch, H.A., J.W. Shay, R.J. Alpern & P.A. Preisig. 1995. Involvement of pRB family in TGF-beta–dependent epithelial cell hypertrophy. J. Cell Biol. **129:** 245–254.
25. Riley, D.J., E.Y.-H.P. Lee & W.-H. Lee. 1994. The retinoblastoma protein: More than a tumor suppressor. Annu. Rev. Cell Biol. **10:** 1–29.
26. Weinberg, R. 1995. The retinoblastoma protein and cell cycle control. Cell **81:** 323–330.
27. Roberts, A.B. & M.B. Sporn. 1990. The transforming growth factors-beta. Handb. Exp. Pharmacol. **95:** 419.
28. Sakata, Y. 1993. Tissue factors contributing to cardiac hypertrophy in cardiomyopathic hamsters (BIO14.6): Involvement of transforming growth factor-beta 1 and tissue renin-angiotensin system in the progression of cardiac hypertrophy. Hokkaido Igaku Zasshi **68:** 18–28.

29. SADOSHIMA, J., Y.H. XU, H.S. SLAYTER & S. IZUMO. 1993. Autocrine release of angiotensin-II mediates stretch-induced hypertrophy of cardiac myocytes in vitro. Cell **75:** 977–984.
30. PARKER, T.G., S.E. PARKER & M.D. SCHNEIDER. 1990. Peptide growth factors can provoke "fetal" contractile protein gene expression in rat cardiac myocytes. J. Clin. Invest. **85:** 507–514.
31. WOLF, G.E. MUELLER, R.A.K. STAHL & F.N. ZIYADEH. 1993. Angitensin-II-induced hypertrophy of cultured murine proximal tubular cells is mediated by endogenous transforming growth factor-beta. J. Clin. Invest. **92:** 1366–1372.
32. LEE, A.A., W.H. DILLMANN, A.D. MCCULLOCH & F.J. VILLARREAL. 1995. Angiotensin II stimulates the autocrine production of transforming growth factor-beta1 in adult rat cardiac fibroblasts. J. Mol. Cardiol. **27:** 2347–2357.
33. LAU, C.L. 1993. Behavior of embryonic chick heart cells in culture. 2. Cellular responses to epidermal growth factor and other growth signals. Tissue Cell **25:** 681–693.
34. EWEN, M.E., X. YIGONG, J.B. LAWRENCE & D.M. LIVINGSTON. 1991. Molecular cloning, chromosomal mapping and expression of the cDNA for p107, a retinoblastoma gene product-related protein. Cell **66:** 1155–1164.
35. HASEGAWA, K., M.B. MEYERS & R.N. KITSIS. 1997. Transcriptional coactivator p300 stimulates cell-type specific gene expression in cardiac myocytes. J. Biol. Chem. **272:** 20049–20054.
36. KIM, K.K., M.H. SOONPA, H. WANG & L.J. FIELD. 1995. Developmental expression of p107 mRNA and evidence for alternative splicing of the p107 (RBL1) gene product. Genomics **28:** 520–529.

The Ins and Outs of Caveolar Signaling

m2 Muscarinic Cholinergic Receptors and eNOS Activation versus Neuregulin and ErbB4 Signaling in Cardiac Myocytes[a]

OLIVIER FERON,[b] YOU-YANG ZHAO, AND RALPH A. KELLY[c]

Department of Medicine, Cardiovascular Division, Brigham and Women's Hospital and Harvard Medical School, Boston, Massachusetts 02115, USA

[b]*Department of Medicine, University of Louvain, Brussels, Belgium*

ABSTRACT: Endothelial cells constitutively express the NOS isoform eNOS, which generates NO in response to specific extracellular signals to regulate vascular smooth muscle tone, vascular permeability, and platelet adhesion, among other actions. In addition to coronary vascular and endocardial endothelium, both atrial and ventricular myocytes express eNOS, the activation of which is also dependent on specific intracellular and extracellular signals. eNOS is targeted in cardiac myocytes to caveolae in plasma membranes and, in the case of cardiac myocytes, possibly T-tubular membranes as well. eNOS targeting to caveolae in cardiac myocytes requires co-translational myristoylation and subsequent palmitoylation for efficient targeting of the enzyme to the specialized lipid microdomains characteristic of caveolae. Although eNOS also contains a caveolin binding motif, this is insufficient for correct targeting of eNOS to caveolae. Recent evidence obtained from ventricular myocytes of mice with targeted disruption of the eNOS gene indicates that the lack of functional eNOS interrupts muscarinic cholinergic control of I_{Ca-L} in these cells. eNOS-/- mice are hypertensive and develop cardiac hypertrophy as they age, and these animals also exhibit an accelerated degree of vascular remodeling in response to injury. Reconstitution experiments confirm both the essential role of eNOS in coupling m2 AchR signaling to the control of I_{Ca-L} and myocyte automaticity and the importance of eNOS subcellular localization within caveolae in mediating this signal transduction pathway. It appears that translocation into caveolae is essential for signaling. However, this is not the case with all receptors associated with caveolae.

THE INS: m2 AchR TRANSLOCATION AND eNOS ACTIVATION

The principal source of nitric oxide (NO) within the normal myocardium is the endothelium of the coronary vasculature and endocardium. Endothelial cells constitutively express the NOS isoform, termed eNOS, which generates NO in response to

[a]This work was supported by grants HL52320 and HL36141 from the National Institutes of Health (RA.K.).

[c]Address correspondence to: Ralph A. Kelly, M.D., Cardiovascular Division, Brigham and Women's Hospital, 75 Francis Street, Boston, Massachusetts 02115; Telephone: 617/732-7503; Fax: 617/732-5132; E-mail: rakelly@rics.bwh.harvard.edu

specific extracellular signals to regulate vascular smooth muscle tone, vascular permeability, and platelet adhesion, among other actions. In addition to coronary vascular and endocardial endothelium, both atrial and ventricular myocytes—including specialized pacemaker tissue, such as sinoatrial and atrioventricular nodal cells—express eNOS as well, the activation of which is also dependent on specific intracellular and extracellular signals (see Kelly and coworkers[1] and Kelly and Han[2] and references therein). As in endothelial cells, eNOS is targeted in cardiac myocytes to caveolae in plasma membranes and, in the case of cardiac myocytes, possibly T-tubular membranes as well.[3,4] Also, as in endothelial cells, eNOS targeting to caveolae in cardiac myocytes requires co-translational myristoylation and subsequent palmitoylation for efficient targeting of the enzyme to the specialized lipid microdomains characteristic of caveolae (reviewed in Michel and Feron[4]). Although eNOS also contains a caveolin binding motif (see below), this is insufficient for correct targeting of eNOS to caveolae.

Although not yet formally demonstrated in cardiac myocytes, it is presumed that eNOS in myocytes participates in a Ca^{2+}-calmodulin-caveolin regulatory cycle similar to that described in endothelial cells. When the Ca^{2+} concentration increases in the vicinity of caveolae containing eNOS, Ca^{2+}-activated calmodulin removes eNOS from its inactive heterodimer conformation with caveolin (caveolin-3 in cardiac myocytes), with subsequent activation of eNOS.[4] With the decline of Ca^{2+} towards basal levels, calmodulin dissociates from eNOS, and eNOS reassociates with caveolin (a process believed to be facilitated by palmitoylation).

Although it appears clear that myocyte eNOS is targeted to sarcolemmal caveolae, the possibility that eNOS might also be localized within the T-tubular system may have important consequences for the regulation of several signal transduction pathways and for excitation-contraction coupling. More than 30 years ago, Ishikawa[5] hypothesized that the development of the T-tubular system in fetal cardiac muscle occurred by successive caveolar fission and coalescence events, beginning with a single caveola or clusters of caveolae at the sarcolemmal membrane. It had been known that the lipid composition of the T-tubular system—enriched in glycosphingolipids and cholesterol with a low phospholipid content—was similar to that of caveolae. Recently, using antibodies to caveolin-3, the muscle-specific caveolin, Parton and his colleagues[6] confirmed that the T-tubular system in both skeletal and cardiac muscle contained caveolin-3. Interestingly, while caveolin-3 disappears from T-tubular membranes in skeletal muscle after development, caveolin-3 expression in T-tubules is sustained in cardiac muscle.

The potential localization of eNOS to T-tubular membranes is of interest in the context of recent work by Meszaros and colleagues[7,8] and Stamler and coworkers[9] on the effects of NO on the cardiac ryanodine receptor Ca^{2+} release channel (CRC), which is localized to T-tubular membranes. Building on their original observations of the skeletal muscle CRC, in which Meszaros and colleages[7] demonstrated that NO decreased CRC activity by a mechanism that appeared to be independent of cGMP generation, this laboratory went on to document a similar response in CRC in canine cardiac muscle-derived sarcoplasmic reticulum microsomes.[8] Importantly, they demonstrated regulation of channel activity both with NO donors and by activation of NOS activity within the microsomal preparations (presumably eNOS, since eNOS was detectable by Western blot in these microsomal fractions). These authors concluded that eNOS in cardiac muscle, which, like the CRC, is a Ca^{2+}-activated protein, may act to downregulate CRC activation during muscle depolarization. This interpretation is supported by preliminary data from this group that activation of eNOS in intact cells suppresses the frequency and duration of Ca^{2+} "sparks" generated in intact cardiac myocytes.[10] That the underlying biochemistry is complex, however, is highlighted in the work of Xu and coworkers[9] who, also working in CRC purified from canine cardiac muscle, found that addition of S-nitrosothiol NO donors results in reversible activation of CRC activity when measured after their incorporation into plasma lipid bilayers. Indeed, the CRC has an unusually large number of reactive intramolecular cysteines—the usual oxidation target of S-nitrosothiols. These data are supported by work by Salama and colleagues[11] that documents activation of both skeletal and cardiac CRCs by NO donors. Further work will obviously be needed to clarify the role(s) of NO and S-nitrosothiols in the regulation of CRC activity, but there now seems little doubt that an important regulatory role exists.

eNOS, in cardiac myocytes, is also activated by muscarinic, cholinergic, and purinergic agonists.[12–14] An increasing number of reports support the concept that m2 AchR and A_1 purinergic receptor control of $I_{Ca\text{-}L}$ in some cardiac myocyte phenotypes is dependent on activation of myocyte eNOS (reviewed in Kelly and Han[2]). The principal subcellular target of NO generated by eNOS in cardiac myocytes is the heme moiety in soluble guanylyl cyclase. Aside from the effects on CRC noted above, several non–cGMP-mediated effects of NO on $I_{Ca\text{-}L}$ have also been demonstrated, but their importance in the physiological regulation of these channels remains to be determined.[14] The net effect of an increase in myocyte intracellular cGMP will depend on the extent of activation of adenylyl cyclase and the activities of potential downstream target proteins (e.g., protein kinase G, cGMP-regulated PDEs [i.e., types 2 and 3]) and the activity of cGMP-hydrolyzing PDEs (i.e., PDEs 3 and 5). A small increase in myocyte cGMP, whether the result of increased NO delivered by a nitrovasodilator or eNOS activation in myocytes or adjacent endothelium, could enhance cAMP levels by inhibiting PDE 3 activity. Larger amounts of NO would lead to larger increases in cGMP levels, thereby decreasing cAMP content (by activating a type 2 PDE) and inhibiting downstream cAMP signaling (by activating a protein kinase G).

Recent evidence obtained from ventricular myocytes of mice with targeted disruption of the eNOS gene (i.e., eNOS–/–) indicates that the lack of functional eNOS interrupts muscarinic cholinergic control of $I_{Ca\text{-}L}$ in these cells.[16] eNOS–/– mice are hypertensive, develop cardiac hypertrophy as they age, and exhibit an accelerated degree of vascular remodeling in response to injury.[17–19] We isolated atrial and ventricular myocytes from neonatal and adult eNOS–/– animals and their eNOS+/+ littermates. Compared to wild-type (WT) ventricular myocytes, eNOS–/– myocytes exhibited little or no suppression of isoproterenol-induced increases in $I_{Ca\text{-}L}$ contractile amplitude in response to muscarinic cholinergic agonists (e.g., carbachol).[16] The absence of an effect on m2 AchR control of $I_{Ca\text{-}L}$ in ventricular myocytes from eNOS–/– animals was reflected in the absence of any increase in cGMP levels in response to carbachol in eNOS–/– cells.

We have recently confirmed and extended these observations in neonatal murine ventricular myocytes, which beat spontaneously in primary culture. Neonatal ventricular myocytes from eNOS+/+ animals respond to isoproterenol with an increase in beating rate, which can be suppressed with muscarinic cholinergic agonists, while myocytes from eNOS–/– fail to respond to cholinergic agonists. However, the responsiveness of eNOS–/– neonatal myocytes can be restored by transfection with wild-type eNOS, but not with a myristoylation-deficient eNOS. These reconstitution experiments confirm both the essential role of eNOS in coupling m2 AchR signaling to the control of $I_{Ca\text{-}L}$ and myocyte automaticity and the importance of eNOS subcellular localization within caveolae in mediating this signal transduction pathway (O. Feron, C. Dessy, D.J. Opel, M.A. Arstall, R.A. Kelly & T. Michel, manuscript under review).

Diminished eNOS expression and activity in myocytes, due to inflammatory cytokines or to agents that cause sustained intracellular cAMP elevations (such as catecholamines or phosphodiesterase inhibitors, such as milrinone), may have important consequences for parasympathetic nervous system regulation of myocardial electrophysiology and contractile function. Sustained increases in cAMP directly diminish eNOS transcription as well as interrupt post-translational processing and targeting of eNOS to sarcolemmal caveolae.[20,21] Indeed, this decreased expression of myocyte eNOS by drugs that elevate cAMP would be predicted to diminish parasympathetic nervous system control of $I_{Ca\text{-}L}$, and perhaps contribute to the generation of arrhythmias. With reference to human disease, heart failure is characterized by high levels of sympathetic nervous system tone and is often treated, during short-term decompensation of advanced heart failure, with sympathomimetic drugs that increase intracellular cAMP. The relevance of these observations to the pathophysiology of heart failure in humans is enhanced by recent data from our laboratory that implicate eNOS-derived NO in the suppression of some cardiac arrhythmias. We have found recently that adult ventricular myocytes from eNOS–/– mice were more susceptible to cardiac glycoside (ouabain)-induced afterdepolarizations than myocytes from wild-type mice (I. Kubota, X. Han, D. Opel, M.A. Arstall, T. Michel & R.A. Kelly, manuscript under review). Ouabain-induced afterdepolarization in eNOS–/– myocytes could be suppressed by a pharmacologic NO donor, but this protective effect could be ablated by ODQ, a specific inhibitor of guanylyl cyclase, implicating NO-dependent generation of cGMP in mediating the anti-arrhythmic effect of eNOS activation.

While many of the details of the Ca^{2+}/calmodulin-eNOS regulatory cycle within caveolae are now understood, the sequence of events leading to Ca^{2+} influx within caveolae remains unclear. Some G protein–coupled receptors, such as endothelin receptors, appear to be constitutively present within caveolae, but this is clearly not the case for a number of other G protein–coupled receptors, including the m2 AchR. Using two complementary approaches, (1) density gradient (isopycnic) centrifugation following detergent-free preparation of adult rat ventricular myocyte lysates and (2) co-immunoprecipitation protocols using antibodies to caveolin-3, eNOS, and the m2 AchR, we demonstrated that eNOS and caveolin-3 were present in caveolar fractions in the absence of muscarinic cholinergic agonists, but the m2 AchR was not.[21] Following exposure to the muscarinic agonist carbachol—but not the antagonist, atropine—the m2 AchR (tracked by [^{3}H]QNB binding) moved into myocyte caveolar microdomains. Moreover, in the presence of agonist (but not antagonist), the m2 AchR could be co-immunoprecipitated by anti–caveolin-3 antibodies.[21]

The relevance of this intracellular trafficking of ligand–m2 AchR complexes into caveolae to receptor desensitization remains controversial. Nevertheless, it appears that translocation into caveolae is essential for signaling. However, as will be discussed below, this is not the case with all receptors that are associated with caveolae.

THE OUTS: NEUREGULIN SIGNALING AND ErbB4 TRANSLOCATION

The list of biologic mediators that induce a growth response in cardiac myocytes continues to grow. These include agents that signal through G protein–coupled receptors (including biogenic amines, muscarinic cholinergic agonists, angiotensin II and endothelins, and others) receptor tyrosine kinases (EGF, HB-EGF, bFGF, and others) and cytokine receptors (IL-1β, IFNγ, IL-6, CT-1, and others). In many cases, these biologic mediators are produced either by other parenchymal cells within cardiac muscle (such as adjacent endocardial or microvessel endothelium) or by the myocytes themselves. Targeted disruptions of the gene for neuregulin 1 (NRG1), a family of autocrine, paracrine, and juxtacrine signaling proteins known to be important in neuronal and skeletal muscle development, or two of their cognate receptors (ErbB2 and ErbB4), unexpectedly resulted in embryonic lethality due to defects in the developing myocardium.[23–26] The absence of NRG1 in the endocardial endothelium or of functioning receptors in subjacent ventricular muscle resulted in the failure of the muscle to undergo normal trabeculation.

Neuregulins (i.e., NRG1) include the growth-regulatory proteins glial growth factor (GGF), Neu differentiation factor, heregulin, and acetylcholine receptor–inducing activity (ARIA). All of these proteins are encoded by a single gene but exist in at least fifteen isoforms, including both integral membrane and soluble signaling proteins.[27] Recently, two additional genes coding for neuregulin-like signaling proteins have been identified, "neuregulin-2" (NRG2), and "neuregulin-3" (NRG3).[28–30] Products of the originally identified neuregulin family, "neuregulin-1" (NRG1), share about 40% and 20% amino acid sequence identity with NRG2 and NRG3, respectively. Unlike NRG1-derived mRNAs, which within the developing heart are limited largely to the endocardial endothelium of ventricular muscle, NRG2 mRNAs are found primarily in the endothelium of developing atrial muscle, while no NRG3 mRNA has been detected by *in situ* hybridization in the heart at midembryogenesis.[28–30]

Neuregulins, which are produced by either neuronal or mesenchymal cells, mediate their effects by binding to and signaling via the ErbB family of receptors, including ErbB1/epidermal growth factor receptor, Neu/ErbB2/HER2, ErbB3/HER3, and ErbB4/HER4.[27] All neuregulins (i.e., NRG1, NRG2, and NRG3) identified to date bind to either ErbB3 or ErbB4, subsequently recruiting another ErbB receptor (including ErbB1 or ErbB2) as co-receptors to initiate signaling. While all possible hetero- and homodimers of the ErbB receptor family can be formed, there is no known high affinity ligand for ErbB2, and ErbB3 homodimers have diminished intrinsic tyrosine kinase activity, suggesting that there is a limited and hierarchical structure to neuregulin/ErbB signaling in target cells.[27] In the case of myocardial development, for example, animals lacking functional ErbB2 (ErbB2–/–) exhibited a cardiac phenotype similar to that of animals with a targeted disruption of the NRG1 gene, indicating that ErbB4 homodimers could not substitute for ErbB2 in fetal ventricular myocytes at this point in development.[23]

Peptide ligands other than products of the known neuregulin genes may also initiate ErbB signaling. Heparin-binding epidermal growth factor–like growth factor, which we have demonstrated can act as an autocrine growth stimulus in both neonatal and adult ventricular myocytes,[31] has been shown also to act as a ligand for both the ErbB1 and ErbB4 receptors. Indeed, as noted by Burden and Yarden,[27] this abundance of potential ligands suggests that the spatial and temporal restriction of soluble and membrane-bound neuregulins and other ErbB-receptor ligands provides the necessary specificity for ErbB-dependent signaling. Finally, recent evidence suggests that these receptors participate in crosstalk among differing classes of receptors. For example, ErbB2 can be recruited by IL-6 to the gp130 subunit of the IL-6 receptor complex to facilitate signal transduction.[32] While such signaling crosstalk has not yet been demonstrated in cardiac myocytes, it is unlikely that myocytes differ importantly from other cell types in this regard.

Although expression of both NRG1 and ErbB-mediated signaling pathways declines during later stages of embryonic development, as noted above, both ErbB2 and ErbB4 continue to be expressed in late postnatal and adult myocardium.[33] Both neonatal and adult rat ventricular myocytes in primary culture exhibit a hypertrophic growth response to a soluble NRG1 (recombinant human glial growth factor-2, rhGGF-2), a growth response that also appeared selective for cardiac myocytes, with no detectable mitogenic effect on non-myocyte cell types also isolated from hearts. Moreover, NRG1 suppressed baseline rates of apoptotic cell death in both neonatal and adult ventricular myocytes in primary culture maintained in serum-free medium.[33] Finally, as in the developing heart, endothelial cells may be the source of neuregulins in the postnatal myocardium. Primary cultures of coronary microvascular endothelial cells (CMEC) isolated from adult rat ventricular muscle exhibit robust induction of NRG1 expression in response to hypertrophic stimuli, such as endothelin-1.[33]

Ligand-induced desensitization and downregulation mechanisms are important aspects of the regulation of transmembrane receptors. Ligand binding to the ErbB1 receptor rapidly induces receptor-mediated endocytosis through clathrin-coated pits, and the internalized complexes are subsequently degraded in lysosomes. In contrast to the ErbB1/EGF receptor, all other ErbB family members, including ErbB4, are not rapidly internalized in the presence of ligand, although Carpenter and his colleagues[34,35] have demonstrated recently that activation of a PKC isoenzyme in a number of cell types that constitutively express ErbB4, including the AT-1 cardiac muscle-like cell line, results in proteolytic cleavage of the 120 kD ectodomain of the receptor, probably by a metalloproteinase. The membrane-spanning and cytoplasmic domains were subsequently shown to undergo ubiquination and targeting to the proteosome.[35]

Recently, the ErbB1/EGF receptor was identified to interact directly with caveolins in caveolae in mammalian A431 cells.[36] All caveolins share common cytoplasmic scaffolding domains that mediate the interactions of caveolins with themselves and other proteins. Furthermore, two caveolin-binding motifs, ϕxϕxxxxϕ and ϕxxxxϕxxϕ (ϕ represents aromatic amino acids Trp, Phe, or Tyr) have been identified and found in most caveolin-associated proteins. The motif <u>W</u>S<u>Y</u>GVTI<u>W</u> within the kinase domain of ErbB1/EGFR has been shown to be responsible for binding of this receptor tyrosine kinase to caveolins. This motif is identical to the corresponding sequence within ErbB2 and ErbB3, while only one amino acid is different (I→V) in ErbB4.

As with the m2 AchR internalization into caveolae, noted above, we employed two complementary approaches to investigate the subcellular localization of ErbB4 receptor in cardiac myocytes. In the absence of ligand binding, this receptor tyrosine kinase was localized to caveolae as determined both by density gradient (isopycnic) centrifugation of myocyte lysates and by co-immunoprecipitation of caveolin-3 with ErbB4. In the presence of a soluble NRG1 (recombinant human glial growth factor [rhGGF2]), ErbB4 rapidly (within minutes) translocated out of caveolae (Y.-Y. Zhao, O. Feron, X. Han, M.A. Marchionni & R.A. Kelly, manuscript under review). This is unlike what has been reported for the EGF receptor, which remains in caveolae after stimulation of the A431 cells with EGF,[37] and similar to the PDGF receptor, which has been demonstrated to translocate from caveolae after ligand binding, although with a time course somewhat less rapid than we have described for ErbB4.

The caveolin scaffolding domain also binds to a ϕxxxxϕxxϕ motif in the catalytic domain of eNOS (FSAAPFSGCQ) which, as in the case of ErbB4, locks the receptor in an inactive conformation. Indeed, Sessa and his colleagues[39] have demonstrated that site-directed mutagenesis of the aromatic amino acid moieties in eNOS caveolin binding motif results in the inability of caveolin to inhibit eNOS activity. As detailed above, eNOS targeting to caveolae, however, appears to be independent of its association with caveolins,[4] with correct targeting to caveolar microdomains requiring acylation.

In the case of ErbB4 (and likely ErbB3 and ErbB2 as well, which as mentioned above, typically undergo heterodimerization to facilitate signaling), caveolar localization upon ligand binding facilitates initiation of downstream signaling cascades. Whether additional motifs are present on ErbB4 (or other neuregulin receptors) that facilitate caveolar targeting and whether rapid translocation out of caveolar microdomains upon ligand binding occurs are unknown.

REFERENCES

1. KELLY, R.A., J.-L. BALLIGAND & T.W. SMITH. 1996. Nitric oxide and cardiac function. Circ. Res. **79:** 363–380.
2. KELLY, R.A. & X. HAN. 1997. Nitrovasodilators have (small) direct effects on cardiac contractility. Is this important? Circulation **96:** 2493–2495.
3. FERON, O., L. BELHASSEN, L. KOBZIK, T.W. SMITH, R.A. KELLY & T. MICHEL. 1996. Endothelial nitric oxide synthase targeting to caveolae: specific interactions with caveolin isoforms in cardiac myocytes and endothelial cells. J. Biol. Chem. **271:** 22810–22814.
4. MICHEL, T. & O. FERON. 1997. Nitric oxide synthases: which, where, how, and why? J. Clin. Invest. **100:** 1–7.
5. ISHIKAWA, H. 1968. Formation of elaborate networks of T-system tubules in cultured skeletal muscle with special reference to the T-system formation. J. Cell Biol. **38:** 51–66.
6. PARTON, R.G., M. WAY, N. ZORZI & E. STANG. 1997. Caveolin-3 associates with developing T-tubules during muscle differentiation. J. Cell Biol. **136:** 137–154.
7. MESZAROS, L.G., I. MINAROVIC & A. ZABRADNIKOVA. 1996. Inhibition of the skeletal muscle ryanodine receptor calcium release channel by nitric oxide. FEBS Lett. **380:** 49–52.

8. ZAHRADNIKOVA, A., I. MINAROVIC, R.C. VENEMA & L.G. MESZAROS. 1997. Inactivation of the cardiac ryanodine receptor calcium release channel by nitric oxide. Cell Calcium **22:** 447–453.
9. XU, L., J.P. EU, G. MEISSNER & J.S. STAMLER. 1998. Activation of the cardiac calcium release channel (ryanodine receptor) by poly-s-nitrosylation. Science **279:** 234–237.
10. MESZAROS, L.G. & V. LUKYANENKO. 1998. Nitric oxide reduces spontaneous calcium release activity in isolated rat ventricular myocytes—a confocal Ca-imaging study. Presented at the 42nd Annual Meeting of the Biophysical Society. Kansas City, MO, USA, 1998. Abstract submitted.
11. STOYANOVSKY, D., T. MURPHY, P.R. ANNO, Y.-M. KIM & G. SALAMA. 1997. Nitric oxide activates skeletal and cardiac ryanodine receptors. Cell Calcium **21:** 19–29.
12. ELVAN, A., M. RUBART & D.P. ZIPES. 1997. NO modulates autonomic effects on sinus discharge rate and AV nodal conduction in open-chest dogs. Am. J. Physiol. **272:** H263–H271.
13. SHIMONI, Y., X. HAN, D. SEVERSON & W.R. GILES. 1996. Mediation by nitric oxide of the indirect effects of adenosine on calcium current in rabbit heart pacemaker cells. Br. J. Pharmacol. **119:** 1463–1469.
14. MARTYNYUK, A.G., K.A. KANE, S.M. COBBE & A.C. RANKIN. 1996. Nitric oxide mediates the anti-adrenergic effect of adenosine on calcium current in isolated rabbit atrioventricular nodal cells. Pflugers Arch. **431:** 452–457.
15. CAMPBELL, D.L., J.S. STAMLER & H.C. STRAUSS. 1996. Redox modulation of L-type calcium channels in ferret ventricular myocytes: dual mechanism regulation by nitric oxide and S-nitrosothiols. J. Gen. Physiol. **108:** 277–293.
16. HAN, X., I. KUBOTA, O. FERON, D.J. OPEL, M.A. ARSTALL, Y.-Y. ZHAO, P. HUANG, M.C. FISHMAN, T. MICHEL & R. A. KELLY. 1998. Muscarinic cholinergic regulation of cardiac myocyte $I_{Ca\text{-}L}$ is absent in mice with targeted disruption of endothelial nitric oxide synthase (eNOS). Proc. Natl. Acad. Sci. USA **95:** 6510–6515.
17. HUANG, P.L., Z. HUANG, H. MASHIMO, K.D. BLOCH, M.A. MOSKOWITZ, J.A. BEVAN & M.C. FISHMAN. 1995. Hypertension in mice lacking the gene for endothelial nitric oxide synthase. Nature **377:** 239–242.
18. MOROI, M., L. ZHANG, T. YASUDA, R. VIRMANI, H.K. GOLD, M. C. FISHMAN & P. L. HUANG. 1998. Interaction of genetic deficiency of endothelial nitric oxide, gender, and pregnancy in vascular response to injury in mice. J. Clin. Invest. **101:** 1225–1232.
19. RUDIC, R.D., E.G. SHESELY, N. MAEDA, O. SMITHIES, S.S. SEGAL & W.C. SESSA. 1998. Direct evidence for the importance of endothelium-derived nitric oxide in vascular remodeling. J. Clin. Invest. **101:** 731–736.
20. BELHASSEN, L., R.A. KELLY, T.W. SMITH & J.-L. BALLIGAND. 1996. Nitric oxide synthase (NOS3) and contractile responsiveness to adrenergic and cholinergic agonists in the heart: regulation of NOS3 transcription in vitro and in vivo by cAMP in rat cardiac myocytes. J. Clin. Invest. **97:** 1908–1915.
21. BELHASSEN, L., O. FERON, D.M. KAYE, T. MICHEL & R.A. KELLY. 1997. Regulation by cAMP of post-translational processing and subcellular targeting of endothelial nitric oxide synthase (type 3) in cardiac myocytes. J. Biol. Chem. **272:** 11198–11204.
22. FERON, O., T.W. SMITH, T. MICHEL & R.A. KELLY. 1997. Dynamic targeting of the agonist-stimulated m2 muscarinic acetylcholine receptor to caveolae in cardiac myocytes. J. Biol. Chem. **272:** 17744–17748.
23. MARCHIONNI, M.A. 1995. *neu* tack on neuregulin. Nature **378:** 334–335.
24. MEYER, D. & C. BIRCHMEIER. 1995. Multiple essential functions of neuregulin in development. Nature **378:** 386–390.
25. LEE, K.-F., H. SIMON, H. CHEN, B. BATES, M.-C. HUNG & C. HAUSER. 1995. Requirement for neuregulin receptor *erb*B2 on neural and cardiac development. Nature **378:** 394–398.
26. GASSMAN, M., F. CASAGRANDA, D. ORIOLI, H. SIMON, C. LAL, R. KLEIN & G. LEMKE. 1995. Aberrant neural and cardiac development in mice lacking the *erb*B4 neuregulin receptor. Nature **378**: 390–394.

27. Burden, S. & Y. Yarden. 1997. Neuregulins and their receptors: a versatile signaling module in organogenesis and oncogenesis. Neuron **18:** 847–855.
28. Chang, H., D.J. Riese II, W. Gilbert, D.F. Stern & U.J. McMahan. 1997. Ligands for ErbB-family receptors encoded by a neuregulin-like gene. Nature **387:** 509–512.
29. Carraway, K.L. III, J.L. Weber, M.J. Unger, J. Ledesma, N. Yu, M. Gassmann & C. Lai. 1997. Neuregulin-2, a new ligand of ErbB3/ErbB4-receptor tyrosine kinases. Nature **387:** 512–516.
30. Zhang, D., M.X. Sliwkowski, M. Mark, G. Frantz, R. Akita, Y. Sun, K. Hillan, C. Crowley, J. Brush & P.J. Godowski. 1997. Neuregulin-3 (NRG3): a novel neural tissue-enriched protein that binds and activates ErbB4. Proc. Natl. Acad. Sci. USA **94:** 9562–9567.
31. Perrella, M.A.T. Maki, S. Prasad, D. Pimental, K. Singh, N. Takahashi, M. Yoshizumi, A. Alali, S. Higashiyama, R.A. Kelly, M. Lee & T.W. Smith. 1994. Regulation of heparin-binding epidermal growth factor-like growth factor mRNA levels by hypertrophic stimuli in neonatal and adult rat cardiac myocytes. J. Biol. Chem. **269:** 27045–27050.
32. Qiu, Y., R. Lakshmeswari & H.-J. Kung. 1998. Requirement of ErbB2 for signaling by interleukin-6 in prostate carcinoma cells. Nature **393:** 83–85.
33. Zhao, Y.-Y., D.R. Sawyer, R. R. Baliga, D.J. Opel, X. Han, M.A. Marchionni & R.A. Kelly. 1998. Neuregulins promote survival and growth of cardiac myocytes. Persistence of ErbB2 and ErbB4 expression in neonatal and adult ventricular myocytes. J. Biol. Chem. **273:** 10261–10269.
34. Vecchi, M., J. Baulida & G. Carpenter. 1996. Selective cleavage of the heregulin receptor ErbB-4 by protein kinase C activation. J. Biol. Chem. **271:** 18989–18995.
35. Vecchi, M. & G. Carpenter. 1997. Constitutive proteolysis of the ErbB-4 receptor tyrosine kinase by a unique, sequential mechanism. J. Cell Biol. **139:** 995–1003.
36. Okamoto, T., A. Schlegel, P.E. Scherer & M. P. Lisanti. 1998. Caveolins, a family of scaffolding proteins for organizing "preassembled signaling complexes" at the plasma membrane. J. Biol. Chem. **273:** 5419–5422.
37. Couet, J., M. Sargiacomo & M.P. Lisanti. 1997. Interaction of a receptor tyrosine kinase, EGF-R, with caveolins — caveolin. Binding negatively regulates tyrosine and serine/threonine kinase activities. J. Biol. Chem. **272:** 30429–30438.
38. Liu, P.S., Y.S. Ying, Y.G. Ko & R.G.W. Anderson. 1996. Localization of platelet-derived growth factor-stimulated phosphorylation. Cascade to caveolae. J. Biol. Chem. **271:** 10299–10303.
39. Garcia-Cardena, G., P. Martasek, B.S.S. Masters, P.M. Skidd, J. Couet, S.W. Li, M.P. Lisanti & W.C. Sessa. 1997. Dissecting the interaction between nitric oxide synthase (NOS) and caveolin — Functional significance of the NOS caveolin binding domain *in vivo*. J. Biol. Chem. **272:** 25437–25440.

Amplification of Angiotensin II Signaling in Cardiac Myocytes by Adenovirus-Mediated Overexpression of the AT_1 Receptor[a]

GEORGE W. BOOZ,[b] LOIS L. CARL, AND KENNETH M. BAKER

Henry Hood MD Research Program, The Pennsylvania State University College of Medicine, Weis Center for Research, Danville, Pennsylvania 17822-2611, USA

ABSTRACT: Low levels of AT_1 receptor can make studying the growth-related signal transduction events mediated by this angiotensin II receptor in cardiac myocytes technically difficult. The purpose of the present study was to establish whether an adenovirus expression system could be used to increase the number of plasma membrane AT_1 receptors in neonatal rat ventricular myocytes, thereby amplifying the signaling pathways activated by this receptor. Cardiac myocytes infected with adenovirus expressing the AT_1 receptor exhibited increased ligand binding. The overexpressed receptor appeared to function like the endogenous receptor, in regard to agonist-induced internalization, as well as coupling to MAPK activation and protein tyrosine phosphorylation events. In addition, adenovirus-mediated overexpression of the AT_1 receptor resulted in the amplification of angiotensin II intracellular signaling. In conclusion, adenovirus-mediated overexpression of angiotensin II receptors appears to be a useful strategy for studying the signal transduction events activated by this hormone in cardiac myocytes and for unraveling the molecular means by which this receptor type couples to a hypertrophic pattern of growth and gene expression.

INTRODUCTION

Left ventricular hypertrophy occurs in many common cardiovascular pathologies and represents an important risk factor for heart failure and death.[1] Clinical studies, as well as studies on animals and cultured cells, have implicated angiotensin II (Ang II) in the left ventricular hypertrophy associated with myocardial infarction and hypertension.[2,3] The growth-promoting effects of Ang II are mediated by the AT_1, $G_q/G_{i/o}$-coupled receptor, which activates conventional and novel signaling pathways.[3,4] We previously reported that the growth-promoting effects of Ang II on neonatal rat ventricular myocytes are tempered in part by low AT_1 receptor levels.[5] The hypothesis was proposed that increased AT_1 receptor expression, which occurs with myocardial

[a]This work was supported by grants from the National Heart, Lung, and Blood Institute (HL-44883 and HL-60529, Dr. Baker), National American Heart Association (9650210N, Dr. Baker), and Pennsylvania Affiliate of the American Heart Association (GWB). Dr. Baker is an Established Investigator of the American Heart Association.

[b]Address correspondence to: George W. Booz, Ph.D., Henry Hood MD Research Program, Penn State University College of Medicine, Weis Center for Research, 100 N. Academy Avenue, Danville, Pennsylvania 17822-2611, USA; Phone: 717-271-6815; Fax: 717-271-6701; E-mail: gbooz@psghs.edu

infarction or hypertension,[3,6,7] may amplify the growth effects of Ang II on cardiac myocytes. Evidence was also found that the other major class of Ang II receptor AT_2 opposes the actions of the AT_1 receptor by mediating an anti-growth effect on neonatal rat ventricular myocytes.[5]

The low number of AT_1 receptors, as well as the presence of a near equal number of AT_2 receptors, can make studying the signal transduction events mediated by the AT_1 receptor in cardiac myocytes technically difficult. The purpose of the present study was to establish whether adenovirus-mediated delivery into cardiac myocytes of DNA coding for the AT_1 receptor would result in an increased number of plasma membrane AT_1 receptors and, thus, amplification of signaling pathways activated by this receptor. The efficacy of adenovirus for expressing foreign DNA in cardiac myocytes is well established.[8] Unlike conventional transfection procedures, which have levels of efficiency in primary cultures of <10%, adenovirus can be used to infect nearly all cardiac myocytes with DNA.

METHODS

Tissue Culture

Cardiac myocytes were isolated as previously described[5] from the ventricles of Sprague-Dawley neonatal rat pups, and seeded (1.2×10^6 cells) onto 35-mm, 6-well plates in medium containing 10% newborn calf serum and 5-bromo-2′-deoxyuridine to inhibit fibroblast proliferation. After 22 h, the medium was changed to a serum-substitute medium.[5] All experiments were performed within 6 days following isolation of the cardiac myocytes.

Construction of AT_1-Expressing Adenovirus

Recombinant adenovirus (Ad) were generated from the Ad-5–derived plasmids, pJM17 and pCA13, as recommended by the supplier (Microbix Biosystems, Toronto, Canada). pJM17 is the circularized Ad-5 genome with deletions/substitutions in the E1 and E3 regions. pCA13 is a left-end, E1-deleted shuttle plasmid. The Hind III fragment, containing the coding region of the AT_{1A} receptor gene, was excised from the previously described[9] pBluescript II (Stratagene, La Jolla, CA)–derived vector, and subcloned into pCA13 behind the cytomegalovirus (CMV) promoter to generate pCA13-AT1. Proper orientation of the insert was established by sequencing and performing binding studies on CHO cells transfected with pCA13-AT1. Adenovirus expressing the AT_1 receptor (Ad-AT1) was generated by homologous recombination in HEK293 cells, which were cotransfected with pJM17 and pCA13-AT1 by the calcium-phosphate method. Ad-AT1 was purified by successive plaque assays. Final high titres of Ad-AT1 were purified by two discontinuous cesium chloride gradient ultracentrifugation steps. Using lacZ expressing adenovirus and staining for β-galactosidase activity, we established that a multiplicity of infection (MOI) of 10 plaque-forming units per cell will infect >95% of neonatal rat ventricular myocytes in our cultures (unpublished observation).

Angiotensin II Binding

Radioligand binding studies with 0.2 nM ^{125}I-[Tyr^4]Ang II (NEN Life Science Products, Boston, MA) were performed as previously described.[5] Binding medium was Minimum Essential Medium (Gibco BRL, Gaithersburg, MD) with 50 mM Tris (pH 7.4), 2.5% bovine serum albumin (BSA), and 0.01 mg/ml bacitracin. Surface (receptor)-bound ligand was distinguished from internalized ligand by acid-washing the cells.[5]

Tyrosine Phosphorylation and MAPK Activation

After treatment, cells were washed twice with ice-cold Hanks' buffered salt solution, and scraped at 4°C into 200 μl lysis buffer (20 mM Tris [pH 7.5], 2 mM EGTA, 1 mM sodium orthovanadate, 10 mM β-glycerophosphate) containing 0.5% Triton X-100, 0.15 mg/ml dithiothreitol, 0.03 mg/ml aprotinin, and 0.2 mM phenylmethylsulfonyl fluoride. Cell scrapings from three similarly treated wells were pooled, homogenized, and centrifuged at 100,000 ×*g* for 20 min (4°C). Proteins (15 μg) in the supernatants were separated by SDS-PAGE (10% gel) and transferred to Hybond ECL nitrocellulose membranes (Amersham Life Science, Arlington Heights, IL). To block nonspecific sites, membranes were incubated overnight at 4°C in TBS (10 mM Tris [pH 7.4], 100 mM NaCl, and 0.025% Tween 20) with 1% BSA. Membranes

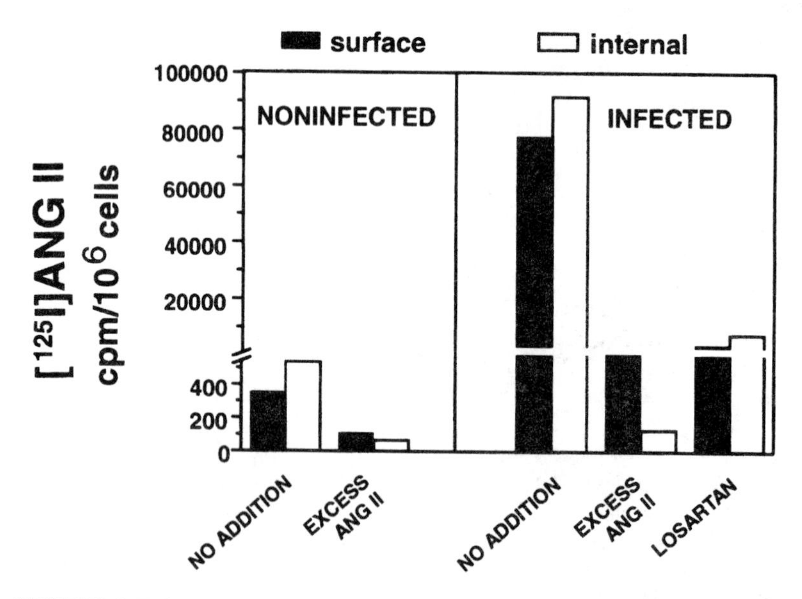

FIGURE 1. Enhanced equilibrium binding of radiolabeled Ang II binding to cardiac myocytes infected with adenovirus overexpressing the AT_1 receptor. Infection (MOI = 10) with adenovirus was carried out 48 h earlier. Cells were incubated for 1 h with 0.2 nM ^{125}I-[Tyr^4]Ang I in the presence or absence of 1 μM Ang II (excess Ang II) or 1 μM losartan. Surface (receptor)-bound ligand was distinguished from internalized ligand by acid-washing the cells. Results shown are representative of six experiments.

were incubated for 90 min at room temperature with either anti-phosphotyrosine (anti-P-Tyr) monoclonal $IgG2b_k$ (Upstate Biotechnology, Lake Placid, NY) or anti-active mitogen-activated protein kinase (MAPK) antibody (Promega, Madison, WI), diluted (1:4,000 and 1:20,000, respectively) in TBS with 1% BSA. After washing (5 × 5 min in TBS), membranes were incubated 20 min at room temperature with anti-rabbit or anti-mouse IgG peroxidase-conjugated antibody in TBS with 5% nonfat dry milk (1:8,000 dilution). After washing (5 × 5 min in TBS) the membranes, immunoreactive proteins were detected by enhanced chemiluminescence using Renaissance reagents and exposure to reflection autoradiography film (NEN Life Science Products, Boston, MA).

RESULTS AND DISCUSSION

Equilibrium binding of radiolabeled Ang II to the cell surface was measured 48 h after cardiac myocytes were infected with adenovirus expressing the AT_1 receptor. As FIGURE 1 shows, at that time there was a dramatic increase in surface binding of labeled Ang II. The majority of the increased surface binding could be displaced by excess nonlabeled Ang II (>98%), indicating that it was specific, as well as by the AT_1 nonpeptide receptor antagonist losartan (95%). Over 1 h, an appreciable amount of labeled Ang II was internalized, i.e., 54% of total cell-associated label (FIG. 1). This internalization process was competed for by excess nonlabeled Ang II and was attenuated by losartan, indicating that it represented internalization of the AT_1 receptor. Agonist-induced internalization is a characteristic of the AT_1 receptor,[10] and has

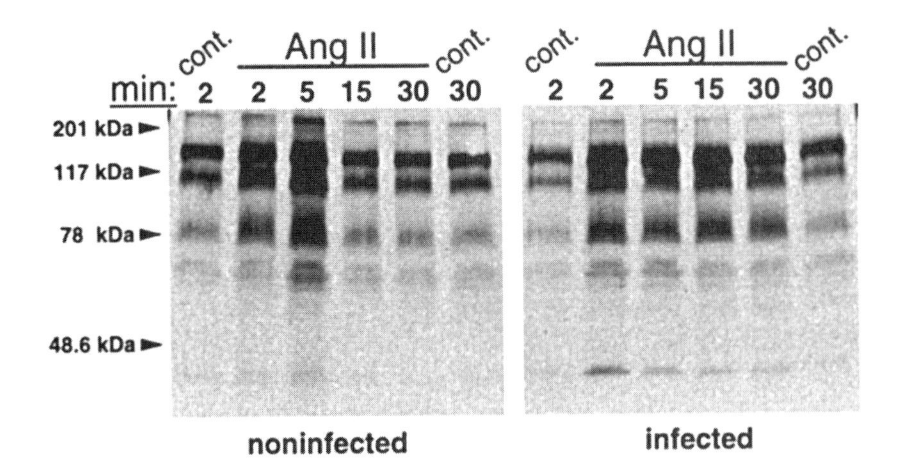

FIGURE 2. Amplification of Ang II-induced protein tyrosine phosphorylation. Noninfected or adenovirus-infected neonatal rat ventricular myocytes were incubated with vehicle (cont.) or 100 nM Ang II for the indicated times. Infection (MOI = 20) with adenovirus expressing the AT_1 receptor was carried out 48 h earlier. Proteins in cell lysates were separated by SDS-PAGE, transferred to nitrocellulose membranes, and immunoblotted with anti-P-Tyr antibody. Enhanced chemiluminescence was used in secondary detection. Result shown is representative of three experiments.

been suggested to function in Ang II signaling.[11] Thus, the present observation indicates that the overexpressed AT_1 receptors in cardiac myocytes functioned normally in this regard. In contrast, the AT_2 receptor does not undergo agonist-induced internalization,[10] and our observations on adenovirus-mediated overexpression of the AT_2 receptor in cardiac myocytes are consistent with that fact (unpublished observation).

We have determined that the adenovirus expression system can be used to enhance signal transduction events associated with the AT_1 receptor in cardiac myocytes, including protein tyrosine phosphorylation (FIG. 2). In noninfected cells, tyrosine phosphorylation of a number of proteins occurs rapidly following treatment with Ang II, but is short-lived. In adenovirus-infected cells overexpressing the AT_1 receptor, protein tyrosine phosphorylation events are more sustained, lasting for at least 30 min in the case of some proteins. Protein bands that exhibited enhanced phosphorylation in response to Ang II have molecular weights (kD) of 200, 100–150, 80, 60–65, 42, and 44. Similar patterns of protein tyrosine phosphorylation are induced in cardiac myocytes by other hypertrophic agonists, such as fetal calf serum,[12] ET-1 and PMA (unpublished observation), and insulin-like growth factor-1.[13] The identity of these proteins has not been established, nor is it known what role these proteins have in hypertrophic growth. The 42 and 44 kD bands, which are prominent in cardiac myocytes that overexpress the AT_1 receptor, most likely represent the MAP kinases ERK1 and ERK2.

Using an antibody that recognizes only the active form of ERK1 and ERK2, we have found greater activation of both of these MAP kinases by Ang II in cardiac myocytes that have increased levels of the AT_1 receptor. In noninfected cells, Ang II produced a modest increase in ERK1 (p44) and ERK2 (p42) activities (FIG. 3). In

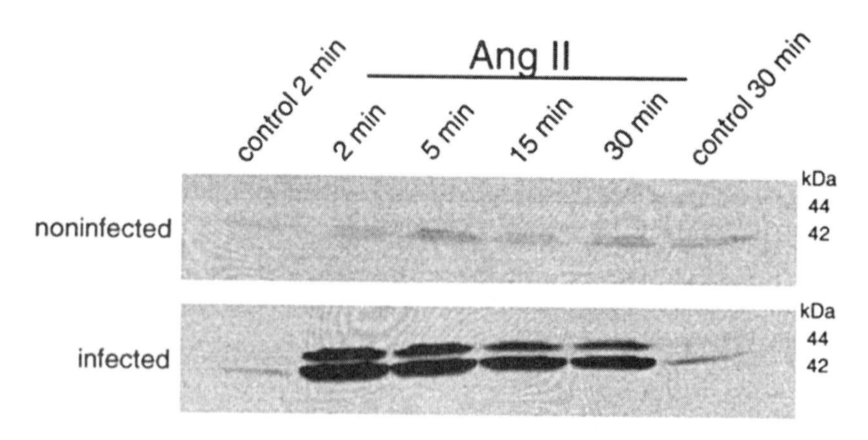

FIGURE 3. Amplification of Ang II-induced mitogen-activated protein kinase (MAPK) activity in neonatal rat ventricular myocytes. Lysates were prepared at the indicated times from noninfected or adenovirus-infected (AT_1 overexpressing) cardiac myocytes incubated with vehicle (control) or 100 nM Ang II. Proteins in cell lysates were separated by SDS-PAGE, transferred to nitrocellulose membranes, and immunoblotted with an antibody specific for activated (i.e., dually phosphorylated) p42 (ERK2) and p44 (ERK1) MAPK enzymes. Shown is a representative blot of three experiments. *See* FIGURE 2 legend for additional details.

myocytes infected with an adenovirus that expresses the AT_1 receptor, treatment with Ang II robustly stimulated both ERK1 and ERK2 for longer than 30 min. Available evidence indicates that MAPK activation in cardiac myocytes is necessary, though not sufficient, for induction of hypertrophic cell growth.[14-16] Conflicting findings have been reported on whether MAPK activation mediates changes in gene expression associated with the hypertrophic phenotype, in particular ANF expression.[15,17,18]

CONCLUSIONS

Adenovirus-mediated overexpression of Ang II receptors appears to be a useful strategy for amplifying the signal transduction events activated by this hormone in cardiac myocytes. Given the normally low levels of both AT_1 and AT_2 receptors in cardiac myocytes, this experimental approach should prove useful in unraveling the molecular means by which these receptor types couple to hypertrophic or apoptotic growth responses. In addition, adenovirus-mediated overexpression of the AT_1 receptor should be of value in clarifying the role of internalized Ang II in nuclear signaling and gene expression in cardiac myocytes.

REFERENCES

1. LEVY, D., R.J. GARRISON, D.D. SAVAGE, W.B. KANNEL & W.P. CASTELLI. 1990. Prognostic implications of echocardiographically determined left ventricular mass in the Framingham heart study. N. Eng. J. Med. **322** (22)**:** 1561–1566.
2. BAKER, K.M., G.W. BOOZ & D.E. DOSTAL. 1992. Cardiac actions of angiotensin II: Role of an intracardiac renin-angiotensin system. Annu. Rev. Physiol. **54:** 227–241.
3. BOOZ, G.W. & K.M. BAKER. 1996. The role of the renin-angiotensin system in the pathophysiology of cardiac remodeling. Blood Pressure **5** (Suppl. 2)**:** 10–18.
4. DOSTAL, D.E., G.W. BOOZ & K.M. BAKER. 1996. Angiotensin II signalling pathways in cardiac fibroblasts: Conventional versus novel mechanisms in mediating cardiac growth and function. Mol. Cell. Biochem. **157:** 15–21.
5. BOOZ, G.W. & K.M. BAKER. 1996. Role of type 1 and type 2 angiotensin receptors in angiotensin II-induced cardiomyocyte hypertrophy. Hypertension **28** (4)**:** 635–640.
6. NIO, Y., H. MATSUBARA, S. MURASAWA, M. KANASAKI & M. INADA. 1995. Regulation of gene transcription by angiotensin II receptor subtypes in myocardial infarction. J. Clin. Invest. **95** (1)**:** 46–54.
7. SUZUKI, J., H. MATSUBARA, M. URAKAMI & M. INADA. 1993. Rat angiotensin II (type 1A) mRNA regulation and subtype expression in the myocardial growth and hypertrophy. Circ. Res. **73** (3)**:** 439–447.
8. KASS-EISLER, A., E. FALCK-PEDERSEN, M. ALVIRA, J. RIVERA, P.M. BUTTRICK, B.A. WITTENBERG, L. CIPRIANI & L. A. LEINWAND. 1993. Quantitative determination of adenovirus-mediated gene delivery into rat cardiac myocytes *in vitro* and *in vivo*. Proc. Natl. Acad. Sci. USA **90:** 11498–11502.
9. THEKKUMKARA, T.J., J. DU, D.E. DOSTAL, T.J. MOTEL, W.G. THOMAS & K.M. BAKER. 1995. Stable expression of a functional rat angiotensin II (AT_{1A}) receptor in CHO-K1 cells: Rapid desensitization by angiotensin II. Mol. Cell. Biochem. **146:** 79–89.
10. THOMAS, W.G., T.J. THEKKUMKARA & K.M. BAKER. 1996. Cardiac actions of AII: AT_{1A} receptor signaling, desensitization, and internalization. Adv. Exp. Med. Biol. **396:** 59–69.
11. BOOZ, G.W., D.E. DOSTAL & K.M. BAKER. 1994. Regulation of cardiac second messengers by angiotensins. *In* Cardiac Renin-Angiotensin System. K. Lindpaintner & D. Ganten, Eds.: 101–124. Futura Medical Publishers. New York, NY.

12. SADOSHIMA, J., Z. QIU, J.P. MORGAN & S. IZUMO. 1995. Angiotensin II and other hypertrophic stimuli mediated by G-protein-coupled receptors activate tyrosine kinase, mitogen-activated protein kinase, and 90-kDa S6 kinase in cardiac myocytes. The critical role of Ca^{2+}-dependent signaling. Circ. Res. **76** (1)**:** 1–15.
13. FONCEA, R., M. ANDERSSON, A. KETTERMAN, V. BLAKESLEY, M. SAPAG-HAGAR, P.H. SUGDEN, D. LEROITH & S. LAVANDERO. 1997. Insulin-like growth factor-1 rapidly activates multiple signal transduction pathways in cultured rat cardiac myocytes. J. Biol. Chem. **272** (31)**:** 19115–19124.
14. GLENNON, P.E., S. KADDOURA, E.M. SALE, G.J. SALE, S.J. FULLER & P.H. SUGDEN. 1996. Depletion of mitogen-activated protein kinase using an antisense oligodeoxynucleotide approach downregulates the phenylephrine-induced hypertrophic response in rat cardiac myocytes. Circ. Res. **78** (6)**:** 954–961.
15. POST, G.R., D. GOLDSTEIN, D.J. THUERAUF, C.C. GLEMBOTSKI & J.H. BROWN. 1996. Dissociation of p44 and p42 mitogen-activated protein kinase activation from receptor-induced hypertrophy in neonatal rat ventricular myocytes. J. Biol. Chem. **271** (14)**:** 8452–8457.
16. CLERK, A., J. GILLESPIE-BROWN, S.J. FULLER & P.H. SUGDEN. 1996. Stimulation of phosphatidylinositol hydrolysis, protein kinase C translocation, and mitogen-activated protein kinase activity by bradykinin in rat ventricular myocytes: Dissociation from the hypertrophic response. Biochemical J. **317** (1)**:** 109–118.
17. THORBURN, J., J.A. FROST & A. THORBURN. 1994. Mitogen-activated protein kinases mediate changes in gene expression, but not cytoskeletal organization associated with cardiac muscle hypertrophy. J. Cell Biol. **126** (6)**:** 1565–1572.
18. GILLESPIE-BROWN, J., S.J. FULLER, M.A. BOGOYEVITCH, S. COWLEY & P.H. SUGDEN. 1995. The mitogen-activated protein kinase kinase MEK1 stimulates a pattern of gene expression typical of the hypertrophic phenotype in rat ventricular cardiomyocytes. J. Biol. Chem. **270** (47)**:** 28092–28096.

Mitochondrial ATP-Dependent Potassium Channels

Viable Candidate Effectors of Ischemic Preconditioning[a]

YONGGE LIU,[b] TOSHIAKI SATO, JEGATHEESAN SEHARASEYON, ADAM SZEWCZYK, BRIAN O'ROURKE, AND EDUARDO MARBÁN[c]

Section of Molecular and Cellular Cardiology, Department of Medicine, Johns Hopkins University, Baltimore, Maryland 21205, USA

ABSTRACT: Pharmacological evidence has implicated ATP-dependent potassium (K_{ATP}) channels in the mechanism of ischemic preconditioning; however, the effects of sarcolemmal K_{ATP} channels on excitability cannot account for the protection. K_{ATP} channels also exist in mitochondrial inner membrane. To test whether such channels play a role in cardioprotection, we simultaneously measured flavoprotein fluorescence, an index of mitochondrial redox state, and sarcolemmal K_{ATP} currents in intact rabbit ventricular myocytes. Our results show that diazoxide, a K_{ATP} channel opener, induced reversible oxidation of flavoproteins, but did not activate sarcolemmal K_{ATP} channels. This effect of diazoxide was blocked by 5-hydroxydecanoic acid (5-HD). We further verified that 5-HD is a selective blocker of the mitochondrial K_{ATP} channels. These methods have enabled us to demonstrate that the activity of mitochondrial K_{ATP} channels can be regulated by protein kinase C. In a cellular model of simulated ischemia, inclusion of diazoxide decreased the rate of cell death to about half of that in control. Such protection is inhibited by 5-HD. In conclusion, our results demonstrate that diazoxide targets mitochondrial but not sarcolemmal K_{ATP} channels, and imply that mitochondrial K_{ATP} channels may mediate preconditioning.

INTRODUCTION

This paper summarizes recent work from our laboratory,[1,2] which implicates mitochondrial ATP-dependent potassium (K_{ATP}) channels in the mechanism of ischemic preconditioning. The reader is referred to the original articles for full details.

[a]This work was supported by the National Institutes of Health (R01 HL44065 to E.M. and F32 HL09586 to J.S.).

[b]Current address: Maryland Research Laboratories, Otsuka America Pharmaceutical Inc., Rockville, Maryland 20850.

[c]Address correspondence to: Eduardo Marbán, M.D., Ph.D., Section of Molecular and Cellular Cardiology, Department of Medicine, Johns Hopkins University, Ross 844, 720 Rutland Avenue, Baltimore, Maryland 21205, USA; Phone: 410-955-2776; Fax: 410-955-7953; E-mail: marban@welchlink.welch.jhu.edu

K_{ATP} CHANNELS AND ISCHEMIC PRECONDITIONING

Lethal injury to the heart can be dramatically blunted by brief conditioning periods of ischemia. Such "ischemic preconditioning"[3] exists in all species examined including the human.[4] Despite intensive investigation, the mechanism of preconditioning remains poorly understood. One of the early hypotheses proposed that opening of sarcolemmal K_{ATP} (surfaceK_{ATP}) channels shortens the action potential duration. By a cardioplegic effect, energy consumption and calcium overload would be attenuated during ischemia. Although preconditioning has been shown to accelerate action potential shortening slightly during lethal ischemia,[5] several recent studies indicate that abbreviation of action potential duration may not be necessary for the protection from preconditioning and K_{ATP} channel openers. Grover and colleagues showed that dofetilide, a class III antiarrhythmic agent, abolished the action potential shortening during ischemia but did not abolish ischemic preconditioning in dogs.[6] Yao and colleagues found that bimakalim, a K_{ATP} channel opener, had minimal effect on action potential duration, but still reduced the extent of infarction.[7] Such dissociation has also been shown in several other studies.[8,9] Furthermore, K_{ATP} channel openers and ischemic preconditioning are protective even in models using unstimulated cardiac myocytes.[10,11] Since adult ventricular myocytes are electrically quiescent in these models, action potential duration shortening should not be a factor in these models. These experimental results challenge the idea that the protective effect of K_{ATP} channels is targeted to surfaceK_{ATP} channels, and prompted the investigation of potential intracellular channels.

K_{ATP} CHANNELS IN MITOCHONDRIA INNER MEMBRANE

Inoue and colleagues were the first to demonstrate the existence of K_{ATP} channels in the inner mitochondrial membrane by patch clamping mitoplasts prepared from rat liver mitochondria.[12] Later on, a fraction containing mitochondrial K_{ATP} (mitoK_{ATP}) channel activity was purified from the inner membranes of rat liver and beef heart mitochondria.[13] The molecular identity of mitoK_{ATP} channels is unknown at the present time. Much more is known about surfaceK_{ATP} channels, which are octamers of four sulfonylurea receptors and four pore-forming subunits of the Kir6 family.[14] Several observations hint that mitoK_{ATP} channels also have a similar complex.[15,16] The functional roles of mitoK_{ATP} channels are not very clear either. One known function of mitoK_{ATP} channels, in concert with K^+/H^+ exchange, is to maintain potassium homeostasis within the mitochondria and thereby to regulate mitochondrial osmotic pressure and volume, which in turn influences bioenergetics. In this article, we present evidence that suggests a novel role of mitoK_{ATP} channels in cardioprotection.

DIAZOXIDE IS A SELECTIVE MITOK_{ATP} CHANNEL OPENER

Using reconstituted mitochondrial vesicles or isolated mitochondria and measuring potassium flux, Garlid and colleagues demonstrated that heart and liver mi-

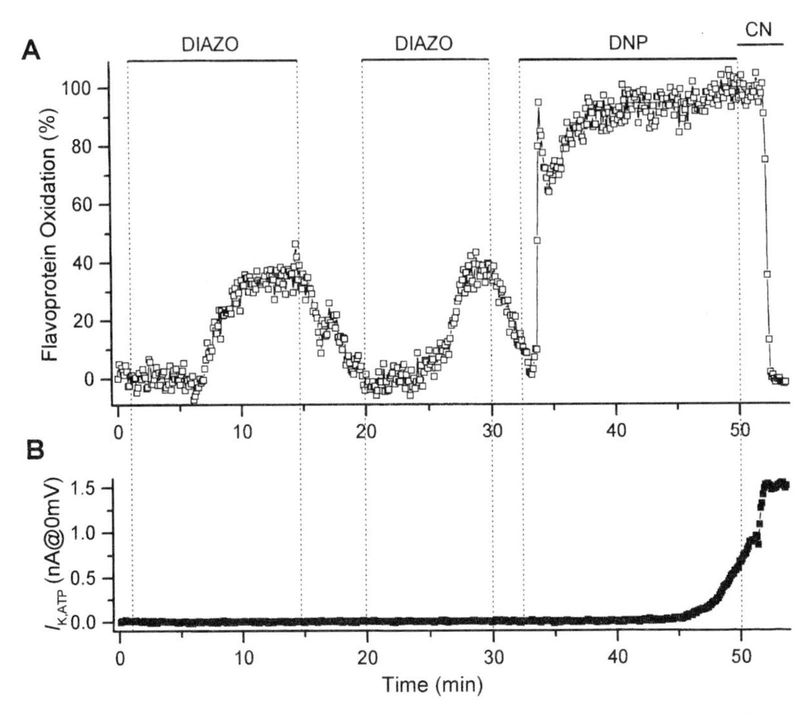

FIGURE 1. Diazoxide effect on flavoprotein fluorescence and $I_{K,ATP}$. **(A)** 100 μM diazoxide (DIAZO) induced a reversible increase of mitochondrial oxidation. **(B)** Diazoxide did not activate $I_{K,ATP}$. **(C)** 500 μM 5-HD completely blocked the oxidative effect of diazoxide. **(D)** Diazoxide and 5-HD did not activate $I_{K,ATP}$. **(E)** and **(F)** Pooled data for fluorescence and $I_{K,ATP}$. DIAZO(1), first exposure to diazoxide; DIAZO+5-HD(100), diazoxide in the presence of 100 μM 5-HD; DIAZO+5-HD(500), diazoxide in the presence of 500 μM 5-HD; DIAZO(2), second exposure to diazoxide; and DNP, exposure to dinitrophenol. The bar indicates the periods when cells were exposed to drug. **(G)** Dose-response curve for diazoxide. Each point constitutes measurements from 5–6 cells. $*p < 0.01$ versus DIAZO(1), DIAZO(2), and DNP groups. (Reproduced with permission from Liu *et al.*[1])

toK_{ATP} channels share some pharmacological properties with the channels found in sarcolemma, while possessing a distinct profile.[15] The outstanding pharmacological signature of mitochondrial channels is their high sensitivity to opening by diazoxide, exceeding the sensitivity of sarcolemmal channels 2,000-fold.[15] Although the physiological and pathophysiological roles of the mitoK_{ATP} channel are not yet very clear, opening of mitoK_{ATP} channels dissipates the inner mitochondrial membrane potential established by the proton pump. This dissipation accelerates the electron transfer of the respiratory chain and, if uncompensated by increased production of electron donors (such as NADH), leads to net oxidation of the mitochondria. Mitochondrial redox state can be monitored by recording the fluorescence of FAD-linked enzymes in the mitochondria.[17,18] Low concentrations of the K_{ATP} channel opener diazoxide (1–100 μM) have been reported to activate mitoK_{ATP} channels,[15] while cardiac surface K_{ATP} channels are quite resistant to this drug.[15,19] To determine

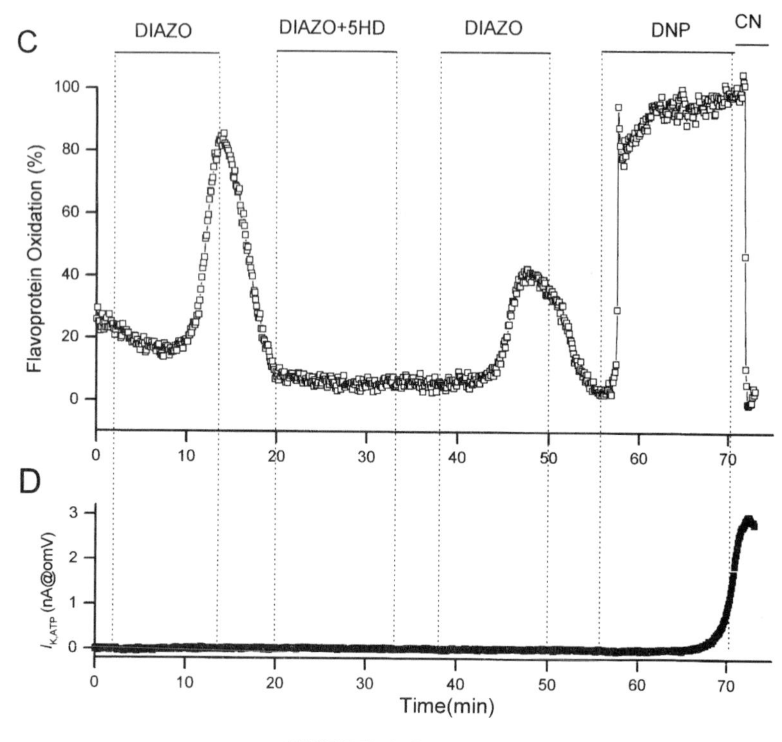

FIGURE 1, C and D

whether diazoxide can selectively open mitoK_{ATP} channels in intact living cells, we simultaneously measured flavoprotein fluorescence, an index of mitochondrial redox state, and surfaceK_{ATP} currents ($I_{K,ATP}$) in intact rabbit ventricular myocytes.

FIGURE 1 shows results from simultaneous measurements of flavoprotein fluorescence and membrane $I_{K,ATP}$ in cells exposed to diazoxide.[1] The periods of drug treatments are marked with horizontal bars. Diazoxide (100 μM) induced reversible oxidation of the flavoproteins (FIG. 1A) but did not activate $I_{K,ATP}$ (FIG. 1B). The redox signal was calibrated by exposing the cells to 2,4-dinitrophenol (DNP) followed by sodium cyanide (CN) at the end of the experiments. DNP, a protonophore that uncouples respiration from ATP synthesis and collapses the mitochondrial potential, induced maximal oxidation, while CN, which inhibits cytochrome oxidase and thus stops electron transfer, caused complete reduction of the flavoproteins (FIG.1A and C). Although membrane currents were unchanged by diazoxide, $I_{K,ATP}$ eventually turned on after prolonged exposure to DNP (FIG. 1B and D), indicating that these channels are operable under our experimental conditions despite diazoxide's inability to open them. Diazoxide [100 μM, DIAZO(1)] reversibly increased mitochondrial oxidation to 48 ± 3% of the DNP value (FIG. 1E). This oxidation was reproducible, since after washout of the response a second exposure to diazoxide [DIAZO(2)] in the same cells increased flavoprotein oxidation to 43 ± 5%. 5-hydroxydecanoic acid (5-HD) (100 μM) [DIAZO+5-HD(100)] attenuated the oxida-

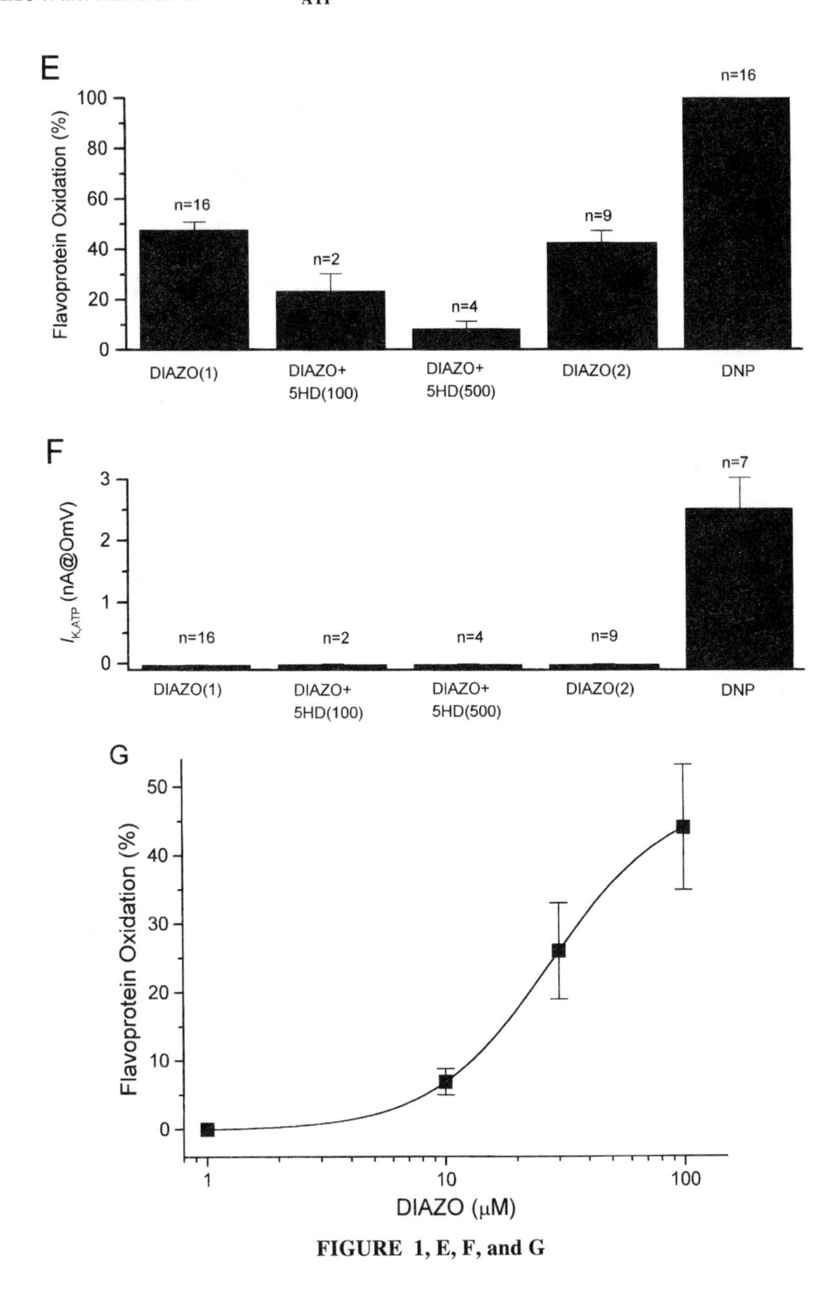

FIGURE 1, E, F, and G

tive effect of diazoxide by about half, while 500 μM 5-HD [(DIAZO+5-HD(500)] further reduced oxidation to 8 ± 3% [$p < 0.01$ versus DIAZO(1), DIAZO(2), and DIAZO+5-HD(100) groups]. Treatment with diazoxide and 5-HD did not activate $I_{K,ATP}$, while prolonged exposure (>6 min) to DNP did turn on $I_{K,ATP}$ (FIG. 1F). The

EC_{50} for diazoxide to induce mitochondrial oxidation is 27 μM (FIG. 1G). The subcellular site of diazoxide action was co-localized to mitochondria by confocal imaging of flavoprotein fluorescence and mitochondria (stained with tetramethylrhodamine ethyl ester).[1]

Our data show that diazoxide reversibly oxidizes the mitochondrial matrix, as expected if it opens the mitoK_{ATP} channel. Diazoxide had no effect on surfaceK_{ATP} channels. This insensitivity is consistent with the phenotype of the cardiac sarcolemmal isoform of K_{ATP} channels.[19] Considering the diffusion barriers between extracellularly applied diazoxide and the mitochondria and other differences in the experimental conditions, our value of 27 μM for the EC_{50} of diazoxide induction of mitochondrial oxidation is not inconsistent with the EC_{50} of ~3 μM for enhanced potassium flux in isolated mitochondria.[15]

5-HD IS A SELECTIVE MITOK_{ATP} CHANNEL BLOCKER

5-HD is widely used to block ischemic preconditioning and cardioprotection induced by K_{ATP} channel openers. Results from this study as well others[20] show that 5-HD is an effective blocker of mitoK_{ATP} channels. The possibility that 5-HD is selective for mitoK_{ATP} channels was then tested. We first demonstrated that, unlike diazoxide, the K_{ATP} channel opener pinacidil targets both mitoK_{ATP} and surfaceK_{ATP} channels (FIG. 2).[2] Pinacidil at 100 μM reversibly increased both flavoprotein oxidation and $I_{K,ATP}$. In the presence of 5-HD (500 μM), a second exposure to pinacidil failed to increase flavoprotein oxidation, whereas $I_{K,ATP}$ turned on without impediment after exposure to pinacidil. These results indicate that 5-HD selectively inhibits mitoK_{ATP} channels without affecting surfaceK_{ATP} channels.

We also tested glibenclamide, another K_{ATP} channel inhibitor. We did not observe consistent blockade of mitochondria oxidation, probably because glibenclamide alone caused oxidation of the flavoproteins especially at concentrations higher than 1 μM (data not shown). This is consistent with the finding that glibenclamide uncouples mitochondria with K_d of 4 μM.[21] Similarly, high concentrations of glibenclamide have been shown to affect the function of isolated mitochondria nonspecifically.[20] Therefore, we caution against the interpretation at face value of studies using glibenclamide to test the involvement of K_{ATP} channels in cardioprotection.

REGULATION OF MITOK_{ATP} CHANNELS

We have previously shown that adenosine and protein kinase C (PKC) can synergistically activate sarcolemmal $I_{K,ATP}$.[22] Recently, we found that PKC activation can also augment diazoxide-induced flavoprotein fluorescence.[2] Exposure to the PKC activator PMA potentiated and accelerated the effect of diazoxide on mitoK_{ATP} channels. These PMA effects were blocked by 5-HD. An inactive phorbol did not alter the effects of diazoxide. These results provide a direct mechanistic link between signal transduction and K_{ATP} channels for cardioprotection. The effects of adenosine on mitoK_{ATP} channels are currently under investigation.

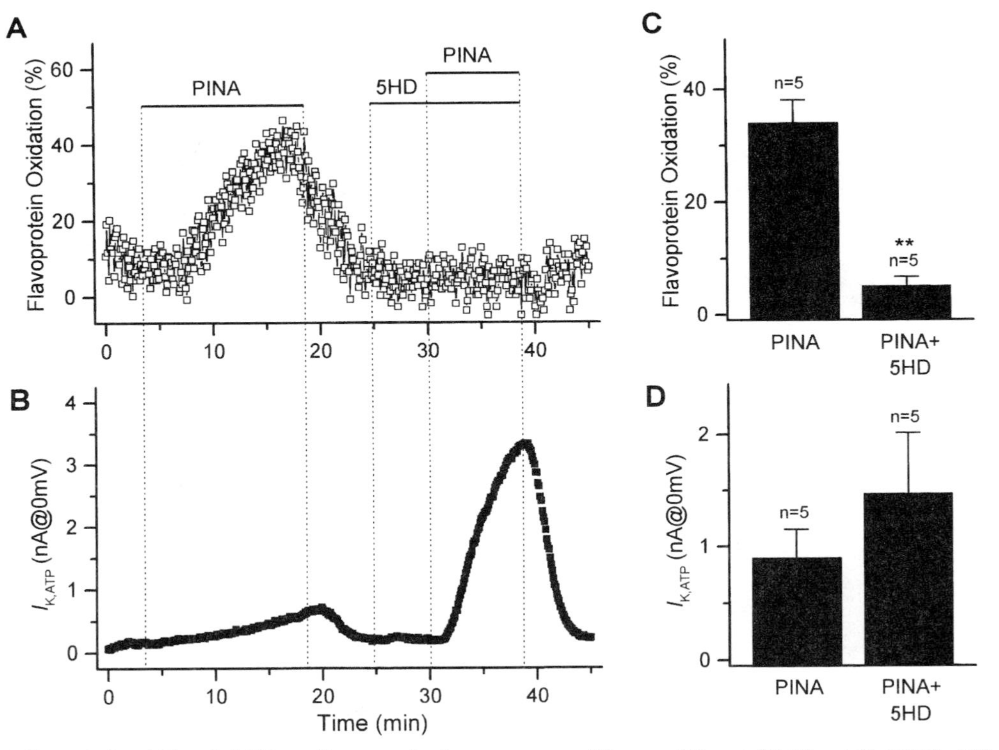

FIGURE 2. Effect of pinacidil and 5-HD on flavoprotein fluorescence and $I_{K,ATP}$. **(A)** and **(B)** Pinacidil (PINA, 100 μM) reversibly increased both flavoprotein oxidation and $I_{K,ATP}$. 5-HD (500 μM) completely inhibited pinacidil-induced flavoprotein oxidation but not $I_{K,ATP}$. **(C)** and **(D)** Summarized data for pinacidil-induced flavoprotein and $I_{K,ATP}$ measured in the absence (PINA group) and presence of 5-HD (PINA+5HD group), respectively. $^{**}p < 0.01$ versus PINA group. Bar indicates periods when the cells were exposed to drugs. (Reproduced with permission from Liu *et al.*[1])

It would be logical and desirable to extend this kind of study to the structural level to determine whether the mitoK_{ATP} channels are phosphorylated and, if so, how this alters their function. Such studies are not yet possible because the molecular identity of the channel is unknown.

DIAZOXIDE PROTECTS ISCHEMIC MYOCYTES

To test the idea that mitoK_{ATP} channels may play a role in cardioprotection, we examined the effect of diazoxide in a cellular ischemia model. Isolated rabbit ventricular myocytes were centrifuged into a pellet to simulate the restricted extracellular space and reduced oxygen supply during ischemia, sampled at designated time points, and stained with a hypotonic (85 mOsm) trypan blue solution to test the osmotic fragility of the membrane.[23] Diazoxide was added at 15 min and 5-HD was added at 20 min into the incubation buffer before pelleting and were not washed out.

FIGURE 3 plots the fraction of cells killed by 60 or 120 min of ischemia as a percentage of the total number of viable cells prior to ischemia.[1] Pelleting for 60 min and 120 min killed 35 ± 2% and 46 ± 4% of cells, respectively, in the control (Cont). However, inclusion of 50 μM diazoxide significantly decreased cell death during simulated ischemia to about half of that in the controls (18 ± 3% after 60 min, and

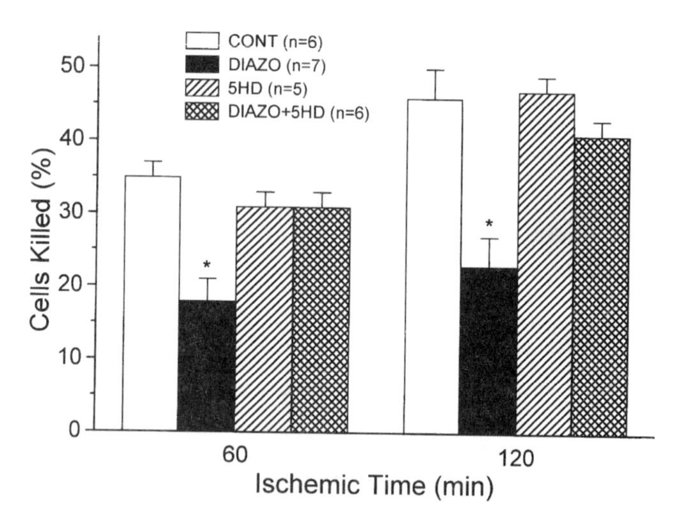

FIGURE 3. Pooled data show that diazoxide protects rabbit ventricular myocytes from ischemia. Cell killed (%) was calculated as number of cells killed by ischemia as a percentage of the total viable cells prior to ischemia. In the control group (Cont), cells were pelleted and sampled at 60 min and 120 min. For the diazoxide-treated group (DIAZO), diazoxide was added into the solution (final concentration: 50 μM) 15 min before pelleting. In the third group (5-HD), 5-HD was added in to the cell suspension (final concentration: 100 μM) 20 min prior to pelleting. Cells in the DIAZO+5HD group were treated the same as in the third group except that diazoxide was added into the cell suspension (final concentration: 50 μM) 15 min before pelleting. $*p < 0.01$ versus the other three groups. (Reproduced with permission from Liu *et al.*[1])

23 ± 4% after 120 min, $p < 0.01$ versus Cont). The protection by diazoxide was completely blocked by 100 μM 5-HD (31 ± 2% after 60 min and 41 ± 2% after 120 min). 5-HD alone did not significantly alter the percentage of fractions of cells killed by simulated ischemia: 31 ± 2% after 60 min and 47 ± 2% after 120 min. Glibenclamide (1 μM) also blocked the protection from diazoxide (data not shown). Diazoxide at 100 μM had a similar protective effect (data not shown). For each experiment, there was always an isochronal nonischemic group in which cells were not pelleted. In these groups, less than 5% of trypan blue–resistant cells became permeable to trypan blue during the 120-min experiments.

Our results demonstrated that diazoxide treatment protects rabbit ventricular myocytes to the same extent as preconditioning in our previously published results.[11] Interestingly, a cardioprotective EC_{25} of 11 μM diazoxide has been reported in intact hearts.[24] This concentration corresponds closely to that which we observed to induce flavoprotein oxidation (FIG. 1G).

Because we used a single-cell model, we were unable to investigate the involvement of mitoK_{ATP} channels in genuine ischemic preconditioning in the present experimental system. There are known important differences between ischemic preconditioning and cardioprotective effects of K_{ATP} channel openers in terms of efficacy and memory.[25] Nevertheless, the protection from ischemic preconditioning and K_{ATP} channel openers is blocked by glibenclamide and 5-HD.[26] Thus, while it is reasonable to propose that mitoK_{ATP} is the target for both, further studies are warranted to bolster the links between pharmacological and genuine ischemic preconditioning. The selectivity of diazoxide and 5-HD on the mitoK_{ATP} channel will facilitate such studies.

Our results demonstrate that diazoxide targets only mitoK_{ATP} channels—not surfaceK_{ATP} channels—and suggest that mitoK_{ATP} channels may serve as effectors of cardioprotection by K_{ATP} channel openers. The question remains as to how opening of mitoK_{ATP} channels might protect myocytes against ischemic damage. One possibility is that dissipation of mitochondrial membrane potential decreases the driving force for calcium influx through the calcium uniporter. Inhibition of the mitochondrial calcium uniporter by ruthenium red protects hearts against ischemia and reperfusion injury,[27–29] consistent with this hypothesis. Another possibility is that opening of mitoK_{ATP} channels decreases the proton gradient, which may promote the binding of the endogenous mitochondrial ATPase inhibitor IF_1[30] and thus conserve ATP during ischemia. Finally, a change of mitochondrial membrane potential could alter glycolytic pathways during ischemia in favor of myocyte survival. Further studies on mitoK_{ATP} channels will help us not only to dissect the mechanism of cardioprotection from K_{ATP} channels and ischemic preconditioning, but also to understand the pathogenesis of ischemic and reperfusion injury. In addition, recognition of this role for mitoK_{ATP} channels identifies a promising new target for the development of cardioprotective drugs.

REFERENCES

1. LIU, Y., T. SATO, B. O'ROURKE & E. MARBAN. 1998. Mitochondrial ATP-sensitive potassium channels: novel effectors of cardioprotection? Circulation **97:** 2463–2469.
2. SATO, T., B. O'ROURKE & E. MARBAN. 1998. Modulation of mitochondrial ATP-dependent potassium channels by protein kinase C. Circ. Res. **83:** 110–114.

3. MURRY, C.E., R.B. JENNINGS & K.A. REIMER. 1986. Preconditioning with ischemia: a delay of lethal cell injury in ischemic myocardium. Circulation **74:** 1124–1136.
4. COHEN, M.V. & J. M. DOWNEY. 1993. Ischaemic preconditioning: can the protection be bottled? Lancet **342:** 6.
5. SCHULZ, R., J. ROSE & G. HEUSCH. 1994. Involvement of activation of ATP-dependent potassium channels in ischemic preconditioning in swine. Am. J. Physiol. **267:** H1341–H1352.
6. GROVER, G.J., A.J. D'ALONZO, S. DZWONCZYK, C.S. PARHAM & R.B. DARBENZIO. 1996. Preconditioning is not abolished by the delayed rectifier K^+ blocker dofetilide. Am. J. Physiol. **40:** H1207–H1214.
7. YAO, Z. & G.J. GROSS. 1994. Effects of the K_{ATP} channel opener bimakalim on coronary blood flow, monophasic action potential duration, and infarct size in dogs. Circulation **89:** 1769–1775.
8. GROVER, G.J., A.J. D'ALONZO, T.A. HESS, P.G. SLEPH & R.B. DARBENZIO. 1995. Glyburide-reversible cardioprotective effect of BMS-180448 is independent of action potential shortening in guinea pig hearts. Cardiovasc. Res. **30:** 731–738.
9. GROVER, G.J., A.J. D'ALONZO, C.S. PARHAM & R.B. DARBENZIO. 1995. Cardioprotection with the K_{ATP} opener cromakalim is not correlated with ischemic myocardial action potential duration. J. Cardiovasc. Pharmacol. **26:** 145–152.
10. LIANG, B.T. 1996. Direct preconditioning of cardiac ventricular myocytes via adenosine A1 receptor and K_{ATP} channel. Am. J. Physiol. **40:** H1769–H1777.
11. LIU, Y., W.D. GAO, B. O'ROURKE & E. MARBAN. 1996. Cell-type specificity of preconditioning in an in vitro model. Basic Res. Cardiol. **91:** 450–457.
12. INOUE, I., H. NAGASE, K. KISHI & T. HIGUTI. 1991. ATP-sensitive K^+ channel in the mitochondrial inner membrane. Nature **352:** 244–247.
13. PAUCEK, P., G. MIRONOVA, F. MAHDI, A.D. BEAVIS, G. WOLDEGIORGIS & K.D. GARLID. 1992. Reconstitution and partial purification of the glybenclamide-dependent, ATP-dependent K^+ channels from rat liver and beef heart mitochondria. J. Biol. Chem. **267:** 26062–26069.
14. INAGAKI, N., T. GONOI, J.P.I. CLEMENT, N. NAMBA, J. INAZAWA, G. GONZALEZ, L. AGUILAR-BRYAN, S. SEINO & J. BRYAN. 1995. Reconstitution of I_{KATP}: an inward rectifier subunit plus the sulfonylurea receptor. Science **270:** 1166–1170.
15. GARLID, K.D., P. PAUCEK, V. YAROV-YAROVOY, X. SUN & P.A. SCHINDLER. 1996. The mitochondrial K_{ATP} channel as a receptor for potassium channel openers. J. Biol. Chem. **271:** 8796–8799.
16. SUZUKI, M., K. KOTAKE, K. FUJIKURA, N. INAGAKI, T. SUZUKI, T. GONOI, S. SEINO & K. TAKATA. 1997. Kir6.1: a possible subunit of ATP-sensitive K^+ channels in mitochondria. Biochem. Biophys. Res. Commun. **241:** 693–697.
17. CHANCE, B., I.A. SALKOVITZ & A.G. KOVACH. 1972. Kinetics of mitochondrial flavoprotein and pyridine nucleotide in perfused heart. Am. J. Physiol. **223:** 207–218.
18. HAJNOCZKY, G., L.D. ROBB-GASPERS, M.B. SEITZ & A.P. THOMAS. 1995. Decoding of cytosolic calcium oscillations in the mitochondria. Cell **82:** 415–424.
19. INAGAKI, N., T. GONOI, J.P. CLEMENT, C. WANG, L. AGUILAR-BRYAN, J. BRYAN & S. SEINO. 1996. A family of sulfonylurea receptors determines the pharmacological properties of ATP-sensitive K^+ channels. Neuron **16:** 1011–1017.
20. GARLID, K.D., M. JABUREK, V. YAROV-YAROVOY & P. PAUCEK. 1997. Sulfonylurea receptor—K^+ channel coupling in the mitochondrial K_{ATP} channels. Biophy. J. **72:** A39. (Abstract)
21. SZEWCZYK, A., A. CZYZ & M.J. NALECZ. 1997. ATP-regulated potassium channel blocker, glybenclamide, uncouples mitochondria. Pol. J. Pharmacol. **49:** 49–52.
22. LIU, Y., W.D. GAO, B. O'ROURKE & E. MARBAN. 1996. Synergistic modulation of ATP-sensitive K^+ currents by protein kinase C and adenosine: implications for ischemic preconditioning. Circ. Res. **78:** 443–454.
23. VANDER HEIDE, R.S., D. RIM, C.M. HOHL & C.E. GANOTE. 1990. An in vitro model of myocardial ischemia utilizing isolated adult rat myocytes. J. Mol. Cell. Cardiol. **22:** 165–181.
24. GARLID, K.D., P. PAUCEK, V. YAROV-YAROVOY, H.N. MURRAY, R.B. DARBENZIO, A. J. D'ALONZO, N.J. LODGE, M.A. SMITH & G.J. GROVER. 1997. Cardioprotective

effect of diazoxide and its interaction with mitochondrial ATP-sensitive K^+ channels: Possible mechanism of cardioprotection. Circ. Res. **81:** 1072–1082.
25. YAO, Z., T. MIZUMURA, D.A. MEI & G.J. GROSS. 1997. K_{ATP} channels and memory of ischemic preconditioning in dogs: synergism between adenosine and K_{ATP} channels. Am. J. Physiol. **272:** H334–H342.
26. GROSS, G.J., Z. YAO & J.A. AUCHAMPACH. 1994. Role of ATP-sensitive potassium channels in ischemic preconditioning. Dev. Cardiovasc. Med. **148:** 125–135.
27. FIGUEREDO, V.M., K.P. DRESDNER, A.C. WOLNEY & A.M. KELLER. 1991. Postischaemic reperfusion injury in the isolated rat heart: effect of ruthenium red. Cardiovasc. Res. **25:** 337–342.
28. MIYAMAE, M., S.A. CAMACHO, M.W. WEINER & V.M. FIGUEREDO. 1996. Attenuation of postischemic reperfusion injury is related to prevention of $[Ca^{2+}]_m$ overload in rat heart. Am. J. Physiol. **271:** H1245–H2153.
29. PARK, Y., D.K. BOWLES & J.P. KEHRER. 1990. Protection against injury in isolated-perfused rat heart by ruthenium red. J. Pharmacol. Exp. Ther. **253:** 628–635.
30. ROUSLIN, W. 1991. Regulation of the mitochondrial ATPase in situ in cardiac muscle: role of the inhibitor subunit. J. Bioenerg. Biomembr. **23:** 873–888.

The Molecular Mechanism of Cardiac Hypertrophy and Failure

TSUTOMU YAMAZAKI,[a,b] ISSEI KOMURO,[a] ICHIRO SHIOJIMA,[a] AND YOSHIO YAZAKI[a,c]

[a]*Department of Cardiovascular Medicine, Faculty of Medicine, University of Tokyo, 7-3-1 Hongo, Bunkyo-ku, Tokyo 113-8655, Japan*

[b]*Health Service Center, University of Tokyo, 7-3-1 Hongo, Bunkyo-ku, Tokyo 113-0033, Japan*

ABSTRACT: Mechanical stretch induced by high blood pressure is an initial factor leading to cardiac hypertrophy. In an *in vivo* study, an angiotensin II (AngII) type 1 receptor antagonist TCV116 reduced left ventricular (LV) weight, LV wall thickness, transverse myocyte diameter, relative amount of V3 myosin heavy chain, and interstitial fibrosis, while treatment with hydralazine did not. In an *in vitro* study using cultured cardiomyocytes, mechanical stretch activated second messengers such as mitogen-activated protein (MAP) kinase, followed by increased protein synthesis. Additionally, in the stretch-conditioned medium AngII and endothelin-1 concentrations were increased. Furthermore, the Na^+/H^+ exchanger activated by mechanical stretch modulated the hypertrophic responses of cardiomyocytes. The pathways leading to MAP kinase activation differed between cell types. In cardiac fibroblasts AngII activated MAP kinase via Gβγ subunit of Gi, Src, Shc, Grb2, and Ras, whereas Gq and protein kinase C were critical in cardiomyocytes.

MECHANICAL OVERLOAD ACTIVATES THE CARDIAC RENIN–ANGIOTENSIN SYSTEM

Mechanical stress per se is a major factor for cardiac hypertrophy at the pressure or volume overload. The first reported effect of mechanical stress on the heart was that stretching quiescent papillary muscles of rabbits accelerates protein synthesis.[1] It was successively shown that elevation of aortic pressure increases protein synthesis in beating perfused rat hearts.[2] Cooper and colleagues[3] also reported that in aorta-constricted cats, papillary muscles whose tendon had been cut to release the tension do not represent hypertrophy, whereas neighboring uncut papillary muscles show marked hypertrophy and that the hypertrophy is induced even under the denervation of ventricular adrenoreceptors. On the other hand, in a series of *in vitro* studies, stretching cultured cardiomyocytes of neonatal rats drastically induced protein synthesis and specific gene expression without participation of neural and humoral factors.[4,5]

[c]Address correspondence to: Yoshio Yazaki M.D., Ph.D., Department of Cardiovascular Medicine, Faculty of Medicine, University of Tokyo, 7-3-1 Hongo, Bunkyo-ku, Tokyo 113-8655, Japan; Phone: 81-3-3815-5411 ext. 5013; Fax: 81-3-3815-2087; E-mail: yazaki-tky@umin.ac.jp

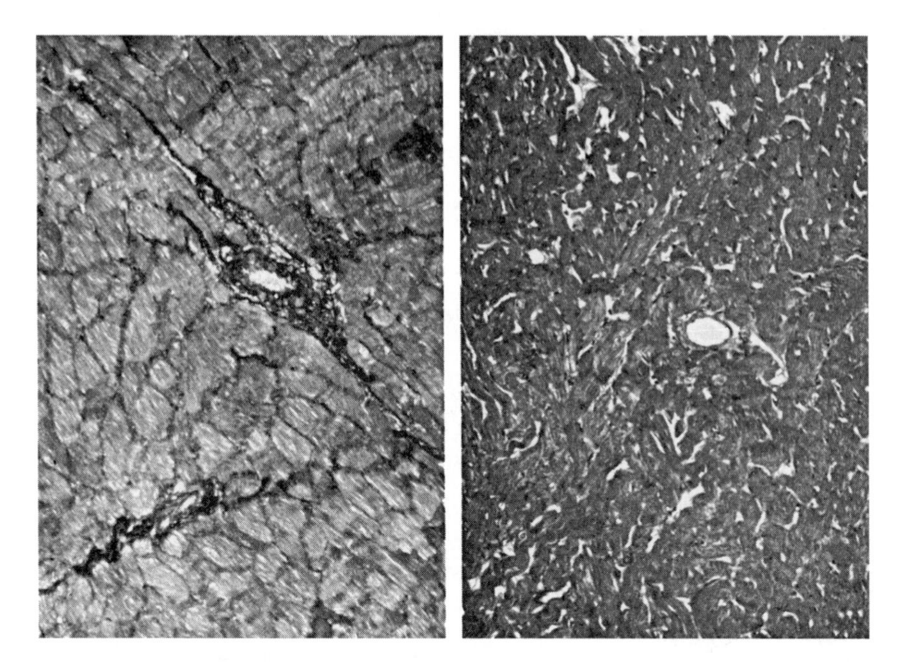

FIGURE 1. Histological examination of left ventricular fibrosis by Azan staining. (*Left*) Perivascular and interstitial fibrosis in vehicle-treated 25-week-old SHR. (*Right*) Suppression of the fibrosis in TCV116-treated 25-week-old SHR.

With regard to the molecular mechanisms by which external overload evokes cardiac hypertrophy, protein kinase cascades are the focus of much attention.[6] Some groups including ours have shown that mechanical stretch of cardiomyocytes activates second messengers such as phosphatidylinositol, protein kinase C (PKC), Raf-1 kinase, and mitogen-activated protein (MAP) kinase. All of these second messengers are involved in re-expression of a number of genes, including atrial natriuretic peptide, skeletal α actin, and β myosin heavy chain (MHC), and subsequent increased protein synthesis.[4,5,7–9]

Much evidence demonstrates that the cardiac renin-angiotensin system is linked to the formation of pressure-overload hypertrophy. It has been shown that all components of the renin-angiotensin system [e.g., renin, angiotensinogen, angiotensin-converting enzyme (ACE), and angiotensin II (AngII) receptors] are identified in the heart at both the mRNA and the protein levels[10] and that the renin-angiotensin system is activated in experimental left ventricular (LV) hypertrophy induced by hemodynamic overload.[10–13] Shyu and colleagues[14] have also shown that cyclical stretch of cultured cardiac myocytes accelerates angiotensinogen gene expression. Moreover, an increase in LV mass produced by abdominal aortic constriction can be completely prevented by an ACE inhibitor with no change in afterload and plasma renin activity.[15] We further investigated the relationship between hypertensive cardiac hypertrophy and the cardiac renin-angiotensin system.[16] Spontaneously hypertensive rats (SHR) were assigned to the treatment with an AngII type

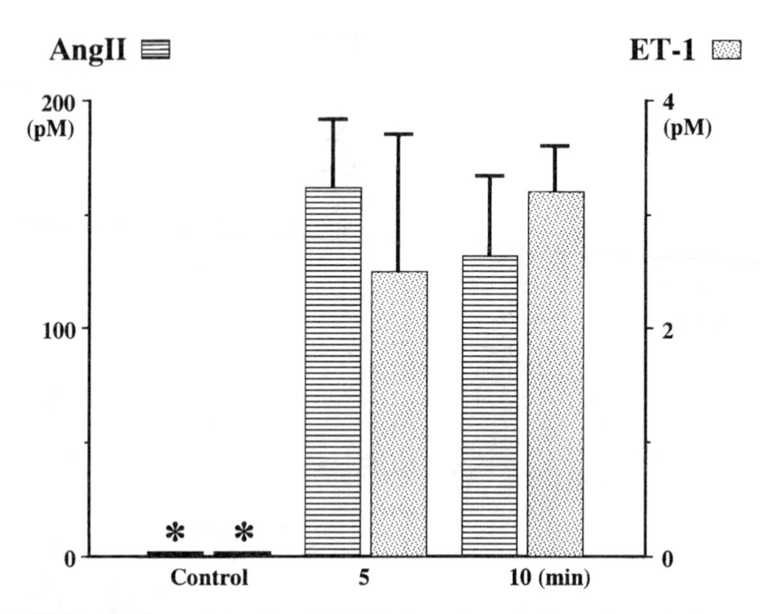

FIGURE 2. Release of AngII and ET-1 in the culture medium of stretched myocytes. The results were indicated as mean±S.E. for four to six independent experiments. Asterisks indicate undetectable levels.

1 receptor antagonist (TCV116) or a vasodilating agent (hydralazine). LV wall thickness was serially monitored using M-mode echocardiography, and LV weight, transverse diameter of cardiomyocytes, relative amount of V3 MHC, and degree of interstitial collagen accumulation were examined. Untreated SHR progressively developed severe hypertension with increasing age. Treatment with TCV116 or hydralazine completely blunted the increase in blood pressure. Treatment with TCV116 ameliorated LV weight, LV wall thickness, transverse diameter of myocytes, relative amount of V3 MHC, and fibrotic changes (FIG. 1), whereas treatment with hydralazine slightly prevented an increase in LV wall thickness but did not exert significant restoration of other parameters. These results suggest a crucial role of the cardiac renin-angiotensin system in the development of LV hypertrophy by pressure overload.

To further gain insight into the role of AngII in mechanical stress–induced cardiac hypertrophy, cardiac myocytes in culture were stretched in the absence or presence of saralasin (an antagonist of AngII type 1 and type 2 receptors), TCV116, or PD123319 (an AngII type 2 receptor-specific antagonist).[17] Stretching myocytes rapidly increased the activities of Raf-1 kinase and MAP kinase. Both saralasin and TCV116 partly inhibited the stretch-induced increase in the activities of Raf-1 kinase and MAP kinase, whereas PD123319 was without inhibitory effects. Amino acid incorporation into cells was enhanced by mechanical stretch, which was also partly diminished by the pretreatment with saralasin or TCV116 but not by PD123319. Further, when the culture medium conditioned by stretching cardiocytes was transferred to unstretched cardiac myocytes, MAP kinase activity was slightly enhanced, and the increase was completely suppressed by saralasin or TCV116. Taken collectively, the locally activated cardiac renin-angiotensin system may play a pivotal role in pressure-overload cardiac hypertrophy, and AngII may act to promote the growth of cardiomyocytes by an autocrine or paracrine mechanism. In fact, we and others[18] have shown that mechanical stretch induces secretion of AngII from cardiac myocytes of neonatal rats (FIG. 2).

ENDOTHELIN-1 AND Na^+/H^+ EXCHANGER ARE ALSO INVOLVED IN PRESSURE-OVERLOAD CARDIAC HYPERTROPHY

We have recently clarified the association of endothelin-1 (ET-1) with mechanical stretch–induced hypertrophic responses of cardiomyocytes.[19] BQ123, an antagonist selective for the ETA receptor subtype, diminished stretch-induced activation of MAP kinase and an increase in phenylalanine uptake by approximately 60% and 50%, respectively, but not an ETB receptor–specific antagonist BQ788. ET-1 was constitutively secreted from cardiomyocytes, and a significant increase in ET-1 concentration was observed in the culture medium of cardiomyocytes in response to stretch (FIG. 2). ET-1 mRNA induction was also enhanced at 30 minutes after stretch. Moreover, ET-1 and AngII synergistically activated Raf-1 kinase and MAP kinase in cardiac myocytes. These results suggest that ET-1 as well as AngII modulate mechanical stress–induced cardiac hypertrophy.

Many cells rapidly respond to a variety of environmental stimuli by ion channels or exchangers in the plasma membrane. Mechanosensitive ion channels have been observed with single-channel recordings in more than 30 cell types of prokaryotes, plants, fungi, and all animals so far examined.[20] The activation of mechanosensitive ion channels has been proposed as the transduction mechanism between load and protein synthesis in cardiac hypertrophy.[21] When cardiomyocytes were exposed to a Na^+ ionophore, *c-fos* expression was transiently induced, possibly because of increased Ca^{2+} uptake by the Na^+/Ca^{2+} exchange mechanism.[22] However, the expression of fetal-type genes was not induced by Na^+ increase (unpublished data). On the other hand, we have recently indicated that the Na^+/H^+ exchanger (NHE) mediates mechanical stretch–induced hypertrophic responses (such as Raf-1 kinase and MAP kinase activation) followed by increased protein synthesis in cardiomyocytes.[23,24] To determine the involvement of mechanosensitive ion channels and exchangers in stretch-induced hypertrophic responses, cardiomyocytes were stretched after pretreatment with a specific inhibitor of stretch-sensitive cation channels (gadolinium and streptomycin), of ATP-sensitive K^+ channels (glibenclamide), of hyperpolarization-activated inward channels (CsCl), or of the NHE (HOE 694). Gadolinium, streptomycin, glibenclamide, and CsCl did not have any inhibitory effects on MAP kinase activation by mechanical stretch. HOE 694, however, markedly diminished stretch-induced activation of Raf-1 kinase and MAP kinase and attenuated stretch-induced increase in phenylalanine uptake into cells. Furthermore, the NHE inhibitor HOE 694 in combination with an AngII type 1 receptor antagonist TCV116 and an ETA receptor antagonist BQ123 almost completely suppressed mechanical stretch–induced MAP kinase activation (FIG. 3). Taken collectively, the NHE and autocrinely released vasoactive peptides AngII and ET-1 represent at least two differ-

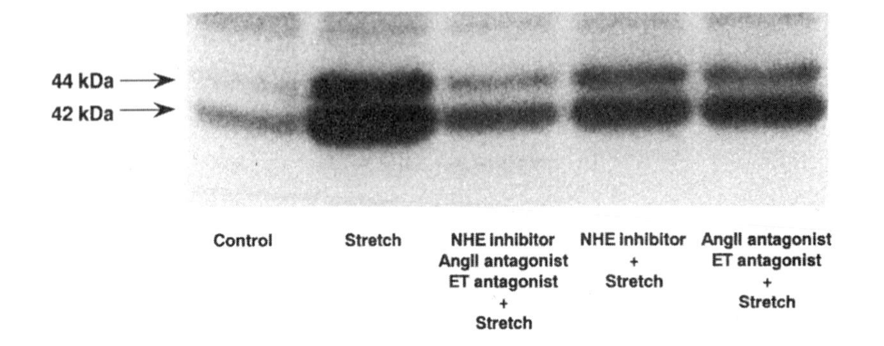

FIGURE 3. Effects of BQ 123, TCV116, or HOE 694 on stretch-induced MAP kinase activation. After pretreatment with BQ 123 (ETA receptor antagonist), TCV116 (AngII type 1 receptor antagonist), and HOE 694 (NHE inhibitor) for 30 minutes, cardiocytes were stretched by 20% for 8 minutes, and MAP kinase activities were analyzed.

ent signaling pathways by which mechanical stretch can activate the hypertrophic responses of cardiomyocytes.

EXTRACELLULAR MATRIX AND CYTOSKELETON

There is abundant data indicating that mechanical stress is transduced into cells from the sites at which cells attach to the extracellular matrix (ECM).[25] Therefore, transmembrane ECM receptors, such as the integrin family adhesion molecules, are good candidates for mechnoreceptors. A large extracellular domain of integrin receptor complex binds to various ECM proteins, while a cytoplasmic domain interacts with the cytoskeleton in the cell.[26] Integrins, which are heterodimeric proteins composed of α and β subunits, can transmit signals not only by organizing the cytoskeleton but also by altering biochemical properties such as the extent of tyrosine phosphorylation of a complex of proteins including the integrin-linked focal adhesion kinase $pp125^{FAK}$.[25] In addition, since cytoskeleton proteins can potentially regulate plasma membrane proteins such as enzymes, ion channels, and antiporters, mechanical stress could modulate these membrane-associated proteins and stimulate second messenger systems through the cytoskeleton. In this regard, $pp125^{FAK}$ has been reported to exhibit extracellular matrix–dependent phosphorylation on tyrosine and to physically associate with nonreceptor protein kinases via their Src homology 2 domains.[27] Furthermore, the Rho family small GTP-binding proteins, which play a key part in regulating the actin cytoskeleton and cell adhesion through the integrin receptors, are activated in stretched cardiocytes independently of autocrinely released AngII and ET-1(unpublished data). Mechanical stress may first be received by integrin and then interlinked actin microfilaments transduce mechanical stress in concert with microtubles and intermediate filaments.

SIGNAL TRANSDUCTION PATHWAYS ACTIVATED BY ANGII

AngII directly induces cardiomyocyte hypertrophy even without an increase in vascular resistance or cardiac afterload.[12] We therefore examined AngII-evoked signal transduction pathways leading to activation of MAP kinase in cultured cardiac myocytes by using a variety of inhibitors.[28] Inhibition of PKC with calphostin C or downregulation of PKC by pretreatment with a phorbol ester for 24 hours abolished AngII-induced activation of Raf-1 kinase and MAP kinase. But pretreatment with tyrosine kinase inhibitors, genistein and tyrphostin, did not attenuate AngII-induced activation of MAP kinase. Overexpression of C-terminal Src kinase (Csk), which inhibits the function of Src family tyrosine kinases, had no effect on AngII-induced activation of transfected MAP kinase in cardiac myocytes. Although pretreatment with manumycin, a Ras farnesyltransferase inhibitor, or overexpression of dominant negative (DN) mutant of Ras inhibited insulin-induced MAP kinase activation, neither of them affected AngII-induced activation of MAP kinase. By contrast, overexpression of DN mutant of Raf-1 kinase completely suppressed MAP kinase activation by AngII. These results, together with the previous data,[9] indicate that AngII induces cardiomyocyte hypertrophy through the PKC–Raf-1 kinase–MAP kinase cascade (FIG. 4).

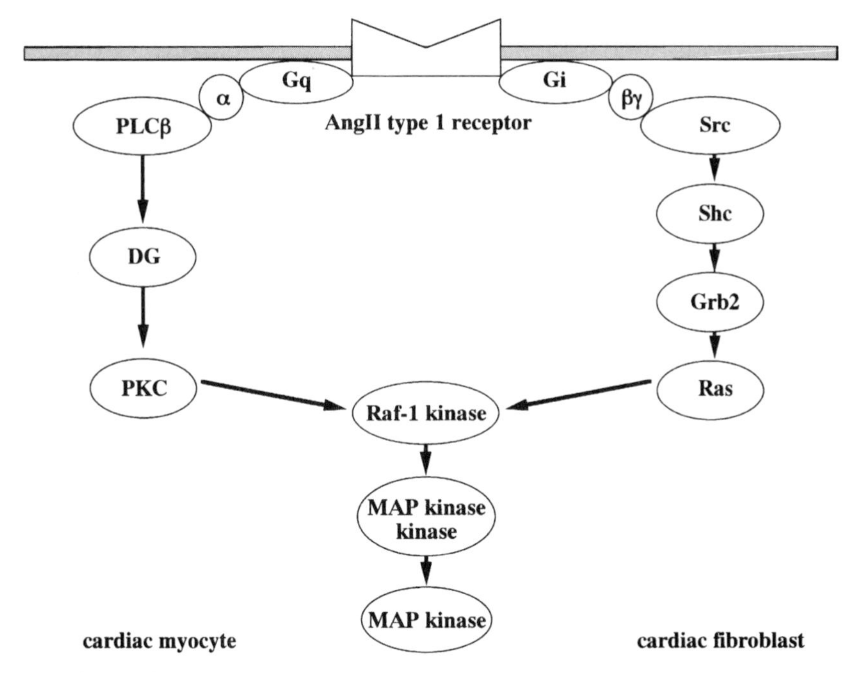

FIGURE 4. Signaling pathways induced by AngII. In cardiac myocytes, AngII-induced MAP kinase activation is independent of βγ subunit of Gi, Src, Shc, Grb2, and Ras, but dependent on PKC. By contrast, in cardiac fibroblasts, AngII activates Gβγ subunit derived from Gi protein, which in turn leads to the phosphorylation cascade including Src, Shc, Grb2, and Ras followed by activation of the Raf-1 kinase/MAP kinase cascade. PLC, phospholipase; DG, diacylglycerol; PKC, protein kinase C.

AngII also evokes a variety of signals and induces proliferation of cardiac fibroblasts.[29] We have recently shown that unlike in cardiac myocytes, AngII-induced MAP kinase activation is suppressed by tyrosine kinase inhibitors but is not affected by PKC downregulation in cardiac fibroblasts.[30] AngII-induced MAP kinase activation was abolished by pretreatment with pertussis toxin and by overexpression of the Gβγ subunit-binding domain of the β-adrenergic receptor kinase 1 in cardiac fibroblasts. Inhibition of tyrosine kinases but not of PKC abolished AngII-induced MAP kinase activation in cardiac fibroblasts. Overexpression of Csk or DN mutant of Ras in cardiac fibroblasts completely suppressed the activation of MAP kinase. Moreover, AngII rapidly induced phosphorylation of Shc and association of Shc with Grb2 adapter protein in cardiac fibroblasts but not in cardiac myocytes.[30] These findings suggest that AngII-evoked signal transduction pathways differ among cell types. In cardiac fibroblasts, AngII activates MAP kinases through a pathway including the Gβγ subunit of Gi protein, tyrosine kinases including Src family tyrosine kinases, Shc, Grb2, Ras, and Raf-1 kinase, while Gq and PKC are critical in cardiac myocytes (FIG. 4)

DIASTOLIC DYSFUNCTION IN THE HYPERTROPHIED HEART

Cardiac sarcoplasmic reticulum (SR) is a major determinant that sequesters intracellular calcium and influences the relaxation and the tension development of myocardium. Calcium uptake by the SR is driven by a Ca^{2+}-ATPase, which is a membrane protein with a molecular weight of 100 kD and constitutes 35–40% of the proteins in the SR.[31,32] The process of myocardial relaxation is regulated by cellular mechanisms that restore cytosolic calcium to low concentration in diastole, and Ca^{2+}-ATPase of the SR is thought to be foremost among these mechanisms. Some studies have shown that the deterioration of diastolic relaxation in the hypertrophied heart is consistent with depressed Ca^{2+}-ATPase content and resultant decreased calcium uptake by the SR.[33,34] Also, the expression of Ca^{2+}-ATPase mRNA was markedly decreased in the pressure-overloaded heart.[35] We further examined the developmental change of Ca^{2+}-ATPase.[13] The expression of Ca^{2+}-ATPase mRNA was significantly low during the early embryonic period but drastically increased from two days before birth. The mRNA level in 12-day old fetus was approximately 8% compared with 200-day-old adults. Moreover, we assessed Ca^{2+}-ATPase content by measuring the density of the protein band corresponding to the 100 kD Ca^{2+}-ATPase after separating the proteins by electrophoresis. Although there was no significant change in the content of SR protein in aorta-constricted rats compared with sham-operated ones, the Ca^{2+}-ATPase content and calcium uptake by the SR were significantly decreased in rat hearts that received pressure overload for one month. These results indicate that (1) the expression of Ca^{2+}-ATPase is regulated by hemodynamic load and developmental stage at the mRNA levels and (2) the function of the SR is reduced in pressure-overload hypertrophy. Such an altered function of the SR in cardiac hypertrophy may be regarded as a compensatory mechanism because depressed calcium sequestration by the SR may reduce calcium release in systole and thus suppress the oxygen consumption of the hypertrophied myofibrils. At the same time, however, reduced SR function will cause insufficient decrease of intra-cellular calcium in diastole and induce slowing of ventricular relaxation.

Cardiac SR also contains a unique low molecular weight integral protein, phospholamban. The phosphorylation of phospholamban by cAMP-dependent protein kinase accelerates calcium uptake by increasing the turnover rate of the SR Ca^{2+}-ATPase,[36] and the mRNA levels of phospholamban are decreased in the load-induced hypertrophied heart,[37] suggesting that phospholamban may also be involved in the diastolic dysfunction in the hypertrophied heart.

Cardiomyocytes constitute only one third of all cells in myocardium, the remaining two thirds are non-myocytes including fibroblasts, vascular smooth muscle cells, and endothelial cells.[38,39] The remodeling of the interstitial components as well as that of myocytes occurs during the process of cardiac hypertrophy.[40] The existence of extracellular collagen matrix in the mammalian heart has been delineated,[41] and the major part of the collagenous network is produced by non-myocytes, possibly in concert with cardiomyocytes. Previous studies have reported that pathological LV hypertrophy by hemodynamic load is associated with abnormal accumulation of fibrillar collagen within the extracellular space[42] and that the reactive fibrosis might be responsible for the increased ventricular stiffness.[43] We further examined the fibrotic changes of the hearts from abdominal aorta-constricted rats.[13] In sham-operated rat hearts, a slight amount of collagen was detected around the vessel walls. In pressure-overload hearts, on the other hand, much more collagen accumulation was observed within the interstitium as well as in the perivascular area. The mRNA levels of type I and type III collagens also increased progressively after abdominal aorta constriction. It has previously been reported that the relative amount of type III collagen to type I is increased in pressure-overload hypertrophy.[40] Taken together, qualitative and quantitative changes in the extracellular matrix of the heart are induced by hemodynamic overload. Perivascular fibrosis leads to myocardial ischemia, and the accumulation of interstitial collagen contributes to the increase of ventricular stiffness, both of which may play important roles in the mechanism of impaired diastolic function in the hypertrophied heart.

CONCLUSIONS

Mechanical stretch–induced AngII and ET-1 produce cardiac hypertrophy, and the NHE directly activated by mechanical stretch also induces the hypertrophic responses independently of autocrinely released AngII and ET-1. Furthermore, AngII-induced signal transduction pathways leading to MAP kinase activation are divergent among cell types. Acting via the different signaling pathways, AngII evokes cardiac myocyte hypertrophy and fibroblast proliferation. Further investigation will lead to the development of novel strategies for the prevention and treatment of cardiac hypertrophy and failure. Additionally, the depressed function of the cardiac SR may be responsible for the impaired diastolic function in pressure-overloaded hearts. The remodeling of extracellular matrix by pressure overload is an adaptational phenomenon because the accumulation of collagen fibers might be necessary to support the hypertrophied myofibrils. Such fibrotic changes, however, increase chamber stiffness and may also cause diastolic dysfunction in the hypertrophied heart.

REFERENCES

1. PETERSON, M.B. & M. LESCH. 1972. Protein synthesis and amino acid transport in isolated rabbit right ventricular muscle. Circ. Res. **31:** 317–327.
2. KIRA, Y., P.J. KOCHEL, E.E. GORDON & H.E. MORGAN. 1984. Aortic perfusion pressure as a determinant of cardiac protein synthesis. Am. J. Physiol. **246:** C247–C258.
3. COOPER, G., R.L. KENT, C.E. UBOH, E.W. THOMPSON & T.A. MARINO. 1985. Hemodynamic versus adrenergic control of cat right ventricular hypertrophy. J. Clin. Invest. **75:** 1403–1414.
4. KOMURO, I., T. KAIDA, Y. SHIBAZAKI, M. KURABAYASHI, F. TAKAKU & Y. YAZAKI. 1990. Stretching cardiac myocytes stimulates proto-oncogene expression. J. Biol. Chem. **265:** 3595–3598.
5. KOMURO, I., Y. KATOH, T. KAIDA, Y. SHIBAZAKI, M. KURABAYASHI, F. TAKAKU & Y. YAZAKI. 1991. Mechanical loading stimulates cell hypertrophy and specific gene expression in cultured rat cardiac myocytes. J. Biol. Chem. **266:** 1265–1268.
6. YAMAZAKI, T., I. KOMURO & Y. YAZAKI. 1995. Molecular mechanism of cardiac cellular hypertrophy by mechanical stress. J. Mol. Cell. Cardiol. **27:** 133–140.
7. SADOSHIMA, J. & S. IZUMO. 1993. Mechanical stretch rapidly activates multiple signal transduction pathways in cardiac myocytes: potential involvement of an autocrine/paracrine mechanism. EMBO J. **12:** 1681–1692.
8. YAMAZAKI, T., K. TOBE, E. HOH, K. MAEMURA, T. KAIDA, I. KOMURO, H. TAMEMOTO, T. KADOWAKI, R. NAGAI & Y. YAZAKI. 1993. Mechanical loading activates mitogen-activated protein kinase and S6 peptide kinase in cultured rat cardiac myocytes. J. Biol. Chem. **268:** 12069–12076.
9. YAMAZAKI, T., I. KOMURO, S. KUDOH, Y. ZOU, I. SHIOJIMA, T. MIZUNO, H. TAKANO, Y. HIROI, K. UEKI, K. TOBE, T. KADOWAKI, R. NAGAI & Y. YAZAKI. 1995. Mechanical stress activates protein kinase cascade of phosphorylation in neonatal rat cardiac myocytes. J. Clin. Invest. **96:** 438–446.
10. SUZUKI, J., H. MATSUBARA, M. URAKAMI & M. INADA. 1993. Rat angiotensin II (type 1A) receptor mRNA regulation and subtype expression in myocardial growth and hypertrophy. Circ. Res. **73:** 439–447.
11. SCHUNKERT, H., V.J. DZAU, S.S. TANG, A.T. HIRSCH, C.S. APSTEIN & B.H. LORELL. 1990. Increased rat cardiac angiotensin converting enzyme activity and mRNA expression in pressure overload left ventricular hypertrophy: effect on coronary resistance, contractility, and relaxation. J. Clin. Invest. **86:** 1913–1920.
12. BAKER, K.M., G.W. BOOZ & D.E. DOSTAL. 1992. Cardiac actions of angiotensin II: role of an intracardiac renin-angiotensin system. Annu. Rev. Physiol. **54:** 227–241.
13. SHIOJIMA, I., I. KOMURO, T. YAMAZAKI, R. NAGAI & Y. YAZAKI. 1994. Molecular aspects of the control of myocardial relaxation. *In* Diastolic Relaxation of the Heart. B. H. Lorell & W. Grossman, Eds.: 25–32. Kluwer Academic Publishers.
14. SHYU, K.G., J.J. CHEN, N.L. SHIH, H. CHANG, D.L. WANG, W.P. LIEN & C.C. LIEW. 1995. Angiotensinogen gene expression is induced by cyclical mechanical stretch in cultured rat cardiomyocytes Biochem. Biophys. Res. Commun. **211:** 241–248.
15. BAKER, K.M., M.I. CHERIN, S.K. WIXON & J.F. ACETO. 1990. Renin-angiotensin system involvement in pressure-overload cardiac hypertrophy in rats. Am. J. Physiol. **259:** H324–H332.
16. KOJIMA, M., I. SHIOJIMA, T. YAMAZAKI, I. KOMURO, Y. ZOU, Y. WANG, T. MIZUNO, K. UEKI, K. TOBE, T. KADOWAKI, R. NAGAI & Y. YAZAKI. 1994. Angiotensin II receptor antagonist TCV-116 induces regression of hypertensive left ventricular hypertrophy in vivo and inhibits intracellular signaling pathway of stretch-mediated cardiomyocyte hypertrophy in vitro. Circulation **89:** 2204–2211.
17. YAMAZAKI, T., I. KOMURO, S. KUDOH, Y. ZOU, I. SHIOJIMA, T. MIZUNO, H. TAKANO, Y. HIROI, K. UEKI, K. TOBE, T. KADOWAKI, R. NAGAI & Y. YAZAKI. 1995. Angiotensin II partly mediates mechanical stress-induced cardiac hypertrophy. Circ. Res. **77:** 258–265.
18. SADOSHIMA, J., Y. XU, H.S. SLAYTER & S. IZUMO. 1993. Autocrine release of angiotensin II mediates stretch-induced hypertrophy of cardiac myocytes in vitro. Cell **75:** 977–984.

19. YAMAZAKI, T., I. KOMURO, S. KUDOH, Y. ZOU, I. SHIOJIMA, Y. HIROI, T. MIZUNO, K. MAEMURA, H. KURIHARA, R. AIKAWA, H. TAKANO & Y. YAZAKI. 1996. Endothelin-1 is involved in mechanical stress-induced cardiomyocyte hypertrophy. J. Biol. Chem. **271:** 3221–3228.
20. MORRIS, C.E. 1990. Mechanosensitive ion channels. J. Membr. Biol. **113:** 93–107.
21. KENT, R.L., K. HOOBER & G. COOPER IV. 1989. Load responsiveness of protein synthesis in adult mammalian myocardium: role of cardiac deformation linked to sodium influx. Circ. Res. **64:** 74–85.
22. KOMURO, I., Y. KATOH, E. HOH, F. TAKAKU & Y. YAZAKI. 1991. Mechanisms of cardiac hypertrophy and injury: possible role of protein kinase C activation. Jpn. Circ. J. **55:** 1149–1157.
23. TAKEWAKI, S., M. KURO-O, Y. HIROI, T. YAMAZAKI, T. NOGUCHI, A. MIYAGISHI, K. NAKAHARA, M. AIKAWA, I. MANABE, Y. YAZAKI & R. NAGAI. 1995. Activation of Na^+-H^+ antiporter (NHE-1) gene expression during growth, hypertrophy and proliferation of the rabbit cardiovascular system. J. Mol. Cell. Cardiol. **27:** 729–742.
24. YAMAZAKI, T., I. KOMURO, S. KUDOH, Y. ZOU, R. NAGAI, R. AIKAWA, H. UOZUMI & Y. YAZAKI. 1998. Role of ion channels and exchangers in mechanical stretch-induced cardiomyocyte hypertrophy. Circ. Res. **82:** 430–437.
25. JULIANO, R.L. & S. HASKILL. 1993. Signal transduction from the extracellular matrix. J. Cell Biol. **120:** 577–585.
26. HYNES, R. 1992. Integrins: versatility, modulation and signaling in cell adhesion. Cell **69:** 11–25.
27. SCHALLER, M.D., J.D. HILDEBRAND, J.D. SHAMMON, J.W. FOX, R.R. VINES & J.T. PARSONS. 1994. Autophosphorylation of the focal adhesion kinase, $pp125^{FAK}$, directs SH2-dependent binding of $pp60^{Src}$. Mol. Cell. Biol. **14:** 1680–1688.
28. ZOU, Y., I. KOMURO, T. YAMAZAKI, R. AIKAWA, S. KUDOH, I. SHIOJIMA, Y. HIROI, T. MIZUNO & Y. YAZAKI. 1996. Protein kinase C, but not tyrosine kinases or Ras, plays a critical role in angiotensin II-induced activation of Raf-1 kinase and extracellular signal-regulated protein kinases in cardiac myocytes. J. Biol. Chem. **271:** 33592–33597.
29. SCHORB, W., G.W. BOOZ, D.E. DOSTAL, K.M. CONRAD, K.C. CHANG & K.M. BAKER. 1993. Angiotensin II is mitogenic in neonatal rat cardiac fibroblasts. Circ. Res. **72:** 1245–1254.
30. ZOU, Y., I. KOMURO, T. YAMAZAKI, S. KUDOH, R. AIKAWA, W. ZHU, I. SHIOJIMA, Y. HIROI, K. TOBE, T. KADOWAKI & Y. YAZAKI. 1998. Cell type–specific angiotensin II–evoked signal transduction pathways. Critical roles of $G\beta\gamma$ subunit, Src family, and Ras in cardiac fibroblasts. Circ. Res. **82:** 337–345.
31. MACLENNAN, D. H. & P. C. HOLLAND. 1975. Calcium transport in sarcoplasmic reticulum. Annu. Rev. Biophys. Bioeng. **4:** 377–404.
32. TADA, M., T. YAMAMOTO & Y. TONOMURA. 1978. Molecular mechanism of active transport by sarcoplasmic reticulum. Physiol. Rev. **58:** 1–79.
33. SUKO, J., J.H. VOGEL & C.A. CHIDSEY. 1970. Intracellular calcium and myocardial contractility. 3. Reduced calcium uptake and ATPase of sarcoplasmic reticulum fraction prepared from chronically failing calf hearts. Circ. Res. **27:** 235–247.
34. SORDAHL, L.A., W.B. MCCOLLUM, W.G. WOOD & A. SCHWARTZ. 1973. Mitochondria and sarcoplasmic reticulum function in cardiac hypertrophy and failure. Am. J. Physiol. **224:** 497–502.
35. KOMURO, I., M. KURABAYASHI, Y. SHIBAZAKI, F. TAKAKU & Y. YAZAKI. 1989. Molecular cloning and characterization of a Ca^{2+} + Mg^{2+}-dependent adenosine triphosphatase from rat cardiac sarcoplasmic reticulum. J. Clin. Invest. **83:** 1102–1108.
36. TADA, M. & A.M. KATZ. 1982. Phosphorylation of the sarcoplasmic reticulum and sarcolemma. Annu. Rev. Physiol. **44:** 401–423.
37. NAGAI, R., A. ZARAIN-HERZBERG, C.J. BRANDL, J. FUJII & M. TADA. 1989. Regulation of myocardial Ca^{2+}-ATPase and phospholamban mRNA expression in response to pressure overload and thyroid hormone. Proc. Natl. Acad. Sci. USA **86:** 2966–2970.
38. ZAK, R. 1973. Cell proliferation during cardiac growth. Am. J. Cardiol. **31:** 211–219.

39. FRANK, J.S. & G.A. LANGER. 1974. The myocardial interstitium: its structure and its role in ionic exchange. J. Cell Biol. **60:** 586–601.
40. WEBER, K.T., J.S. JANICKI, S.G. SHROFF, R. PICK, R.M. CHEN & R.I. BASHEY. 1988. Collagen remodeling of the pressure-overloaded hypertrophied nonhuman primate myocardium. Circ. Res. **62:** 757–765.
41. CAULFIELD, J.B. & T.K. BORG. 1979. The collagen network of the heart. Lab. Invest. **40:** 364–372.
42. CASPARI, P.G., M. NEWCOMB, K. GIBSON & P. HARRIS. 1977. Collagen in the normal and hypertrophied human ventricle. Cardiovasc. Res. **11:** 554–558.
43. JALIL, J.E., C.W. DOERING, J.S. JANICKI, S.G. SHROFF & K.T. WEBER. 1989. Fibrillar collagen and myocardial stiffness in the intact hypertrophied rat left ventricle. Circ. Res. **64:** 1041–1050.

Oxygen Free Radical Signaling in Ischemic Preconditioning[a]

DIPAK K. DAS, RICHARD M. ENGELMAN, AND NILANJANA MAULIK

University of Connecticut School of Medicine, Farmington, Connecticut, USA
Baystate Medical Center, Springfield, Massachusetts, USA

ABSTRACT: This review will focus on the free radical signaling mechanism of preconditioning. The results from our laboratory as well as studies from other laboratories suggest that reactive oxygen species function as second messenger during myocardial adaptation to ischemia. This review provides evidence for the first time that tyrosine kinase and MAP kinases are the targets for reactive oxygen species generated in the preconditioned myocardium. The finding that p38 MAP kinase might be upstream of NFκB further supports our previous reports that MAPKAP kinase 2 could be the most likely link between the preconditioning and adaptation mediated by gene expression. p38 activation appears to be an important step in the translocation and activation of the nuclear transcription factor NFκB, which in turn may be involved in the induction of the expression of a variety of stress-inducible genes.

INTRODUCTION

Prokaryotic and eukaryotic cells exhibit specific responses when confronted with sudden changes in their environmental conditions. The ability of the cells to acclimate to a new environment is the integral driving force for adaptive modification of cells. Such adaptation involves a number of cellular and biochemical alterations including metabolic homeostasis and reprogramming of gene expression. The changes in the metabolic pathways are generally short-lived and reversible; while the consequences of gene expression are a long-term process and may lead to the permanent alteration in the pattern of gene expression. It has been shown that stress-preconditioning of heart by repeated ischemia and reperfusion can delay the onset of further irreversible injury[1,2] or even reduce the subsequent post-ischemic ventricular dysfunction[3–6] and incidence of ventricular arrhythmias.[2,7] Such myocardial preservation by repeated short-term reversible ischemia leads to the development of the concept of stress adaptation. Consequently, new ideas of stress-preconditioning have been developed that include preconditioning with adenosine,[8] potassium channel opening,[9] α_1-receptor,[10,11] hypoxia,[12,13] oxidative stress,[14–16] drug,[17] and heat shock.[18]

Ischemic preconditioning is the manifestation of the earlier stress response that occurs during repeated episodes of brief ischemia and reperfusion, and can render the myocardium more tolerant to a subsequent, potentially lethal, ischemic injury. The adaptive protection has been found to be mediated by gene expression and tran-

[a]This study was supported by National Institutes of Health grants HL 34360, HL 22559, HL 33889, HL 56803, as well as by a Grant-in-Aid from the American Heart Association.

scriptional regulation.[19,20] Our laboratory demonstrated that ischemic preconditioning triggers a signaling pathway by potentiating tyrosine kinase phosphorylation.[21,22] The signal transduction involves phospholipase D, which subsequently transmits the signal via the activation of MAP kinases. Our results clearly indicated a role for tyrosine kinase, because inhibition of tyrosine kinase phosphorylation by genistein almost completely blocked the activation of protein kinase C, MAP kinases, and MAPKAP kinase 2. Subsequently, we were able to identify p38 MAP kinase as one of the potential targets for tyrosine kinase phosphorylation.[23]

Recently, oxygen-derived free radicals have been implicated in the transmembrane signaling process.[24] In this study, the authors provided evidence that a tyrosine kinase inhibitor, herbimycin A, and a free radical scavenger, N-acetyl-cysteine, inhibit free radical–induced activation of NFκB, indicating that activation triggered by reactive oxygen species is dependent on tyrosine kinase activity. A large number of studies from different laboratories including our own showed the induction of the expression of antioxidant genes during the preconditioning.[24] We recently demonstrated nuclear translocation and activation of NFκB in response to preconditioning.[25] Increased binding of NFκB was found to be dependent on both tyrosine kinase and p38 MAP kinase.

This review will focus on the free radical–signaling mechanism of preconditioning. The results from our laboratory as well as studies from other laboratories suggest that reactive oxygen species function as second messenger during myocardial adaptation to ischemia.

ISCHEMIC PRECONDITIONING

As mentioned earlier, mammalian heart can be adapted to ischemia by repeatedly subjecting it to short-term, reversible ischemic episodes, each followed by short durations of reperfusion. This phenomenon, known as ischemic preconditioning, causes oxidative stress leading to the induction of gene expression, which is subsequently translated into the development of several stress-related proteins responsible for the heart's defense.

Myocardial Protection

Preconditioning of heart by repeated ischemia and reperfusion cycles was thought to delay the onset of further irreversible injury.[26] It is now apparent that preconditioning provides cardioprotection by reducing subsequent post-ischemic ventricular dysfunction, decreasing incidence of arrhythmias, and decreasing infarct size. Our laboratory has demonstrated that repeated ischemia can reduce subsequent ischemia-reperfusion injury, post-ischemic ventricular fibrillation, and infarct size. Such myocardial preservation by repeated short-term reversible ischemia leads to the development of the concept of stress adaptation.

Role of Stress Proteins

Experimental approaches such as heat shock were used to precondition the heart against ischemic injury. Our laboratory developed techniques to precondition the heart by heat shock in the setting of open heart surgery.[18] Another recent study from our laboratory used a drug to induce whole body heat shock, each resulted in myocardial preservation.[27] In addition, oxidative stress has also been used to induce preconditioning.[13,28,29] Interestingly, irrespective of the type of approaches used in these studies, all stresses including ischemic stress have been found to enhance the heart's defense system, as evidenced by increased heat shock proteins (HSPs) and antioxidant enzymes, which are believed to constitute the body's defense system.[30]

Stress proteins, including HSP 27, HSP 32, HSP 60, HSP 70, and HSP 89, have been found to be induced during ischemic preconditioning.[31] Some of these HSPs are known to play a role in myocardial protection. Recently, HSP 27 and HSP 32 were implicated in myocardial protection against ischemia-reperfusion injury.[32,33] Oxidative stress–inducible proteins like SOD, catalase, glutathione peroxidase, and heme oxygenase, also play a crucial role in ischemic preconditioning.[29,31]

SIGNAL TRANSDUCTION

A signal transduction pathway involving tyrosine kinase, MAP kinases, and protein kinase C appears to be involved in transmitting the extracellular ischemic stress signal inside the cell.[34] However, the precise function of each kinase is not known. A recent study from our laboratory indicated that stress induced by oxidants and heat shock could rapidly activate p38 MAP kinase and MAPKAP kinase 2 leading to the phosphorylation of HSP 27.[35] The results of this study indicate that p38 MAP kinase and MAPKAP kinase 2 are also involved in myocardial adaptation to ischemia. MAPKAP kinase 2, which has been found to phosphorylate small heat shock proteins like HSP 27, is likely to play a role in the activation of transcription factors. Phosphorylation of HSP 27 is instrumental for the polymerization of actin thereby counteracting the disruptive effects of ischemia on actin microfilaments.

Tyrosine Kinase

Protein phosphorylation plays a crucial role in a wide variety of cellular processes that control the signal transduction. It must be clearly understood that protein phosphorylation is a rapidly reversible process that regulates intracellular signaling in response to a specific stress, e.g., environmental changes.[36] Protein phosphorylation is mediated by a number of protein kinases that can be grouped into two major classes: (1) protein kinases that phosphorylate serine/threonine residues, e.g., protein kinase A, PKC, casein kinases, and (2) protein kinases that phosphorylate proteins on their tyrosine residues, e.g., tyrosine kinases. Tyrosine kinases can activate a number of different intracellular signaling pathways including tyrosine phosphorylation in the case of PLCγ and phospholipase D,[37] conformational changes induced by binding of the SH2 domain to phosphotyrosine for P13 kinases,[38] as well as translocation to the plasma membrane for stimulation of Ras guanine nucleotide exchange by Sos.[39]

As mentioned earlier, ischemic preconditioning has been found to trigger a signaling pathway by potentiating tyrosine kinase phosphorylation that involved phospholipase D and MAP kinases.[21,22] Inhibition of tyrosine kinase phosphorylation by genistein almost blocked the activation of protein kinase C, MAP kinases, and MAPKAP kinase 2.

Protein Kinase C

A role of protein kinase C (PKC) in ischemic preconditioning has been suggested. A short-term ischemia as well as ischemia followed by reperfusion were previously shown to translocate and activate PKC.[40] Furthermore, both α_1-receptor stimulation and Ca^{2+} ion can translocate and activate PKC.[41,42] Given the fact that both α_1-receptor activation and intracellular Ca^{2+} overloading are the manifestations of ischemia-reperfusion injury, it was not surprising when ischemic preconditioning consisting of repeated ischemia and reperfusion was also found to translocate and activate PKC.[43,44] Interestingly, it has long been known that PKC can activate the transcription of genes.[45] Indeed, many genes were found to be activated in the preconditioned myocardium.[31,32,46,47] Thus PKC, which is activated as a result of the events controlled by endogenous compounds (*viz.*, α_1-receptor, adenosine, and diacylglycerol), can be instrumental for gene expression leading to the translation into proteins.

As mentioned earlier, it has been demonstrated that cellular PKC activation is an important step in the mechanism of adaptive protection of the heart.[43,48] The PKC hypothesis received further support from the observations that any agent that can activate PKC can also precondition the heart. For example, phenylephrine, an α_1 agonist, angiotensin AT_1, and bradykinin B_2 receptors can activate PKC.[49] Phenylephrine, angiotensin AT_1, and bradykinin B_2 have been shown to precondition the hearts when infused prior to ischemia.[50,51]

A variety of stress signals have been found to translocate and activate PKC. For example, mechanical stress induced by stretching can activate PKC in cultured myocytes.[52] Immediately after stretching, activation of phosphatidylinositol turnover was observed, suggesting a role of phospholipase C in PKC activation. Our laboratory has demonstrated that even a short-term ischemia or ischemia followed by reperfusion could translocate and activate PKC.[40] Furthermore, both α_1-receptor stimulation and Ca^{2+} can translocate and activate PKC.[46, 47]

P38 MAP Kinase and MAPKAP Kinase 2

The results of a number of recent studies from our laboratory now indicate that PKC may not be the only link between ischemic preconditioning and myocardial adaptation. It appears that MAPKAP kinase 2 also plays an important role in preconditioning. This concept receives support from the presence of abundant MAPKAP kinase 2 in heart, rapid activation of MAPKAP kinase 2 by stresses, such as heat stress, oxidative stress and ischemia-reperfusion; and most importantly, it is MAPKAP kinase 2, not PKC, that can phosphorylate small heat shock proteins HSP 25 and HSP 27, which are also activated by ischemic preconditioning. Recently, we have demonstrated for the first time that activation of protein tyrosine kinase is coupled with the activation of phospholipase D in ischemic preconditioning. Inhibition of tyrosine kinase results not only in the inhibition of phospholipase D, but also abolishes preconditioning-mediated activation of protein kinase C, MAP kinase, and MAPKAP kinase 2.

As mentioned earlier, stress mediated by repeated ischemia and reperfusion has been shown to trigger a tyrosine kinase–dependent signaling pathway leading to the activation of MAP kinases and MAPKAP kinase 2.[34] More recently, we have shown that both oxidative and heat stresses rapidly activated p38MAPK and MAPKAP kinase 2, leading to the phosphorylation of HSP 27.[33] To further define the role of MAPKAP kinase 2 in ischemia-reperfusion–mediated stress signaling pathway, we used a specific blocker for p38MAPK prior to ischemia and reperfusion. The results of our study demonstrated that ischemia-reperfusion resulted in the translocation of p38MAPK into the cytoplasm and that the beneficial effects of myocardial adaptation to the stress of repeated ischemia-reperfusion were abolished by inhibiting p38MAPK with simultaneous inhibition of MAPKAP kinase 2. These results suggest a role of p38MAPK-MAPKAP kinase 2 signaling pathway in myocardial adaptation to stress.

MAP kinases and MAPKAP kinase 2 have recently been shown to play a role in mediating intracellular signal transduction events associated with ischemia and reperfusion.[21,22] In mammalian cells, the mitogenic signal is transmitted from the cytoplasm into the nucleus by the nuclear translocation of p42/p44MAPK isoforms (extracellular signal regulated kinases ERK1 and ERK2).[53] Although the kinase cascades have been well characterized for the prokaryotic system, their precise role in the mammalian system is far from clear. Three distinct mammalian MAP kinases, each with apparently unique signaling pathways, have been identified: the ERK group (p42/p44MAPK), the SAPK group (also known as JNK), and the p38 MAP kinase (a mammalian homologue of HOG1).[54]

P38 MAP kinase[54] has a very specific cellular target—MAPKAP kinase 2.[55] Unlike p42/p44MAPK, which are readily activated by growth signals via a Ras-dependent signal transduction pathway,[56] the activation of JNKs and p38MAPK is potentiated by diverse stresses and pro-inflammatory cytokines.[57] However the JNK and p38MAPK cascades appear to be involved in distinct cellular functions because they possess different cellular targets and are located on different signaling pathways. For example, JNK kinases activate c-Jun while p38MAPK stimulates MAPKAP kinase 2.[58,59] Upon activation by upstream kinases, p38 MAP kinase phosphorylates and activates MAPKAP kinase 2, which in turn leads to the phosphorylation of HSP 27.[60] The precise mechanism of p38 MAP kinase activation is not known, but its activation appears to be regulated by dual phosphorylation of Thr and Tyr within the motif Thr-Gly-Tyr.[61] Recently, the nucleus has been shown to be a target for the p38 MAP kinases signal transduction.[58]

It has been universally accepted that although the activation of p38 MAP kinase requires dual phosphorylation like other members of MAP kinases family, the substrate specificity of p38 MAP kinase is quite different from that of JNK or ERK subgroups of MAP kinases. Thus, unlike other MAP kinases, p38 MAP kinase activates the MAPKAP kinase 2. It is speculated that P38 MAP kinase signaling has a distinct function in the cell and this was supported by the recent findings that pro-inflammatory cytokines lead to the activation of p38 MAP kinase, which in turn results in the phosphorylation of HSP 27.[62,63] Recently, two MAP kinase kinases (MKK3 and MKK4) have been discovered, the former being specific for p38 MAP kinase while the latter can activate both p38 and JNK MAP kinases,[64] suggesting that p38 and JNK may sit at the crossroads of stress-activated signal transduction pathways.

MAP kinases signal transduction pathway is likely to involve activation of Ras or Raf-1, which in turn induces mitogen-activated protein kinase kinase (MKK) and MAP kinases. It is also known that Raf-1 kinases possesses MAPKKK activity and lies upstream from MAPKK and MAP kinases in various cell types.[65]

Oxygen Free Radicals

Evidence is rapidly accumulating to support a role of oxygen free radicals as a signaling molecule. For example, a recent study indicated that reactive oxygen species are involved in the Ca^{2+} signaling in the regulation of vascular endothelium.[66] Oxygen free radicals were found to alter key enzymes, including cAMP-dependent protein kinases, in certain pathological states.[67] In another study, amyloid beta-peptide stimulated nitric oxide production in astrocytes through an NFκB-dependent mechanism.[68] Free radicals was found to activate the guanylate cyclase-cyclic guanosine–3′-5′ monophosphate system.[69] The present study shows that the infarct size–limiting effect of ischemic preconditioning was abolished by either DMTU, a hydroxyl radical scavenger, or SN 50 peptide, a NFκB inhibitor, suggesting that both reactive oxygen species and nuclear transcription factor NFκB play crucial roles in preconditioning. Multiple kinases including PKC, p38 MAP kinase, and MAPKAP kinase 2 were activated by preconditioning supporting a number of previous reports.[34,70–71] DMTU reduced the preconditioning-mediated increase in the activation of p38 MAP kinase and MAPKAP kinase 2. However, DMTU had no effects on PKC suggesting that free radicals potentiate a signal transduction process independent of PKC.

The results of our study support the previous reports that free radical signaling involves p38 MAP kinase. A recent study showed potent activation of extracellular signal–regulated ERK2 kinase within 10 min of H_2O_2 treatment.[72] This study also showed that H_2O_2 moderately activated other kinases including p38 MAP kinase. Lipopolysaccharides, which can adapt the heart to oxidative stress, have been found to induce tyrosine phosphorylation of p38 protein.[73] Phosphorylation of p38 was blocked by treatment of cells with a protein tyrosine kinase inhibitor, herbimycin A, suggesting that tyrosine phosphorylation is involved in lipopolysaccharide-induced oxygen free radical signaling.

Our results indicate that reactive oxygen species provoke a signal transduction pathway through the activation of tyrosine kinase phosphorylation and then function either independent of PKC or act downstream of PKC leading to the activation of p38 MAP kinase and MAPKAP kinase 2. A recent study has demonstrated that hypoxia and hypoxia/reoxygenation activated Raf-1, MKK, and MAP kinases in cultured rat cardiomyocytes. Raf-1 operates downstream from cell surface–associated tyrosine kinases and upstream from MAP kinases. Raf is not strictly a member of the MEKK family, but it is functionally analogous. Ras is part of the signal transduction chain extending from extracellular signals to transcriptional regulation in the nucleus. Upon activation, tyrosine kinase recruits a number of proteins including Ras-specific guanine nucleotide releasing proteins, which then regulate the binding of Ras with GTP, thereby potentiating the Ras signal. Ras proteins then interact with Raf kinases to induce downstream signals activating MAP kinases and other protein kinases. Once Raf is activated, then Ras is no longer required. The precise mechanism by which Ras controls Raf-1 is poorly understood. The binding of Raf-1 to Ras is largely GTP dependent and requires the effector region of Ras and the regulatory region of Raf-1.

PRECONDITIONING, APOPTOSIS, AND OXYGEN FREE RADICALS

Cardiomyocytes undergo apoptotic cell death in a variety of coronary diseases including heart failure,[74] myocardial infarction,[75] and ischemia-reperfusion.[76–84] Both necrosis and apoptosis contribute to the pathophysiology of ischemic and reperfusion injury. Most of the studies so far have been reported for rat hearts where no evidence of apoptosis were found in hearts subjected to up to 2 hours of ischemia. For example, recent studies from our laboratory found no evidence for apoptosis in rat hearts subjected to 2 h of ischemia, but apoptosis became evident when these hearts were subjected to 15 min of ischemia followed by 90 min of reperfusion.[79,80,83,84] Another related study showed that apoptotic and necrotic myocyte cell deaths have been shown to independently contribute to infarct size in rats, but apoptosis did not become evident for up to 2 h of ischemia.[76] In a more recent study, characteristic signs of apoptosis were shown to appear only after 2.25 h of ischemia.[77] By contrast, hearts subjected to relatively short periods of ischemia followed by reperfusion result in apoptosis. This result was independently shown by our group[78,83,84] and two other groups.[77,82] In another study, as with rat and rabbits hearts, cardiomyocytes from mouse heart did not show any signs of apoptosis and DNA fragmentation for up to 30 min of ischemia, but these cells underwent apoptosis after 60 min of reperfusion following 30 min of ischemia.[85] This raises the interesting possibility that reperfusion of ischemic myocardium triggers some distinct signal for apoptosis that is not mediated by up to 30 min of ischemia.

Substantial evidence exists in the literature to support that reperfusion of the ischemic heart generates oxygen free radicals, which contribute to the pathogenesis of reperfusion injury.[86–88] Interestingly, free radicals and/or oxidative stress are also common mediators of apoptosis, perhaps via the formation of lipid peroxidation and lipid hydroperoxides.[89–91] A direct role of oxygen free radicals has also been implicated in the pathogenesis of apoptosis. For example, superoxide dismutase (SOD) or an expression vector containing SOD cDNA was found to delay apoptotic cell death[92] and free radical–mediated apoptosis was found to be modulated by protooncogene expression.[93] In fact, reactive oxygen species and prooxidants may act through mobilization of Ca^{2+}.[94] In cultured sympathetic neurons, when injected with SOD or with an expression vector containing SOD cDNA, apoptosis was delayed by a considerable amount.[92] Injection of antisense SOD expression vector into the neurons decreased the amount of SOD simultaneously delaying apoptosis. This study also demonstrated that if SOD was injected after the development of oxidative stress, it had no effect on apoptosis. A recent study from our laboratory demonstrated that a seleno peroxide mimic, ebselen, could reduce apoptotic cell death and DNA fragmentation in concert with reduction of myocardial ischemia-reperfusion injury.[85] The precise mechanism by which ebselen reduced apoptosis was not clearly understood. Ebselen, a synthetic selenium-containing heterocycle, is known to function as an antioxidant by its ability to reduce lipid hydroperoxides.[96] Ebselen suppresses free radical formation from hydroperoxides and hydrogen peroxide, which have been implicated in the pathogenesis of ischemia-reperfusion injury. Indeed, this compound was also shown to reduce ischemia reperfusion injury.[97]

The role of free radical signaling in apoptotic cell death is further supported from the results of our recent study that ischemic preconditioning attenuates apoptotic cell death.[84] In this study, preconditioning reduced apoptosis and DNA fragmentation presumably by reducing the oxidative stress developed during ischemia and reperfusion.

GENE EXPRESSION

The acutely developing adaptive effect is short-lived, lasting for only up to 2 to 3 hours. Hearts can subsequently undergo a secondary and delayed adaptation to stress presumably through the induction of the expression of new genes and their subsequent translation into proteins. A number of genes and proteins have been identified as possibly involved in the development of "second window" or delay preconditioning including HSPs, SOD, catalase, nitric oxide synthase, as well as ATPase 6 and cytochrome *b* subunits. Such an adaptive response becomes evident only after approximately 24 h of stress treatment and may include stress induced by heat shock, oxidant, or other stress-inducible agents. MAPKAP kinase 2 appears to link the early preconditioning effect to the delayed adaptative response.

Induction of the Expression of Genes

Evidence exists to support that preconditioning rapidly induces the expression of a large variety of mRNAs of the stress-related proteins in mammalian hearts. These include mRNAs of HSP,[17,18,20,31] antioxidants,[13–16,31] Ca^{2+}-regulated proteins,[98] and growth hormones.[99] Most of these stress genes are also induced when hearts are subjected to heat shock or oxidative stress. It seems, therefore, reasonable to postulate that there is a common inducible pathway for the stress-mediated induction of gene expression.

A variety of stresses including ischemia, hypoxia, heat shock, and oxidative stress have been found to stimulate the expression of early responsive genes such as *c-fos*, *c-myc*, and *c-jun*. Genes of antioxidants (e.g., SOD, catalase, glutathione peroxidase, and heme oxygenase) and genes of HSPs (e.g., HSP 27, HSP 32, HSP 70, and HSP[89]) are expressed during myocardial adaptation to ischemia. Subtractive hybridization and differential display techniques revealed that preconditioning results in the induction of the expression of several mitochondrial genes such as ATPase 6 and cytochrome *b* as well as a gene encoding ribosomal protein L23a.[19,20]

Transcription Regulation

A recent study from our laboratory demonstrated that the infarct size–limiting effect of ischemic preconditioning was abolished by either DMTU, a hydroxyl radical scavenger, or SN 50 peptide, a NFκB blocker, suggesting that both reactive oxygen species and nuclear transcription factor NFκB play crucial roles in preconditioning. It seems logical to assume that ischemia-reperfusion–induced oxidative stress caused translocation of NFκB, which might be involved in the regulation of the activation of MAP kinases observed in conjunction with myocardial stress adaptation. To examine the role of NFκB in tyrosine kinase signaling during myocardial adaptation to ischemia, isolated rat hearts were adapted to ischemic stress by repeated ischemia and reperfusion. The adapted heart resulted in the nuclear translocation and activation of NFκB, which was completely blocked by both DMTU and SN 50 peptide. In conjunction, the beneficial effects of ischemic adaptation were blocked by pretreating the hearts with SN 50 peptide or DMTU. These results support our previous observation[100] and further suggest that NFκB, located downstream of p38 MAP kinase, plays a crucial role in myocardial adaptation to ischemia. A more recent study from our laboratory also indicated a role of another transcription factor AP-1 in ischemic preconditioning.[101]

IMPLICATION OF PKC-DEPENDENT AND PKC-INDEPENDENT PATHWAYS

As mentioned earlier, multiple kinases including PKC, p38 MAP kinase, and MAPKAP kinase 2, are activated by preconditioning. DMTU reduced preconditioning-mediated increase in the activation of p38 MAP kinase and MAPKAP kinase 2. However, DMTU had no effects on PKC suggesting that free radicals potentiate a signal transduction process independent of PKC. On the other hand, PKC is modulated when the effects of preconditioning are blocked by inhibiting tyrosine kinase with genestein. Thus, it seems reasonable to assume that preconditioning potentiates signal transduction through both PKC-dependent and PKC-independent pathways.

SUMMARY AND CONCLUSION

Although the beneficial effects of ischemic stress adaptation are well recognized, controversies exist regarding the mechanism of signal transduction by which ischemic stress builds up the heart's defense. Myocardial adaptation to ischemia has recently been shown to be mediated through the activation of tyrosine kinase receptor protein. The signal transduction process appears to involve tyrosine kinase coupled to phospholipase D and MAP kinases, which leads to the activation of MAPKAP kinase 2. Our recent study demonstrated that the ischemic stress specifically translocates and activates p38 MAP kinases which directly activates MAPKAP kinase 2.[21,71]

The results of our study demonstrate that free radical signaling plays a crucial role in ischemic preconditioning (FIG. 1). For example, enhanced tyrosine kinase phosphorylation during ischemic preconditioning, which was blocked by DMTU and inhibited preconditioning mediated phosphorylation of p38 MAP kinase and MAPKAP kinase 2 activity.[100] In concert, the cardioprotective effect of preconditioning was abolished by DMTU. Preconditioning mediated nuclear translocation and activation of NFκB was blocked by DMTU.

Reactive oxygen species appear to provoke a signal transduction pathway through the activation of tyrosine kinase phosphorylation and then function either through

PKC or act downstream of PKC leading to the activation of p38 MAP kinase and MAPKAP kinase 2. MAP kinases' signal transduction pathway is likely to involve activation of Ras or Raf-1 which in turn induces mitogen-activated protein kinase kinase and MAP kinases. It is also known that Raf-1 kinases possesses MAPKKK activity and lies upstream from MAPKK and MAP kinases in various cell types.

The nuclear transcription factor NFκB seems to play a crucial role in ischemic preconditioning, further supporting a role of free radical signaling in preconditioning. NFκB is translocated in response to oxidative stress from its inactive cytoplasmic form by releasing the inhibitory subunit IκB from NFκB. Activation of NFκB is likely to be involved in the induction of gene expression associated with the ischemic adaptation, since this transcription factor has recently been found to play a crucial role in the regulation of ischemia-reperfusion–mediated gene expression.

Evidence is rapidly accumulating to indicate that oxidative stress and free radicals lead to the activation of NFκB, which in turn induces the expression of genes.[102,103] Interestingly, H_2O_2 was found to activate DNA binding of NFκB *in vivo* but not *in vitro,*[104] suggesting that a byproduct of H_2O_2 and not H_2O_2 by itself may be responsible for the activation of NFκB. Another related study using transient catalase overexpression in cos-1 cells showed that H_2O_2 may not serve as a messenger for TNFα or phorbol ester–induced NFκB activation.[105] It is possible that hydroxyl radicals formed by a transient metal-catalyzed Fenton reaction during the reperfusion of ischemic heart[106] can induce NFκB activation. Inhibition of NFκB by antioxidants further supports a role of free radicals in NFκB activation.[107]

In summary, this review provides evidence for the first time that tyrosine kinase and MAP kinases are the targets for reactive oxygen species generated in the preconditioned myocardium. The finding that p38 MAP kinase might be upstream of NFκB further supports our previous reports that MAPKAP kinase 2 could be the most likely link between the preconditioning and adaptation mediated by gene expression. p38 activation appears to be an important step in the translocation and activation of the nuclear transcription factor NFκB, which in turn may be involved the induction of the expression of a variety of stress-inducible genes.

The evidence presented above indicates a vital role for the reactive oxygen species generated during preconditioning in mediating cellular responses through diverse intracellular and extracellular ligands. Stimulation of protein phosphorylation by oxygen free radicals as observed in the present study appears to be a feasible mechanism for subsequent signal transduction leading to the activation of the transcription factor NFκB. A large number of reports exist in the literature to show the induction of antioxidant gene expression during preconditioning. It seems, therefore, quite logical to assume that the reactive oxygen species function as "second messengers" during ischemic preconditioning. This is substantiated from our observation that free radicals generated during preconditioning trigger a tyrosine kinase–dependent signal transduction resulting in enhanced phosphorylation and activation of MAP kinase cascade leading to the activation of NFκB. It is interesting to note that PKC is not a potential target for oxygen free radicals in the preconditioning process. Activation of NFκB seems to be regulated by MAP kinases independent of PKC. The induction of the antioxidant genes and enzymes observed by many investigators is likely to be mediated by NFκB.

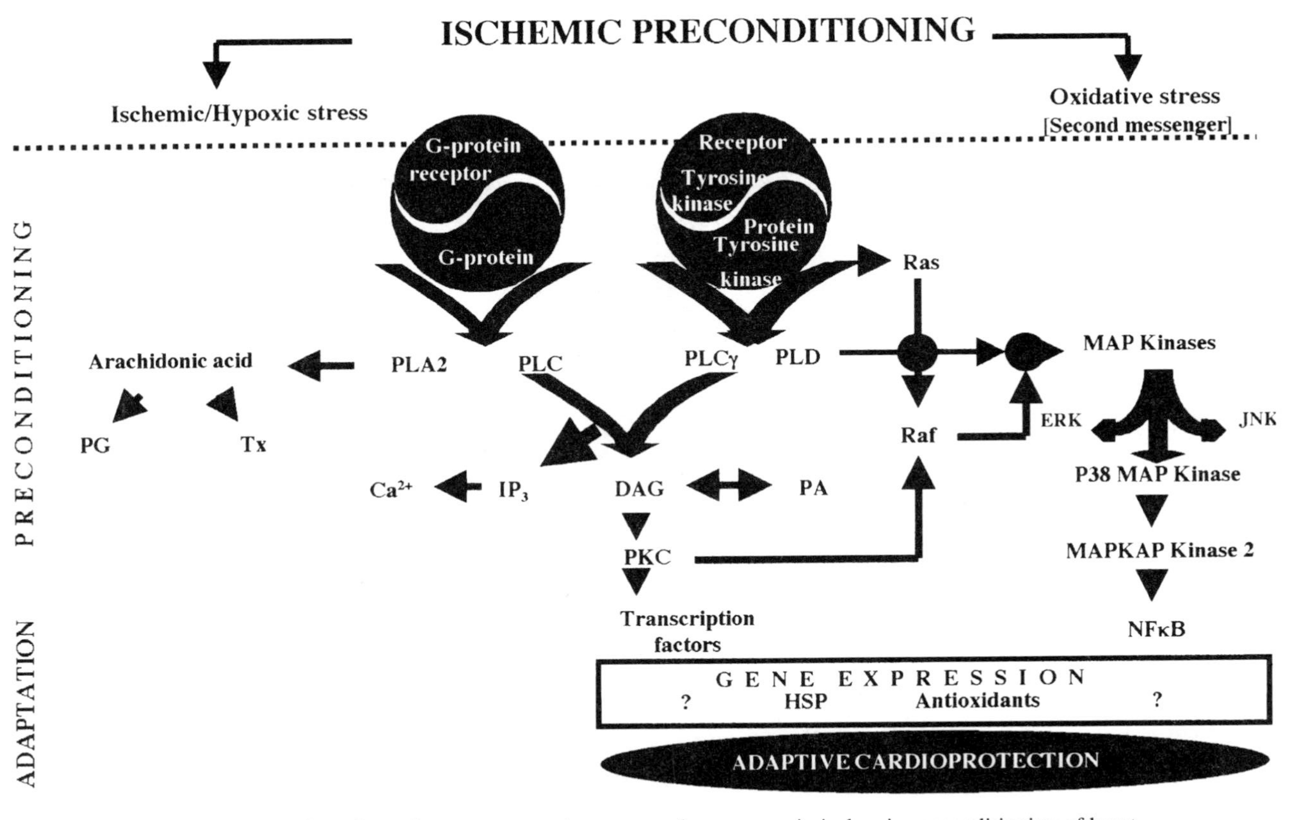

FIGURE 1. Function of reactive oxygen species as second messenger in ischemic preconditioning of heart.

REFERENCES

1. FLACK, J., Y. KIMURA, R.M. ENGELMAN & D.K. DAS. 1991. Preconditioning the heart by repeated stunning improves myocardial salvage. Circulation **84:** III369–III374.
2. TOSAKI, A., G.A. CORDIS, P. SZERDAHELYI, R.M. ENGELMAN & D.K. DAS. 1994. Effects of preconditioning on reperfusion arrhythmias, myocardial functions, formation of free radicals and ion shifts in isolated ischemic/reperfused rat hearts. J. Cardiovasc. Pharmacol. **23:** 365–373.
3. KIMURA, Y., J. IYENGAR, R. SUBRAMANIAN, G.A. CORDIS & D.K. DAS. 1992. Myocardial adaptation by repeated short term ischemia reduces post-ischemic dysfunction. Basic Res. Cardiol. **87:** 128–138.
4. ASIMAKIS, G.K., K. INNERS-MCBRIDE, G. MEDELLIN & V.R. CONTI. 1992. Ischemic preconditioning attenuates acidosis and postischemic dysfunction in isolated rat heart. Am. J. Physiol. **263:** H887–H894.
5. SCHOTT, R.J., S. ROHMANN, E.R. BRAUN & W. SCHAPER. 1990. Ischemic preconditioning reduces infarct size in swine myocardium. Circ. Res. **66:** 1133–1142.
6. LI, G.C., B.S. VASQUEZ, K.P. GALLAGHER & B.R. LUCCHESI. 1990. Myocardial protection with preconditioning. Circulation **82:** 609–619.
7. LAWSON, C.S., D.J.O. COLTART & D.J. HEARSE. 1992. Ischemic preconditioning and protection against reperfusion-induced arrhythmias, reduction in vulnerability or delay in onset? Studies in the isolated blood perfused rat heart. Eur. Heart J. **13:** 23–34.
8. LIU, G.S., J. THORNTON, D.M. VANWINKLE, A.W.H. STANLEY, R.A. OLSSON & J.M. DOWNEY. 1991. Protection against infarction afforded by preconditioning is mediated by A1 adenosine receptors in rabbit heart. Circulation **84:** 350–356.
9. GROSS, G.J. & J.A. AUCHAMPACH. 1991. Blockade of ATP-sensitive potassium channels prevents myocardial preconditioning in dogs. Circ. Res. **70:** 223–233.
10. BANERJEE, A., C. LOCKE-WINTER, K.B. ROGERS, M.B. MITCHELL, E.C. BREW, C.B. CAIRNS, D.D. BENSARD & A.H. HARKEN. 1993. Preconditioning against myocardial dysfunction after ischemia and reperfusion by an alpha 1-adrenergic mechanism. Circ. Res. **73:** 656–670.
11. TOSAKI, A., N.S. BEHJET, D.T. ENGELMAN, R.M. ENGELMAN & D.K. DAS. 1995. α-1 adrenergic agonist-induced preconditioning in isolated working rat hearts. J. Pharmacol. Exp. Ther. **273:** 689–694.
12. SHIZUKUDA, Y., T. IWAMOTO, R.T. MALLET & H.F. DOWNEY. 1993. Hypoxic preconditioning attenuates stunning caused by repeated coronary artery occlusions in dog heart. Cardiovasc. Res. **27:** 559–564.
13. ENGELMAN, R.M., M. WATANABE, R.M. ENGELMAN, J.A. ROUSOU, E. KISIN, V.E. KAGAN, N. MAULIK & D.K. DAS. 1995. Hypoxic preconditioning preserves antioxidant reserve in the working rat heart. Cardiovasc. Res. **29:** 133–140.
14. MAULIK, N., M. WATANABE, D. ENGELMAN, R.M. ENGELMAN & D.K. DAS. 1995. Oxidative stress adaptation improves postischemic ventricular recovery. Mol. Cell. Biochem. **144:** 67–74.
15. MAULIK, N., W. WATANABE, D. ENGELMAN, R.M. ENGELMAN, V.E. KAGAN, E. KISIN, V. TYURIN, G.A. CORDIS & D.K. DAS. 1995. Myocardial adaptation to ischemia by oxidative stress induced by endotoxin. Am J. Physiol. **269:** C907–C916.
16. MAULIK, N., R.M. ENGELMAN, Z. WEI, D. LU, J.A. ROUSOU & D.K. DAS. 1993. Interleukin-1α preconditioning reduces myocardial ischemia reperfusion injury. Circulation **88**(suppl II): 387–394.
17. MAULIK, N., Z. WEI, X. LIU, R.M. ENGELMAN, J.A. ROUSOU & D.K. DAS. 1994. Improved postischemic ventricular recovery by amphetamine is linked with its ability to induce heat shock. Mol. Cell. Biochem. **137:** 17–24.
18. LIU, X., R.M. ENGELMAN, I.I. MORARU, J.A. ROUSOU, J.E. FLACK, D.W. DEATON, N. MAULIK & D.K. DAS. 1992. Heat Shock: A new approach for myocardial preservation in cardiac surgery. Circulation **86** (suppl II): 358–363.
19. MAULIK, N. & D.K. DAS. 1996. Hunting for differentially expressed mRNA species in preconditioned myocardium. Ann. N.Y. Acad. Sci. **793:** 240–258.

20. DAS, D.K., I.I. MORARU, N. MAULIK & R.M. ENGELMAN. 1994. Gene expression during myocardial adaptation to ischemia and reperfusion. Ann. N.Y. Acad. Sci. **723:** 292–307.
21. MAULIK, N., M. WATANABE, Y.L. ZU, C.K. HUANG, G.A. CORDIS, J.A. SCHLEY & D.K. DAS. 1996. Ischemic preconditioning triggers the activation of MAP kinases and MAPKAP kinase 2 in rat hearts. FEBS Lett. **396:** 233–237.
22. DAS, D.K., N. MAULIK, T. YOSHIDA, R.M. ENGELMAN & Y.L. ZU. 1996. Preconditioning potentiates molecular signaling for myocardial adaptation to ischemia. Ann. N.Y. Acad. Sci. **793:** 191–209.
23. MAULIK, N., M. WATANABE, A. TOSAKI, D.T. ENGELMAN, R.M. ENGELMAN, J.A. ROUSOU, D.W. DEATON, J.E. FLACK & D.K. DAS. 1996. Tyrosine kinase regulation of phospholipase D–protein C kinase pathway in ischemic preconditioning. J. Am. Coll. Cardiol. **27:** 385A.
24. SCHIEVEN, G.L., J.M. KIRIHARA, D.E. MYERS, J.A. LEDBETTER & F.M. UCKUN. 1993. Reactive oxygen intermediates activate NFkB in a tyrosine kinase-dependent mechanism and in combination with vanadate activate the p56 lck and p59 fyn tyrosine kinases in human lymphocytes. Blood **82:** 1212–1220.
25. MAULIK, N., M. SATO, B.D. PRICE & D.K. DAS. 1998. An essential role of NFκB in tyrosine kinase signaling of p38 MAP kinase regulation of myocardial adaptation to ischemia. FEBS Lett. **429:** 365–369.
26. MURRY, C.E., R.B. JENNINGS & K.A. REIMER. 1986. Preconditioning with ischemia: a delay of lethal cell injury in ischemic myocardium. Circulation **74:** 1124–1136.
27. MAULIK, N., R.M. ENGELMAN, Z. WEI, X. LIU, J.A. ROUSOU, J. FLACK, D. DEATON & D.K. DAS. 1995. Drug-induced heat shock improves post-ischemic ventricular recovery after cardiopulmonary bypass. Circulation **92**(Suppl II)**:** 381–388.
28. MAULIK, N., M. WATANABE, R.M. ENGELMAN, V.E. KAGAN, E. KISIN, V. TYURIN, G.A. CORDIS & D.K. DAS. 1995. Myocardial adaptation to ischemia by oxidative stress induced by endotoxin. Am. J. Physiol. (Cell Physiol.) **269:** C907–C916.
29. DAS, D.K. & N. MAULIK. 1995. Cross talk between heat shock and oxidative stress inducible genes during myocardial adaptation to ischemia. *In* Cell Biology of Trauma. J.J. Lemasters & C. Oliver, Eds.: 193–211. CRC Press. Florida.
30. DAS, D.K., N. MAULIK & I.I. MORARU. 1995. Gene expression in acute myocardial stress. J. Mol. Cell. Cardiol. **27:** 181–193.
31. DAS, D.K., R.M. ENGELMAN & Y. KIMURA. 1993. Molecular adaptation of cellular defences following preconditioning of the heart by repeated ischemia. Cardiovasc. Res. **27:** 578–584.
32. MAULIK, N., H.S. SHARMA & D.K. DAS. 1996. Induction of the heme oxygenase gene expression during the reperfusion of ischemic rat myocardium. J. Mol. Cell. Cardiol. **28:** 1261–1270.
33. DAS, D.K., N. MAULIK, R.M. ENGELMAN, J.A. ROUSOU, D. DEATON & J.E. FLACK. 1999. Signal transduction pathway leading to HSP 27 and HSP 70 gene expression during myocardial adaptation to stress. Ann. N.Y. Acad. Sci. This volume.
34. ZU, Y.-L., Y. AI, A. GILCHRIST, N. MAULIK, J. WATRAS, R.I. SHA'AFI, D.K. DAS & C.-K. HUANG. 1997. High expression and activation of MAP kinase-activated protein kinase 2 in myocardium. J. Mol. Cell. Cardiol. **29:** 2150–2168.
35. DAS, D.K. 1998. Intracellular signaling mechanisms in delayed preconditioning. *In* Delayed Preconditioning and Adaptive Cardioprotection. G. Baxter & D. Yellon, Eds.: 91–103. Kluwer Academic Publishers. The Netherlands.
36. HUNTER, T., C.B. ALEXANDER & J.A. COOPER. 1985. Protein tyrosine kinases. Annu. Rev. Biochem. **54:** 897–930.
37. SADOWSKI, H.B., K. SHUAI, J.E. DARNELL & M.Z. GILMAN. 1993. A common nuclear signal transduction pathway activated by growth factor and cytokine receptors. Science **261:** 1739–1744.
38. CARPENTER, C.L., K.R. AUGER, M. CHANUDHURI, M. YOAKIM, B. SCHAFFHAUSEN, S. SHOELSON & L.C. CANTLEY. 1993. Phosphoinositide 3-kinase is activated by phosphopeptides that bind to the SH2 domains of the 85-kDa subunit. J. Biol. Chem. **268:** 9478–9483.

39. QUILLIAM, L.A., S.Y. HUFF, K.M. RABUN, W. WEI, W. PARK, D. BROEK & C.J. DER. 1994. Membrane-targeting potentiates guanine nucleotide exchange factor CDC25 and SOS1 activation of Ras transforming activity. Proc. Natl. Acad. Sci. USA **91:** 8512–8516.
40. PRASAD, M.R. & R.M. JONES. 1992. Enhanced membrane protein kinase C activity in myocardial ischemia. Basic Res. Cardiol. **87:** 19–26.
41. HENRICH, C.J. & P.C. SIMPSON. 1988. Differential acute and chronic response of protein kinase C in cultured neonatal rat heart myocytes to a1-adrenergic and phorbol ester stimulation. J. Mol. Cell. Cardiol. **20:** 1081–1085.
42. FEARON, C.W. & A.H. TASHJIAN. 1985. Thyrotropin-releasing hormone induces redistribution of protein kinase C in GH4C1 rat pitutary cells. J. Biol. Chem. **260**: 8366–8371.
43. YTREHUS, K., Y. LIU & J.M. DOWNEY. 1994. Preconditioning protects ischemic rabbit heart by protein kinase C activation. Am. J. Physiol. **266:** H1145–H1152.
44. MITCHELL, M.B., X. MENG, J. BROWN, A.H. HARKEN & A. BANERJEE. 1994. Preconditioning of isolated rat heart is mediated by protein kinase C activation. Am. J. Physiol. **266:** H1145–H1152.
45. NISHIZUKA, Y. 1996. Studies and perspectives of protein kinase C. Science **233:** 305–312.
46. BRAND, T., H.S. SHARMA, K.E. FLEISCHMANN, D.J. DUNCKER, E.O. MCFALLA, P.D. VERDOUW & W. SCHAPER. 1992. Proto-oncogene expression in porcine myocardium subjected to ischemia and reperfusion. Circ. Res. **71:** 1351–1360.
47. HEADS, R.J., D.S. LATCHMAN & D.M. YELLON. 1995. Differential stress protein mRNA expression during early ischemic preconditioning in the rabbit heart and its relationship to adenosine receptor function. J. Mol. Cell. Cardiol. **27:** 2133–2148.
48. BUGGE, E. & K. YTREHUS. 1995. Ischemic preconditioning is protein kinase C dependent but not through stimulation of α adrenergic or adenosine receptors in the isolated rat heart. Cardiovasc. Res. **29:** 401–406.
49. DIXON, B.S, R.V. SHARMA, T. DICKERSON & J. FORTUNE. 1994. Bradykinin and angiotensin II: activation of protein kinase C in arterial muscle. Am. J. Physiol. **266:** C1406–C1420.
50. GOTO, M., Y. LIU, X.M. YANG, J.L. ARDELL, M.V. COHEN & J.M. DOWNEY. 1995. Role of bradykinin in protection of ischemic preconditioning in rabbit hearts. Circ. Res. **77:** 611–621.
51. LIU, Y., A. TSUCHIDA, M.V. COHEN & J.M. DOWNEY. 1995. Pretreatment with angiotensin II activates protein kinase C and limits myocardial infarction in isolated rabbit hearts. J. Mol. Cell. Cardiol. **27:** 883–892.
52. YAMAZAKI, T., I. KOMURO, S. KUDOH, Y. ZOU, I. SHIOJIMA, Y. HIROI, T. MIZUNO, K. MAEMURA, H. KURIHARA, R. AIKAWA, H. TAKANO & Y. YAZAKI. 1996. Endothelin-1 is involved in mechanical stress-induced cardiomyocyte hypertrophy. J. Biol. Chem. **271:** 3221–3228.
53. LENORMAND, P., C. SARDET, G. PAGES, G. L'ALLEMAIN, A. BRUNET & J. POUYSSEGUR. 1993. Growth factors induce nuclear translocation of MAP kinases (p42MAPK and p44 MAPK) but not of their activator MAP kinase kinase (P45 MAPKK) in fibroblasts. J. Cell. Biol. **122:** 1079–1088.
54. HAN, J., J.D. LEE, L. BIBBS & R.J. ULEVITCH. 1994. A MAP kinase targeted by endotoxin and hyperosmolarity in mammalian cells. Science **265:** 808–811.
55. FRESHNEY, N.W., L. RAWLINSON, F. GUESDON, E. JONES, S. COWLEY, J. HSUAN & J. SAKLATVALA. 1994. Interleukin-1 activates a novel protein kinase cascade that results in the phosphorylation of HSP 27. Cell **78:** 1039–1049.
56. EGAN, S.E. & R.A. WEINBERG. 1993. The pathway to signal achievement. Nature **65:** 781–783.
57. DAVIS, R.J. 1994. MAPKs: New JNK expands the group. Trends Biochem. Sci. **19:** 470–477.
58. RAINGEAUD, J., A.J. WHITMARSH, T. BARRETT, B. DERIJARD & R.J. DAVIES. 1996. MKK3- and MKK6-regulated gene expression is mediated by the p38 mitogen-activated protein kinase signal transduction pathway. Mol. Cell. Biol. **16:** 1247–1255.

59. OLSON, M.F., A. ASHWORTH & A. HALL. 1995. An essential role for Rho, Rac, and Cdc 42 GTPases in cell cycle. Science **269:** 1270–1272.
60. DOZA, Y.N., A. CUENDA, G.M. THOMAS, P. COHEN & A.R. NEBREDA. 1995. Activation of the MAP kinase homologue RK requires the phosphorylation of Thr-180 and Tyr-182 and both residues are phosphorylated in chemically stressed KB cells. FEBS Lett. **364:** 223–228.
61. RAINGEAUD, J., S. GUPTA, J. ROGERS, M. DICKENS, J. HAN, R.J. ULEVITCH & R.J. DAVIS. 1995. Pro-inflammatory cytokines and environmental stress cause p38 mitogen-activated protein kinase activation by dual phosphorylation on tyrosine and threonine. J. Biol. Chem. **270:** 7420–7426.
62. ROUSE, J., P. COHEN, S. TRIGON, M. MORANGE, A. ALONSO-LLAMAZARES, D. ZAMANILLO, T. HUNT & A.R. NEBREDA. 1994. A novel kinase cascade triggered by stress and heat shock that stimulates MAPKAP kinase 2 and phosphorylation of the small heat shock proteins. Cell **78:** 1027–1037.
63. LEE, J.C., J.T. LAYDON, P.C. MCDONNELL, T.F. GALLAGHER, S. KUMAR, D. GREEN, D. MCNULTY, M.J. BLUMENTHAL, J.R. HEYS, S.W. LANDVATTER, J.E. STRICKLER, M.M. MCLAUGHLIN, I.R. SIEMENS, S.M. FISHER, G.P. LIVI, J.R. WHITE, J.L. ADAMS & P.R. YOUNG. 1994. A protein kinase involved in the regulation of inflammatory cytokine biosynthesis. Nature **372:** 739–746.
64. DERIJARD, B., J. RAINGEAUD, T. BARRETT, I.H. WU, J. HAN, R.J. ULEVITCH & R.J. DAVIS. 1995. Independent human MAP kinase signal transduction pathways defined by MEK and MKK isoforms. Science **269:** 17.
65. FORCE, T., J.V. BONVENTREM, G. HEIDECKER, U. RAPP, J. AVRUCH & L.M. KYRIAKIS. 1994. Enzymatic characteristics of the Raf-1 protein kinase. Proc. Natl. Acad. Sci. USA **91:** 1270–1274.
66. GRAIER, W.F., B.G. HOEBEL, J. PALTAUF-DOBURZYNSKA & G.M. KOSTNER. 1998. Effects of superoxide anions on endothelial Ca^{2+} signaling pathways. Arterioscler. Thromb. Vasc. Biol. **18:** 1470–1479.
67. DIMON-GADAL, S., P. GERBAUD, G. KERYER, W. ANDERSON, D. EVAIN-BRION & F. RAYNAUD. 1998. In vitro effects of oxygen-derived free radicals in type I and type II c-AMP-dependent protein kinases. J. Biol. Chem. **273:** 22833–22840.
68. AKAMA, K.T., C. ALBANESE, R.G. PESTELL & L.J. VAN ELDIK. 1998. Amyloid beta-peptide stimulated nitric oxide production in astrocytes through an NFκB-dependent mechanism. Proc. Natl. Acad. Sci. USA **95:** 5795–5800.
69. VESELY, D.L. 1997. Signal transduction: activation of the guanylate cyclase-cyclic guanosine-3′-5′ monophosphate system by hormones and free radicals. Am. J. Med. Sci. **314:** 311–323.
70. COHEN, M.V., Y. LIU, G. LIU, P. WANG, C. WEINBRENNER, G.A. CORDIS, D.K. DAS & J.M. DOWNEY. 1996. Phospholipase D plays a role in ischemic preconditioning in rabbit heart. Circulation **94:** 1713–1718.
71. MAULIK, N., T. YOSHIDA, Y.-L. ZU, M. SATO, A. BANERJEE & D.K. DAS. 1998. Ischemic stress adaptation of heart triggers a tyrosine kinase regulated signaling pathway. A potential role for MAPKAP kinase 2. Am. J. Physiol. **275:** H1857–H1864.
72. GUYTON, K.Z., Y. LIU, M. GOROSPE & Q. XU. 1996. Activation of mitogen-activated protein kinase by H_2O_2. Role in cell survival following oxidant injury. J. Biol. Chem. **271:** 4138–4142.
73. HAN, J., J.-D. LEE, P.S. TOBIAS & R.J. ULEVITCH. 1993. Endotoxin induces rapid protein tyrosine phosphorylation in 70z/3 cells expression cD14. J. Biol. Chem. **268:** 25009–25014.
74. SHAROV, V.G., H.N. SABBAH, H. SHIMOYAMA, A.V. GOUSSEV, M. LESCH & S. GOLDSTEIN. 1996. Evidence of cardiocyte apoptosis in myocardium of dogs with chronic heart failure. Am. J. Pathol. **148:** 141–149.
75. BROMME, H.J. & J. HOLTZ. 1996. Apoptosis in the heart: when and why? Mol. Cell. Biochem. **163/164:** 261–275.
76. KAJSTURA, J., W. CHENG, K. REISS, W.A. CLARK, E.H. SONNENBLICK, S. KRAJEWSKI, J.C. REED, G. OLIVETTI & P. ANVERSA. 1996. Apoptotic and necrotic myocyte cell

deaths are independent contributing variables of infarct size in rats. Lab. Invest. **74:** 86–107.
77. Fliss, H. & D. Gattinger. 1996. Apoptosis in ischemic and reperfused rat myocardsium. Circ. Res. **79:** 949–956.
78. Maulik, N., R.M. Engelman, D. Deaton, J.E. Flack, J.A. Rousou & D.K. Das. 1996. Reperfusion of ischemic myocardium induces apoptosis and DNA laddering with enhanced expression of protooncogene c-myc mRNA. Circulation **94:** I415.
79. Maulik, N., T. Yoshida & D.K. Das. 1998. Oxidative stress developed during the reperfusion of ischemic myocardium induces apoptosis. Free Radical Biol. Med. **24:** 869–875.
80. Maulik, N., V.E. Kagan, A. Vladimir & D.K. Das. 1998. Redistribution of phosphatidylethanolamine and phosphatidylserine precedes reperfusion-induced apoptosis. Am. J. Physiol. **274:** H242–H248.
81. Buerke, M., T. Murohara, C. Shurk, C. Nuss, K. Tomaselli & A.M. Lefer. 1995. Cardioprotective effect of insulin-like growth factor 1 in myocardial ischemia followed by reperfusion. Proc. Natl. Acad. Sci. USA **92:** 8031–8035.
82. Gottlieb, R.A., K.O. Burleson, R.A. Kloner, B.M. Babior & R.L. Engler. 1994. Reperfusion injury induces apoptosis in rabbit cardiomyocytes. J. Clin. Invest. **94:** 1621–1628.
83. Maulik, N., T. Yoshida, R.M. Engelman, J.A. Rousou, J.E. Flack, D. Deaton & D.K. Das. 1997. Oxidative stress developed during reperfusion of ischemic myocardium downregulates BCL-2 gene and induces apoptosis and DNA laddering. Surg. Forum **48:** 245–248.
84. Maulik, N., T. Yoshida, R.M. Engelman, D. Deaton, J.E. Flack, J.A. Rousou & D.K. Das. 1999. Ischemic preconditioning attenuates apoptotic cell death associated with ischemia/reperfusion. Mol. Cell. Biochem. In press.
85. Maulik, N. & D.K. Das. 1999. Regulation of cardiomyocyte apoptosis in ischemic reperfused mouse heart by glutathione peroxidase. Mol. Cell. Biochem. In press.
86. Das, D.K. & N. Maulik. 1994. Evaluation of antioxidant effectiveness in ischemia reperfusion tissue injury methods. Methods Enzymol. **233:** 601–610.
87. Tosaki, A., D. Bagchi, A. Hellegouarch, T. Pali, G.A. Cordis & D.K. Das. 1993. Comparisons of ESR and HPLC methods for the detection of hydroxyl radicals in ischemic/reperfused hearts. A relationship between the genesis of oxygen-free radicals and reperfusion-induced arrhythmias. Biochem. Pharmacol. **45:** 961–969.
88. Kramer, J.H., V. Misik & W.B. Weglicki. 1994. Lipid peroxidation-derived free radical production and postischemic myocardial reperfusion injury. Ann. N.Y. Acad. Sci. **723:** 180–196.
89. Buttke, T.M. & P.A. Sandstrom. 1994. Oxidative stress as a mediator of apoptosis. Immunol. Today **15:** 7–10.
90. Hockenbery, D.M., Z.N. Oltvai, X.M. Yin, C.L. Milliman & S.J. Korsmeyer. 1993. Bcl-2 functions in an antioxidant pathway to prevent apoptosis. Cell **75:** 241–251.
91. Kane, D.J., T.J. Sarafian, R. Anton, H. Hahn, E.B. Gralla, J.S. Valentine & D.E. Bredesen. 1997. Bcl-2 inhibition of neuronal death: Decreased generation of reactive oxygen species. Science **262:** 1274–1277.
92. Greenlund, L.J., T.L. Deckwerth & E.M. Johnson, Jr. 1995. Superoxide dismutase delays neuronal apoptosis: A role for reactive oxygen species in programmed neuronal death. Neuron **14:** 303–315.
93. Verity, M.A., D.E. Bredesen & T. Sarafian. 1995. Role of reactive oxygen species in neuronal degeneration. Ann. N.Y. Acad. Sci. **765:** 340–345.
94. Muehlematter, D., R. Larsson & P. Cerutti. 1988. Active oxygen induced DNA strand breakage and poly ADP-ribosylation in promotable and non-promotable JB6 mouse epidermal cells. Carcinogenesis **9:** 239–245.
95. Das, D.K. & N. Maulik. 1998. Apoptosis in ischemia reperfusion injury. *In* Biological Oxidants and Antioxidants. L. Packer & A.S.H. Ong, Eds.: 165–177. AOCS Press. Champaign, IL.

96. NOGUCHI, N., Y. YOSHIDA, H. KANEDA, Y. YAMAMOTO & E. NIKI. 1992. Action of ebselen as an antioxidant against lipid peroxidation. Biochem. Pharmacol. **44:** 39–44.
97. UEDA, S., T. YOSHIKAWA, S. TAKAHASHI, Y. NAITO, H. OYAMADA, T. TAKEMURA, Y. MORITA, T. TANIGAWA, S. SUGINO & M. KONDO. 1990. Protection by seleno-organic compound, ebselen, against acute gastric mucosal injury induced by ischemia-reperfusion in rats. *In* Antioxidant in Therapy and Preventive Medicine. I. Emerit, Ed.: 187–191. Plenum. New York, NY.
98. FRASS, O., H.S. SHARMA, R. KNOLL, D.J. DUNCKER, E.O. MCFALLS, P.D. VERDOUW & W. SCHAPER. 1993. Enhanced gene expression of calcium regulatory proteins in stunned porcine myocardium. Cardiovasc. Res. **27:** 2037–2043.
99. SHARMA, H.S., M. WUNCH, R. KANDOLF & W. SCHAPER. 1989. Angiogenesis by slow coronary artery occlusion in the pig heart: Expression of different growth factors mRNAs. J. Mol. Cell. Cardiol. **21**(Suppl III)**:** 69.
100. DAS, D.K., N. MAULIK, M. SATO & P. RAY. 1999. Reactive oxygen species function as second messenger during ischemic preconditioning of heart. Mol. Cell. Biochem. In press.
101. MAULIK, N., S. GOSWAMI, N. GALANG & D.K. DAS. 1999. Differential regulation of Bcl-2, AP-1 and NFkB on cardiomyocyte apoptosis during myocardial ischemic stress adaptation. FEBS Lett. **443:** 331–336.
102. TOLEDANO, M. & W.J. LEONARD. 1991. Modulation of transcription factor NF-kappa B binding activity by oxidation-reduction in vitro. Proc. Natl. Acad. Sci. USA **86:** 5974–5978.
103. MEYER, M., R. SCHRECK & P.A. BAEUERLE. 1993. H_2O_2 and antioxidants have opposite effects on activation of NF-kappa B and AP-1 in intact cells: AP-1 as secondary antioxidant-responsive factor. EMBO J. **12:** 2005–2015.
104. SCHRECK, R., P. RIEBER & P.A. BAEUERLE. 1991. Reactive oxygen intermediates as apparently widely used messengers in the activation of the NF-kappa B transcription factor and HIV-1. EMBO J. **10:** 2247–2258.
105. SUZUKI, Y.J., M. MIZUNO & L. PACKER. 1994. Signal transduction for nuclear factor-kappa B activation. Proposed location of antioxidant inhibitable step. Biochem. Biophys. Res. Commun. **210:** 537–541.
106. BAGCHI, D., D.K. DAS, R.M. ENGELMAN, M.R. PRASAD & R. SUBRAMANIAN. 1990. Polymorphonuclear leucocytes as potential source of free radicals in the ischemia-reperfused myocardium. Eur. Heart J. **11:** 800–813.
107. GHOSH, S., A.M. GIFFORD, L.R. RIVIERE, P. TEMPST, G.P. NOLAN & D. BALTIMORE. 1990. Cloning of the p50 DNA binding subunit of NF-kappa B: homology to rel and dorsal. Cell **62:** 1019–1029.

Small Heat Shock Proteins and Protection against Injury

WOLFGANG H. DILLMANN[b]

Department of Medicine, University of California, San Diego, La Jolla, California 92093, USA

ABSTRACT: The small heat shock proteins αB crystallin and HSP27 exert a protective effect in response to simulated ischemia. A model is proposed whereby proteins not in their final folding state bind to the outside of the large oligomeric small heat shock protein complexes thus finding a safe haven during ischemia. After the ischemia is resolved, these proteins may be released and, with the help of HSP70, are shuttled to a productive refolding pathway resulting in proteins in their final folding state, which can assume their normal activity in cells recovered from ischemic injury.

INTRODUCTION

Heat shock proteins are a diverse group of proteins classified according to their molecular weights. They form different structures that exert protective effects by different mechanisms, but all involve the prevention of aggregation of proteins that are not in their final folding stage or they allow proteins to reach their folding state avoiding structures which would trap them in aggregates.[1] This review will focus on the group of small heat shock proteins that includes heat shock protein 32 (HSP32) or hemoxogenase heat shock protein 27 (HSP27) in humans or heat shock protein 25 in rodents and αB crystallin. These small heat shock proteins arose from a primordial gene and have a 3 Exon structure.[2] They form large multimeric units to which proteins not in their final folding stage bind on the outside. In contrast, heat shock proteins forming barrel-like structures, in which folding occurs in the inside, are termed chaperonins and include the mitochondrial heat shock protein 10 and 60 and the CCT (chaperonin-containing TCPI) complex in the cytosol. In these complexes, heat shock proteins are folded in the inside of a barrel-like structure.[1] In contrast, heat shock protein 70 (HSP70) acts as a single molecule attaching to hydrophobic loops of a protein that would normally be localized inside the globular protein structure.[3] HSP27 and αB crystallin differ in their concentrations during development with HSP27 being at very high levels in neonatal animals and decreasing with increasing age.[4] In contrast, αB crystallin occurs at relatively lower levels immediately after parturition and increases with increasing age.[5] The tissue's specific expression is also different for the two small heat shock proteins. αB crystallin is expressed, for example, in high levels in striated muscle.[6] This may be due to the fact

[b]Address correspondence to: Wolfgang H. Dillmann, M.D., University of California, San Diego, Department of Medicine, 9500 Gilman Drive, La Jolla, California 92093-0618; Telephone: (619) 534-9934; Fax: (619) 534-9932; E-mail: wdillmann@ucsd.edu

that an E-box and CAr G box occur in the promoter of αB crystallin.[7] HSP27 is, in contrast, widely expressed.[4]

SPECIFIC FUNCTIONS AND PROTECTIVE EFFECTS OF αB CRYSTALLIN

As indicated, αB crystallin is expressed in high levels in striated muscle, e.g., the heart.[6] It binds to Z-lines and the I band. In contrast to other heat shock proteins, αB crystallin does not contain any ATPase activity. With ischemia and a lowering of the pH, αB crystallin binds with an increased affinity to actin and desmin-based filaments.[8] The area of the I band where myofibrils are attached to the structures of the Z-line is a critical region for ischemic damage. We wanted to determine if increased expression of the small heat shock proteins would lead to additional protective effects against ischemic injury. We therefore cloned αB crystallin into a human adenovirus viral vector. The adenovirus, which is infective but replication deficient, was then used to infect cardiac myocytes. Subsequently, the cardiac myocytes are exposed to a simulated ischemia in a specially prepared incubation chamber. Oxygen is blown out by argon and the cells are maintained in the presence of low glucose. The damage was quantitated by the release of creatine kinase or lactate dehydrogenase into the medium. These experiments showed that increased expression of αB crystallin led to a significant decrease in creatine kinase release from myocytes made ischemic.[5] Using an αB crystallin mutant in which a C-terminal lysine was changed to glycine led to increased damage in myocytes exposed to simulated ischemia. In addition we found that such a mutant forms oligomers of the lower molecular size than the wildtype αB crystallin.[9]

In order to explore the mechanisms underlying the protective effect of αB crystallin we determined the intactness of the microtubular structure using an antibody to the α-subunit of tubulin using a confocal microscopic approach. Exposing neonatal myocytes to simulated ischemia led to significant disruption of the tubular structure.[10] Infecting such myocytes with αB crystallin led to a markedly better preservation of the microtubular structure. Part of the protective effects of αB crystallin are therefore most likely exerted by protecting specific elements of the cytoskeleton in myocytes exposed to an ischemic milieu.

PROTECTIVE EFFECTS OF HSP27

HSP27 associates primarily with F-acting based microfilaments. It contains three serines, which are phosphorylated by P38 stimulated activity of MAPKAP kinase 2. The role that phosphorylation plays in the overall protective effects of HSP27 is currently unclear. Infecting neonatal myocytes with HSP27 and exposing them to simulated ischemia did not lead to increased protection against ischemic injury. This is most likely related to the fact that in neonatal myocytes HSP27 is already present at very high levels. Constructing an HSP27 antisense expressing adenovirus led to a significant decrease in the level of HSP27 and increased injury in neonatal cardiac myocytes. We also used the serine-to-alanine mutants to explore the role of phosphorylation for the protective effect of HSP27. In these mutants, serines 15, 78, and 82 were changed to alanine or glycine. Using these phosphorylation mutants, we obtained similar protective effects to that obtained with wildtype HSP27. It appears, therefore, that for the general chaperonin effects of HSP27 phosphorylation at the serines is not an essential requirement. In addition, we determined if combined expression of heat shock proteins with each other led to an enhanced protective effect. A higher protective effect were observed, for example, from combining HSP27 with αB crystallin than from αB crystallin or HSP27 alone. Similarly, an increased protective effect was observed by a combination of αB crystallin and HSP70.

SUMMARY

In summary, small heat shock proteins, αB crystallin, and HSP27 exert a protective effect against simulated ischemia. One could propose a model whereby proteins that are not in their final folding state bind to the outside of the large oligomeric small heat shock protein complexes, finding a safe haven. After the ischemia is resolved these proteins may be released and, with the help of HSP70, are shuttled to a productive refolding pathway resulting in proteins in their final folding state, which can assume their normal activity in cells recovered from ischemic injury.

REFERENCES

1. Welch, W.J., L.A. Mizzen & A.-P. Arrigo. 1989. Structure and function of mammalian stress proteins. *In* Stress-induced Proteins. M.L. Pardue, J.R. Feramisco & S. Lindquist, Eds.: 187–202. Alan R. Liss, Inc. New York.
2. Wistow, G. 1985. Domain structure and evolution in α-crystallins and small heat-shock proteins. FEBS Lett. **181:** 1–6.
3. Rudiger, S., A. Buchberger & B. Bukau. 1997. Interaction of Hsp70 chaperones with substrates. Nature Structural Bio. **4:** 342–349.
4. Gernold, M., U. Knauf, M. Gaestel, J. Stahl & P.M. Kloetzel. 1993. Development and tissue-specific distribution of mouse small heat shock protein Hsp25. Dev. Genet. **14:** 103–111.
5. Martin, J.L., R. Mestril, R. Hilal-Dandan, L.L. Brunton & W.H. Dillmann. 1997. Small heat shock proteins and protection against ischemic injury in cardiac myocytes. Circulation **96:** 4343–4348.
6. Longoni, S., S. Lattonen, G. Bullock & M. Chiesi. 1990. Cardiac alpha-crystallin. Mol. Cell. Biochem. **97:** 113–120.
7. Gopal-Srivastava, R., J.I. Haynes II, & J. Piatigorsky. 1995. Regulation of the murine αB-crystallin/small heat shock protein gene in cardiac muscle. Mol. Cell. Biol. **15**(12)**:** 7081–7090.
8. Chies, M., S. Longoni & U. Limbruno. 1990. Cardiac alpha-crystallin: III involvement during heart ischemia. Mol. Cell. Biochem. **97:** 129–136.
9. Martin, J.L. & R. Mestril. 1998. Small heat shock proteins and protection against ischemic damage to cardiomyocytes. Circulation **98** (17)**:** I-620(abstract).
10. Bluhm, W.F., J.L. Martin, R. Mestril & W.H. Dillmann. 1998. Specific heat shock proteins protect microtubules during simulated ischemia in cardiac myocytes. Am. J. Physiol. **275** (Heart Circ. Physiol.)**:** H2243–H2249.

Inhibition of Myocardial TNF-α Production by Heat Shock

A Potential Mechanism of Stress-Induced Cardioprotection against Postischemic Dysfunction[a]

XIANZHONG MENG,[b] ANIRBAN BANERJEE, LIHUA AO,
DANIEL R. MELDRUM, BRIAN S. CAIN, BRIAN D. SHAMES,
AND ALDEN H. HARKEN

Department of Surgery, University of Colorado Health Sciences Center, Denver, Colorado 80262, USA

ABSTRACT: Overproduction of tumor necrosis factor-α (TNF-α) contributes to cardiac dysfunction associated with systemic or myocardial stress, such as endotoxemia and myocardial ischemia/reperfusion (I/R). Heat shock has been demonstrated to enhance cardiac functional resistance to I/R. However, the protective mechanisms remain unclear. The purpose of this study was to determine: (1) whether cardiac macrophages express heat shock protein 72 (HSP72) after heat shock, (2) whether induced cardiac HSP72 suppresses myocardial TNF-α production during I/R, and (3) whether preservation of postischemic myocardial function by heat shock is correlated with attenuated TNF-α production during I/R. Rats were subjected to heat shock (42°C for 15 min) and 24 h recovery. Immunoblotting confirmed the expression of cardiac HSP72. Immunofluorescent staining detected HSP72 in cardiac interstitial cells including resident macrophages rather than myocytes. Global I/R caused a significant increase in myocardial TNF-α. The increase in myocardial TNF-α was blunted by prior heat shock and the reduced myocardial TNF-α level was correlated with improved cardiac functional recovery. This study demonstrates for the first time that heat shock induces HSP72 in cardiac resident macrophages and inhibits myocardial TNF-α production during I/R. These observations suggest that inhibition of myocardial TNF-α production may be a mechanism by which HSP72 protects the heart against postischemic dysfunction.

INTRODUCTION

Expression of heat shock protein 72 (HSP72), an inducible isoform of the 70 kD major stress protein family, is an endogenous mechanism by which living cells adapt to stress. Although the precise functions of this family of stress proteins remain to

[a]This work was supported in part by National Institutes of Health grants GM-08315 and GM-49222.

[b]Address correspondence to: Xianzhong Meng, M.D., Department of Surgery, Box C-320, University of Colorado Health Sciences Center, 4200 E. Ninth Avenue, Denver, Colorado 80262; Telephone: 303/315-8055; Fax: 303/315-0007.

be defined, HSP72 is known to be involved in the folding, assembly, and stabilization of newly synthesized proteins, and may play an important role in processing denatured proteins.[1]

In vivo synthesis of cardiac HSP72 occurs in response to a variety of noxious stimuli, such as heat shock,[2,3] hypoxia,[4] mobility restraint,[5] endotoxemia,[6] hemodynamic stress,[7,8] myocardial ischemia,[9–11] and myocardial oxidant stress.[12] Induction of cardiac HSP72 has been demonstrated to protect myocardium against dysfunction caused by ischemia/reperfusion (I/R).[2,5,8,13–15] Recent studies using an *in vivo* transfection model[16] or transgenic models[17–20] have provided direct evidence demonstrating an important role of cardiac HSP72 in preservation of myocardial function after I/R. However, the mechanism by which HSP72 protects myocardium against an ischemic insult is unknown.

Heat shock is a vigorous stimulus to induce cardiac HSP72.[2] Previous studies using immunoblotting or two-dimensional gel electrophoresis have demonstrated an increased level of cardiac HSP72 24 h after heat shock. However, the cellular distribution of hyperthermia-induced HSP72 expression in the myocardium remains to be defined. The heart is composed of heterogeneous cell populations. Cardiac myocytes express HSP72 after hemodynamic overload[21] or noradrenergic stress.[8] However, cardiac cell populations expressing HSP72 may be dependent upon the stressor faced by the heart. Indeed, we have observed that heat shock induces cardiac HSP72 in interstitial cells rather than myocytes of rat heart.[6] Macrophages (Mϕ) express HSP72 after *in vitro* heat stress.[22–24] Whether cardiac resident Mϕ express HSP72 after *in vivo* heat stress remains unknown.

Tumor necrosis factor-α (TNF-α) is a cytokine produced by monocytes and Mϕ and has been recognized as a myocardial depressant factor in sepsis-induced myocardial dysfunction.[25] A number of studies have demonstrated that TNF-α directly depresses myocardial contractility.[26,27] Cardiac resident Mϕ produce TNF-α when stimulated,[28,29] suggesting that cardiac resident Mϕ and locally produced TNF-α may regulate cardiac contractility. It has been reported that increased cardiac expression of TNF-α occurs in animal models of myocardial I/R[30–35] and in humans after coronary bypass surgery.[36,37] These studies suggest a link between cardiac TNF-α and myocardial dysfunction after I/R. In this regard, our recent study demonstrates that adenosine inhibits myocardial TNF-α production and preserves myocardial function in rat heart after I/R.[34] Thus, suppression of myocardial TNF-α production may be a permissive strategy for preservation of myocardial function.

Prior heat stress to monocytes or Mϕ *in vitro* inhibits TNF-α production when the cells are subsequently stimulated with bacterial lipopolysaccharide.[22–24] This inhibition appears at the transcriptional level and is associated with an increased cellular level of HSP72.[23] However, it remains unknown whether induction of cardiac HSP72 by heat shock inhibits myocardial TNF-α production.

We hypothesized that heat shock induces HSP72 in cardiac resident Mϕ and that induced cardiac HSP72 preserves postischemic myocardial function by suppression of TNF-α production. The purpose of this study was to examine: (1) whether cardiac Mϕ express HSP72 after heat shock, (2) whether induced cardiac HSP72 suppresses myocardial TNF-α production during I/R, and (3) whether preservation of postischemic myocardial function by heat shock is correlated with attenuated TNF-α production during I/R.

MATERIALS AND METHODS

Animals

Male Sprague-Dawley rats, body weight 300–325 g (Sasco, Omaha, NE), were acclimated in a quarantine room and maintained on a standard pellet diet for two weeks before initiation of the experiments. All animal experiments were approved by the Animal Care and Research Committee, University of Colorado Health Sciences Center. All animals received humane care in compliance with the "Guide for the Care and Use of Laboratory Animals" (NIH Publication No. 85-23, revised 1985).

Chemicals and Reagents

Mouse monoclonal anti-HSP72 (clone C92) was purchased from Stressgen Inc. (Victoria, British Columbia, Canada). Rabbit antiserum to rat Mϕ was obtained from Accurate Chemical & Scientific Co. (Westbury, NY). Cy3-labeled goat anti-mouse IgG and fluorescein-labeled goat anti-rabbit IgG were obtained from Jackson ImmunoResearch Laboratories, Inc. (West Grove, PA). Fluorescein-labeled wheat germ agglutinin was purchased from Molecular Probes (Eugene, OR). Peroxidase-labeled sheep anti-mouse IgG was purchased from Amersham Corporation (Arlington Heights, IL). Enhanced chemiluminescent assay kit was purchased from Pierce Chemical Co. (Rockford, IL). TNF-α assay kit was obtained from Genzyme Corporation (Cambridge, MA). All other chemicals were obtained from Sigma Chemical Co. (St. Louis, MO).

Heat Shock

The protocol for heat shock used by our laboratory has been previously reported[6] and is outlined in FIGURE 1. Briefly, rats were anesthetized with sodium pentobarbital (50 mg/kg i.p.), and 5 ml of bacteriostatic normal saline was administered through a tail vein to compensate the loss of body fluid during heating. A digital thermometer was inserted into the colon, 5 cm from the anus, to monitor core body temperature. Body temperature was gradually heated to 42°C with a heating blanket and maintained for 15 min. Animals were allowed to recover at room temperature. Sham control rats were anesthetized and wrapped with the blanket without heating. After 24 h of recovery, hearts were rapidly removed from hyperthermia-treated rats and sham controls. Four hearts from each group were processed for detection of HSP72. Coronary vessels of each heart were flushed by retrograde perfusion with 10 ml of cold

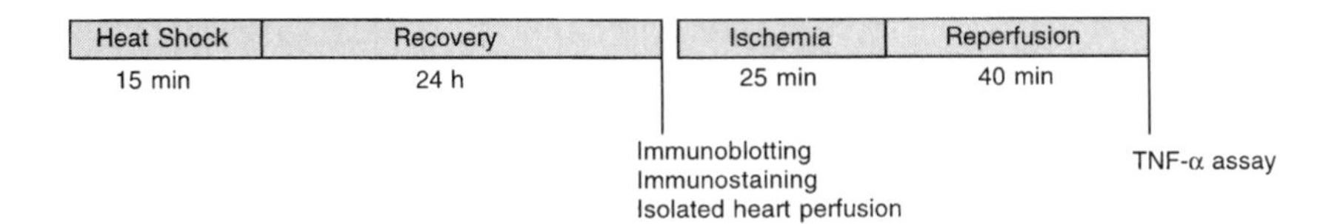

FIGURE 1. Experimental protocols.

(4°C) phosphate-buffered saline (PBS). A portion of ventricular tissue (including both ventricles) of each heart was frozen in liquid nitrogen and stored at –70°C for immunoblotting of HSP 72. The remaining ventricular tissue (including both ventricles) was embedded in OCT compound (Miles Inc., Elkhart, IN), frozen in dry ice-cold isopentane, and stored at –70°C for immunofluorescent detection and localization of HSP72. Additional hearts from each group were subjected to global I/R for the examination of cardiac functional resistance to I/R.

Acrylamide Gel Electrophoresis and Immunoblotting

Ventricular tissue from rats treated with heat shock or sham control rats was minced on ice in four parts of homogenate buffer (50 mM Tris-HCl, pH 7.0; 2 mM EGTA; 1.0 mM benzamidine; 1.0 mM phenylmethylsulfonyl fluoride). Homogenate was prepared with a tissue homogenizer (Tekmar Co, Cincinnati, OH) at highest speed, 20 strokes. Centrifugation was carried out with a Beckman centrifuge (Model J2-21 with a JA-17 rotor, Beckman Instruments, Inc., Palo Alto, CA) at 4°C, 10,000 ×*g* for 15 min. The supernatant was transferred to a plastic test tube. Protein concentration was determined by the Lowry method.[38] An aliquot of the supernatant was mixed with an equal volume of sample buffer (62.5 mM Tris-HCl, pH to 6.8 and 1% SDS).

Acrylamide gel electrophoresis and electrophoresis transfer of crude proteins were performed by the previously described method.[39] Size fraction of crude proteins was performed by electrophoresis (Mini-Protean II Electrophoresis System, Bio-Rad Laboratories, Hercules, CA) with 20 µg of crude protein on 4–20% gradient acrylamide gel (Bio-Rad Laboratories, Hercules, CA). Fractioned proteins were transferred onto a nitrocellulose membrane. Immunodetection of HSP72 was carried out by the enhanced chemiluminescence method. The membrane was incubated in 5% nonfat dry milk (Nestle Food Co., Glendale, CA) in PBS for 1 h to block nonspecific binding. The membrane was subsequently incubated with a monoclonal antibody against HSP72 [1 µg/ml in antibody buffer (PBS containing 5% dry milk and 0.05% Tween 20)] for 2 h and with peroxidase-linked sheep anti-mouse IgG (1:5,000 dilution with antibody buffer) for 1 h. After a thorough wash with PBS, signal development was carried out by incubating the membrane in chemiluminescence solution (Luminol/enhancer/stable peroxide) for 2 min. The membrane was then exposed to Kodak X-Omat film (Eastman Kodak Co. Rochester, NY). Densitometry of HSP72 band was performed with a computerized laser densitometer (Molecular Dynamics, Sunnyvale, CA).

Immunofluorescent Staining

Immunolocalization of HSP72 was performed with an indirect immunofluorescence technique as described previously.[6,40] Transverse sections (5 µm thick) of ventricular myocardium were cut with an IEC cryotome (Minotome Plus, Needham Heights, MA) and then dried at room temperature for 1 h. Sections were fixed in a mixture of 30% methanol and 70% acetone at –20°C for 10 min, and then washed with PBS. Unless indicated, all incubations were performed at room temperature. To block nonspecific binding, sections were incubated for 30 min with 10% goat serum in PBS. Sections were then incubated for 90 min with mouse monoclonal antibody against HSP72 (5 μg/ml in PBS containing 1% bovine serum albumin). After three washes with PBS, sections were incubated for 45 min with Cy3-labeled goat anti-mouse IgG (1:250 dilution with PBS containing 1% bovine serum albumin). After thorough washing with PBS, specimens were counterstained with fluorescein-labeled wheat germ agglutinin (5 μg/ml, for cell surface staining) and *bis*-benzimide (2 μg/ml, for nuclear staining). The sections were then mounted with aqueous anti-quenching media. To assess the specificity of the immunostaining, adjacent sections were incubated with non-immune mouse IgG (5 μg/ml in PBS containing 1% bovine serum albumin) in replacement of the primary antibody and then processed in identical conditions. Microscopic observation and photography were performed with a Leica DMRXA confocal microscope (Germany).

Isolated Heart Perfusion and Assessment of Cardiac Contractile Function

Intrinsic cardiac contractility was determined by a modified isovolumetric Langendorff technique as described elsewhere.[6,8] At the termination of the experiments, beating hearts were rapidly excised into oxygenated Krebs-Henseleit solution containing (in mmol/L) glucose 5.5, $CaCl_2$ 1.2, KCl 4.7, $NaHCO_3$ 25, NaCl 119, $MgSO_4$ 1.17, and KH_2PO_4 1.18. Normothermic retrograde perfusion was performed with the same solution in the isovolumetric and non-recirculating mode. Perfusion buffer was saturated with a gas mixture of 92.5% O_2 and 7.5% CO_2 to achieve a pO_2 of 450 mm Hg, pCO_2 of 40 mm Hg, and pH of 7.4. Perfusion pressure was maintained at 70 mm Hg. A latex balloon was inserted through the left atrium into the left ventricle, and the balloon was filled with water to achieve a left ventricular end-diastolic pressure (LVEDP) of 5 to 10 mm Hg. Pacing wires were fixed to the right atrium, and heart was paced at 6.0 Hz. The myocardial temperature was maintained by placing the heart in a jacketed tissue chamber kept at 37°C by circulating warm water. A three-way stopcock was mounted above the aorta cannula to create global ischemia. After 15 min of perfusion (equilibration), hearts were subjected to normothermic global ischemia for 25 min followed by 40-min reperfusion. Left ventricular developed pressure (LVDP) and LVEDP were continuously recorded with a computerized pressure amplifier/digitizer (Maclab 8, AD Instrument, Cupertino, CA).

TNF-α Assay

Myocardial homogenate was used for TNF-α assay. TNF-α level was measured using an enzyme-linked immunosorbent assay (ELISA) system containing a hamster anti-mouse TNF-α antibody (cross-reaction with rat TNF-α). Recombinant rat TNF-α was used to construct a standard curve. Absorbance of standards and samples were determined spectrophotometrically at 450 nm using a microplate reader (Bio-Rad Laboratories, Hercules, CA). Results were plotted against the linear portion of the standard curve. TNF-α in myocardium was expressed as picograms per milligram of protein.

Statistical Analysis

Data were expressed as mean ± standard error of the mean (SEM). An analysis of variance (ANOVA) was performed, and a difference was accepted as significant with $p < 0.05$ verified by Bonferroni/Dunn post hoc test.

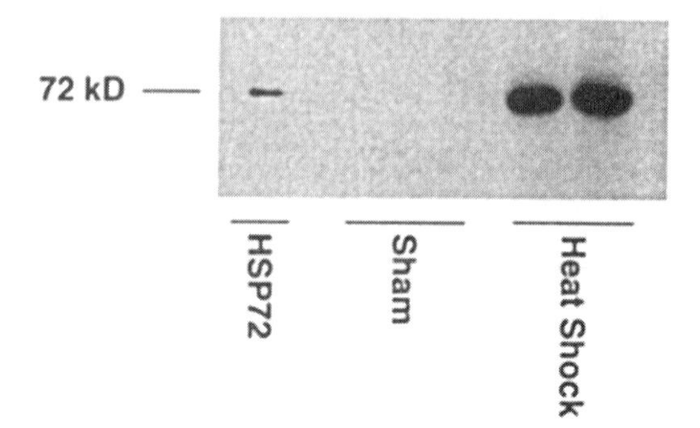

FIGURE 2. Expression of cardiac HSP72 after heat shock. Rats were subjected to heat shock (42°C for 15 min), and hearts were isolated 24 h after the treatment. After flushing coronary blood vessels, ventricular myocardium was homogenized. Myocardial crude protein was size-fractionated and immunoblotted for HSP72 with mouse monoclonal anti-HSP72. A representative blot of two separate experiments shows that cardiac HSP72 was induced at 24 h after heat shock.

RESULTS

Heat Shock Induces HSP72 in Cardiac Mϕ

Cardiac HSP72 was induced at 24 h after heat shock, whereas it was undetectable in sham control hearts (FIG. 2). To examine the cellular distribution of HSP72 in ventricular myocardium, a heterogeneous cell population, immunofluorescent staining (using a monoclonal antibody to HSP72) and confocal microscopy were performed. As shown in FIGURE 3, HSP72 immunoreactivity was not present in sham control hearts. HSP72 immunoreactivity was detected in ventricular myocardium at 24 h after heat shock, and the immunoreactivity was localized in interstitial cells, but not in myocytes. In the positively stained cells, HSP72 immunoreactivity was localized in both the cytoplasm and the nucleus. When sections from heat-shocked hearts were incubated with non-immune mouse IgG in replacement of the monoclonal antibody, immunoreactivity was not present (not shown). To examine whether cardiac resident Mϕ express HSP72 after heat shock, double immunofluorescent staining was performed using the monoclonal antibody to HSP72 and a polyclonal antibody to rat Mϕ. As shown in FIGURE 4, HSP72 immunoreactivity was detected in Mϕ after heat shock. These cells were identified as cardiac resident Mϕ rather than peripheral monocytes because they were in the interstitial space and the coronary vessels had been flushed before tissue embedding.

Induction of Cardiac HSP72 Attenuates Myocardial TNF-α Production during I/R

To examine whether induced cardiac HSP72 inhibits myocardial TNF-α production during I/R, isolated hearts were subjected to I/R using a Langendorff apparatus. This method enabled us to eliminate the influences of elevated circulating TNF-α on myocardial TNF-α level and myocardial function. As presented in FIGURE 5, there

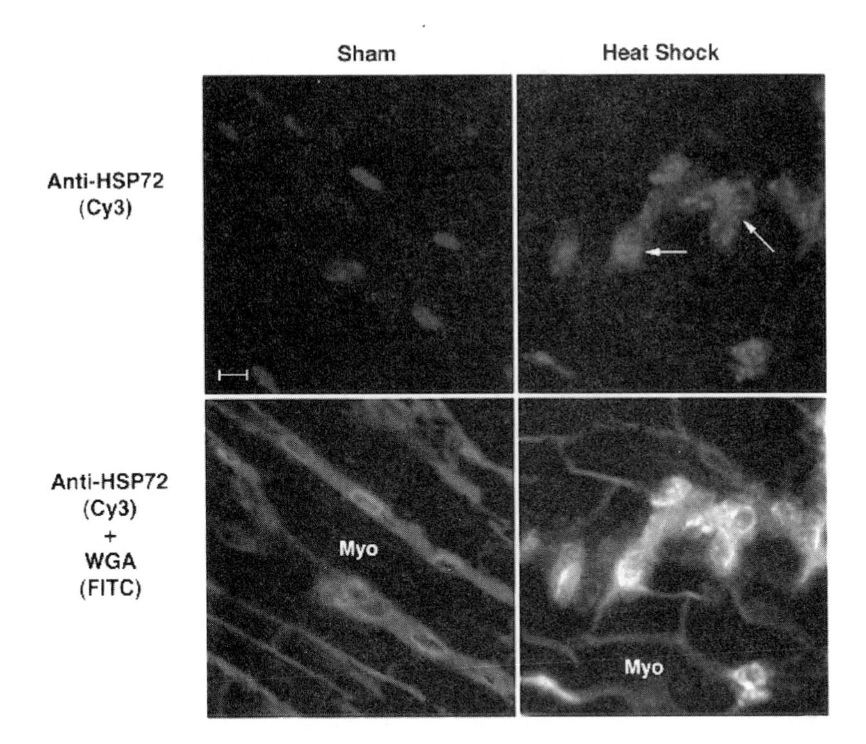

FIGURE 3. Localization of HSP72 in ventricular myocardium. Rats were subjected to heat shock (42°C for 15 min), and hearts were isolated 24 h after treatment. After flushing coronary blood vessels, ventricular myocardium was embedded in OCT compound and frozen on dry ice. Cryosection was stained with mouse monoclonal anti-HSP72 followed by Cy3-labeled goat anti-mouse IgG. The nucleus was counterstained with *bis*-benzimide and the cell surface was counterstained with wheat germ agglutinin (WGA). In ventricular myocardium of sham-treated heart, HSP72 was undetectable. Heat shock induced HSP72 in cardiac interstitial cells (*arrows*) but not in myocytes (Myo). Bar = 10 μm.

was a baseline level of TNF-α in untreated ventricular myocardium (4.6 ± 0.7 pg/mg protein). I/R resulted in an increase in myocardial TNF-α (21.0 ± 2.5 pg/mg protein at the end of reperfusion, $p < 0.01$ versus non I/R). Sham treatment before heart isolation did not affect postischemic myocardial TNF-α level (18.4 ± 2.4 pg/mg protein at the end of reperfusion, $p > 0.05$ versus I/R control). However, prior heat shock significantly reduced myocardial TNF-α (8.7 ± 0.6 pg/mg protein, $p < 0.01$ versus either I/R or sham plus I/R controls).

Induction of Cardiac HSP72 Preserves Myocardial Function after I/R

To examine whether reduced myocardial TNF-α correlates with an improved myocardial function, LVDP and LVEDP of isolated hearts were recorded during perfusion, ischemia, and reperfusion. As presented in FIGURE 6, LVDP declined rapidly to an undetectable level within 5 min of global ischemia regardless of the pretreatment. LVEDP increased progressively in all hearts during ischemia, and the peak is-

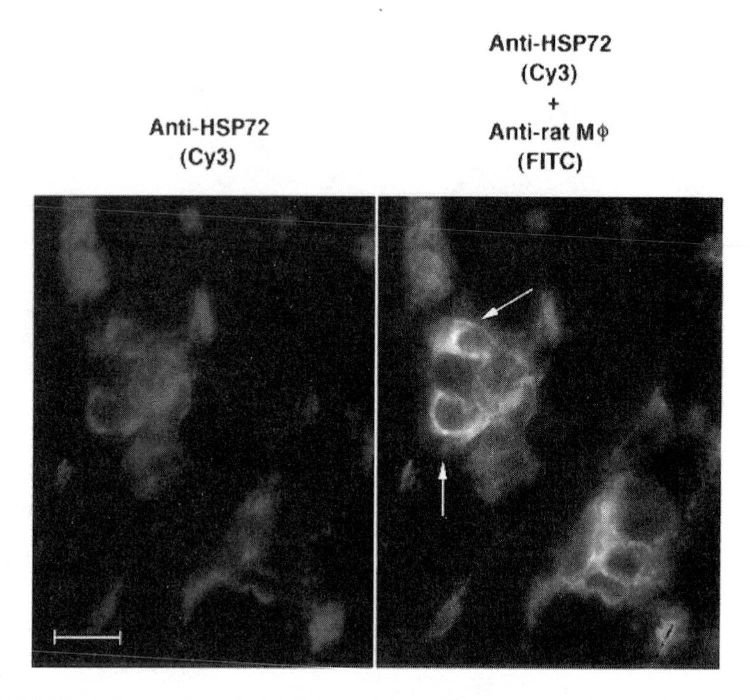

FIGURE 4. Expression of HSP72 in cardiac resident Mϕ. Rats were subjected to heat shock (42°C for 15 min), and hearts were isolated at 24 h after treatment. After flushing coronary blood vessels, ventricular myocardium was embedded in OCT compound and frozen on dry ice. The cryosection was stained with a combination of mouse monoclonal anti-HSP72 and rabbit polyclonal anti-rat Mϕ and then with Cy3-labeled goat anti-mouse IgG and fluorescein-labeled goat anti-rabbit IgG. The nucleus was counterstained with *bis*-benzimide. HSP72 was induced in cardiac resident Mϕ (*arrow*) and localized in both the cytoplasm and the nucleus. Bar = 10 μm.

chemic contracture did not differ between sham control and heat shock group. Heat shock 24 h before heart isolation improved postischemic recovery of LVDP and LVEDP. At the end of reperfusion, LVDP recovered to 41.5 ± 10.0 mm Hg in sham control hearts ($p > 0.05$ versus I/R control) whereas LVDP recovered to 72.8 ± 4.0 mm Hg in hyperthermia-pretreated hearts ($p < 0.01$ versus sham control, FIG. 6, left). LVEDP recovered to 52.3 ± 5.3 mm Hg in sham control ($p > 0.05$ versus I/R control) whereas LVEDP recovered to 30.7 ± 2.1 mm Hg in heat shock group ($p < 0.01$ versus sham control, FIG. 6, right).

DISCUSSION

The results of the present study demonstrate that (1) cardiac resident Mϕ express HSP72 after heat shock, (2) induction of cardiac HSP72 inhibits myocardial TNF-α production during I/R, and (3) the attenuated myocardial TNF-α production is cor-

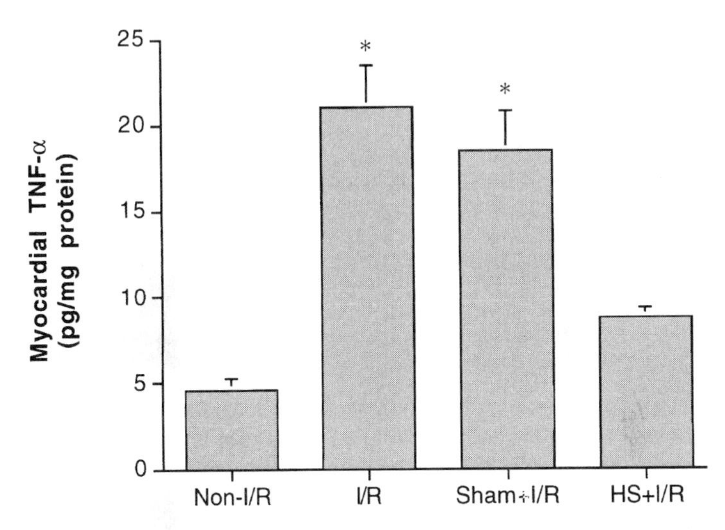

FIGURE 5. The effect of induction of cardiac HSP72 on myocardial TNF-α level after ischemia/reperfusion (I/R). Hearts were isolated from rats without pretreatment, pretreated with heat shock or sham and subjected to global I/R (25/40 min). Ventricular myocardium was homogenized after I/R. Myocardial TNF-α was determined by ELISA and compared with myocardium without I/R (Non-I/R). Data are mean ± SEM. $N = 6$ hearts in each group; $*p < 0.01$ versus Non-I/R. HS, heat shock.

related with improved postischemic myocardial functional recovery. These results suggest that suppressing I/R-induced production of cardiac TNF-α may be a mechanism by which induced cardiac HSP72 preserves myocardial function.

Heat shock induces HSP72 in the myocardium. The immunoblotting results of the present study confirmed that HSP72 was induced in ventricular myocardium at 24 h after heat shock. Immunoblotting or two-dimensional gel analysis using myocardial homogenate has been applied in previous studies to detect myocardial HSP72. Neither of these techniques was able to determine which cell types express HSP72 in the heterogeneous myocardium. Examination of HSP72-expressing cell types is important for understanding how myocardium adapts to thermal stress. Furthermore, characterization of cellular expression of HSP72 is critical for the elucidation of the mechanisms by which HSP72 protects myocardium against an ischemic insult. We have immunohistochemically examined the expression of HSP72 in the rat heart after heat shock.[6] Surprisingly, HSP72 is localized primarily in the interstitial cells. Some of the HSP72-immunoreactive cells appear to be cardiac resident Mϕ. In this study, we examined whether cardiac resident Mϕ express HSP72 after heat shock. Coronary vessels were flushed to eliminate circulating monocytes, and double immunofluorescent staining (with an monoclonal antibody against HSP72 and a polyclonal antibody against rat Mϕ) was applied to co-localize HSP72 and Mϕ. HSP72 was localized in cardiac resident Mϕ and other interstitial cells after heat shock. However, HSP72 was not detectable by immunofluorescent staining in cardiac myocytes. This pattern of myocardial cellular expression of

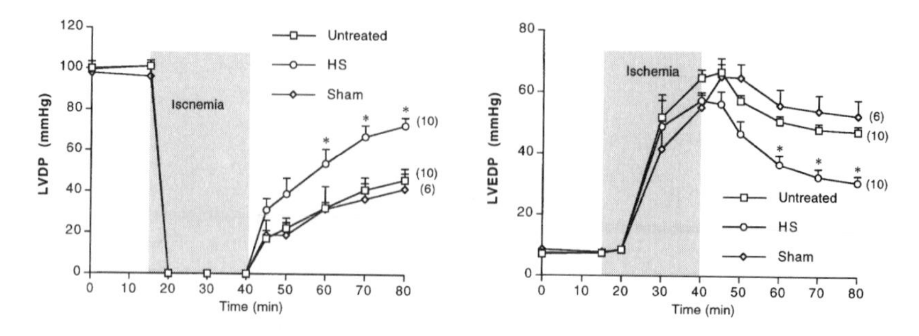

FIGURE 6. The effect of induction of cardiac HSP72 on myocardial function after ischemia/reperfusion (I/R). Hearts were isolated from rats without pretreatment, pretreated with heat shock or sham, and subjected to global I/R (25/40 min). Left ventricular developed pressure (LVDP, **left**) and left ventricular end-diastolic pressure (LVEDP, **right**) were continuously recorded. Data are mean ± SEM. *N* is shown in parentheses as number of hearts. $^*p < 0.01$ versus both untreated and sham controls. HS, heat shock.

HSP72 seems to be related to the stimulus rather than the species since we have observed that myocytes of rat heart express HSP72 after hemodynamic stress.[8] Cardiac myocytes express HSP72 after *in vitro* heat stress.[41] It appears that the *in vivo* heat stress used in the present study is insufficient to induce detectable amount of HSP72 in this cell type. The expression of HSP72 selectively in cardiac interstitial cells suggests that these cells play important roles in myocardial adaptation to stress.

It has been generally assumed that increased myocardial resistance to I/R after heat shock is due to the induction of HSP72 in cardiac myocytes. Indeed, the increased cardiac functional resistance to I/R was associated with the induction of cardiac HSP72 in this study. However, it was related to the expression of this stress protein in interstitial cells including resident Mϕ rather than myocytes.

Interestingly, induction of HSP72 in cardiac resident Mϕ resulted in reduced myocardial TNF-α production during I/R. TNF-α is a well-known myocardial depressant factor[26,27] and myocardial TNF-α production is enhanced in animal models during I/R[30–33,35] and in humans during cardiopulmonary bypass surgery.[36,37] The mechanisms by which TNF-α causes myocardial dysfunction have been reviewed[42] and appear to be complicated, including disruption of calcium homeostasis,[43] induction of oxidant stress,[44] attenuation of cardiac myocyte responsiveness to adrenergic stimulation,[45] and promotion of cardiac myocyte apoptosis.[46] The definitive role of TNF-α in postischemic myocardial dysfunction in this model remains to be determined. It is possible, however, that TNF-α impedes functional recovery in the late phase of reperfusion because the induction of cardiac HSP72 by heat shock improved postischemic recovery of LVDP and LVEDP at 20 to 40 min of reperfusion. We have recently observed that preservation of postischemic function of rat heart by adenosine is associated with attenuated myocardial TNF-α production.[34] Furthermore, neutralization of TNF-α by TNF-binding proteins preserves myocardial contractility of isolated rat heart[47] and human ventricular muscle preparation[48] after I/R. Thus, inhibition of myocardial TNF-α production or neutralization of TNF-α during I/R can be a therapeutic strategy for the preservation of cardiac function. Cardiac resident Mϕ are the main sources of myocardial TNF-α. Induction of HSP72 in cardiac resident Mϕ by heat shock may downregulate their response to I/R, leading to a reduced myocardial TNF-α level. The induction of HSP72 in cardiac resident Mϕ and the subsequent inhibition of myocardial TNF-α production during I/R imply a novel mechanism by which stresses induce myocardial adaptation to ischemia.

In vitro heat stress has been previously shown to inhibit TNF-α production by Mϕ and peripheral monocytes without influences on their phagocytic functions.[22–24] Inhibition of TNF-α production appears to occur at transcription level and is associated with an increased level of cellular HSP72.[23] However, heat stress may promote changes in gene expression as well as in cellular metabolism. It remains unknown whether HSP72 per se is an important factor in the modulation of Mϕ TNF-α production. TNF-α gene transcription in most cell types is regulated by transcription factor NF-κB.[49] Feinstein and colleagues[50] demonstrate in rat fibroblasts that overexpression of HSP70 attenuates NF-κB intranuclear accumulation when the cells are stimulated with lipopolysaccharide plus cytokines. Induction of HSP70 has also been found to prevent stress-induced activation of stress-activated protein kinase and p38 mitogen-activated protein kinase.[51] These protein kinases are important in the signal transduction pathways leading to NF-κB activation. Thus, it is possible that HSP72 suppresses Mϕ TNF-α gene transcription by inhibition of NF-κB. The role of HSP72 in the regulation of Mϕ TNF-α production and the mechanism of this regulation await further determination.

REFERENCES

1. RUDIGER, S., A. BUCHBERGER & B. BUKAU. 1997. Interaction of Hsp70 chaperones with substrates. Nature Struct. Biol. **4:** 342–349.
2. CURRIE, R.W., M. KARMAZYN, M. KLOC & K. MAILER. 1988. Heat-shock response is associated with enhanced post-ischemic ventricular recovery. Circ. Res. **63:** 543–549.
3. DONNELLY, T., R. SIEVERS, F. VISSERN, W. WELCH & C. WOLFE. 1992. Heat shock protein induction in rat hearts. A role for improved myocardial salvage after ischemia and reperfusion. Circulation **85:** 769–778.
4. HOWARD, G. & T.E. GEORGHEGAN. 1986. Altered cardiac tissue gene expression during acute hypoxia exposure. Mol. Cell. Biochem. **69:** 155–160.
5. MEERSON, F.Z., I.Y. MALYSHEV & A.V. ZAMOTRINSKY. 1992. Differences in adaptive stabilization of structures in response to stress and hypoxia relate with the accumulation of hsp70 isoforms. Mol. Cell. Biochem. **111:** 87–95.
6. MENG, X., J.M. BROWN, L. AO, S.K. NORDEEN, W. FRANKLIN, A.H. HARKEN & A. BANERJEE. 1996. Endotoxin induces cardiac heat shock protein 70 and resistance to endotoxemic myocardial dysfunction. Am. J. Physiol. **271:** C1316–C1324.
7. DELCAYRE, C., J.L. SAMUEL, F. MAROTTE, M. BEST-BELPOMME, J.J. MERCADIER & L. RAPPAPORT. 1988. Synthesis of stress proteins in rat cardiac myocytes 2–4 days after imposition of hemodynamic overload. J. Clin. Invest. **82:** 460–468.
8. MENG, X., J.M. BROWN, L. AO, A. BANERJEE & A.H. HARKEN. 1996. Norepinephrine induces cardiac heat shock protein and delayed cardioprotection in the rat through α1-adrenoceptors. Cardiovasc. Res. **32:** 374–383.
9. DILLMANN, W.H., H.B. MEHTA, A. BARRIEUX, B.D. GUTH, W.E. NEELEY & J. ROSS. 1986. Ischemia of the dog heart induces the appearance of a cardiac mRNA coding for a protein with migration characteristics similar to heat shock/stress protein 71. Circ. Res. **59:** 110–114.
10. KNOWLTON, A.A., P. BRECHER & C.S. APSTEIN. 1991. Rapid expression of heat shock protein in the rabbit after brief cardiac ischemia. J. Clin. Invest. **87:** 139–147.

11. MARBER, M., D. LATCHMAN, J. WALKER & D. YELLON. 1993. Cardiac stress protein elevation 24 hours after brief ischemia or heat stress is associated with resistance to myocardial infarction. Circulation **88:** 1264–1272.
12. KUKREJA, R.C., M.C. Kontos, K.E. LOESSER, S.K. BATRA, Y.Z. QIAN, C.J. GBUR, S.A. NASEEM, R.L. JESSE & M.L. HESS. 1994. Oxidant stress increases heat shock protein 70 mRNA in isolated perfused rat heart. Am. J. Physiol. **267:** H2213–H2219.
13. KARMAZYN, M., K. MAILER & R. W. CURRIE. 1990. Acquisition and decay of heat-shock–enhanced post-ischemic ventricular recovery. Am. J. Physiol. **259:** H424–H431.
14. YELLON, D.M., E. PASINI, A. CARGNONI, M.S. MARBER, D.S. LATCHMAN & R. FERRARI. 1992. The protective role of heat stress in the ischemic and reperfused rabbit myocardium. J. Mol. Cell. Cardiol. **24:** 895–907.
15. KONTOS, M.C., J.B. SHIPLEY & R.C. KUKREJA. 1996. Heat stress improves functional recovery and induces synthesis of 27- and 72-kDa heat shock proteins without preserving sarcoplasmic reticulum function in the ischemic rat heart. J. Mol. Cell. Cardiol. **28:** 1885–1894.
16. SUZUKI, K., Y. SAWA, Y. KANEDA, H. ICHIKAWA, R. SHIRAKURA & H. MATSUDA. 1997. In vivo gene transfection with heat shock protein 70 enhances myocardial tolerance to ischemia-reperfusion injury in the rat. J. Clin. Invest. **99:** 1645–1650.
17. MARBER, M.S., R. MESTRIL, S.H. CHI, M.R. SAYEN, D.M. YELLON & W.H. DILLMANN. 1995. Overexpression of the rat inducible 70-kD heat stress protein in a transgenic mouse increases the resistance of the heart to ischemic injury. J. Clin. Invest. **95:** 1446–1456.
18. PLUMIER, J.L., B.M. ROSS, R.W. CURRIE, C.E. ANGELIDIS, H. KAZLARIS, G. KOLLIAS & G.N. PAGOULATOS. 1995. Transgenic mice expressing the human heat shock protein 70 have improved post-ischemic myocardial recovery. J. Clin. Invest. **95:** 1854–1860.
19. RADFORD, N.B., M. FINA, I.J. BENJAMIN, R.W. MOREADITH, K.H. GRAVES, P. ZHAO, S. GAVVA, A. WIETHOFF, A.D. SHERRY, C.R. MALLOY & R.S. WILLIAMS. 1996. Cardioprotective effects of 70-KDa heat shock protein in transgenic mice. Proc. Natl. Acad. Sci. USA **93:** 2339–2342.
20. TROST, S.U., J.H. OMENS, W.J. KARLON, M. MEYER, R. MESTRIL, J.W. COVELL & W.H. DILLMANN. 1998. Protection against myocardial dysfunction after a brief ischemic period in transgenic mice expressing inducible heat shock protein 70. J. Clin. Invest. **101:** 855–862.
21. SNOECKX, L.H., F. CONTARD, J.L. SAMUEL, F. MAROTTE & L. RAPPAPORT. 1991. Expression and cellular distribution of heat-shock and nuclear oncogene proteins in rat hearts. Am. J. Physiol. **261:** H1443–H1451.
22. FOUQUERAY, B., C. PHILIPPE, A. AMRANI, J. PEREZ & L. BAUD. 1992. Heat shock prevents lipopolysaccharide-induced tumor necrosis factor-α synthesis by rat mononuclear phagocytes. Eur. J. Immunol. **22:** 2983–2987.
23. SNYDER, Y.M., L. GUTHRIE, G.F. EVANS & S.H. ZUCKERMAN. 1992. Transcriptional inhibition of endotoxin-induced monokine synthesis following heat shock in murine peritoneal macrophages. J. Leukoc. Biol. **51:** 181–187.
24. ENSOR, J.E., S.M. WIENER, K.A. MCCREA, R.M. VISCARDI, E.K. CRAWFORD & J.D. HASDAY. 1994. Differential effects of hyperthermia on macrophage interleukin-6 and tumor necrosis factor-α expression. Am. J. Physiol. **266:** C967–C974.
25. KUMAR, A., V. THOTA, L. DEE, J. OLSON, E. URETZ & J.E. PARRILLO. 1996. Tumor necrosis factor-alpha and interleukin 1-beta are responsible for the in vitro myocardial cell depression induced by human septic shock serum. J. Exp. Med. **183:** 949–958.
26. FINKEL, M.S., C.V. ODDIS, T.D. JACOB, S.C. WATKINS, B.G. HATTLER & R.L. SIMMONS. 1992. Negative inotropic effects of cytokines on the heart mediated by nitric oxide. Science **257:** 387–389.
27. KAPADIA, S., G. TORRE-AMIONE, T. YOKAHAMA & D.L. MANN. 1995. Soluble TNF binding proteins modulate the negative inotropic properties of TNF alpha *in vitro.* Am. J. Physiol. **268:** H517–H525.

28. KAPADIA, S., J. LEE, G. TORRE-AMIONE, H.H. BIRDSALL, T.S. MA & D.L. MANN. 1995. Tumor necrosis factor-α gene and protein expression in adult feline myocardium after endotoxin administration. J. Clin. Invest. **96:** 1042–1052.
29. ARRAS, M., A. HOCHE, R. BOHLE, P. ECKERT, W. RIEDEL & J. SCHAPER. 1996. Tumor necrosis factor-alpha in macrophages of heart, liver, kidney, and in the pituitary gland. Cell Tissue Res. **285:** 39–49.
30. SQUADRITO, F., D. ALTAVILLA, B. ZINGARELLI, M. IOCULANO, G. CALAPAI, G.M. CAMPO, A. MICELI & A. P. CAPUTI. 1993. Tumor necrosis factor involvement in myocardial ischemia-reperfusion injury. Eur. J. Pharmacol. **237:** 223–230.
31. HERSKOWITZ, A., S. CHOI, A.A. ANSARI & S. WESSELINGH. 1995. Cytokine mRNA expression in postischemic/reperfused myocardium. Am. J. Pathol. **146:** 419–428.
32. GUREVITCH, J., I. FROLKIS, Y. YUHAS, Y. PAZ, M. MATSA, R. MOHR & V. YAKIREVITCH. 1996. Tumor necrosis factor-alpha is released from the isolated heart undergoing ischemia and reperfusion. J. Am. Coll. Cardiol. **28:** 247–252.
33. CHANDRASEKAR, B., J.T. COLSTON & G.L. FREEMAN. 1997. Induction of proinflammatory cytokine and antioxidant enzyme gene expression following brief myocardial ischemia. Clin. Exp. Immunol. **108:** 346–351.
34. MELDRUM, D.R., B.S. CAIN, J.C. CLEVELAND, X. MENG, A. AYALA, A. BANERJEE & A.H. HARKEN. 1997. Adenosine decreases post-ischemic myocardial TNF-α: anti-inflammatory implications for preconditioning and transplantation. Immunology **92:** 472–477.
35. MELDRUM, D.R., J.C. CLEVELAND, B.S. CAIN, X. MENG & A.H. HARKEN. 1998. Increased myocardial tumor necrosis factor-α in a crystalloid-perfused model of cardiac ischemia-reperfusion injury. Ann. Thorac. Surg. **65:** 439–443.
36. HATTLER, B.G., A. ZEEVI, C.V. ODDIS & M.S. FINKEL. 1995. Cytokine induction during cardiac surgery: analysis of TNF-alpha expression pre- and postcardiopulmonary bypass. J. Card. Surg. **10:** 418–422.
37. WAN, S., J.M. DESMET, L. BARVAIS, M. GOLDSTEIN, J.L. VINCENT & J.L. LECLERC. 1996. Myocardium is a major source of proinflammatory cytokines in patients undergoing cardiopulmonary bypass. J. Thorac. Cardiovasc. Surg. **112:** 806–811.
38. LOWRY, O., N. ROSEBROUGH, A. FARR & R. RANDALL. 1951. Protein measurement with the folin phenol reagent. J. Biol. Chem. **193:** 265–275.
39. TOWBIN, H., T. STAEHELIN & J. GORDON. 1979. Electrophoretic transfer of proteins from polyacrylamide gels to nitrocellulose sheets: procedure and some applications. Proc. Natl. Acad. Sci. USA **76:** 4350–4354.
40. MITCHELL, M.B., X. MENG, C.G. PARKER, A.H. HARKEN & A. BANERJEE. 1995. Preconditioning of isolated rat heart is mediated by protein kinase C. Circ. Res. **76:** 73–81.
41. NAKANO, M., A.A. KNOWLTON, T. YOKOYAMA, W. LESSLAUER, D.L. MANN. 1996. Tumor necrosis factor-alpha-induced expression of heat shock protein 72 in adult feline cardiac myocytes. Am. J. Physiol. **270:** H1231–H1239.
42. MELDRUM, D.R. 1998. Tumor necrosis factor in the heart. Am. J. Physiol. **274:** R577–R595.
43. KROWN, K.A., Y. YASUI, M. BROOKER, A. DUBIN, C. NGUYEN, G. HARRIS, P. MCDONOUGH, C.G. GLEMBOTSKI, P. PALADE & R.A. SABBADINI. 1995. TNFα receptor expression in rat cardiac myocytes: TNF inhibition of L-type Ca^{2+} current and Ca^{2+} transients. FEBS Lett. **376:** 24–30.
44. MAYER, A.M.S., R.A. PITTNER, G.E. LIPSCOMB & J.A. SPITZER. 1993. Effect of in vivo TNF administration on superoxide production. Am. J. Physiol. **264:** L43–L52.
45. GULICK, T., M.K. CHUNG, S.J. PIEPER, L.G. LANGE & G.F. SCHREINER. 1989. Interleukin 1 and tumor necrosis factor inhibit cardiac myocyte adrenergic responsiveness. Proc. Natl. Acad. Sci. USA **86:** 6753–6757.
46. KROWN, K.A., M.T. PAGE, C. NGUYEN, D. ZECHNER, V. GUTIERREZ, K.L. COMSTOCK, C.G. GLEMBOTSKI, P.J.E. QUINTANA & R.A. SABBADINI. 1996. Tumor necrosis factor alpha-induced apoptosis in cardiac myocytes: Involvement of the sphingolipid signaling cascade in cardiac cell death. J. Clin. Invest. **98:** 2854–2865.
47. MELDRUM, D.R., C.A. DINARELLO, X. MENG, L. SHAPIRO & A.H. HARKEN. 1997. P38 MAP kinase-mediated myocardial TNFα production contributes to post-ischemic

cardiac dysfunction. Circulation **96** (suppl)**:** I-556.

48. CAIN, B.S., D.R. MELDRUM, C.A. DINARELLO, X. MENG, A. BANERJEE & A.H. HARKEN. 1998. Adenosine reduces cardiac TNF-α production and human myocardial injury following ischemia-reperfusion. J. Surg. Res. **76:** 117–123.
49. KUPRASH, D.V., I.A. UDALOVA, R.L. TURETSKAYA, N.R. RICE & S.A. NEDOSPASOV. 1995. Conserved κB element located downstream of the tumor necrosis factor α gene: distinct NF-κB binding pattern and enhancer activity in LPS activated murine macrophages. Oncogene **11:** 97–106.
50. FEINSTEIN, D.L., E. GALEA, D.A. AQUINO, G.C. LI, H. XU & D.J. REIS. 1996. Heat shock protein 70 suppresses astroglial inducible nitric oxide synthesis expression by decreasing NFκB activation. J. Biol. Chem. **271:** 17724–17732.
51. GABAI, V.L., A.B. MERIIN, D.D. MOSSER, A.W. CARON, S. RITS, V.I. SHIFRIN & M.Y. SHERMAN. 1997. Hsp70 prevents activation of stress kinases. A novel pathway of cellular thermotolerance. J. Biol. Chem. **272:** 18033–18037.

Cardiac Adaptation to Ischemia-Reperfusion Injury[a]

JOHN G. KINGMA, JR.[b]

Department of Medicine, Faculty of Medicine, Laval University, Cité Universitaire, Ste.-Foy, Québec G1K 7P4, Canada

ABSTRACT: Acute myocardial ischemia initiates a cascade of cellular events that lead to irreversible injury. We previously described the transient nature of heat-shock induced cardioprotection; treatment with a catalase inhibitor abolished the cytoprotective actions without affecting expression levels of HSP71. Repeated, transient ischemic episodes augment the ischemic tolerance of affected myocardium but the fundamental cytoprotective mechanism(s) for both "early" and "delayed" preconditioning remains unclear. Increased cellular induction of protooncogenes, heat shock genes, and downstream effector proteins might play critical roles in the cytoprotection afforded by delayed preconditioning. We measured *c-fos*, *c-jun*, *c-myc,* and *hsp70* induction in preconditioned (2 × 5-min ischemia/10-min reperfusion) and control rabbit hearts that either underwent 30- or 120-min coronary occlusion and 60-min reperfusion, or did not undergo subsequent sustained ischemia; the latter hearts were allowed to recover for 0, 1, 3, 6, 24, 48, 72, or 96 hours. Both *c-fos* and *c-jun* in ischemic tissue were strongly induced by ischemia-reperfusion injury and preconditioning pretreatment. However, expression levels diminished significantly by 1-h reperfusion and remained depressed during the 96-h recovery period. *Hsp70* (inducible) mRNA expression levels were highest primarily in ischemic myocardium after 6-h recovery post-preconditioning; *Hsp70* levels in ischemic myocardium were slightly stronger after 48-h recovery but subsequently diminished to barely detectable levels by 96-h post-preconditioning. Induction of *c-fos* and *c-jun* preceded that of *Hsp70*. These findings support the concept that upregulation of immediate early genes and heat shock genes plays an important role in myocardial adaptation to acute ischemic stress.

INTRODUCTION

The ability of cardiac myocytes to adapt to potentially lethal exogenous stresses has been documented in many different experimental models, yet the underlying cytoprotective mechanisms remain elusive. In 1986, Murry and colleagues reported increased tolerance to sustained ischemic insult in myocardium previously exposed to repeated episodes of ischemic stress.[1] Since then hundreds of studies in numerous experimental models have been published confirming the protection of ischemic my-

[a]Studies described in this paper were supported, in part, by grants from the Heart and Stroke Foundation of Quebec. J.G.K. was supported by a Senior Chercheur-Boursier Fellowship from the Fonds de la recherche en sante du Quebec.

[b]Address all correspondence to: Dr. J. G. Kingma Jr., Research Center, Laval Hospital, 2725, Chemin Ste.-Foy, Ste.-Foy, Québec, Canada G1V 4G5; Telephone: 418-656-4760; Fax: 418-656-4509; E-mail: john.kingma@med.ulaval.ca

ocardium following pretreatment with preconditioning and attempting to determine the cytoprotective mechanisms. Current dogma holds that preconditioning-mediated protection comprises an "early" and "delayed" phase, that, in turn, are believed to comprise different cellular mechanisms.[2,3]

Early Phase of Cytoprotection

The early phase of protection, initially defined as being 1–2 hours of increased myocardial resistance to sustained ischemia when preceded by a period of sublethal ischemia and reperfusion, is probably triggered via stimulation of various receptors and/or upregulation of the signal transduction pathway particularly by activation of protein kinase C (PKC).[4–6] Activation of bradykinin and opioid receptors may also participate equally with adenosine to trigger cytoprotection[7]—probably because their receptors are PKC coupled. PKC isoforms are present within the cell, each with a slightly different structure (amino acid sequence) and function; activation of the PKC isoforms involves physical binding to specific RACK (receptor for activated C kinase). Numerous protein kinases exist within the cell, each controlled by intracellular regulatory processes. They appear to be arranged in an elaborate cascade where one kinase phosphorylates another until the end-effector protein is phosphorylated. Kinases are also believed to be intimately involved in gene expression. Although PKC may be a critical component of preconditioning-mediated cytoprotection, experimental findings are not unanimous.[8,9] Recent interest has also focused on the mitogen-activated protein kinases (MAPK).[10,11] For example, activation of p38 MAPK results in phosphorylation of MAPKAP kinase-2 (mitogen-activated protein kinase-activated protein kinase-2).[12] MAPKAP kinase-2, in turn, phosphorylates a small heat shock protein (HSP27) which, when phosphorylated, promotes polymerization of cytoskeletal actin filaments.[13,14] Furthermore, blockade of p38 MAPK phosphorylation has been shown to abolish preconditioning-mediated cytoprotection.[15]

Delayed Phase of Cytoprotection

A substantially growing database supports the concept that a second or "delayed" phase of protection, more commonly referred to as the "second window of protection (SWOP),"[2] contributes to preconditioning-mediated cytoprotection. This particular phase appears to be initiated between 24 and 72 hours after the initial preconditioning stimulus.[2,16–20] The mechanisms involved have not been determined, however, activation of PKC may be involved in triggering the SWOP.[2] Nuclear proto-oncogenes are activated by various physiologic stimuli but the significance of increased post-ischemic expression levels of these genes remains undetermined.[21,22] Post-ischemic induction of immediate early genes, among them *c-fos*, *c-jun,* and *c-myc,* is a dynamic process—mRNA expression levels and time course vary in relation to the severity and duration of ischemic insult.[23–25] The products of *c-fos* and *c-jun* form a complex associated with transcriptional control elements; this complex may act as a master switch to upregulate various genes in response to exogenous stimuli.

Heat shock genes are induced by ischemia and other exogenous stimuli.[26–28] Many heat shock proteins are involved in the control of conformation, stabilization, and transport of normal and partially denatured proteins.[29,30] The mechanism for hyperthermia-mediated cytoprotection after induction of heat shock proteins has not been established. The heat-shock response has been reported to alter intracellular calcium, pH,[31] tissue high-energy phosphates,[32] and the level of intracellular catalase.[33–36] Immediate early genes are upregulated before induction of heat shock proteins. Heat shock proteins may stabilize or solubilize damaged proteins within the nucleus, nucleolus, and/or ribosomes after an acute stress. Consequently, upregulation of heat shock proteins probably facilitates removal or repair of damaged proteins during post-stress recovery. In fact, several investigators have suggested a possible correlation between the degree of induction of heat shock proteins and extent of post-ischemic myocardial salvage in rat myocardium.[37,38]

The purpose of this study was (1) to examine the cytoprotective efficacy of whole-body hyperthermia against ischemia-reperfusion injury and (2) to characterize the temporal upregulation of immediate early genes during ischemic preconditioning followed by up to 96-h reperfusion of the ischemia-related arterial bed. The latter hearts did not undergo sustained myocardial ischemia since we wished to determine if the delayed phase of preconditioning might be due to induction of various nuclear proto-oncogenes, including *c-fos*, *c-jun*, and *c-myc* or heat shock proteins (*Hsp70*) within the 24–72 h post-preconditioning time period.

MATERIALS AND METHODS

Animals

Male New Zealand White rabbits (2.0–3.0 kg body weight) obtained from Charles River Laboratories were used in all studies. All animals were cared for in accordance with the "Guide to the Care and Use of Experimental Animals of the Canadian Council on Animal Care"; the Laval University Animal Ethics Committee also approved these studies. Two different experimental approaches were used: whole-body hyperthermia and ischemic preconditioning.

Surgical Protocol

Pentobarbital-anesthetized rabbits were intubated and mechanically ventilated with room air; drugs and essential fluids were administered through a cannula in the right jugular vein. Surgical preparation, hemodynamic measurements, and the ischemia-reperfusion model have been described in detail elsewhere.[39] Briefly, following a left thoracotomy in the fifth intercostal space, a snare (4-0 silk; Ethicon) was placed around the first anterolateral branch of the main circumflex artery midway between the atrioventricular groove and apex of the heart.

Heat Shock Protocol

Whole-body hyperthermia was induced as previously described.[36,40] Lightly anesthetized rabbits were placed between two temperature-controlled heating pads; body temperature was progressively increased over 45 min, monitored with a rectal thermometer and maintained at 42°C for 15 minutes. All rabbits were given intravenous saline during the hyperthermia protocol to prevent undue fluid loss. Subsequently, animals were allowed to recover for at least 24 h after which they were re-anesthetized and underwent 30-min regional coronary occlusion followed by 3-h reperfusion.

Ischemic Preconditioning Protocol

After cardiac hemodynamic parameters were stable (i.e., 20 min) rabbits underwent two cycles of 5-min regional coronary occlusion and 10-min reperfusion.[41] Absolute control hearts were allowed to stabilize for 30 min (to limit potential influence of shorter anesthetic durations on overall infarct size). In the first study, rabbits underwent preconditioning pretreatment followed by 30-min regional coronary occlusion and 3-h reperfusion. In the second study, rabbits underwent preconditioning pretreatment without the subsequent 30-min coronary occlusion; hearts were allowed to recover for 0, 1, 3, 6, 24, 48, 72 or 96 h before animals were killed.

In all rabbits, ischemia was verified visually by the appearance of regional epicardial cyanosis and elevation of the ST segment on the lead II electrocardiogram.

Post-mortem Analysis

Experiments were terminated by intravenous injection of hypertonic potassium chloride, hearts were quickly extirpated and placed in cold saline. At this time the heart was assigned to either the infarct size or immunochemical parts of this study.

For the infarct size studies, hearts were perfused via an aortic cannula with 2,3,5-triphenyltetrazolium chloride at 37°C for 30 min to delineate infarcted myocardium. The heart was then removed from the perfusion apparatus, the atria and right ventricle were trimmed away, and the left ventricle (LV) weighed and fixed by immersion in buffered 10% formalin. Anatomic risk zones were determined by autoradiography (radiolabeled microspheres were injected into the left atrium after 15-min coronary occlusion). Infarct and risk areas were determined from enlarged tracings using computerized planimetry (SigmaScan, San Rafael, CA). Infarct size was normalized to anatomic risk zone size for each heart.

For the immunochemical studies, myocardial tissue from ischemic and non-ischemic portions of the LV were freeze-clamped in liquid nitrogen and stored at −80°C until analysis.

Northern Blot Analysis

Total RNA was extracted from ischemic and nonischemic myocardium using previously described methods.[42] Concentration and purity of the RNA preparation were determined spectrophotometrically and directly used for Northern blot analysis. A 10 μg sample of denatured RNA was resolved by electrophoresis on 1.2% agarose gels in phosphate buffer (10 mM, pH 7.0). RNA was then transferred by suction onto a nylon membrane (Hybond, Amersham) using a vacublot apparatus (Vacuogene, Pharmacia) and fixed by UV irradiation for 3 min.[43] Glyoxal was removed by rinsing in a 20 mM Tris-Cl solution (pH 8.0) at 100 ± 2°C for 10 min. Membranes were prehybridized at 65°C for 4 h in 1 ml/5–10 cm^2 of a 5× standard saline citrate buffer (SSC), 5× Denhardt's, 50 mM sodium phosphate pH 6.9, 250 μg/ml ssDNA and 0.1% SDS. The membranes were exposed to Kodak BioMax films at −80°C with intensifying screens for detection of mRNA. The following cDNA probes were used: (1) *c-fos,* 2.2 kb rat cDNA (Dr. L. Belanger, Hotel Dieu de Quebec); (2) *c-jun*, 2.6 kb human cDNA (Dr. L. Belanger, Hotel Dieu de Quebec); (3) *c-myc*, 2.4 kb mouse cDNA; or (4) HSP70 (inducible), 2.3 kb human hsp70 cDNA (Dr. J. Landry, Hotel Dieu de Quebec). Each hybridization was repeated twice. After each hybridization bound cDNA was stripped by two incubations in 0.1 SSC/0.5% SDS at 95°C for 20 min. Stripped membranes were then rehybridized. Membranes were also probed with ^{32}P-labeled 18S rRNA cDNA (Dr. P. Poyet, Hopital St-Francois d'Assise) as a control. The integrity of RNA was determined by the appearance of the 18S and 28S ribosomal RNA bands after agarose-formaldehyde gel electrophoresis and ethidium bromide staining.

Immunoblotting Procedures

Ventricular biopsies were homogenized in 10 volumes of sample buffer (62.5 mM Tris, pH 6.8, 2% SDS, 5% 2-mercaptoethanol, and 0.001% bromophenol blue). After centrifugation, the supernatant fraction was diluted with sample buffer and frozen at –80°C or directly loaded onto polyacrylamide gels. Cardiac proteins were transferred to Immobilon polyvinyledine difluoride membranes (Millipore, Toronto, CAN) overnight. Membranes were incubated in phosphate-buffered saline containing 5% skim milk powder to block nonspecific binding sites on the membranes and immunoreacted with a 1:7,500 dilution of a rabbit polyclonal anti-HSP70 antibody to the highly inducible human HSP71. Membranes were then incubated with a peroxidase-conjugated goat anti-rabbit immunoglobulin G (Organon Teknika, Scarborough, CAN). 4-Chloro-1-naphthol was used as substrate to visualize the immunoreaction.

Data Analysis

Variables that were measured once, including infarct area, risk zone, and percent tissue necrosis, were compared using a one-way ANOVA model. Duncan's test was performed on all main effect means to determine statistical differences between experimental groups. A p value of ≤ 0.05 was considered statistically significant.

RESULTS

Infarct Size Studies

Rabbit hearts were either pretreated by whole-body hyperthermia or ischemic preconditioning.

Heart rate and systolic LV pressure were similar for each of the experimental groups (TABLE 1). The similarity of hemodynamic parameters during the infarct protocol indicates that cardiac hemodynamics had little influence on the development of infarction in this model. The absence of preformed coronary collateral vessels in the rabbit heart precludes the necessity to incorporate collateral flow as a covariate in the infarct size analysis.[39,44]

Infarct size (normalized to risk zone size) was significantly reduced in hearts previously exposed to acute ischemic preconditioning (i.e., early protection) and whole-body hyperthermia plus 24 h recovery (i.e., delayed protection) compared to untreated control animals (49.3 ± 3.0%; mean ± SEM) as shown in FIGURE 1. Risk

TABLE 1. Summary of heart rate and mean arterial pressure

	Pre-Occlusion		Occlusion		Reperfusion	
	HR	MAP	HR	MAP	HR	MAP
Con	241 ± 7	105 ± 13	222 ± 8	78 ± 5	201 ± 9	90 ± 4
PC	272 ± 7	102 ± 5	238 ± 7	94 ± 4	187 ± 5	95 ± 5
HS-24	266 ± 17	99 ± 7	256 ± 12	75 ± 9	265 ± 11	88 ± 7

Note: Values are mean±SEM. HR = heart rate (beats/min); MAP = mean arterial pressure (mm Hg); Con = control animals; PC = preconditioned animals (2 cycles of 5-min ischemia and 10-min reperfusion); HS-24 = whole-body hyperthermia pretreatment followed by 24 h recovery before being subjected to ischemia-reperfusion injury.

zone size averaged 40% of the LV and was comparable for the different experimental groups. Myocardial catalase activity in hyperthermia-pretreated rabbits (47 ± 4 U/mg protein, $p \leq 0.02$) was substantially increased compared to untreated controls (33 ± 2 U/mg protein). Catalase activity was not assessed in preconditioned rabbits.

Northern and Western Immunoblot Analysis

HSP71, determined using the Northern hybridization technique, was undetectable in untreated control hearts. Peak expression of the inducible HSP71 transcript was obtained between 1.5 and 3 h post-hyperthermia (FIG. 2A). Six hours post-hyperthermia, HSP71 mRNA expression levels decreased below the detectable range;

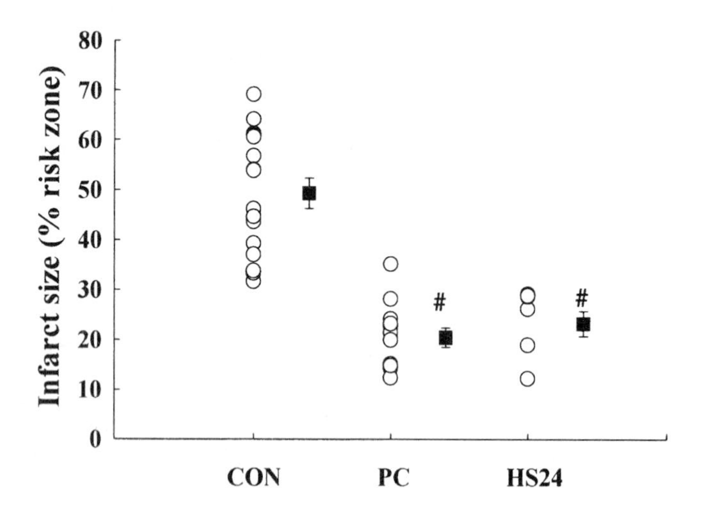

FIGURE 1. Infarct size (expressed as percent of area at risk) is shown for control (CON), preconditioned (PC), and whole-body hyperthermia followed by 24-h recovery (HS-24) experimental groups. Anatomic risk zone size was delineated using autoradiography and infarct zones by the absence of staining with triphenyl tetrazolium chloride. Both PC and HS-24 were associated with a significant reduction in tissue necrosis; compared by ANOVA ($^{\#}p = 0.02$ versus controls).

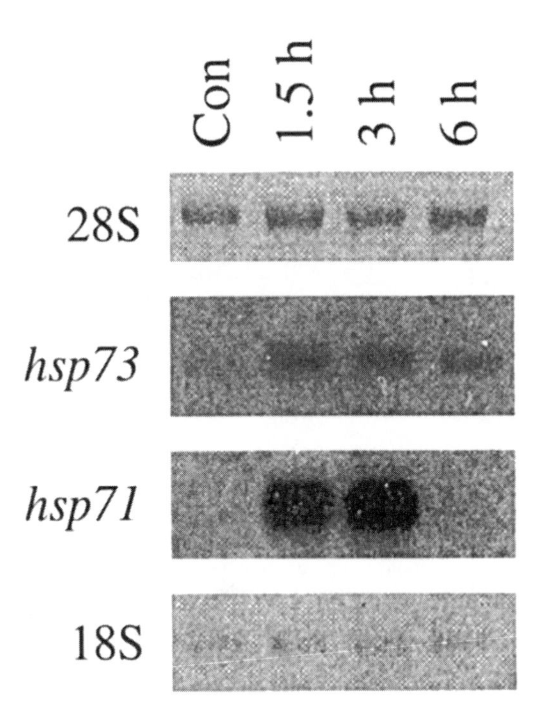

FIGURE 2A. Northern blot analysis of RNA from rabbit hearts. Transcripts for the highly inducible HSP71 were not seen in control hearts, but were readily detected at 1.5 and 3 h after hyperthermia pretreatment. At 6 h after hyperthermia pretreatment HSP71 transcripts were not detected. The same membrane was reprobed and revealed transcripts for HSP73 (constitutive) in control hearts. Peak expression of HSP73 transcripts was observed at 1.5 h post-hyperthermia treatment. Molecular weight markers for 28S and 18S ribosomal RNA (methylene blue stain) are also shown.

however, 24 h post-hyperthermia cellular HSP70 protein levels were increased in myocardial biopsies from ischemic myocardium (FIG. 2B). Cellular HSP70 protein levels were diminished in ischemic myocardium subjected to 30-min coronary occlusion and 60-min reperfusion 24 h post-hyperthermia.

Induction of immediate early gene products and heat shock gene products (HSP70 mRNA) in cardiac biopsies from the ischemic and nonischemic regions was detected by Northern blot analysis using specific cDNA probes. *C-fos* mRNA levels increased in ischemic tissues in relation to the duration of coronary occlusion (FIG. 3A). In preconditioned hearts, *c-fos* expression levels were augmented in ischemic myocardium that underwent 30-min coronary occlusion and 60-min reperfusion (FIG. 3B). However, the upregulation of *c-fos* mRNA appeared to be transient since levels were much lower when hearts were subjected to 120-min coronary occlusion and 60-min reperfusion. A similar induction profile for *c-jun* was observed in these cardiac biopsies. Cellular levels of c-FOS and c-JUN protein were not assessed in

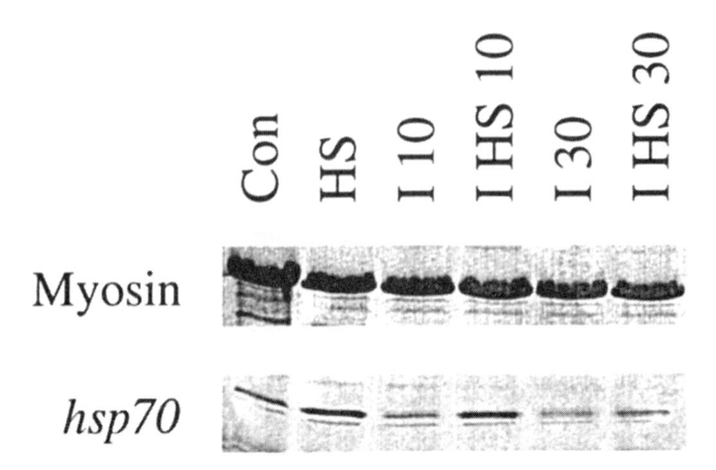

FIGURE 2B. Immunoblot showing the relative distribution of HSP70 within ischemic tissues from control (Con) and hyperthermia-pretreated (HS) rabbits subjected to either 10- or 30-min coronary occlusion (I) followed by 60-min reperfusion. Approximately 10 μg of protein was loaded on each gel. Proteins were transferred to membranes as described in *Materials and Methods* and immunoreacted with a mouse monoclonal anti-71-kd HSP70 antibody. Cellular HSP70 protein levels were increased in hyperthermia-pretreated rabbits. However, HSP70 levels were lower in ischemic tissues from rabbits subjected to 30-min coronary occlusion and 60-min reperfusion possibly due to a more rapid degradation of the protein following ischemic injury. HSP70 levels in control animals undergoing ischemia-reperfusion injury were comparable.

these hearts. *C-myc* was not detectable in either ischemic or nonischemic myocardial regions.

In preconditioned hearts that were not reperfused (i.e., rabbits sacrificed at the end of the second reperfusion period in the preconditioning protocol), *c-fos* was strongly induced in both ischemic and nonischemic myocardium. *Hsp70* (inducible) was not increased in either ischemic or nonischemic myocardium. When the reperfusion period was extended beyond 1 h, mRNA expression levels for both *c-fos* and *c-jun* in ischemic and nonischemic regions were much lower (i.e., undetectable) as shown in FIGURE 4. *Hsp70* mRNA levels within the ischemic region increased at 3 h, but peaked at 6 h after preconditioning pretreatment. At 48-h reperfusion, *Hsp70* mRNA levels increased slightly. At 72 and 96 h post-reperfusion *Hsp70* mRNA was not detectable within the ischemic region. In the nonischemic myocardium *Hsp70* levels increased slightly at 3 h reperfusion following preconditioning pretreatment but remained at low levels subsequently.

DISCUSSION

Pre-treatment with whole-body hyperthermia resulted in significant induction of myocardial HSP71 mRNA and catalase activity. Induction of the heat shock re-

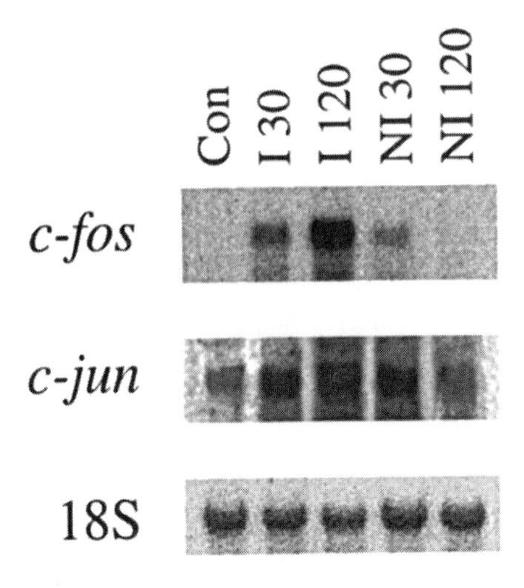

FIGURE 3A. Northern blot hybridization of *c-fos* and *c-jun* in ischemic (I) and nonischemic (NI) rabbit myocardium. Hearts were subjected to either 30- or 120-min regional coronary occlusion followed by 60-min reperfusion. Each lane was loaded with 10 μg of total RNA. *C-fos* and *c-jun* expression levels were increased, compared to controls, after 30-min coronary occlusion and 60-min reperfusion (I 30). Induction of both proto-oncogenes was stronger in ischemic myocardium after 120-min coronary occlusion and 60-min reperfusion (I 120). *C-fos* and *c-jun* were also detected in nonischemic myocardium but at much lower levels (NI 30 and NI 120).

sponse was associated with an important limitation of ischemia-reperfusion injury. Ischemia-reperfusion injury also resulted in a significant rapid induction of several proto-oncogenes, *c-fos* and *c-jun* in myocardial tissues. Expression levels of these proto-oncogenes were greater with longer ischemic durations. Similar results were obtained in hearts pretreated with brief, repetitive ischemic episodes prior to transient coronary occlusion and reperfusion. However, *c-fos* and *c-jun* levels were less pronounced in myocardium undergoing 120-min sustained coronary occlusion followed by 60-min reperfusion. This may be indicative of cell death and an inability of reversibly injured myocytes to induce expression of proto-oncogenes. In hearts that underwent ischemic preconditioning without sustained coronary occlusion, *c-fos* and *c-jun* were highly induced in ischemic and nonischemic myocardium; however, their accumulation was transient, as both were not detectable after 3 h of coronary reperfusion. These myocytes are probably reversibly injured and able to quickly recover from the acute ischemic stress. Induction of *c-myc* was not detected in these experiments; this finding is similar to the data reported by Brand and co-workers.[23] In these hearts, Hsp70 transcripts were readily detected by 3 h post-reperfusion, but peak expression occurred at 6 h reperfusion.

During prolonged myocardial ischemia high-energy phosphate stores are markedly depleted; under these conditions significant alterations occur to protein stability and transcriptional regulation.[45–48] Few studies have addressed the question of the effect of prolonged but reversible ATP depletion on gene expression in ventricular myocytes. This could be important since injured myocytes must rapidly upregulate synthesis of essential proteins post-ischemia to survive. Under normal conditions, *de novo* synthesis of adenine nucleotides is slow in myocardium and resynthesis of ATP occurs preferentially via various salvage pathways (i.e., rephosphorylation of nucleosides).[49,50] Hyperthermia pretreatment appears to induce an ATP-sparing effect in ischemic hearts, but it is not clear that maintaining myocyte high-energy phosphate levels is responsible for hyperthermia-mediated cytoprotection.[40,51] ATP-sparing

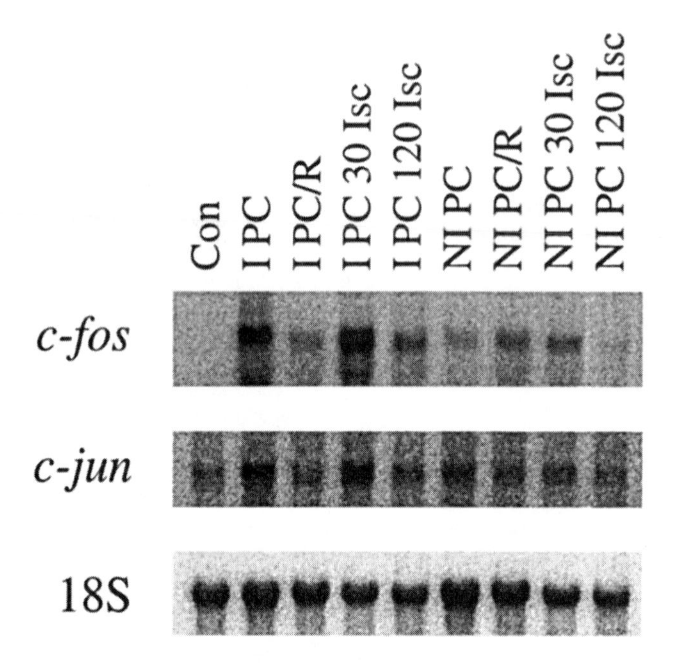

FIGURE 3B. Northern blot hybridization of *c-fos* and *c-jun* in ischemic (I) and nonischemic (NI) rabbit myocardium. Hearts were pre-treated by ischemic preconditioning (PC; 2 × 5-min ischemia and 10-min reperfusion) and then subjected to either 30- or 120-min regional coronary occlusion followed by 60-min reperfusion (I PC 30 Isc and I PC120 Isc). Each lane was loaded with 10 µg of total RNA. *C-fos* and *c-jun* were strongly induced after the preconditioning-pretreatment protocol compared to controls (I PC). Both proto-oncogene levels diminished if hearts were reperfused for 60 min after preconditioning-pretreatment (PC/R) and not subjected to either 30-min or 120-min sustained coronary occlusion (I PC/R). In preconditioned hearts that underwent 30-min coronary occlusion and 60-min reperfusion, *c-fos* and *c-jun* induction in ischemic myocardium was stronger than in hearts subjected to preconditioning alone (I PC 30 Isc versus I PC). After 120-min coronary occlusion proto-oncogene induction levels were diminished in ischemic myocardium (I PC 120 Isc). *C-fos* and *c-jun* levels NI tissues were higher than levels found in Con tissues; however, they did not change compared to Con.

may also be important for preconditioning-mediated protection of ischemic myocardium.[52,53]

Prokaryotic and eukaryotic cells respond to stress by upregulating the synthesis of new proteins including heat shock, oxidative stress-regulated, and calcium- or glucose-regulated proteins.[20,54,55] The role of heat shock proteins in cytoprotection and their possible interaction with other cytoprotective enzymes remain poorly understood. Knowlton recently reviewed the role of heat shock proteins in the heart.[30] In normal cells, HSP70 plays a role in protein folding and trafficking across membranes. Heat shock proteins are important chaperonins—molecules that facilitate passage of macromolecules by unfolding and refolding the macromolecules as they pass through membranes (i.e., nuclear, sarcoplasmic reticular, etc.). Heat shock pro-

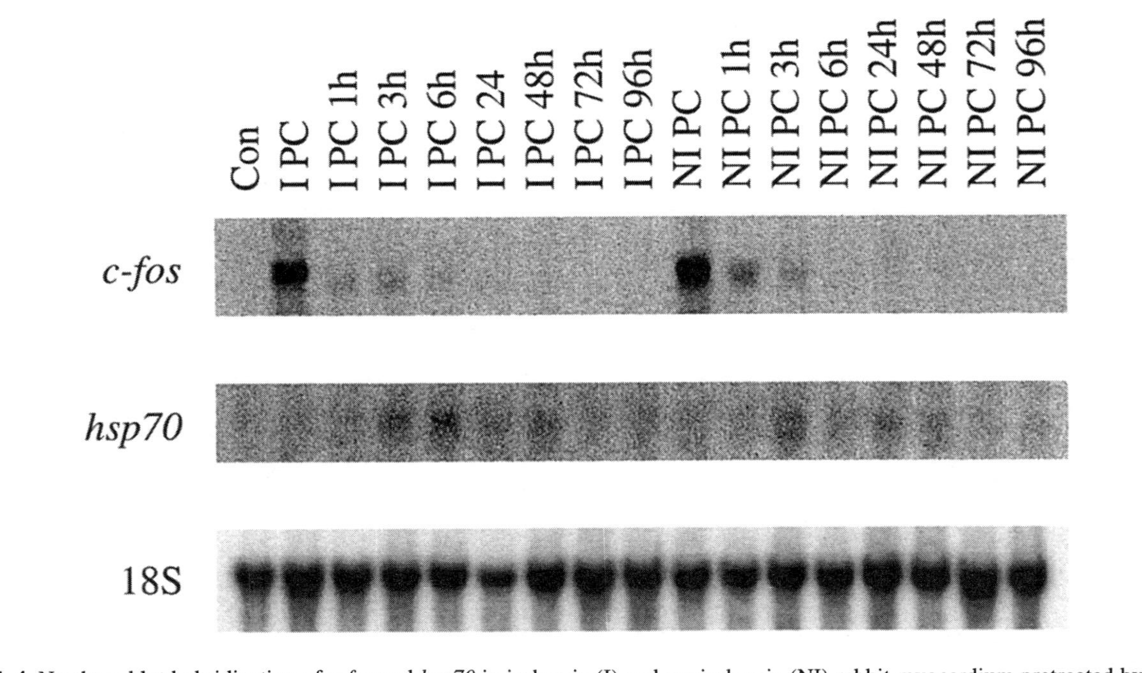

FIGURE 4. Northern blot hybridization of *c-fos* and *hsp70* in ischemic (I) and nonischemic (NI) rabbit myocardium pretreated by ischemic preconditioning (PC) (2 × 5-min ischemia and 10-min reperfusion) followed by 0, 1, 3, 6, 24, 48, 72, or 96 h of coronary reperfusion. These hearts did not undergo sustained ischemia-reperfusion injury following preconditioning pretreatment. Each lane was loaded with 10 μg of total RNA. *C-fos* was strongly induced in both ischemic and nonischemic myocardium during the preconditioning protocol without subsequent reperfusion. Expression of *c-fos* was almost completely absent after 1-h reperfusion and was undetectable between 24–96 h of reperfusion. *Hsp70* expression levels in ischemic myocardium were increased at 3-h reperfusion post-preconditioning. Peak levels were seen at 6 h in both ischemic and nonischemic tissues. *Hsp70* transcripts were also observed in ischemic myocardium at 48-h reperfusion.

teins may stabilize or solubilize damaged proteins within the nucleus, nucleolus, and/or ribosomes after acute ischemic stress. There is experimental evidence suggesting that the extent of post-ischemic cellular repair following hyperthermia-pretreatment depends on the level of induction of heat shock proteins.[37,38]

Higher intracellular levels of antioxidant enzymes post-hyperthermia represent an attractive hypothesis for delayed cytoprotection. A potential relation exists between cellular synthesis of stress proteins and acquisition of thermotolerance.[56,57] Thermotolerance may be a result of improved metabolism of free radical species by stimulation of antioxidative enzymes, catalase in particular.[33,58–61] In the heart, catalase may be important for hyperthermia-mediated cardioprotection for several reasons: (1) it is essential for detoxification of H_2O_2; (2) cofactors are not required for enzymatic activity (glutathione peroxidase must be reduced to glutathione to act as an antioxidant); and (3) it is localized in the cytosol and within peroxisomes (glutathione peroxidase is found in the cytosol and within mitochondria).[35,62,63] Glutathione peroxidase might be more important in limiting peroxidation as peroxidation is increased when cytosolic and mitochondrial glutathione peroxidase levels are reduced.[64]

Several studies have documented significant cardioprotective effects following increased induction of heat shock proteins in various experimental preparations with different study end-points.[33–35,65] Currie and co-workers have documented improved greater recovery of ventricular contractile function in hyperthermia-pretreated rats subjected to global ischemia-reperfusion injury.[33–35] Studies from our laboratory[40] and others[37,38,66] showed increased tolerance to ischemia-reperfusion injury in animals with demonstrated higher myocardial levels of heat shock proteins. Recent findings have also shown a post-ischemic reduction in cardiac contractile dysfunction in transgenic mouse hearts overexpressing inducible HSP70.[17,67] Not all studies report cytoprotection following heat shock: Wall and co-workers were unable to show improved post-ischemic recovery of contractile function in isolated rat hearts despite induction of HSP70 in the heart.[68] Myocardial catalase activity was not augmented in that study. In a recent study from our laboratory we documented increased myocardial catalase activity and significant induction of HSP71 in myocardium within 6 h of hyperthermia pretreatment. Myocardial HSP70 levels were elevated 24 h post-hyperthermia, but a lesser amount of HSP71 was detected in ischemic myocardium after 30-min coronary occlusion followed by 60-min reperfusion. This suggests more rapid degradation of the heat shock proteins in irreversibly injured myocytes. We previously showed that cytoprotection is abolished in hyperthermia-pretreated rabbits administered the irreversible catalase inhibitor 3-aminotriazole prior to coronary occlusion.[36] However, our findings are not in agreement with those of Wolfe and co-workers[69] and Marber and co-workers[17] who showed significant cytoprotection in the absence of increased levels of myocardial catalase activity. These data indicate that there is presently no clear consensus that increased antioxidant enzyme activity is important for hyperthermia-mediated cytoprotection. As such, delayed cytoprotection probably involves other proteins in addition to antioxidants and heat shock proteins.

There is increasing evidence that proto-oncogenes are involved in the transcriptional regulation of various genes including the stress-inducible genes.[70,71] The protein products of *c-fos* and *c-jun* interact to form a heterodimeric transcription factor. *Fos-jun* heterodimers have a high affinity for AP-1 transcription factor.[72] *C-myc*, which is also a transcription factor, has been found to control proliferation and differentiation in many cell types.[73] It also promotes induction of a variety of stress proteins, including heat shock proteins. In the present study, both *c-fos* and *c-jun* were strongly induced in ischemic myocardium during prolonged coronary occlusion followed by reperfusion. Similar findings were obtained in preconditioned hearts that did not undergo a prolonged coronary occlusion. However, with extended coronary reperfusion (i.e., to 96 hours) the myocardial level of these proto-oncogenes was substantially diminished. Whether this is due to reduced, or absent, myocyte necrosis is not clear as infarct size was not assessed in the preconditioning-only studies.

SUMMARY

In summary, acute ischemic stress rapidly potentiates induction of potentially cytoprotective genes including certain members of the stress protein family and nuclear proto-oncogenes. The exact roles that these gene products have in myocardial protection are not known. It is clear that induction of heat shock proteins is associated with cytoprotection against acute ischemic stress. There is evidence to support the hypothesis that increased catalase activity, possibly mediated by enhanced expression of stress proteins, might be involved. We were unable to document significant induction of an immediate early gene within the time period of 24–72 hours after preconditioning pretreatment alone. As such, it is difficult to determine whether these gene products act synergistically or via different independent pathways to promote the cellular adaptive response. Although myocardial *Hsp70* levels declined substantially within 6 hours of the onset of reperfusion, there appeared to be a slight increase in myocardial *Hsp70* levels within ischemic myocardium at 48 hours. It is possible that induction of heat shock gene products at this time period might be involved in the delayed cytoprotective phase of ischemic preconditioning. Finally, whether ischemic preconditioning triggers specific or multiple adaptation processes, it is clear that ultimate cytoprotective mechanisms require participation of the cellular genetic apparatus.

ACKNOWLEDGMENTS

The author would like to thank Drs. Peter Bogaty and Pascal Daleau for reviewing the manuscript. The excellent technical assistance of Monia Michaud is gratefully acknowledged. cDNA probes were generous gifts from Drs. L. Belanger, J. Landry, and P. Poyet.

REFERENCES

1. Murry, C.E., R.B. Jennings & K.A. Reimer. 1986. Preconditioning with ischemia: a delay of lethal cell injury in ischemic myocardium. Circulation **74:** 1124–1136.
2. Yellon, D.M. & G.F. Baxter. 1995. A "Second window of protection" or delayed preconditioning phenomenon: future horizons for myocardial protection? J. Mol. Cell. Cardiol. **27:** 1023–1034.

3. BAXTER, G.F., F.M. GOMA & D.M. YELLON. 1997. Characterisation of the infarct-limiting effect of delayed preconditioning: timecourse and dose-dependency studies in rabbit myocardium. Basic Res. Cardiol. **92:**159–167.
4. YTREHUS, K., Y. LIU & J.M. DOWNEY. 1994. Preconditioning protects ischemic rabbit heart by protein kinase C activation. Am. J. Physiol. (Heart Circ. Physiol.) **266:** H1145–H1152.
5. LI, Y. & R.A. KLONER. 1995. Does protein kinase C play a role in ischemic preconditioning in rat hearts? Am. J. Physiol. (Heart Circ. Physiol.) **268:** H426–H431.
6. COHEN, M.V. & J.M. DOWNEY. 1996. Myocardial preconditioning promises to be a novel approach to the treatment of ischemic heart disease. J. Mol. Cell. Cardiol. **27:** 1623–1632.
7. GOTO, M., Y. LIU, X.-M. YANG, J.L. ARDELL, M.V. COHEN & J. M. DOWNEY. 1995. Role of bradykinin in protection of ischemic preconditioning in rabbit hearts. Circ. Res. **77:** 611–621.
8. VAHLHAUS, C., R. SCHULZ, H. POST, R. ONALLAH & G. HEUSCH. 1996. No prevention of ischemic preconditioning by the protein kinase C inhibitor staurosporine in swine. Circ. Res. **79:** 407–414.
9. BROOKS, G. & D.J. HEARSE. 1996. Role of protein kinase C in ischemic preconditioning: player or spectator? Circ. Res. **79:** 627–630.
10. DOWNEY, J.M. & M.V. COHEN. 1997. Preconditioning: what it is and how it works. Dialogues Cardiovasc. Med. **2:** 179–196.
11. BOGOYEVITCH, M.A., J. GILLESPIE-BROWN, A.J. KETTERMAN, S.J. FULLER, R. BEN-LEVY, A. ASHWORTH, C.J. MARSHALL & P.H. SUGDEN. 1996. Stimulation of the stress-activated mitogen-activated protein kinase subfamilies in perfused heart. p38/RK mitogen-activated protein kinases and c-Jun N-terminal kinases are activated by ischemia/reperfusion. Circ. Res. **79:** 162–173.
12. MAULIK, N., M. WATANABE, Y.L. ZU, C.K. HUANG, G.A. CORDIS, J.A. SCHLEY & D.K. DAS. 1996. Ischemic preconditioning triggers the activation of MAP kinases and MAPKAP kinase 2 in rat hearts. FEBS Lett. **396:** 233–237.
13. HUOT, J., F. HOULE, D.R. SPITZ & J. LANDRY. 1996. HSP27 phosphorylation-mediated resistance against actin fragmentation and cell death induced by oxidative stress. Cancer Res. **56:** 273–279.
14. LANDRY, J. & J. HUOT. 1995. Modulation of actin dynamics during stress and physiological stimulation by a signaling pathway involving p38 MAP kinase and heat-shock protein 27. Biochem. Cell. Biol. **73:** 703–707.
15. WEINBRENNER, C., G.-S. LIU, M.V. COHEN & J.M. DOWNEY. 1997. Phosphorylation of tyrosine 182 of p38 mitogen-activated protein kinase correlates with the protection of preconditioning in the rabbit heart. J. Mol. Cell. Cardiol. **29:** 2383–2391.
16. MARBER, M.S., D.S. LATCHMAN, J.M. WALKER & D.M. YELLON. 1993. Cardiac stress protein elevation 24 hours after brief ischemia or heat stress is associated with resistance to myocardial infarction. Circulation **88:** 1264–1272.
17. MARBER, M.S., R. MESTRIL, S.-H. CHI, M.R. SAYEN, D.M. YELLON & W.H. DILLMANN. 1995. Overexpression of the rat inducible 70-kD heat stress protein in a transgenic mouse increases the resistance of the heart to ischemic injury. J. Clin. Invest. **95:** 1446–1456.
18. KUZUYA, T., S. HOSHIDA, N. YAMASHITA, H. FUJI, H. OE, M. HORI, T. KAMADA & M. TADA. 1993. Delayed effects of sublethal ischemia on the acquisition of tolerance to ischemia. Circ. Res. **72:** 1293–1299.
19. QIU, Y., X.-L. TANG, S.-W. PARK, J.-Z. SUN, A. KALYA & R. BOLLI. 1997. The early and late phases of ischemic preconditioning. A comparative analysis of their effects on infarct size, myocardial stunning, and arrhythmias in conscious pigs undergoing a 40-minute coronary occlusion. Circ. Res. **80:** 730–742.
20. SUN, J.-Z., X.-L. TANG, A.A. KNOWLTON, S.-W. PARK, Y. QIU & R. BOLLI. 1995. Late preconditioning against myocardial stunning. An endogenous protective mechanism that confers resistance to postischemic dysfunction 24 h after brief ischemia in conscious pigs. J. Clin. Invest. **95:** 388–403.
21. PLUMIER, J.-C., H.A. ROBERTSON & R.W. CURRIE. 1996. Differential accumulation of mRNA for immediate early genes and heat shock genes in heart after ischaemic injury. J. Mol. Cell. Cardiol. **28:** 1251–1260.

22. DAS, D.K., N. MAULIK & I.I. MORARU. 1995. Gene expression in acute myocardial stress. Induction by hypoxia, ischemia, reperfusion, hyperthermia and oxidative stress. J. Mol. Cell. Cardiol. **27:** 181–193.
23. BRAND, T., H.S. SHARMA, K.E. FLEISCHMANN, D.J. DUNCKER, E.O. MCFALLS, P.D. VERDOUW & W. SCHAPER. 1992. Proto-oncogene expression in porcine myocardium subjected to ischemia and reperfusion. Circ. Res. **71:** 1351–1360.
24. KNOLL, R., M. ARRAS, R. ZIMMERMANN, J. SCHAPER & W. SCHAPER. 1994. Changes in gene expression following short coronary occlusions studied in porcine hearts with run-on assays. Cardiovasc. Res. **28:** 1062–1069.
25. SCHAPER, W., R. ZIMMERMANN, A. KLUGE, J. ANDRES, H. S. SHARMA, O. FRASS, R. KNOLL, B. WINKLER & P.D. VERDOUW. 1994. Patterns of myocardial gene expression after cycles of brief coronary occlusion and reperfusion. Ann. N.Y. Acad. Sci. **723:** 284–291.
26. MORIMOTO, R.I., A. TISSIERES & C. GEORGOPOULOS. 1990. Stress Proteins in Biology and Medicine. Cold Spring Harbor Laboratory Press. Cold Spring Harbor, NY.
27. MORIMOTO, R.I. 1993. Cells in stress: transcriptional activation of heat shock genes. Science **259:** 1409–1410.
28. CURRIE, R.W. & F.P. WHITE. 1981. Trauma-induced protein in rat tissues: a physiological role for a "heat shock" protein? Science **214:** 72–73.
29. KNOWLTON A.A., P. BRECHER, C. S. APSTEIN, S. NGOY & G. M. ROMO. 1991. Rapid expression of heat shock protein in the rabbit after brief cardiac ischemia. J. Clin. Invest. **87:** 139–147.
30. KNOWLTON, A.A. 1995. The role of heat shock proteins in the heart. J. Mol. Cell. Cardiol. **27:** 121–131.
31. DRUMMOND, I.A., S.A. MCCLURE, M. POENIE, R.Y. TSIEN & R.A. STEINHARDT. 1986. Large changes in intracellular pH and calcium observed during heat shock are not responsible for the induction of heat shock proteins in Drosophila melanogaster. Mol. Cell Biol. **6:** 1767–1775.
32. STEVENSON, M.A., S.K. CALDERWOUD & G.M. HAHN. 1986. Rapid increases in inositol triphosphate and intracellular Ca^{2+} after heat shock. Biochem. Biophys. Res. Commun. **137:** 826–833.
33. CURRIE, R.W., M. KARMAZYN, M. KLOC & K. MAILER. 1988. Heat-shock response is associated with enhanced postischemic ventricular recovery. Circ. Res. **63:** 543–549.
34. CURRIE, R.W. & M. KARMAZYN. 1990. Improved post-ischemic ventricular recovery in the absence of changes in energy metabolism in working rat hearts following heat-shock. J. Mol. Cell. Cardiol. **22:** 631–636.
35. KARMAZYN, M., K. MAILER & R.W. CURRIE. 1990. Acquisition and decay of heat-shock–enhanced postischemic ventricular recovery. Am. J. Physiol. (Heart Circ. Physiol.) **259:** H424–H431.
36. KINGMA, J.G. JR., D. SIMARD, J.R. ROULEAU, R.M. TANGUAY & R.W. CURRIE. 1996. Effect of 3-aminotriazole on hyperthermia-mediated cardioprotection in rabbits. Am. J. Physiol. (Heart Circ. Physiol.) **270:** H1165–H1171.
37. HUTTER, M. M., R. E. SIEVERS, V. BARBOSA & C. L. WOLFE. 1994. Heat shock protein induction in rat hearts: a direct correlation between the amount of heat shock protein induced and the degree of myocardial protection. Circulation **89:** 355–360.
38. DONNELLY, T.J., R.E. SIEVERS, F.L.J. VISSERN, W.J. WELCH & C.L. WOLFE. 1992. Heat shock protein induction in rat hearts. A role for improved myocardial salvage after ischemia and reperfusion? Circulation **85:** 769–778.
39. DORION, M., J.R. ROULEAU & J.G. KINGMA, JR. 1992. Failure of AICA riboside to limit infarct size during acute myocardial infarction in rabbits. J. Cardiovasc. Pharmacol. **19:** 69–77.
40. CURRIE, R.W., R.M. TANGUAY & J.G. KINGMA, JR. 1993. Heat-shock response and limitation of tissue necrosis during occlusion/reperfusion in rabbit hearts. Circulation **87:** 963–971.
41. VAN WINKLE, D.M., J. THORNTON, D.M. DOWNEY & J.M. DOWNEY. 1991. The natural history of preconditioning cardioprotection depends on duration of transient ischemia and time to subsequent ischemia. Coronary Art. Dis. **2:** 613–619.

42. CHIRGWIN, J.M., A.E. PRZYBYLA, R.J. MACDONALD & W.J. RUTTER. 1979. Isolation of biologically active ribonucleic acids from sources enriched in ribonuclease. Biochemistry **18:** 5294–5299.
43. KHANDJIAN, E.W. 1986. UV crosslinking of RNA to nylon membrane enhances hybridization signals. Molec. Biol. Rep. **11:** 107–115.
44. MAXWELL, M.P., D.J. HEARSE & D.M. YELLON. 1987. Species variation in the coronary collateral circulation during regional myocardial ischemia: a critical determinant of the rate of evolution and extent of myocardial infarction. Cardiovasc. Res. **21:** 737–746.
45. STEENBERGEN, C., E. MURPHY, L. LEVY & R.E. LONDON. 1987. Elevation in cytosolic free calcium concentration early in myocardial ischemia in perfused rat heart. Circ. Res. **60:** 700–708.
46. CROALL, D.E. & G.N. DEMARTINO. 1991. Calcium-activated neutral protease (calpain) system: structure, function, and regulation. Physiol. Rev. **71:** 813–847.
47. DARNELL, J., H. LODISH & D. BALTIMORE. 1988. *In* La Cellule, Biologie Moleculaire. pp. 771–854. Ville Mt-Royal. Quebec, Canada.
48. KIHARA, Y., W. GROSSMAN & J.P. MORGAN. 1998. Direct measurement of changes in intracellular calcium transients during hypoxia, ischemia, and reperfusion in the intact mammalian heart. Circ. Res. **65:** 1029–1044.
49. LANGE, R., J. WARE & R.A. KLONER. 1984. Absence of a cumulative deterioration of regional function during three repeated 5 or 15 minute coronary occlusions. Circulation **69:** 400–408.
50. REIBEL, D. K. & M. J. ROVETTO. 1978. Myocardial ATP synthesis and mechanical function following oxygen deficiency. Am. J. Physiol. (Heart Circ. Physiol.) **234:** H620–H624.
51. LEVI, E., M. VIVI, G. NAVON, Y. HASIN & M. HOROWITZ. 1991. Heat acclimation improves cardiac mechanical and metabolic performance during ischemia and reperfusion. Circulation **84**(suppl):II-621(Abstract).
52. MURRY, C.E., V.J. RICHARD, K.A. REIMER & R.B. JENNINGS. 1990. Ischemic preconditioning slows energy metabolism and delays ultrastructural damage during a sustained ischemic episode. Circ. Res. **66:** 913–931.
53. REIMER, K.A., C.E. MURRY, I. YAMASAWA & M.L. HILL. 1986. Four brief periods of myocardial ischemia cause no cumulative ATP loss or necrosis. Am. J. Physiol. (Heart Circ. Physiol.) **251:** H1306–H1315.
54. BURDON, R.H. 1986. Heat shock and the heat shock proteins. Biochem. J. **240:** 313–324.
55. DAS, D.K., R.M. ENGELMAN & Y. KIMURA. 1993. Molecular adaptation of cellular defences during preconditioning of the heart by repeated ischaemia. Cardiovasc. Res. **27:** 578–584.
56. LINDQUIST, S. 1986. The heat-shock response. Ann. Rev. Biochem. **55:** 1151–1191.
57. PELHAM, H.R.B. 1986. Speculations on the functions of the major heat shock and glucose-regulated proteins. Cell **46:** 959–961.
58. LIU, X., R. M. ENGELMAN, I. I. MORARU, J. A. ROUSOU, J. E. FLACK, III, D. W. DEATON, N. MAULIK & D. K. DAS. 1992. Heat shock. A new approach for myocardial preservation in cardiac surgery. Circulation **86**(Suppl): II-358–II-363.
59. HORWITZ, L.D. & J.A. LEFF. 1995. Catalase and hydrogen peroxide cytotoxicity in cultured cardiac myocytes. J. Mol. Cell. Cardiol. **27:** 909–915.
60. STEARE, S.E. & D.M. YELLON. 1993. The protective effect of heat stress against reperfusion arrhythmias in the rat. J. Mol. Cell. Cardiol. **25:** 1471–1481.
61. STEARE, S.E. & D.M. YELLON. 1994. Increased endogenous catalase activity caused by heat stress does not protect the isolated rat heart against exogenous hydrogen peroxide. Cardiovasc. Res. **28:** 1096–1101.
62. NOHL, H. & W. JORDAN. 1980. The metabolic fate of mitochondrial hydrogen peroxide. Int. J. Biochem. **111:** 203–210.
63. TARTAGLIA, L.A., G. STORZ & B.N. AMES. 1989. Identification and molecular analysis of oxyR-regulated promoters important for the bacterial adaptation to oxidative stress. Mol. Biol. **210:** 709–719.

64. SIMMONS, T.W. & I.S. JAMALL. 1989. Relative importance of intracellular glutathione peroxidase and catalase in vivo for prevention of peroxidation to the heart. Cardiovasc. Res. **23:** 774–779.
65. YELLON, D.M., E. PASINI, A. CARGNONI, M.S. MARBER, D.S. LATCHMAN & R. FERRARI. 1992. The protective role of heat stress in the ischemic and reperfused rabbit myocardium. J. Mol. Cell. Cardiol. **24:** 895–907.
66. WALKER, D.M., E. PASINI, S. KUCUKOGLU, M.S. MARBER, E. ILIODROMITIS, R. FERRARI & D.M. YELLON. 1993. Heat stress limits infarct size in the isolated perfused rabbit heart. Cardiovasc. Res. **27:** 962–967.
67. PLUMIER, J.-C., B.M. ROSS, R.W. CURRIE, C.E. ANGELIDIS, H. KAZLARIS, G. KOLLIAS & G.N. PAGOULATOS. 1995. Transgenic mice expressing the human heat shock protein 70 have improved post-ischemic myocardial recovery. J. Clin. Invest. **95:** 1854–1860.
68. WALL, S.R., H. FLISS & B. KORECKY. 1993. Role of catalase in myocardial protection against ischemia in heat shocked rats. Mol. Cell. Biochem. **129:** 187–194.
69. AUYEUNG, Y., R.E. SIEVERS, D. WENG, V. BARBOSA & C.L. WOLFE. 1995. Catalase inhibition with 3-amino-1,2,4-triazole does not abolish infarct size reduction in heat-shocked rats. Circulation **92:** 3318–3322.
70. SADOSHIMA, J.-I., T. TAKAHASHI, L. JAHN & S. IZUMO. 1992. Roles of mechano-sensitive ion channels, cytoskeleton, and contractile activity in stretch-induced immediate-early gene expression and hypertrophy of cardiac myocytes. Proc. Natl. Acad. Sci. USA **89:** 9905–9909.
71. IZUMO, S., B. NADAL-GINARD & V. MAHDAVI. 1988. Proto-oncogene induction and reprogramming of cardiac gene expression produced by pressure overload. Proc. Natl. Acad. Sci. USA **85:** 339–343.
72. BOHMANN, D., T.J. BOS, A. ADMON, T. NISHIMURA, P.K. VOGT & R. TJIAN. 1987. Human proto-oncogene c-jun encodes a DNA binding protein with structural and functional properties of transcription factor AP-1. Science **238:** 1386–1392.
73. COPPOLA, J.A. & M.D. COLEB. 1986. Constitutive c-myc oncogene expression blocks mouse erythroleukemia cell differentiation but not commitment. Nature **320:** 760–763.

Subcellular Remodeling and Heart Dysfunction in Cardiac Hypertrophy due to Pressure Overload[a]

NARANJAN S. DHALLA[b], LEONARD GOLFMAN, XUELIANG LIU, HIDEKI SASAKI, VIJAYAN ELIMBAN, AND HEINZ RUPP

Institute of Cardiovascular Sciences, St. Boniface General Hospital Research Centre, Winnepeg, Manitoba R2H 2A6 Canada

Department of Physiology, Faculty of Medicine, University of Manitoba, Winnipeg, Manitoba R2H 2A6, Canada

ABSTRACT: Rats were treated with etomoxir, an inhibitor of palmitoyltransferase-1, to examine the role of a shift in myocardial metabolism in cardiac hypertrophy. Pressure overload was induced by abdominal aorta banding for 8 weeks. Sham-operated animals served as control. Left ventricular dysfunction, as reflected by decreased LVDP, +dP/dt, –dP/dt, and elevated LVEDP in the pressure overloaded animals, was improved by treatment with etomoxir. Cardiac hypertrophy in pressure-overload rats decreased the sarcoplasmic reticular (SR) Ca^{2+} uptake and Ca^{2+} release as well as myofibrillar Ca^{2+}-stimulated ATPase and myosin Ca^{2+}-ATPase activities; these changes were attenuated by treatment with etomoxir. Steady-state mRNA levels for α- and β-myosin heavy chains, SR Ca^{2+}-pump, and protein content of SR Ca^{2+}-pump were reduced in hypertrophied hearts; these alterations were prevented by etomoxir treatment. The results indicate that modification of changes in myocardial metabolism by etomoxir may prevent remodeling of myofibrils and SR membrane and thereby improve cardiac function in hypertrophied heart.

INTRODUCTION

Although cardiac hypertrophy due to chronic pressure overload is considered to be an adaptive response of the heart at early stages, it is invariably associated with heart dysfunction.[1–5] The sympathetic nervous system and the renin-angiotensin system are activated due to pressure overload.[6,7] Also, a shift in myocardial metabolism may occur during the development of cardiac hypertrophy due to pressure overload.[8,9] On the basis of observations that altered activities of myofibrillar ATPase and the sarcoplasmic reticular (SR) Ca^{2+}-pump may explain the contractile abnormalities in the hypertrophied heart,[5,8,10–20] it was suggested that a remodeling

[a]The research reported in this article was supported by a grant from the Medical Research Council of Canada (MRC Group in Experimental Cardiology). H.R., a Visiting Professor from University of Marburg, Marburg, Germany, was supported by the NATO Research Program (0189/87) and the Science & Technology Cooperation Germany/Canada (HM4).

[b]Address correspondence to: Dr. Naranjan S. Dhalla, Institute of Cardiovascular Sciences, St. Boniface General Hospital Research Centre, 351 Tache Avenue, Winnipeg, Manitoba R2H 2A6, Canada.

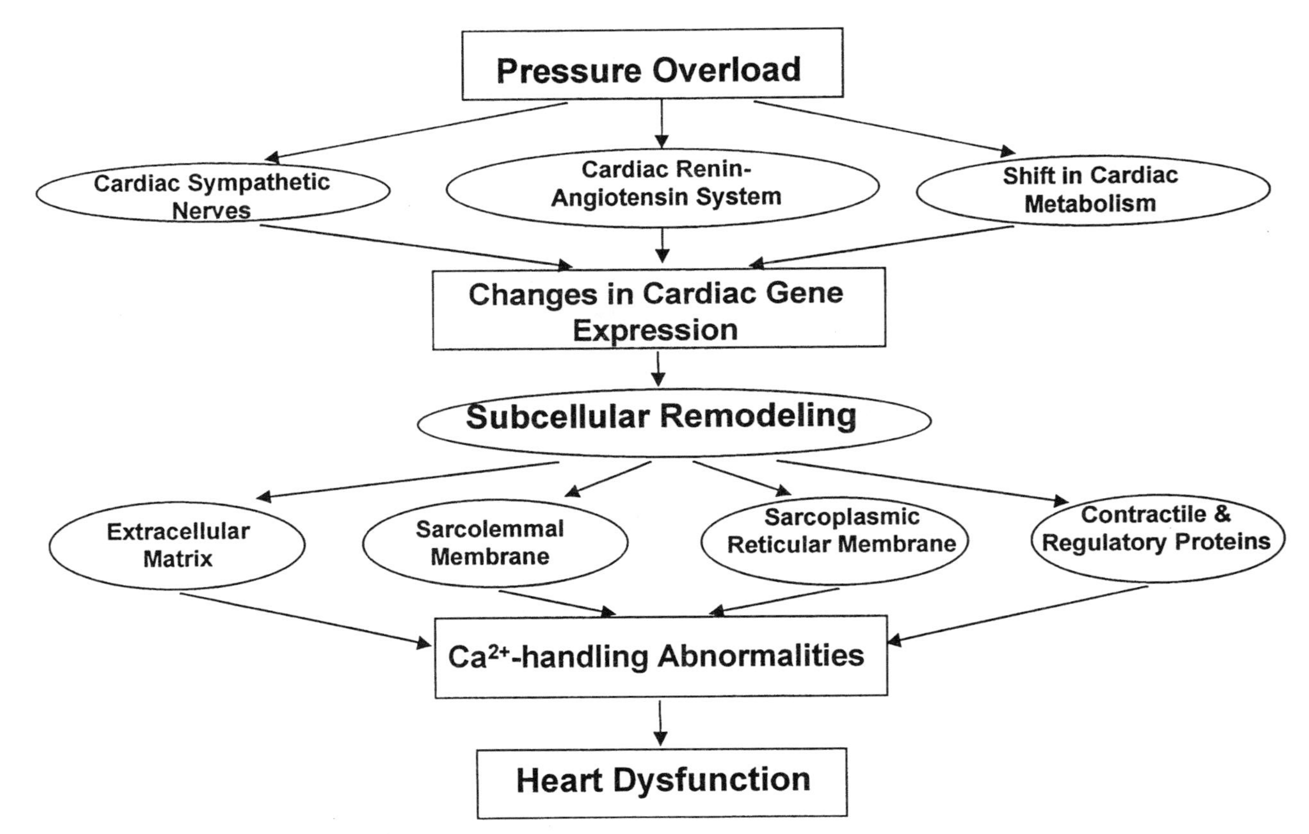

FIGURE 1. Schematic of events leading to subcellular remodeling and heart dysfunction as a consequence of pressure overload.

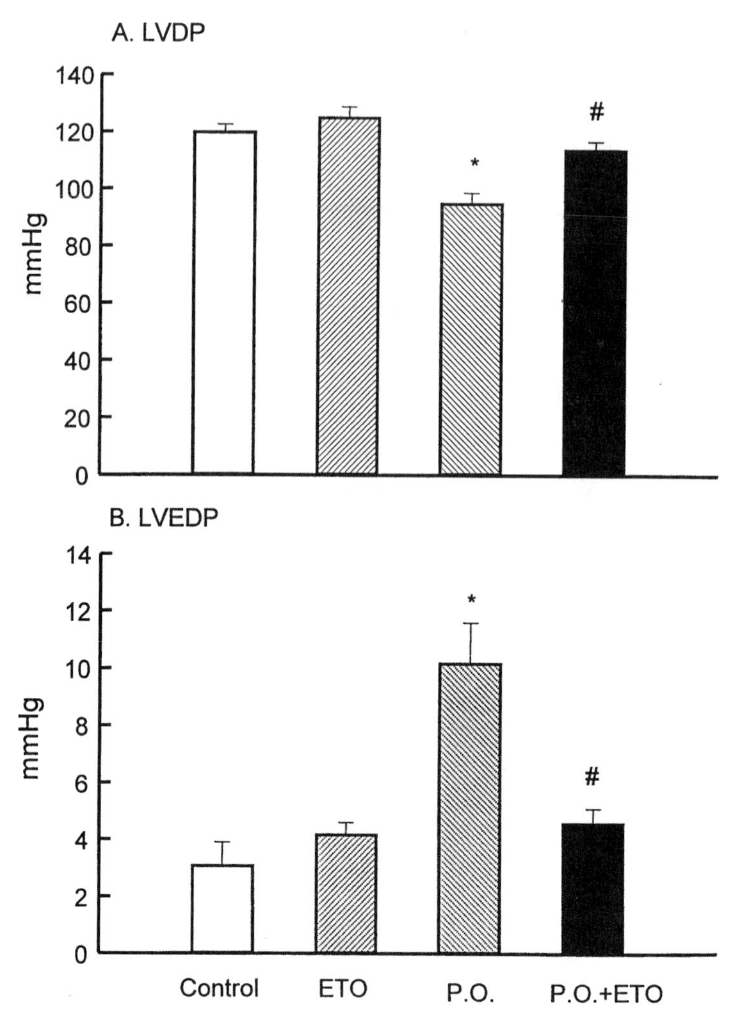

FIGURE 2. Left ventricular developed pressure (LVDP) and end-diastolic pressure (LVEDP) in sham control and pressure-overload (P.O.) rats with or without etomoxir (ETO) treatment. Each value is a mean ± SE of 6 animals in each group. $^{*}p < 0.05$ versus control; $^{\#}p < 0.05$ versus P.O.

of subcellular organelles, including myofibrils and SR membranes, contributes to the development of heart dysfunction in cardiac hypertrophy.[21] FIGURE 1 shows a scheme of events related to chronic pressure overload effects, including changes in gene expression, subcellular remodeling, Ca^{2+}-handling abnormalities, and heart dysfunction. In view of the limited scope of this article, the roles of the sympathetic system and the renin-angiotensin system are not considered. This paper focuses on the role of a cardiac metabolism shift in cardiac hypertrophy. Accordingly, this study

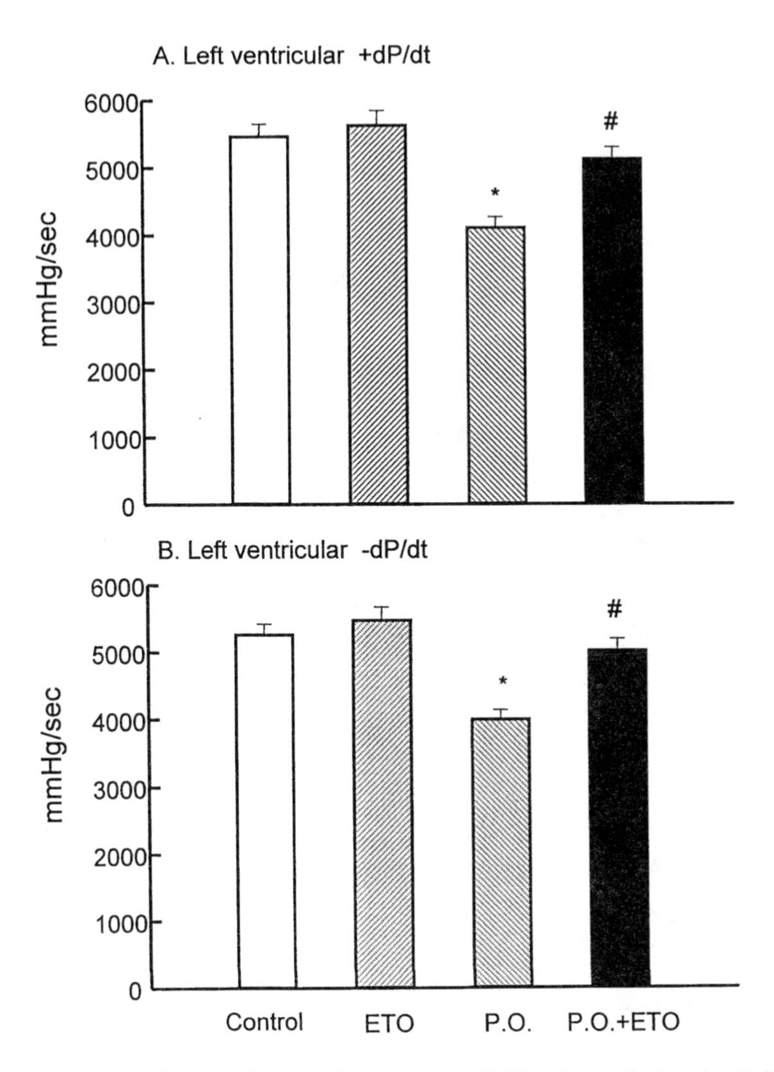

FIGURE 3. Left ventricular rate of contraction (+dP/dt) and rate of relaxation (–dP/dt) in sham control and pressure-overload (P.O.) rats with or without etomoxir (ETO) treatment. Each value is a mean ± SE of 6 animals in each group. $^{*}p < 0.05$ versus control; $^{\#}p < 0.05$ versus P.O.

was undertaken to test whether the prevention of changes in gene expression specific for myofibrillar and SR proteins by etomoxir-induced modification of the shift in cardiac metabolism is associated with the prevention of myofibrillar and SR remodeling as well as improvement of heart function in cardiac hypertrophy due to pressure overload.

MATERIALS AND METHODS

Cardiac hypertrophy due to pressure overload in rats was induced by banding the abdominal aorta for 8 weeks according to the method described elsewhere.[8,9] Sham-operated animals served as control. Both sham-operated and experimental animals were treated with or without etomoxir in the drinking water (12 to 15 mg/kg/day). A group of the animals were employed for hemodynamic assessment in which the left ventricular developed pressure (LVDP), left ventricular end-diastolic pressure (LVEDP), rate of contraction (+dP/dt), and rate of relaxation (–dP/dt) were recorded under anesthesia.[22] All other animals were sacrificed by decapitation, the left ventricular tissue dissected out and used for the isolation of myofibrillar and SR membrane preparations according to the methods described earlier.[23,24] Myofibrillar Ca^{2+}-stimulated ATPase, myosin Ca^{2+}-ATPase, SR Ca^{2+} uptake, and EGTA-induced SR Ca^{2+}-release activities were determined.[23–25] Total cellular RNA was isolated from the left ventricular tissue by the method of Chomczynski and Sacchi[26] and mRNA levels were determined by Northern blot analysis[27] by using molecular probes specific for α-myosin heavy chain, β-myosin heavy chain, SR Ca^{2+}-pump (SERCA2a), and glyceraldehyde-3-phosphate dehydrogenase (GADPH) proteins. The protein content for SERCA2a in the SR membranes was measured by Western blot analysis.[9] After autoradiography, all bands were scanned using GS-670 imaging densitometer with Molecular Analyst computer analysis software (Bio-Rad Laboratories, Hercules, CA). The results were analyzed statistically by Duncan's new multiple comparison as well as by the Mann-Whitney test. A value of $p < 0.05$ was taken to reflect a significant difference between two groups.

RESULTS

Hemodynamic Assessment and Subcellular Activities

In the first series of experiments, the 8-week sham and hypertrophied rats with or without etomoxir treatment were assessed hemodynamically with respect to heart function (FIGS. 2 and 3). Rats with cardiac hypertrophy due to pressure overload showed significant decreases in LVDP, +dP/dt, and –dP/dt, whereas LVEDP was markedly increased. These changes in cardiac function due to pressure overload were prevented by treating the animals with etomoxir. The left ventricular myofibrillar Ca^{2+}-stimulated ATPase and myosin Ca^{2+}-ATPase activities were depressed in the hypertrophied heart and these alterations were attenuated by treatment with etomoxir (FIG. 4). The decreased SR Ca^{2+} uptake and release activities in the hypertrophied heart were also corrected by etomoxir treatment (FIG. 5). As reported earlier,[8] the etomoxir treatment of pressure-overload animals did not prevent cardiac hypertrophy due to pressure overload.

Gene Expression for Myofibrillar and SR Proteins

The second series of experiments were undertaken to examine changes in mRNA levels for α- and β-myosin heavy chains as well as SERCA2a. The results in FIGURES 6 and 7 indicate decreases in mRNA abundance for α-myosin heavy chain and

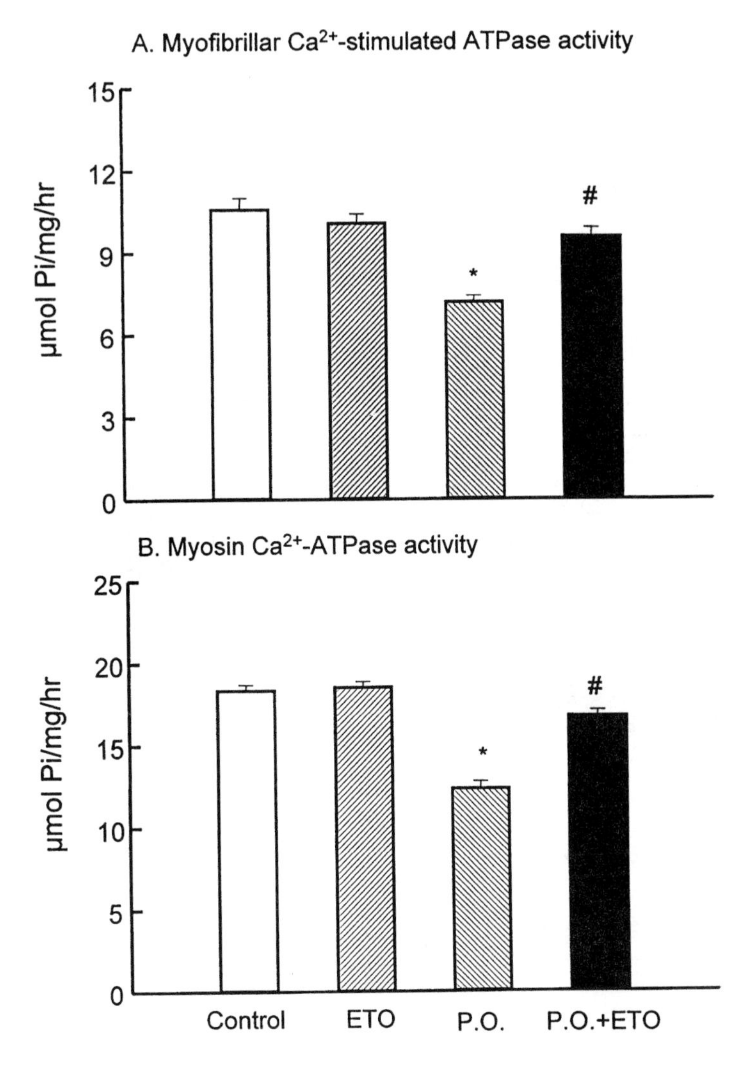

FIGURE 4. Left ventricular myofibrillar Ca^{2+}-stimulated ATPase and myosin Ca^{2+}-ATPase activities in sham control and pressure-overload (P.O.) rats with or without etomoxir (ETO) treatment. Each value is a mean ± SE of 6 samples in each group. $^{*}p < 0.05$ versus control; $^{\#}p < 0.05$ versus P.O.

SERCA2a, whereas the mRNA level for β-myosin heavy chain was increased in the hypertrophied left ventricle; these changes were prevented by treatment with etomoxir. Likewise, the decrease in SERCA2a protein content in SR preparations from hypertrophic hearts was prevented by etomoxir (FIG. 7).

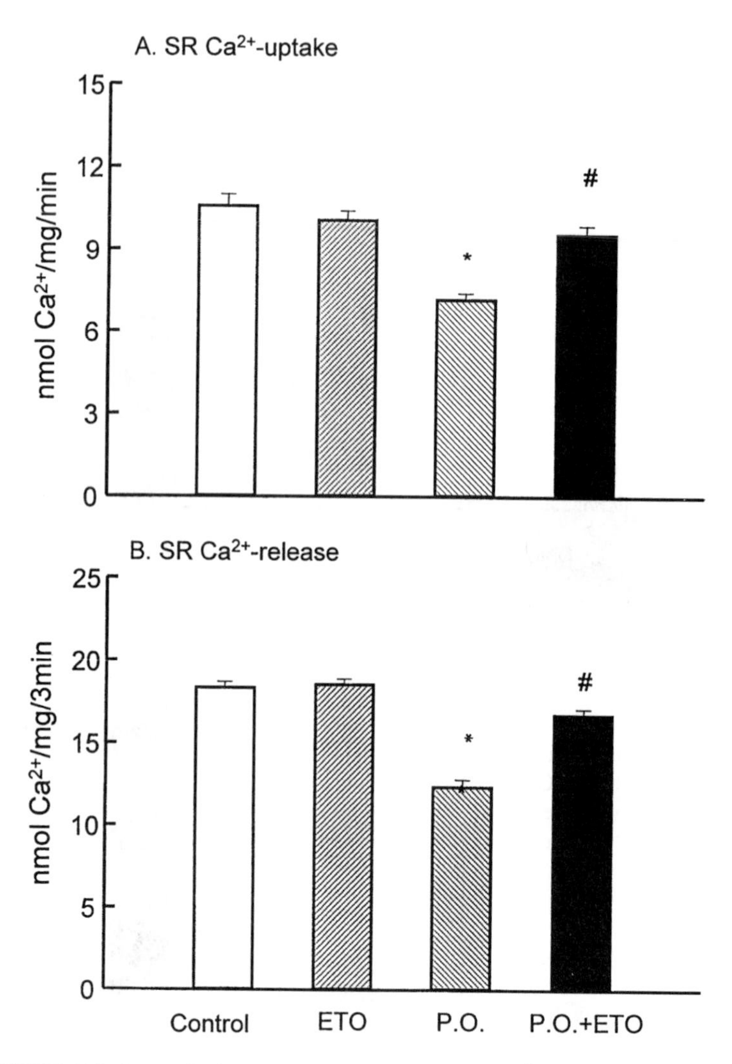

FIGURE 5. Left ventricular sarcoplasmic reticular (SR) Ca^{2+} uptake and release activity in sham control and pressure-overload (P.O.) rats with or without etomoxir (ETO) treatment. Each value is a mean ± SE of 6 samples in each group. $^{*}p < 0.05$ versus control; $^{\#}p < 0.05$ versus P.O.

DISCUSSION

In this study we have shown that heart dysfunction in cardiac hypertrophy due to pressure overload was associated with decreases in the myofibrillar Ca^{2+}-stimulated ATPase, myosin Ca^{2+}-ATPase, and SR Ca^{2+} uptake and release activities. These results are consistent with other reports showing abnormalities in cardiac perfor-

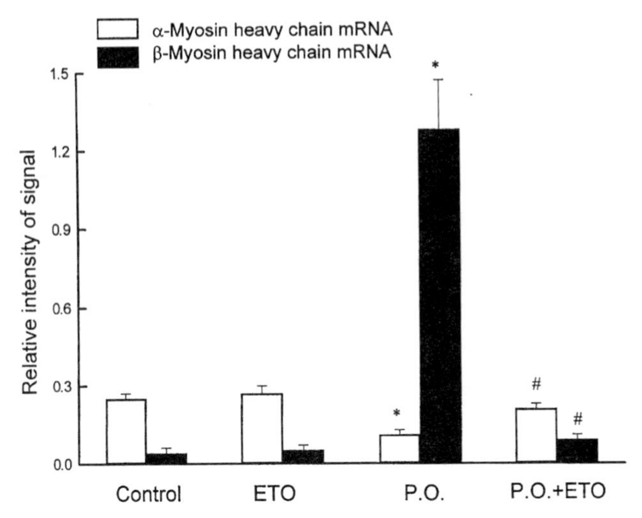

FIGURE 6. Steady-state mRNA abundance for α-myosin heavy chain and β-myosin heavy chain in left ventricles from sham control and pressure-overload (P.O.) rats with or without etomoxir (ETO) treatment. Relative intensity of densitometric signals of mRNA bands for α- and β-myosin heavy chains is a ratio with respect to GADPH mRNA band.

mance,[1–5] contractile proteins,[10–15] and SR Ca^{2+}-transport activities[16–20] in the hypertrophied heart. The decrease in mRNA level for α-myosin heavy chain and increase in β-myosin heavy chain in cardiac hypertrophy may explain the observed decrease in myofibrillar Ca^{2+}-stimulated activities and myosin Ca^{2+}-ATPase activities in the hypertrophied heart. Likewise, the decrease in mRNA level as well as protein content for SERCA2a could explain the decrease in SR Ca^{2+}-pump activity in cardiac hypertrophy due to pressure overload. A decrease in SR Ca^{2+}-release activity in hypertrophied heart may also be due to a decrease in the mRNA levels for SR Ca^{2+}-release channels.[9] These observations are in agreement with the view that remodeling of myofibrils and SR membranes occurs as a consequence of changes in gene expression for proteins of these subcellular organelles during the development of cardiac hypertrophy. Remodeling of subcellular organelles refers to changes in their molecular structure and composition.

The pressure overload–induced changes in heart function, myofibrillar ATPase, and SR Ca^{2+}-transport activities were attenuated by treatment with etomoxir. Beneficial effects of etomoxir treatment on pressure overload–induced changes in contractile proteins, myosin isozyme distribution, SR Ca^{2+}-uptake activities, and mRNA level for SERCA2a have also been reported earlier.[8,9,28–30] Such beneficial effects of etomoxir do not seem to be associated with any decrease in the magnitude of cardiac hypertrophy due to pressure overload.[8,9] On the other hand, these beneficial effects of etomoxir treatment may be due to its ability to prevent remodeling of subcellular organelles because the pressure overload–induced changes in cardiac gene expression were prevented by etomoxir. Since etomoxir has been shown to inhibit the oxidation of free fatty acids and promote the oxidation of glucose,[8,9,28–30] it is possible that the attenuation of changes in cardiac gene expression, prevention

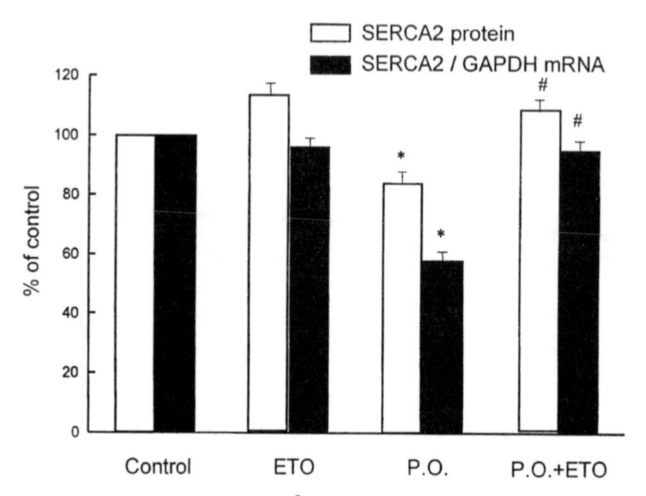

FIGURE 7. Sarcoplasmic reticular Ca^{2+}-pump ATPase (SERCA2a) protein content and steady-state mRNA levels for SERCA2a in left ventricles from sham control and pressure-overload (P.O.) rats with or without etomoxir (ETO) treatment. mRNA abundance was calculated as a ratio for the densitometric signals for SERCA2a and GADPH mRNA bands. The results are expressed as the percentage of the control values for mRNA abundance and protein content. Each value is a mean ± SE of 6 samples in each group. $^{*}p < 0.05$ versus control; $^{\#}p < 0.05$ versus P.O.

of subcellular remodeling, and improvement of cardiac function in hypertrophied hearts by etomoxir may be due to some modification of changes in myocardial fuel utilization and metabolism. It should be emphasized that in this paper the term subcellular remodeling refers to changes in the molecular structure of different proteins as well as composition of the subcellular organelles, such as myofibrils and SR membranes.

SUMMARY

In order to examine the role of a shift in myocardial metabolism in cardiac hypertrophy, rats with or without etomoxir treatment (15 mg/kg/day of etomoxir, an inhibitor of palmitoyltransferase-1, in drinking water) were employed in this study. Pressure overload was induced by banding of the abdominal aorta for 8 weeks; sham-operated animals served as control. Left ventricular dysfunction, as reflected by decreased LVDP, +dP/dt, –dP/dt, and elevated LVEDP in the pressure-overload animals, was improved by treatment with etomoxir. Cardiac hypertrophy in pressure-overload rats decreased the sarcoplasmic reticular (SR) Ca^{2+} uptake and release as well as myofibrillar Ca^{2+}-stimulated ATPase and myosin Ca^{2+}-ATPase activities; these changes were attenuated by treatment with etomoxir. Steady-state mRNA levels for α- and β-myosin heavy chains and SR Ca^{2+}-pump as well as protein content of SR Ca^{2+}-pump were reduced in hypertrophied hearts; these alterations were prevented by etomoxir treatment. The results indicate that modification of changes in myocardial metabolism by etomoxir may prevent remodeling of myofibrils and SR membrane and thereby improve cardiac function in hypertrophied heart.

REFERENCES

1. HAMRELL, B.B. & N.R. ALPERT. 1997. The mechanical characteristics of hypertrophied rabbit cardiac muscle in the absence of congestive heart failure. Circ. Res. **40:** 20–25.
2. WIKMAN-COFFELT, J., W.W. PARMLEY & D.T. MASON. 1979. The cardiac hypertrophy process. Analyses of factors determining pathological vs. physiological development. Circ. Res. **45:** 697–707.
3. JULIAN, F.J., D.L. MORGAN, R.L. MOSS, M. GONZALEZ & P. DWIVEDI. 1981. Myocyte growth without physiological impairment in gradually induced cardiac hypertrophy. Circ. Res. **49:** 1300–1310.
4. SCHEUER, J., A. MALHOTRA, C. HIRSCH, J. CAPASSO & T.F. SHAIBLE. 1982. Physiologic cardiac hypertrophy corrects contractile protein abnormalities associated with pathologic hypertrophy. J. Clin. Invest. **70:** 1300–1305.
5. DHALLA, N.S., C.E. HEYLIGER, R.E. BEAMISH & I.R. INNES. 1987. Pathophysiological aspect of myocardial hypertrophy. Can. J. Cardiol. **3:** 183–196.
6. GANGULY, P.K., S.-L. LEE, R.E. BEAMISH & N.S. DHALLA. 1989. Altered sympathetic system and adrenoceptors during the development of cardiac hypertrophy. Am. Heart J. **118:** 520–525.
7. BAKER, K.M., M.I. CHERMIN, S.K. WIXSON & J.F. ACETO. 1990. Renin-angiotensin system involvement in pressure-overload cardiac hypertrophy in rats. Am. J. Physiol. **259:** H324–H332.
8. RUPP, H., V. ELIMBAN & N.S. DHALLA. 1992. Modification of subcellular organelles in pressure-overloaded heart by etomoxir, a carnitine palmitoyltransferase 1 inhibitor. FASEB J. **6:** 2349–2353.
9. ZARAIN-HERZBERG, A., H. RUPP, V. ELIMBAN & N.S. DHALLA. 1996. Modification of sarcoplasmic reticulum gene expression in pressure overload cardiac hypertrophy by etomoxir. FASEB J. **10:** 1303–1309.
10. SCHAUB, M.C., M.A. HEFTI, R.A. ZUELLIG & I. MARANO. 1997. Modulation of contractility in human cardiac hypertrophy by myosin essential light chain isoforms. Cardiovasc. Res. **37:** 381–404.
11. MERCADIER, J.J., A.M. LOMPRE, C. WISNEWSKY, J.L. SAMUEL, J. BERCOVICI, B. SWYNGHEDAUW & K. SCHWARTZ. 1981. Myosin isoenzyme changes in several models of rat cardiac hypertrophy. Circ. Res. **49:** 525–532.
12. ALPERT, N. & L.A. MULIERI. 1982. Heart mechanics and myosin ATPase in normal and hypertrophied heart muscle. Fed. Proc. **41:** 192–198.
13. RUPP, H. 1981. The adaptive changes in the isoenzyme pattern of myosin from hypertrophied rat myocardium as a result of pressure overload and physical training. Basic Res. Cardiol. **76:** 79–88.
14. SIEMANKOWSKI, R.F. & P. OREIZEN. 1978. Canine cardiac myosin with special reference to pressure overload cardiac hypertrophy. J. Biol. Chem. **253:** 8659–8665.
15. LITTEN, R.Z., J.E. BRAYDEN & N.R. ALPERT. 1978. The ATPase activity of subfragment-1 from the hypertrophied heart. Biochim. Biophys. Acta **523:** 377–384.
16. HEYLIGER, C.E., P.K. GANGULY & N.S. DHALLA. 1985. Sarcoplasmic reticular and mitochondrial calcium transport in cardiac hypertrophy. Can. J. Cardiol. **1:** 401–408.
17. ITO, Y., J. SUKO & C.A. CHIDSEY. 1974. Intracellular calcium and myocardial contractility. V. Calcium uptake of sarcoplasmic reticulum functions in hypertrophied and failing rabbit hearts. J. Mol. Cell. Cardiol. **6:** 237–247.
18. LAMERS, J.M.J. & J.T. STIMIS. 1979. Defective calcium pump in the sarcoplasmic reticulum of the hypertrophied rabbit. Life Sci. **24:** 2313–2320.
19. LIMAS, C.J., S.S. SPIER & J. KAHLON. 1980. Enhanced calcium transport by sarcoplasmic reticulum in mild cardiac hypertrophy. J. Mol. Cell. Cardiol. **12:** 1103–1116.

20. SORDAHL, L.A., W.B. MCCULLUM, W.G. WOOD & A. SCHWARTZ. 1973. Mitochondria and sarcoplasmic reticulum functions in cardiac hypertrophy and failure. Am. J. Physiol. **224:** 497–502.
21. DHALLA, N.S., C. HEYLIGER, K.R. SHAH, R. SETHI, N. TAKEDA & M. NAGANO. 1994. Remodeling of membrane systems during the development of cardiac hypertrophy due to pressure overload. *In* The Adapted Heart. M. Nagano, N. Takeda & N.S. Dhalla, Eds.: 27–49. Raven Press. New York, NY.
22. DIXON, I.M.C., S.-L. LEE & N.S. DHALLA. 1990. Nitrendipine binding in congestive heart failure due to myocardial infarction. Circ. Res. **66:** 782–788.
23. PIERCE, G.N. & N.S. DHALLA. 1985. Mechanisms of the defect in cardiac myofibrillar function during diabetes. Am. J. Physiol. **248:** E170–E175.
24. GANGULY, P.K., G.N. PIERCE & N.S. DHALLA. 1983. Defective sarcoplasmic reticular calcium transport in diabetic cardiomyopathy. Am. J. Physiol. **244:** E528–E535.
25. OSADA, M., T. NETTICADAN, K. TAMURA & N.S. DHALLA. 1998. Modification of ischemia-reperfusion-induced changes in cardiac sarcoplasmic reticulum by preconditioning. Am. J. Physiol. **274:** H2025–H2034.
26. CHOMCZYNSKI, P. & N. SACCHI. 1987. Single-step method of RNA isolation by acid guanidinium thiocyanate-phenol-chloroform extraction. Anal. Biochem. **162:** 156–159.
27. SAMBROOK, J., E.F. FRITSCH & T. MANIATIS. 1989. Molecular Cloning: A Laboratory Manual. 2nd edit. Cold Spring Harbor Laboratory. Cold Spring Harbor, NY.
28. VETTER, R., M. KOTT & H. RUPP. 1995. Differential influences of carnitine palmitoyltransferase-1 inhibition and hyperthyroidism on cardiac growth and sarcoplasmic reticulum phosphorylation. Eur. Heart J. **16:** 15–19.
29. VETTER, R. & H. RUPP. 1994. CPT-1 inhibition by etomoxir has a chamber-related action on cardiac sarcoplasmic reticulum and isoenzymes. Am. J. Physiol. **267:** H2091–H2099.
30. RUPP, H., R. WAHL & M. HANSEN. 1992. Influence of diet and carnitine palmitoyltransferase-1 inhibition on myosin and sarcoplasmic reticulum. J. Appl. Physiol. **72:** 352–360.

In Vitro Analysis of SERCA2 Gene Regulation in Hypertrophic Cardiomyocytes and Increasing Transfection Efficiency by Gene-Gun Biolistics[a]

KARIN EIZEMA, HAN A.A. VAN HEUGTEN, KAREL BEZSTAROSTI, MARGA C. VAN SETTEN, AND JOS M.J. LAMERS[b]

Department of Biochemistry, Cardiovascular Research Institute COEUR, Erasmus University Rotterdam, P.O. Box 1738, 3000 DR Rotterdam, Netherlands

ABSTRACT: The transcriptional downregulation of the SERCA2 gene is studied using neonatal rat cardiomyocytes stimulated with endothelin-1 to induce hypertrophy. Liposome-based transfection of cells with a 1.9 kb SERCA2 promoter fragment directed expression of a reporter gene identical to the downregulation of genomic SERCA2 expression by endothelin-1. Results of a new gene gun technology for transient transfection of cardiomyocytes with a RSV-β-galactosidase construct are reported. This new method for propelling DNA-coated gold beads into cardiomyocytes is extremely suitable for directly testing promoter/reporter gene DNA constructs since the transfection efficiency (approximately 10%) appears to be higher than traditional transfection methods.

INTRODUCTION

In both humans and animal models, sustained increased cardiac workload, as a result, for example, of myocardial infarction, chronic hypertension or valvular insufficiency, elicits a hypertrophic response of the heart, i.e., an increase in the size of individual myocytes. The hypertrophic response is characterized by a period of compensation during which remodeling of the heart normalizes systolic wall stress and basal parameters of contractile function. However, this adaptation carries a price. This apparent salutory response to excess load is accompanied by reversion to a fetal program of cardiac gene expression. The upregulation of cardiac neurohumoral hormones, including angiotensin II, catecholamine, endothelin-1 (ET-1), and atrial natriuretic factor (ANF), is partially involved in mediating the hypertrophic and gene expression responses. The period of adaptation is followed by a transition to cardiac failure. The underlying cause of the negative outcome is believed to reside partially in the reprogramming of gene expression.[1–5] This hypothesis is consistent with the observed relative downregulation of key proteins (indirectly) involved in regulation

[a]This work was supported by Grants M 93.004 and 95.109 from the Netherlands Heart Foundation.

[b]Address correspondence to: J.M.J. Lamers, Ph.D., Department of Biochemistry, Cardiovascular Research Institute (COEUR), Faculty of Medicine and Health Sciences, Erasmus University, P.O.Box 1738, 3000 DR Rotterdam, the Netherlands; Telephone: 00-31-10-4087335; Fax: 00-31-10-4089472; E-mail: lamers@bc1.fgg.eur.nl

of the uptake and release of Ca^{2+} from the cardiac sarcoplasmic reticulum: the β-adrenergic receptor, Ca^{2+} ATPase (SERCA2), and phospholamban (PL).[2–9] On the other hand, the genes encoding ANF, β-myosin heavy chain, α-skeletal actin, for example, are found to be relatively upregulated during hypertrophy.[1,5,10,11] The nuclear mechanisms involved in coordinately regulating these cardiac genes during hypertrophy are fully unknown, although binding sites for several transcription factors, including serum response factor (SRF), transcription enhancer factor (TEF1), AP-1 (a heterodimer of jun/fos), and transcription factor Sp1, were shown to be important for activation of fetal cardiac genes in response to hypertrophy.[12–15]

As to the upstream signaling events, there is abundant evidence that the G_q-coupled phospholipase C-β, which produces Ca^{2+}-releasing inositol 1,4,5-triphosphate and protein kinase C activating 1,2-diacylglycerol, are linked to the receptor-mediated Ras and mitogen-activated (MAP) kinase pathways as transducers of hypertrophic signaling processes.[5,10,14,16] A very recent study of mice, transgenic for dominant-negative G_q-mediated signaling, convincingly demonstrated that receptor-mediated PLC-β is partially involved in pressure overload–induced hypertrophy *in vivo.*[17] The known details of the phosphatidylinositol signaling pathway were reviewed extensively by us.[18]

About the same time, there was a report of the discovery of a Ca^{2+}-calmodulin-dependent pathway via calcineurin in the myocardium during hypertrophy that activated the transcription factor NF-AT3 which, by cooperation with the transcription factor GATA4, induces fetal cardiac gene transcription.[19] In the latter study it was hypothesized that the Ca^{2+} release induced by inositol-1,4,5-triphosphate mainly causes calmodulin-calcineurin complex activation.

Most of the previous studies on nuclear factors concern upregulation of cardiac genes during hypertrophy.[10,12–15,19] To initiate studies on the nuclear factors involved in transcriptional downregulation of the SERCA2 gene during hypertrophy, we employed the model of cultured neonatal rat ventricular myocytes as used successfully by many other groups.[9,19–21] In this model, we were previously able to show that ET-1 is a strong inducer of hypertrophy by its increasing effect on the rate of [^{3}H]leucine incorporation in total protein and protein/DNA ratio.[21,22] Recently, we have isolated, characterized, and tested the activity (by liposome-based transfection) of an isolated SERCA2 promoter fragment as the first step in the search for the *cis*-acting elements and *trans*-acting factors responsible for downregulation of this gene during cardiomyocyte hypertrophy. That study[22] confirmed the general experience of other investigators[12–15,19] that the use of traditional methods (liposomes) for transfection of cardiomyocytes can be of value for studying promoter regulation. However, transfection efficiencies obtained by these methods are still extremely low, generally no more than one percent, and therefore not suitable for functional testing of the effects of overexpression of cardiac proteins. Other transfection methods, including cationic lipid/plasmid DNA complexes, incubations with "naked" plasmid DNA, and calcium phosphate ($CaPO_4$) precipitation, do not achieve higher efficiencies in cardiac cells.[23] A recent report on a new transfection system combined the convenience of plasmid DNA with the unique targeting properties of adenovirus vectors.[24] However, this "component system" gave variable results in our laboratory. In the mean time, it has been demonstrated by several authors that recombinant replication-defective human adenovirus can transfect primary cardiac cultures with close to 100% efficiency.[25–27] These authors could show alterations in cellular Ca^{2+} transients after infecting cardiomyocytes with adenovirus overexpressing SERCA2 (Ad.RSV.SERCA2a[27] or Ad.CMV.SERCA2a[26]) and PL (Ad.RSV.PL[25]). Since recombinant adenoviruses overexpressing cardiac Ca^{2+} handling proteins are time-consuming to prepare, there is a need for methods with high-efficiency transfection of cardiomyocytes with plasmid DNA. Recently, a new product for transfection Fugene6 (Boehringer), and a gold particle–based transfer technology, Helios Gene Gun (Biorad), have become available.[28,29] The Helios Gene Gun uses helium pressure to propel DNA-coated gold particles into cells (biolistics[30]), originally developed for *in vivo* gene transfer into somatic tissues of live animals. Elemental gold has been chosen for mammalian gene transfer because pure gold is chemically inert and does not produce cytotoxicity. The high density of gold also permits greater momentum allowing deeper penetration into target cells. Gene guns have also been used for plant cells and bacteria because these cells have a hard cell wall, whereas other methods require the production of protoplasts before gene introduction (reviewed by Yang and colleagues[28]). So far, several successful applications using the gene gun to transfect primary cultures have been reported.[28] However, to our knowledge no one has reported on adapting this method for use with primary cultures of neonatal rat cardiomyocytes. In this report, we present the first results with the Helios Gene Gun system in cardiomyocytes using a reporter plasmid harboring the β-galactosidase (β-Gal) gene under the control of the Rous sarcoma virus (RSV) promoter. We demonstrate that this method is applicable for transfecting beating rat cardiomyocytes and gives superior results when compared to other—traditional and new—transfection reagents.

METHODS

DNA Constructs

The SERCA2 5′ upstream regulatory region (1.9 kb, including 0.4 kb of the 5′ UTR of the mRNA) was obtained by screening of a rat genomic library with a probe derived by PCR based on published rat SERCA2 promoter sequences, as described in detail elsewhere.[22] After restriction mapping of the obtained genomic fragment (13 kb), the *Bam*HI-*Not*I fragment (1.9 kb) that was promoter-positive in Southern analysis was subcloned in a chloramphenicol acetyltransferase (CAT) reporter vector (pCAT-Basic, Promega) (FIG. 1). The RSV-β-Gal construct was a kind gift from our Department of Endocrinology and Reproduction. The DNAs were isolated and purified with the Wizard Midiprep Kit (Promega) in the study aimed at SERCA2 promoter regulation and purified with CsCl, Wizard, or Qiagen (Endofree Plasmid Maxi Kit; Qiagen, Westburg) for the study aimed at gene gun versus other vehicle-mediated gene transfer.

Transfection and Induction of Hypertrophy by ET-1

Rat neonatal ventricular cardiomyocytes were isolated as described previously,[20] preplated, and cultured in 20 cm^2 (7.5×10^4 cells/cm^2 (SERCA2 promoter regulation)), or 1.8 cm^2 dishes (1.5×10^5 cells/cm^2 (gene gun–mediated gene transfer)) up

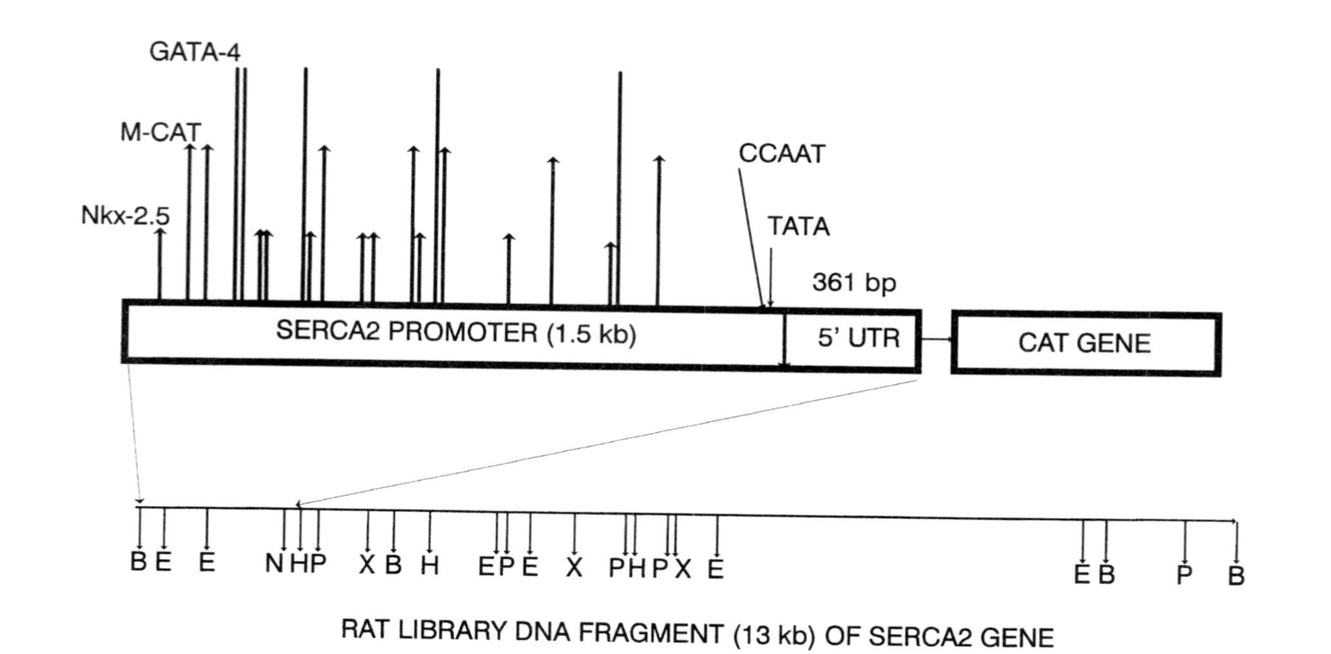

FIGURE 1. Graphical representation of the rat SERCA2 promoter-reporter gene construct. The putative CAAT and TATA sequences are indicated.[22] The rat SERCA2 promoter sequence was analyzed for putative transcription factor binding sites (GATA4, M-CAT, and Nkx2.5) with the Transfac database using the MatInspector program (*Top*). (*Bottom*) The obtained genomic DNA fragment with the locations of the *Bam*HI-*Not*I promoter positive region indicated. Abbreviations: B = *Bam*HI, E = *Eco*RI, H = *Hind*II, N = *Not*I, P = *Pst*I, X = *Xba*I.

to 24 h in DMEM/M199 (4:1) supplemented with 5% fetal calf serum and 5% horse serum (HS). Thereafter, the medium was changed to DMEM/M199 (4:1) with only 5% HS. After 64 h, the medium was changed to serum-free DMEM/M199. Transfection was performed in this serum-free medium by standard $CaPO_4$ (0.5–3 µg DNA per well, HEPES buffer, pH 7.05, overnight incubation), Fugene6, and DOTAP methodologies (according to instructions provided by Boehringer Mannheim, Germany) (Fugene6/DNA ratio: 1.5 µl/0.5 µg DNA or 3.6 µl/1.44 µg DNA) (DOTAP/DNA ratio: 15 µg/5 µg DNA, 18 h) or by gene gun biolistics (see below). Subsequently, cells were washed with serum-free DMEM/M199 (4:1) and fresh medium was added. After 3 h, ET-1 (10 nM) was added for 48 h to induce hypertrophy.[9,21,22]

Gene Gun–Mediated Biolistics Transfection

The most recent hand-held version of the pulse gene gun (Biorad), which uses helium gas–driven force to propel the gold particles into cultured cells, was employed. DNA capsules were 1.2-cm pieces of Tefzel® tubing inner-coated with gold particles and loaded with CsCl-purified DNA. These capsules were then inserted into gene gun cartridges, which hold 12 capsules, allowing 12 transfections per single loading. The cartridges were prepared according to the manufacturer's protocol with slight but essential modifications.[29] Briefly, 200 mg gold particles (0.6 µm diameter) were suspended and sonicated in 1 ml analytically pure (100% is essential) ethanol to facilitate the accurate determination of the amount of gold particles needed per preparation. The exact amount of gold needed (4 mg for 40 cartridges) was transferred to a new tube and dried. Gold particles, DNA, spermidine, and $CaCl_2$ were mixed as described by the manufacturer (Biorad manual), incubated for 10 minutes, centrifuged, washed twice with 100% ethanol, and dried. The DNA-coated particles were suspended in the appropriate amount of 100% ethanol containing 0.015 mg/ml polyvinyl pyrrolidone in a 10-ml glass vial. Thereafter, the solution was transferred into the Tefzel® tubing, which was already inserted into the tubing prep station, by attaching a syringe to the nitrogen inlet. The solution was carefully sucked in just before the O-ring. The solution was left for 10 min to let the gold settle, followed by removal of the ethanol using the still-attached syringe. Immediately thereafter, the tubing chamber was turned by hand and then automatically directed by the apparatus until rings of precipitation of gold particles around the tube became visible (most clearly at the beginning of the tubing). A nitrogen flow (0.5 ml/min) was then applied to dry the DNA-coated gold particles for 15 minutes. After visual examination of the tubing, the parts exhibiting evenly distributed DNA-coated gold particles were cut into 1.2-cm cartridges and stored at 4°C. Per shot 0.5 µg DNA was delivered, which was coated on 0.1 mg gold particles (DLR: 0.5, MLQ: 0.1). Loading of the cartridge was checked by dissociation of the DNA from the gold by adding 100 µl Tris-HCl (10 mM)/EDTA (1 mM) (pH 7.5) buffer to one cartridge followed by vigorous mixing and sonication. The optical density was determined and the concentration of the DNA calculated. On average, within one complete coating of tubing a standard deviation of less than 15% was obtained. A special delivery device on top of the gene gun was developed at our laboratory to specifically enable high efficiency bombardment of 3×10^5 cardiomyocytes in a 1.8-cm^2 well. Medium was first aspirated from the cells followed by immediate bombardment with the Helios Gene Gun system (Biorad) at 100 psi helium pressure, then new serum-free medium was carefully layered back on the cells.

Northern Blotting

Total RNA was isolated by the guanidinium isothiocyanate method, quantified by spectrometry, separated on 1% denaturing formaldehyde-agarose gels, and blotted onto Hybond (Amersham). Probes described below were labeled by random priming using [α-^{32}P]dCTP (Amersham). The CAT probe was excised from the CAT reporter plasmid.[22] The glyceraldehyde phosphate dehydrogenase (GAPDH), PL, and ANF probes were developed by RT-PCR on rat heart RNA based on published sequences. A SERCA2 cDNA (RHCa-117) was a kind gift from Lompre.[31] Hybridization was performed as described.[22] The hybridization signal was quantified by the Molecular Imager (Biorad).

Analysis of β-Gal Gene Expression

Quantification of the β-Gal protein was performed by ELISA according to the manufacturer's protocol (Boehringer Mannheim). Histochemical staining of β-Gal protein was performed overnight according to standard protocols. After staining, cells were refixed and photographed. Cells staining positive for β-Gal were counted per well. Transfection efficiencies were based on this visual examination, as well as by comparing the obtained ELISA results to the amount of β-Gal measured (by ELISA) after 100% infection of cardiomyocytes with an adenovirus encoding β-Gal under the control of a Cowpea Mosaic virus promoter (results not shown).

Statistical Analysis

Significance was set at $p < 0.05$, Student-Newman-Keuls test, for at least four independent experiments.

RESULTS

Changes in Gene Expression in Cardiomyocytes Stimulated by ET-1

Previously, we demonstrated that 24 to 48 h ET-1 stimulation of serum-free cultured cardiomyocytes led to an increase of the rate of protein synthesis and protein/DNA mass ratio, both reminiscent of hypertrophy.[9,21,22] To determine whether ET-1–induced changes in cardiac gene expression are characteristic of hypertrophy and heart failure *in vivo*, we measured the changes in expression of ANF, SERCA2, and PL relative to GAPDH (TABLE 1). The increase in GAPDH mRNA is in accordance with the general increase of total RNA content seen 48 h after stimulation with ET-1.[22] As expected, ANF and SERCA2 (including PL) expression were respectively up- and downregulated. However, it should be noted that the absolute amounts of PL and SERCA2 mRNA levels, i.e., uncorrected for GAPDH levels, did not change significantly when compared to control.

Analysis of Transcriptional Regulation of the SERCA2 Gene

Our observation that the SERCA2 gene was downregulated in hypertrophied cardiomyocytes is consistent with the numerous previous reports (including our own

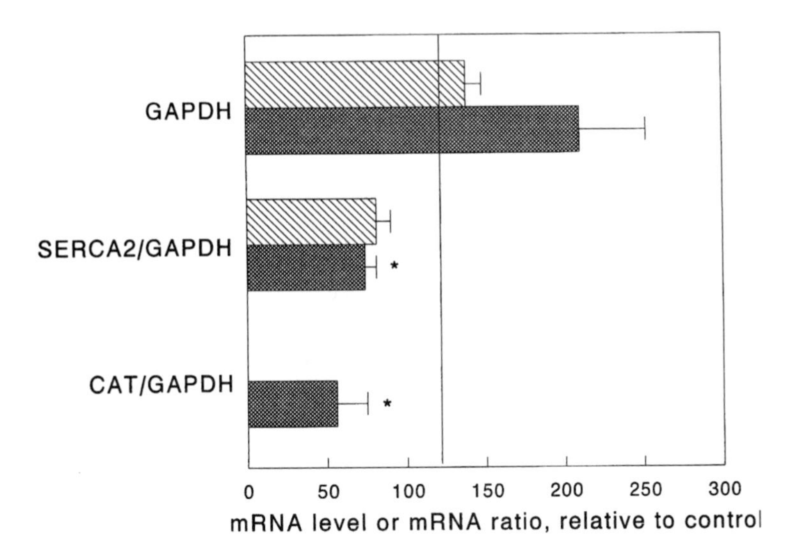

FIGURE 2. Transcriptional regulation of SERCA2 gene in rat cardiomyocytes. The $CATSpro_{1.9}$ DNA construct was transfected into rat cardiomyocytes using DOTAP and hypertrophy was induced by stimulation of the cells with 10^{-8} M ET-1 for 48 h. Subsequently, mRNA levels were quantified as described in *Methods*. Hybridization signals are represented relative to unstimulated control cells for GAPDH mRNA, while the (endogenous) SERCA2 and CAT mRNA signals were first corrected for increase in total RNA by expressing the ratio of these mRNAs relative to GAPDH mRNA before calculating the increase or decrease in expression relative to unstimulated control. GAPDH and SERCA2 expression are assessed in untransfected (*striped bars*) versus transfected cardiomyocytes (*cross-hatched bars*). Data represent mean ± SEM for 4–8 independent experiments. $^{*}p < 0.05$.

reports[32]) on reduced Ca^{2+} pump activity in the hypertrophied (failing) human and animal heart *in vivo* (reviews[1–4]). To perform detailed analysis of SERCA2 promoter regulation and identify *cis*-regulatory elements involved, a pure culture of cardiomyocytes (e.g., free of coronary smooth muscle cells) expressing the splice variant SERCA2a[3] is essential. Furthermore, we have isolated a genomic fragment of the SERCA2 gene containing 1.5 kb of the promoter region and 0.4 kb of the 5′ UTR, which was subcloned into the CAT reporter plasmid (nucleotide sequences were published by van Heugten and colleagues[22]). The sequence of this promoter was analyzed with the Transfac database using the MatInspector program[33] to detect any putative recognition sites for transcription factors, which might be important for the regulation of the SERCA2 promoter. FIGURE 1 represents the SERCA2 promoter-reporter gene construct with indicated recognition sites of putative interacting transcription factors. Indeed many transcription factors (Nkx-2.5, M-CAT, and GATA-4) known to be important for cardiac development and/or hypertrophic responses have putative recognition sites in this promoter.[34–36] To analyze the response of this promoter fragment, we transfected the reporter plasmid into cardiomyocytes that were subsequently stimulated by ET-1 to become hypertrophied. FIGURE 2 illustrates that, also in this separate series of experiments, ET-1 induces a decrease of SERCA2/GAPDH mRNA ratio and an increase in GAPDH mRNA level. Although only a mi-

TABLE 1. Changes in gene expression in cardiomyocytes stimulated by ET-1 for 48 h

	mRNA Level (%)	mRNA Ratio (%)
GAPDH mRNA	170 ± 18	
ANF/GAPDH		247 ± 48
PL/GAPDH		51 ± 8
SERCA2/GAPDH		74 ± 7

Note: Hybridization signals are represented relative to unstimulated control cells for GAPDH mRNA, while the ANF, PL, and SERCA2 signals were first corrected for increase in total RNA by expressing the ratio relative to GAPDH mRNA before calculating the increase or decrease in expression relative to unstimulated control. Data represent mean ± SEM for at least four independent experiments. All values are significantly different from 100%.

nority of cells are transfected by the SERCA2 promoter-reporter plasmid pCAT-$Spro_{1.9}$, the latter result proves that introduction of the SERCA2 promoter fragment did not influence endogenous GAPDH and SERCA2 gene expression. Transfection of pCAT-$Spro_{1.9}$ to cultured cardiomyocytes followed by 48 h of hypertrophy induction with 10^{-8} M ET-1 resulted in decreased reporter CAT mRNA level when compared to unstimulated transfected cells. Absolute CAT mRNA levels (i.e., uncorrected for GAPDH data) remained unchanged under these hypertrophic conditions when compared to unstimulated cardiomyocytes.

Gene Gun–Mediated Biolistic Transfection

The results in TABLE 1 and FIGURE 2 demonstrate that, as expected, it is possible to investigate SERCA2 promoter regulation in neonatal cardiomyocytes using "traditional" transfection methods. However, these methods (liposome- and $CaPO_4$-based methods) are known to have very low transfection efficiencies (less than 1%, see below). Firstly, studying promoters with very low activities may be difficult using these transfection methods. Secondly, high transfection efficiencies are required to study physiological changes of, e.g., overexpressed SERCA2 gene expression or PL synthesis disabled by antisense oligonucleotides, by exogenously introduced DNA constructs in these cardiomyocytes. Therefore, we set out to develop a biolistic technology using the recently commercially available Helios Gene Gun for *in situ* bombardment of tissue. We optimized the biolistics transfection for use with a primary culture of cardiomyocytes and analyzed its efficacy by using a plasmid containing the β-Gal reporter under control of the RSV promoter. Bombarded into the cells was 0.5 μg of DNA coated onto 0.1 mg gold particles (0.6 μm diameter). Forty eight hours after bombardment, cells were stained for β-Gal and the cellular morphology examined (FIG. 3). Transfection efficiencies of maximally up to 10% of the bombarded cells were obtained. Although we occasionally observe some cell death in the center of the bombarded well, this is usually very limited, as checked by the MTT (3-[4,5-dimethylthiazol-2-yl]-2,5-diphenyl tetrazolium bizomid (Sigma) test assay for viable cells) (unpublished results). Next, we examined β-Gal expression in bombarded cells quantitatively by ELISA and compared these results with other traditional transfection reagents (note that in the traditional methods the same low amount of 0.5 μg DNA was also used). FIGURE 4 depicts the comparison of transfec-

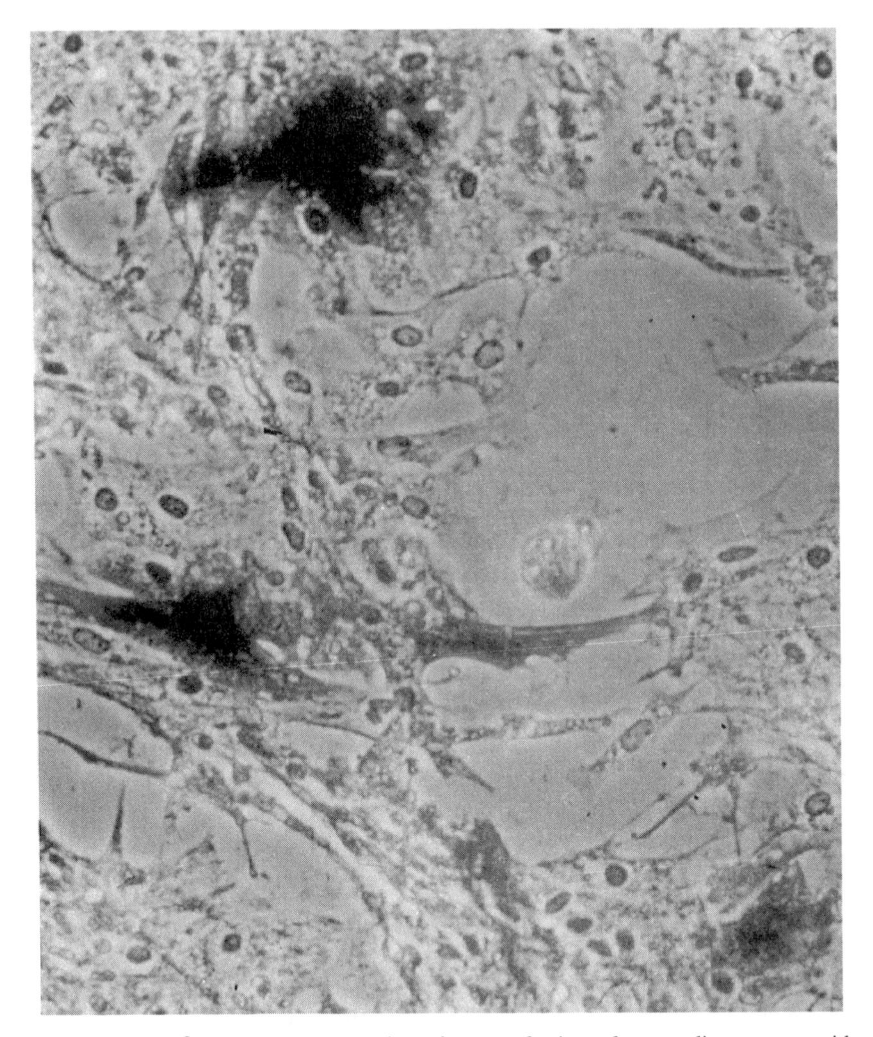

FIGURE 3. β-Gal protein expression after transfection of rat cardiomyocytes with RSV-β-Gal plasmid using gene gun biolistics. Cardiomyocytes were transfected with the biolistic transfection methodology using the RSV-β-Gal plasmid. After 48 h cells were fixed and stained histochemically for β-galactosidase activity (dark staining) to analyze the efficacy of transfection. Up to 10% of the cells are transfected using the gene gun and no gross morphology changes could be observed. Magnification = 200×.

tion methods using the RSV β-Gal DNA construct as measured by ELISA. It is clear that the biolistic method of transfection gives superior results compared to the traditional methods. Using more DNA for transfections with Fugene6 and $CaPO_4$ raises the efficiencies obtained with these methods for only the $CaPO_4$ method, although the amount of β-Gal measured after $CaPO_4$ transfection is still considerably lower compared to the biolistics results (FIG. 4). Recently, Boerhinger, the manufacturer of

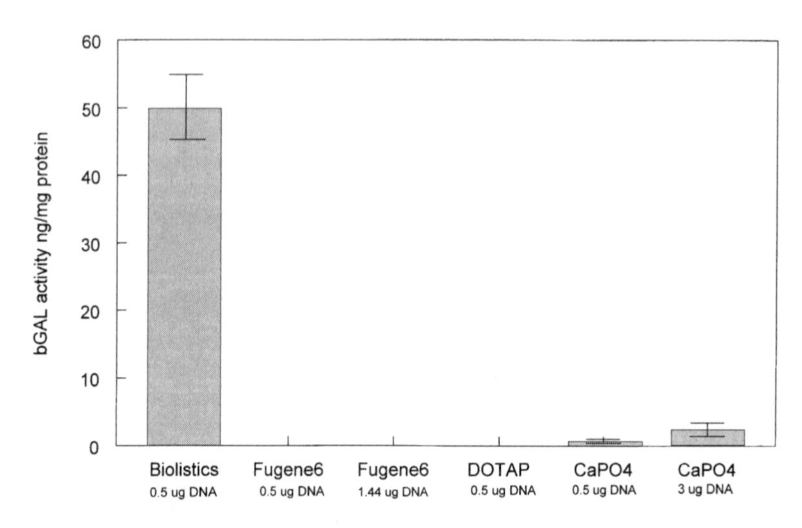

FIGURE 4. Comparison of gene gun versus other vehicle-mediated gene transfer methodologies. In all experiments the same plasmid (RSV-β-Gal) was used. Forty eight hours after transfection cells are homogenized and protein expression measured by ELISA. Data are represented as ng β-Gal/mg protein content±SEM. Cells were subjected to biolistic bombardment using 0.1 mg of gold particles coated with 0.5 μg of DNA (biolistics), or transfected using Fugene6, DOTAP, or $CaPO_4$. The amount of DNA used per 1.8 cm^2 well in the transfection experiments is indicated.

Fugene6, reported that, using mouse cardiomyocytes, approximately 1% of the cells could be transfected. The new Fugene6 transfection reagent did not give any measurable transfection in our test conditions (FIG. 4).

DISCUSSION

We isolated and determined the sequence of the rat SERCA2 gene 5′-regulatory region and analyzed its function in the presence or absence of a hypertrophy inducing stimulus (ET-1). This promoter region appears to contain several recognition sites for cardiac myogenic regulatory factors, e.g., Nkx-2.5, M-CAT, and GATA-4, which could be involved in the observed downregulation of transcription induced by ET-1 (FIGS. 1 and 2). Transfection of the SERCA2 promoter fragment in cultured cardiomyocytes did not change normal downregulation of the endogenous SERCA2 mRNA level during hypertrophy, showing transcription factors not becoming limited by the introduced SERCA2 promoter fragment. A 1.5 kb 5′ regulatory region together with 360 bp 5′ UTR dictated downregulation of a reporter gene similar to that observed for the SERCA2 mRNA (FIG. 2). This suggests that (most) *cis*-acting elements responsible for hypertrophy-associated downregulation of SERCA2 expression are confined to this regulatory region. Expression of the Ca^{2+} pump during hypertrophy was only downregulated when compared to (increased levels of) GAPDH mRNA, but absolute SERCA2 mRNA amounts remained unchanged. Therefore, the downregulation of the SERCA2 promoter may be interpreted as not responding to the general increase in transcription that accompanies hypertrophy. Alterations in mRNA stability could also be an additional regulator of mRNA levels as demonstrated by actinomycin-D mRNA stability assays of cardiomyocytes, treated with phorbol-12-myristate-13-acetate (PMA) to induce hypertrophy, which revealed a marked destabilization of the SERCA2 transcript by PMA treatment.[38] We showed previously that during ET-1 stimulation only PKC-ε becomes redistributed intracellularly, whereas PMA caused redistribution of PKC-α, ε, and δ.[39] Therefore, PMA might act at more cellular sites compared to the physiological stimulus ET-1.

Recently Baker and coworkers,[40] using the rabbit SERCA2 promoter, demonstrated that an E/AT Box located at −1115 bp (corresponding to −1510 in the rat SERCA2 promoter[22,40]) was important for muscle-specific activation of the SERCA2 gene. However, when comparing the sequences of the rat and rabbit SERCA2 promoters it is clear that this E/AT box is not conserved in the rat SERCA2 gene promoter, making this box a less likely candidate for transcriptional regulation of the rat promoter.[22] Whether this E/AT box is important in the response to hypertrophic stimuli has not been investigated so far in the rabbit SERCA2 promoter.

The homology regions previously identified by comparing the rat promoter sequence with the human and rabbit promoter sequences[22] (nt −1520 to −1310, and nt −220 to +363 of the rat sequence) were recently also identified in the mouse SERCA2 promoter[41] (and personal communication, T.D. Reed). Transgenic mice harboring different parts of the mouse SERCA2 promoter clearly demonstrate an important role for these homology regions[41] (and personal communication, T.D. Reed). Future studies will include the role of the homology regions in the transcriptional regulation of the rat SERCA2 promoter and the preparation of deletion constructs of the rat SERCA2 promoter to elucidate the importance of the identified putative transcription factor binding sites.

In this paper we also present the first results using the gene gun technology for transient transfection of cardiomyocytes with a RSV-β-Gal construct. Using helium pressure to propel DNA-coated gold beads into the cardiomyocytes is extremely suitable for directly testing promoter/reporter gene DNA constructs since the transfection efficiency appears to be appreciably higher compared to more traditional transfection methods (FIG. 4). A transfection efficiency of approximately 10% of the cells in the bombarded area can be maximally achieved. This high transfection efficiency opens the possibility to test DNA constructs aimed at overexpressing or oligonucleotide antisense inhibition of specific cardiac Ca^{2+} handling proteins (e.g., SR-Ca^{2+} pump or PL). Up to now this was only feasible using recombinant adenoviruses.[25–27] Several parameters had to be optimized before these results were obtained. The amount of gold used per shot is limited since too much gold bombarded into the cells causes extensive cell damage in the center of the well. The newly developed diffusion screen (Biorad) prevents cell damage in the center of the bombarded area enabling possibly higher amounts of gold to be used. The helium pressure used is relatively low compared to applications using other cell types, due to the fragility of the cardiomyocytes. The most critical factor in achieving reproducible results turned out to be the production of the cartridges, we had to adapt the standard procedure on some essential points (see *Methods*) and used CsCl-purified DNA, which gave remarkably better results compared to DNA purified with the Wizard or Qiagen kits (results not shown).

Taken together, we demonstrate for the first time that the hand-held gene gun is a quick and reliable method to achieve high transfection efficiencies with primary rat neonatal cardiomyocytes as target cells. Experiments on the 5′-flanking regions of SERCA2 and PL genes using the gene gun transfection methodology are currently in progress.

REFERENCES

1. SWYNGHEDAUW, B. 1986. Developmental and functional adaptation of contractile proteins in cardiac and skeletal muscles. Physiol. Rev. **66:** 710–771.
2. MORGAN, J.P., R.E. ERNY, P.D. ALLEN, W. GROSSMAN & J.K. GWATHMEY. 1990. Abnormal intracellular Ca^{2+} handling. A major cause of systolic and diastolic dysfunction in ventricular myocardium from patients with heart failure. Circulation **81** (suppl. III)**:** 21–32.
3. ARAI, M., H. MATSUI & M. PERIASAMY. 1994. Sarcoplasmic reticulum gene expression in cardiac hypertrophy and heart failure. Circ. Res. **74:** 555–564.
4. HASENFUSS, G., M. MEYER, W. SCHILLINGER, M. PREUSS, B. PRISKE & H. JUST. 1997. Calcium handling proteins in the failing human heart. Basic Res. Cardiol. **92** (suppl 1)**:** 87–93.
5. VAN HEUGTEN, H.A.A. & J.M.J. LAMERS. 1997. Changes in cardiac phenotype in hypertrophy and failure: from receptor to gene. Heart Failure Rev. **2:** 95–106.
6. FLESCH, M., R.H.G. SCHWINGER, P. SCHNABEL, F. SCHIFFER, I. VAN GELDER, U. BAVENDIEK, M. SÜDKAMP, F. KUHN-REGNIER & M. BÖHM. 1996. Sarcoplasmic reticulum Ca^{2+}-ATPase and phospholamban mRNA and protein levels in end-stage heart failure due to ischemic or dilated cardiomyopathy. J. Mol. Med. **74:** 321–332.
7. ZARAIN-HERZBERG, A., N. AFZAL, V. ELIMBAN & N. S. DHALLA. 1996. Decreased expression of sarcoplasmic reticulum Ca^{2+} pump ATPase in congestive heart failure due to myocardial infarction. Mol. Cell. Biochem. **163/164:** 285–290.
8. LINCK, B., P. BOKNIK, T. ESCHENHAGEN, F.U. MÜLLER, J. NEUMANN, M. NOSE, L.R. JONES, W. SCHMITZ & H. SCHOLZ. 1996. Messenger RNA expression and immunological quantification of phospholamban and SR-Ca^{2+}-ATPase in failing and nonfailing human hearts. Cardiovasc. Res. **31:** 625–632.
9. VAN HEUGTEN, H.A.A., H.W. DE JONGE, M.A. GOEDBLOED, K. BEZSTAROSTI, H.S. SHARMA, P.D. VERDOUW & J.M.J. LAMERS. 1995. Intracellular signaling and genetic reprogramming during development of hypertrophy in cultured cardiomyocytes. *In* Heart Hypertrophy and Failure. N.S. Dhalla, G.N. Pierce, V.N. Panagia & L. Beamish, Eds.: 79–92.
10. KOMURO, I. & Y. YAZAKI. 1993. Control of cardiac gene expression by mechanical stress. Ann. Rev. Physiol. **55:** 55–75.
11. SCHWARTZ, K., L. CARNER, J-J. MERCADIER, A-M. LOMPRE & K.R. BOHELER. 1993. Molecular phenotype of the hypertrophied and failing myocardium. Circulation **87:** VII5–VII10
12. KOVACIC-MILIVOJEVIZ, B., V.S.H. WONG & D.G. GARDNER. 1996. Selective regulation of the atrial natriuretic peptide gene by individual components of the activatorprotein-1 complex. Endocrinology **137:** 1108–1117.
13. KARNS, L.R., K. KARIYA & P.C. SIMPSON. 1995. M-CAT, CarG, and Sp1 elements are required for α-adrenergic induction of the skeletal α-actin promoter during cardiac myocyte hypertrophy. J. Biol. Chem. **270:** 410–417.
14. SADOSHIMA, J. & S. IZUMO. 1993. Signal transduction pathways of angiotensin II-induced c-fos gene expression in cardiac myocytes *in vitro*. Circ. Res. **73:** 424–438.
15. KARIYA, K., L.R. KARNS & P.C. SIMPSON. 1994. An enhancer core element mediates stimulation of the rat α-myosin heavy chain promoter by an α_1-adrenergic agonist and activated protein kinase C in hypertrophy of cardiac myocytes. J. Biol. Chem. **269:** 3775–3782.

16. FORCE, T., C.M. POMBO, J.A. AVRUCH, J.V. BONVENTRE & J.M. KYRIAKIS. 1996. Stress-activated kinases in cardiovascular disease Circ. Res. **78:** 947–953.
17. AKHTER, S.A., L.M. LUTTRELL, H.A. ROCKMAN, G. IACCARINO, R.J. LEFKOWITZ & W.J. KOCH. 1998. Targeting the receptor-G_q interface to inhibit *in vivo* pressure overload myocardial hypertrophy. Science **280:** 574–577.
18. DE JONGE, G.W., H.A.A. VAN HEUGTEN & J.M.J. LAMERS. 1995. Review. Signal transduction by the phosphatidyl-inositol cycle in myocardium. J. Mol. Cell. Cardiol. **27:** 93–106.
19. MOLKENTIN, J.D., J-R. LU, C.L. ANTOS, B. MARKHAM, J. RICHARDSON, J. ROBBINS, S.R. GRANT & E.N. OLSON. 1998. A calcineurin-dependent transcriptional pathway for cardiac hypertrophy. Cell **93:** 215–228.
20. VAN HEUGTEN, H.A.A., K. BEZSTAROSTI, D.H.W. DEKKERS & J.M.J. LAMERS. 1994. Homologous desensitization of the endothelin-1 receptor evoked phosphoinositide response in cultured neonatal rat cardiomyocytes. J. Mol Cell. Cardiol. **25:** 41–52.
21. VAN HEUGTEN, H.A.A., H.W. DE JONGE, K. BEZSTAROSTI, H.S. SHARMA, P.D. VERDOUW & J.M.J. LAMERS. 1995. Intracellular signalling and genetic reprogramming during agonist-induced hypertrophy of cardiomyocytes. Ann. N.Y. Acad. Sci. **752:** 343–352.
22. VAN HEUGTEN, H.A.A., M.C. VAN SETTEN, K. EIZEMA, P.D. VERDOUW & J.M.J. LAMERS. 1998. Sarcoplasmic reticulum Ca^{2+} ATPase promoter activity during endothelin-1 induced hypertrophy of cultured rat cardiomyocytes. Cardiovasc. Res. **37:** 503–514.
23. ANTIN, P.B., J.H. MAR & C.P. ORDAHL. 1988. Single cell analysis of transfected gene expression in primary heart cell cultures containing multiple cell types. Biotechnology **6:** 630–648.
24. KOHOUT, T.A., J.J. O'BRIAN, S.T. GAA, W.J. LEDERER & T.B. ROGERS. 1996. Novel adenovirus component system that transfects cultured cardiac cells with high efficiency. Circ. Res. **78:** 971–977.
25. HAJJAR, R.J., U. SCHMIDT, J.X. KANG, T. MATSUI & A. ROSENZWEIG. 1997. Adenovirus gene transfer of phospholamban in isolated rat cardiomyocytes. Rescue effects by concomitant gene transfer of sarcoplasmic reticulum Ca^{2+}ATPase. Circ. Res. **81:** 145–153.
26. MEYER, M. & W.H. DILLMANN. 1998. Sarcoplasmic Ca^{2+}ATPase overexpressing by adenovirus mediated gene transfer and in transgenic mice. Cardiovasc. Res. **37:** 360–366.
27. HAJJAR, R.J., J.X. KANG, J.K. GWATHMEY & A. ROSENZWEIG. 1997. Physiological effects of adenoviral gene transfer of sarcoplasmic reticulum Ca^{2+}ATPase in isolated rat myocytes. Circulation **95:** 423–429.
28. YANG, N-S., W.H. SUN & D. MCCABE. 1996. Developing particle-mediated gene-transfer technology for research into gene therapy of cancer. Mol. Med. Today. Nov. 476–481.
29. YOSHIDA, Y. E. KOBAYASHI, H. ENDO, T. HAMAMOTO, T. YAMANAKA, A. FUJIMURA & Y. KAGAWA. 1997. Introduction of DNA into rat liver with a hand-held Gene Gun: Distribution of the expressed enzyme, [^{32}P]DNA, and Ca^{2+} flux. Biochem. Biophys. Res. Commun. **234:** 695–700.
30. SANFORD, J.C. 1988. The biolistic process. Trends Biotechnol. **6:** 299–302.
31. LOMPRE, A-M., D. DE LA BASTIE, K.R. BOHELER & K. SCHWARTZ. 1989. Characterization and expression of the rat sarcoplasmic reticulum Ca^{2+}ATPase mRNA. FEBS Lett. **249:** 35–41.
32. LAMERS, J.M.J. & J.T. STINIS. 1979. Defective Ca^{2+} pump in the sarcoplasmic reticulum of the hypertrophied rabbit heart. Life Sci. **24:** 2313–2320.
33. QUANDT, K., K. FRECH, H. KAVAS, E. WINGENDER & T. WERNER. 1995. MatInd and MatInspector—new, fast and versatile tools for detection of consensus matches in nucleotide sequence data. Nucl. Acids Res. **23:** 4878–4884.
34. VAN BILSEN, M. & K.R. CHIEN. 1993. Growth and hypertrophy of the heart: towards an understanding of cardiac specific and inducible gene expression. Cardiovasc. Res. **27:** 1140–1149.

35. MOLKENTIN, J.D. & E.N. OLSON. 1997. GATA4: A novel transcriptional regulator of cardiac hypertrophy? Circulation **96:** 3833–3835.
36. SANELLO, R.C., J.M. MAR & C.P. ORDAHL. 1991. Characterization of a promoter element required for transcription in myocardial cells. J. Biol. Chem. **266:** 3309–3316.
37. EVANS, T. 1997 Regulation of cardiac gene expression by GATA-4/5/6. Trends Cardiovasc. Med. **7:** 75–83.
38. QI, M., J.W. BASSANI, D.M. BERS & A.M. SAMAREL. 1996. Phorbol 12-myristate 13-acetate alters SR Ca(2+)-ATPase gene expression in cultured neonatal rat heart cells. Am. J. Physiol. **271** (3Pt2)**:** H1031–1039.
39. ESKILDSEN, Y.E.G., K. BEZSTAROSTI, D.H.W. DEKKERS, H.A.A. VAN HEUGTEN & J.M.J. LAMERS. 1997. Cross-talk between receptor-mediated phospholipase C-β and D via protein kinase C as intracellular signal possibly leading to hypertrophy in serum-free cultured cardiomyocytes. J. Mol. Cell. Cardiol. **29:** 2545–2559.
40. BAKER, D.L., V. DAVE, T. REED, S. MISRA & M. PERIASAMY. 1998. A novel E box/AT-rich element is required for muscle-specific expression of the sarcoplasmic reticulum Ca^{2+}-ATPase (SERCA2) gene. Nucl. Acids Res. **26:** 1092-1098.
41. REED, T.D., D. BAKER, R. BLOUGH & M. PERIASAMY. 1998. Characterization of the mouse cardiac/slow-twitch muscle sarco(endo)plasmic reticulum Ca^{2+}-ATPase (SERCA2) promoter. *In* Proceedings of Keystone Symposium on Molecular Biology of the Cardiovascular System: 62. Steamboat Springs, Colorado, March 28–April 3, 1998.

Myocardial Response to Stress in Cardiac Hypertrophy and Heart Failure:

Effect of Antihypertensive Drugs[a]

SUBHA SEN

Department of Molecular Cardiology, The Lerner Research Institute, The Cleveland Clinic Foundation, 9500 Euclid Avenue, Cleveland, Ohio 44195, USA

ABSTRACT: The myocardium's response to increased stress or load is not stereotyped. Differences have been observed in the heart's molecular composition and performance characteristics when exposed to stress. Myosin isoforms gradually change during development of hypertrophy, whereas collagen levels change only during the chronic phase of hypertrophy. Cardiac hypertrophy can regress if treated with antihypertensive drugs, but the myocardium of the post-hypertrophic heart no longer has the same composition as it did before hypertrophy. In rat studies of the effects of antihypertensive drugs on cardiac functional reserve, captopril showed a regression of hypertrophy associated with a lower baseline stroke volume and, after dobutamine stress, a dose-dependent rise in stroke volume. In untreated rates captopril showed no change in stroke volume. In hydralazine-treated rats, there was no change in reserve after dobutamine stress, whereas propranolol treatment resulted in partial regression and a slight change in stroke volume. Overall, our data suggests that development of hypertension and hypertrophy plays a role in changes in the molecular structure of the myocardium, especially during the chronic phase of hypertrophy and heart failure. This complex process cannot be explained by one factor but involves a combination of factors. Identification of each factor would be of importance for the development of appropriate therapeutic agents.

INTRODUCTION

The myocardium's response to increased stress or load is not stereotyped. Marked differences in the heart's biochemical composition, anatomical changes, and performance characteristics as a result of exposure to stress have been reported.[1–4] Hypertrophied ventricles, caused by pressure overload, contain collagen and myosin in disproportionate amounts; as a consequence, ventricular performance is compromised.[1] Sen and colleagues[5,6] have shown that hypertrophy can regress if treated with antihypertensive drugs but that the myocardium of the post-hypertrophic heart does not have the same composition as it did before hypertrophy. Reversal of hypertrophy results in smaller hearts with increased hydroxyproline concentrations due to

[a]This study supported in part by grant R01 HL27838 from the National Institutes of Health to S. Sen.

[b]Address correspondence to: Subha Sen, Ph.D., D.Sc., Department of Molecular Cardiology/FF40, The Cleveland Clinic Foundation, 9500 Euclid Avenue, Cleveland, Ohio 44195, USA; Telephone: 216/444-2056; Fax: 216/444-9263; E-mail: sens@cesmtp.ccf.org

alpha-methyldopa treatment, whereas treatment with the converting enzyme inhibitor captopril both reverses hypertrophy and reduces the amount of collagen.[5,6] Sen and colleagues[7] have demonstrated that just controlling hypertension is not sufficient to reverse hypertrophy. Identification of factors modulating structural responses of the heart will probably lead to more precise therapy, especially functional efficiency when exposed to external stress.[8] This article describes the effects that different antihypertensive drugs (which return blood pressure to normotensive levels) have on the regression of cardiac hypertrophy and on their effects on the molecular composition of the heart after dobutamine challenge.

METHODS

For this hypertrophy regression study, we used male spontaneously hypertensive rats (SHRs, $N = 12$) and male age-matched Wistar-Kyoto rats (WKYs, $N = 12$), all obtained from Taconic Farms (Germantown, NY). Each study group consisted of at least five rats, each 32 weeks old. All animals were kept under the same conditions and fed Purina Rat Chow ad libitum. For antihypertensive treatment, the rats were treated for 13 weeks with either the angiotensin-converting enzyme (ACE) inhibitors captopril (50 mg/kg/day) or hydralazine (80 mg/kg/day) or the beta-blocker propranolol (80 mg/kg/day). The drugs were given in drinking water. Arterial blood pressure was regularly measured every other week using the tail-cuff method described by Sen and colleagues.[5] At the end of the treatment period, an echocardiogram was done on both treated and control rats. The echocardiography was done in the Department of Cardiology of our institution. Rats were killed by pentobarbital anesthesia. Their hearts were excised and drained of blood. The ventricles were blotted dry and stored frozen in liquid nitrogen and transferred to a –80°C freezer until use. All animal experiments were done following the National Institutes of Health guidelines.

Determination of Myosin Isoforms

Myosin was extracted from approximately 300 mg of the ventricle, as described previously.[9] The tissue was homogenized in a saline buffer and centrifuged at 3,000 rpm. The supernatant was discarded and the pellet washed again in phosphate-buffered saline. The pellet was resuspended in 3 ml of extraction solution containing 100 mM sodium pyrophosphate, 5 mM EGTA, and 5 mM dithiothreitol, pH 8.6. After centrifuging, the supernatant pellet was collected and mixed with an equal volume of ice-cold glycerol and stored at 20°C.

Polyacrylamide gels were prepared following the method described previously.[9] Polymerization was initiated by adding 35 µl of freshly prepared ammonium persulfate. The gels used were 9 cm long and 5 mm in internal diameter. Electrophoresis was carried out in a Pharmacia gel electrophoresis apparatus. The electrophoresis buffer contained 20 nM sodium pyrophosphate and 10% glycerol (vol/vol), pH 8.8, at 4°C. The buffer was recirculated during the run by pumping it from the lower to the upper reservoir. The temperature of the electrophoresis was maintained at 2°C in a refrigeration unit. A 60-min pre-run was carried out before myosin was applied to the gel using a current of 2 mA per gel. Myosin (2 µl) in glycerol was loaded directly on top of the gel. The current of 2 mA per gel was maintained for 5 h; then the gels were run for 18 h under a constant voltage of 124 V. The gels were stained with Coomassie brilliant blue solution. The gels were then de-stained in a 7% acetic acid and 30% methanol solution and quantified by densitometric scanning of the gels, using a Quick Scan R&D densitometer from Helena Laboratories.[9]

Determination of Hydroxyproline

The ventricular collagen was quantified from the hydroxyproline content, which was determined by using a modified method of Bergman and Loxley.[10] All tissue samples were taken from the same area of the ventricular wall.[7] The myocardial tissue was homogenized and hydrolyzed with 6 N HCl at 110°C for 24 h under vacuum. Samples were oxidized using chloramine T, and the amount of hydroxyproline was quantified by adding Ehrlich's reagent.[10] A conversion factor of 8.2 was used to convert hydroxyproline to collagen.

Systolic function was evaluated by dobutamine stress echocardiography under pentobarbital anesthesia. Cardiac stress was assessed using a Toshiba Power Vision SHA 380 with a 7-MHz transducer (frame rate up to 168 frames per second) to assess the ability of the dobutamine stress echocardiography to depict changes of cardiac performance under stress. Rats were imaged at the baseline and immediately after administration of dobutamine. Echocardiography was performed in the facilities of the Department of Cardiology at our institution.

RESULTS AND DISCUSSION

Antihypertensive Therapy in Myosin Isoform

Several important aspects associated with the left ventricular hypertrophy (LVH) of hypertension are still not clearly understood, namely, the relationship between the development or regression of myocardial hypertrophy and the changes in biochemical composition of the myocardium, and the relation of both of these elements to cardiac function. Volume-overload hypertrophy is reported to be associated with qualitative changes in cardiac function, particularly changes in the intrinsic mechanical property of cardiac contractility.[13] The development of hypertrophy in rats has also been shown to be accompanied by a decline in maximum velocity of cardiac muscle shortening (V_{max}). Such a decline in V_{max} correlates with the decrease in ATPase activity of myosin.[12,13] It is believed that a reduction in V_{max} is possibly due to a shift of cardiac myosin isoform from a faster migrating V_1 with high ATPase activity as characterized by polyacrylamide gel toward the V_3 form that migrates more slowly, containing low ATPase activity.[14] It has been established that the changes in myosin isoform are expressed as the cellular regulation of myosin biosynthesis. These changes depend on two independent genes that code for different types of myosin—the alpha and beta heavy chains. V_1 and V_3 are the two homodimer phenotypes of the gene, and V_2 is the mixture of a heterodimer phenotype involving both genes.[15,16] We have shown that in renal hypertensive rats, there is a shift from the V_1 to the V_3 type when hypertrophy persisted during hypertension. This shifting of V_1 and V_3 can be reversed to the normal distribution pattern either by antihypertensive therapy with the ACE-inhibitor captopril or by dietary sodium

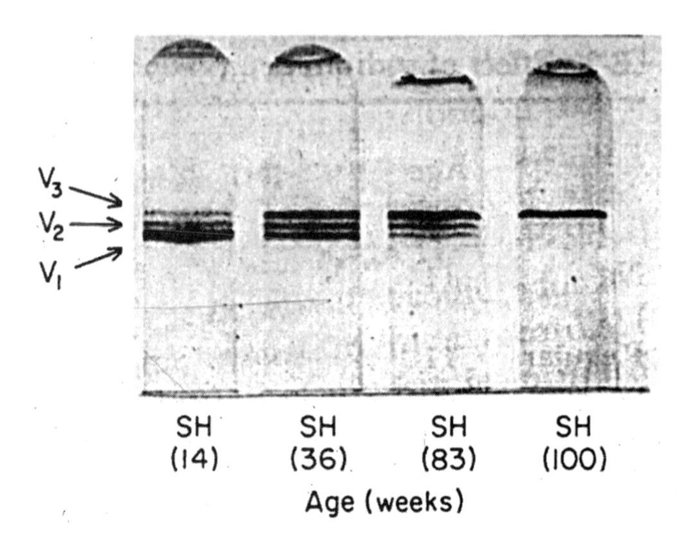

FIGURE 1. Changes in myosin isoform during development of hypertrophy in SHRs. Levels of the V_1 type of myosin isoform decreased gradually from the acute phase of hypertrophy to the chronic phase, whereupon levels of V_3 rose, becoming 100% V_3 during the transition to heart failure.

restriction.[9] The mechanism by which antihypertensive therapy can modulate the shifting of V_1 to V_3, or vice versa, remains unknown.

FIGURE 1 shows the changes in myosin isoforms during development of hypertrophy and hypertension and its transition to heart failure in SHRs. Young animals (14 weeks of age) show a predominance of the V_1 form (high ATPase form), but as hypertension and hypertrophy persist and progress, this gradually changes from V_1 to V_3. Eventually, in the chronic phase of hypertrophy and in heart failure, the isoforms become 100% V_3 type. At 6 months of age, there is about 30–40% V_3; at this time the cardiac function in this animal model starts to become compromised, which suggests that perhaps a 30–40% accumulation of V_3 results in a compromised cardiac function.

The effect of various antihypertensive therapies on heart weight and blood pressure in this animal model is shown in TABLE 1. The data show results from different classes of antihypertensive drugs such as converting enzyme inhibitor diuretics (captopril and Esidrex), sympatholytic drugs (guanethidine and clonidine), vasodilator (minoxidil), and beta blocker (atenolol). Captopril significantly lowered blood pressure in SHRs and switched the isoforms from predominantly the V_3 to the V_1 form. Esidrix, a diuretic, alone also showed some switching, but captopril therapy is more pronounced in switching from V_3 to V_1 as compared to Esidrex. In normotensive rats, treatment with captopril also changed the myosin isozyme pattern, from 73% to 81%.

The effects of clonidine and guanethidine on blood pressure and myosin isoform type are shown in TABLE 1. Both drugs moderately control blood pressure, and this reduction in pressure did not result in a change in heart size (3.44 ± 0.15 mg/g un-

TABLE 1. Relationship between blood pressure, myocardial mass, and myosin isoform after antihypertensive therapy

Treatment	BP (mm Hg)	Mass (mg/g)	V_1 (%)	V_3 (%)
Captopril	↓↓	↓↓	↑↑	↓
Esidrex	↓	→	↑	↓
Guanethidine	↓	↓	↓	↑
Clonidine	↓	↓	↓	↑
Minoxidil	↓↓	↑↑	↓	↑
Atenolol	↓	↓	↓	↑

NOTATION: ↓↓, Normalization; ↓, moderate control; ↑↑, substantial increase; ↑, moderate increase; →, no change.

TABLE 2. Effect of antihypertensive treatment on blood pressure, ventricular mass, and collagen in spontaneously hypertensive rats

Treatment	BP (mm Hg)	Ventricular Mass (mg/g)	Collagen Type I/III	Total Collagen
Captopril	↓↓	↓↓	↑	↓
Hydralazine	↓↓	→	→	→

NOTATION: ↓↓, Normalization; ↓, moderate control; ↑, moderate increase; →, no change.

treated versus 3.2 ± 0.06 mg/g clonidine and 3.12 ± 0.04 mg/g guanethidine, p = N.S.). Each drug independently increased the distribution of the V_3 form from 21% to 48% and 32%, respectively ($p = < 0.01$).

The effect of minoxidil on blood pressure and heart weight is shown in TABLE 1. Minoxidil resulted in a significant reduction in blood pressure in SHRs ($p < 0.001$), associated with an increase in ventricular size (3.44 ± 0.15 mg/g to 3.8 ± 0.12 mg/g, $p < 0.001$). This confirms our previous finding as well. The effect of minoxidil on myosin isoform is shown in TABLE 2. Minoxidil resulted in a significant reduction associated with a significant increase in the V_3 isoform, from 21% to 31% ($p < 0.05$). The effect of atenolol on blood pressure and myosin isoform type is shown in TABLE 1. Treatment with atenolol produced a reduction in blood pressure ($p < 0.001$), associated with a significant reduction in cardiac mass (3.4 ± 0.15 mg/g to 3.0 ± 0.1 mg/g, $p < 0.005$). This treatment resulted in a significant reduction in V_1 and increase in V_3, from 22% to 31% ($p = 0.01$).

Changes in Collagen during Development and Regression of Hypertrophy

Myocardial hypertrophy has been described as an increase in myocardial mass and myocyte size associated with an increase in interstitial collagen within the extracellular matrix. The heart's ability to function is believed to depend considerably on the amount of collagen present in the myocardium, but the quality of the collagen is also important in determining cardiac function,[17] once as the myocardial structure remodels and again to assess the remodeling that occurs after regression of hypertro-

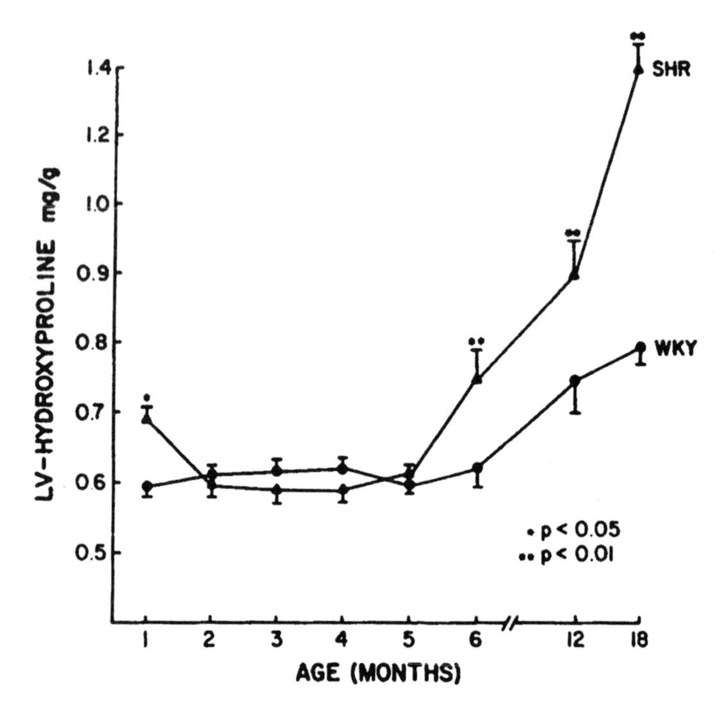

FIGURE 2. Changes in collagen during progression of hypertrophy and its transition to heart failure. During the acute phase of hypertrophy in SHRs up to 6 months of age, there was no change in collagen compared with untreated WKY rat controls. At about 6 months of age, however, there was a significant increase in total collagen, which became substantially increased during the chronic phase of hypertrophy and its transition to heart failure.

phy with antihypertensive therapy. There was also an alteration in the ratio of type I to type III collagen with captopril treatments in both rats and humans.[18]

Changes in Collagen during Progression of Cardiac Hypertrophy

Changes in collagen concentration during development of hypertrophy are shown in FIGURE 2. In rats from 8 to 24 weeks of age, the collagen concentration did not differ between SHRs and WKY rats, despite persistence of hypertension and hypertrophy. However, after 40 weeks of age, the rats showed an unexpected increase in collagen concentration, from 10 mg/g in SHRs versus 7 mg/g in WKYs. The concentrations further increased by 65 weeks, to 23.7 mg/g in SHRs versus 14.4 mg/g in WKYs ($p < 0.001$). These data suggested that despite persistence of high blood pressure and cardiac hypertrophy during the initial phase, the collagen component of the heart was not altered. However, during the chronic phase of hypertrophy the collagen concentration increased in SHRs and remained elevated.

The percent distribution of type I and type III collagen altered with aging. The percent distribution of types I and III collagen did not change until the rats were 40 weeks of age. However, at 40 weeks, type I collagen levels increased and this increase persisted until the rats were 65 weeks old. In SHRs, during progression of hypertrophy up to 40 weeks, no change in collagen was evident, despite the presence of hypertrophy in hypertension; although there was a trend, there was no significant increase in the percent distribution of type I collagen in SHRs during the aging process. On the other hand, type III collagen in WKYs remained unaltered until 40 weeks of age; there was a significant increase compared to the rats in the previous age group and then up to 65 weeks of age. In SHRs, the percent distribution of type III collagen remained the same during the progression of hypertrophy. This resulted in a significant increase in the percent distribution of type III collagen in WKYs compared with SHRs. Our data show that the ratio of type III to type I collagen is significantly different between WKYs and SHRs.[19]

Effect of Antihypertensive Treatment on Collagen

The effect of the ACE inhibitor captopril on blood pressure and collagen phenotypes is shown in TABLE 2. Captopril treatment significantly lowered blood pressure (from 189 mm Hg to 126 mm Hg) and resulted in regression in hypertrophy by normalizing the ratio of heart weight to body weight. The total collagen content was also significantly reduced due to treatment with ACE inhibitors (13 ± .4 mg/g versus 8.8 ± 0.05 mg/g captopril treatment). Treatment with captopril caused a significant decrease in the ratio of type I to type III collagen compared to untreated controls (1.2 ± 0.16 mg/g in untreated versus 0.56 ± 0.04 mg/g in captopril-treated rats, $p < 0.01$). This reduction in ratio of type I to type III collagen is due to an increase in type III collagen during captopril treatment. Captopril treatment resulted in an increase in type III collagen from 2.6 mg/g to 6.4 mg/g ($p < 0.05$). Thus, this study demonstrates that alteration in collagen levels and phenotypes occurs during progression of hypertrophy as well as after its regression by antihypertensive treatment with ACE inhibitors.

Regression of Hypertrophy by Antihypertensive Therapy: Effect of Challenge with Dobutamine-Induced Stress

A noninvasive technique has been used to evaluate the cardiac function in older rats (18 months) before and after treatment with antihypertensive drugs and to study the effect of stress with dobutamine after regression of hypertrophy.

Cardiac functional reserve was compared in rats treated with antihypertensive drugs and in untreated rats, using a similar technique. Three different antihypertensive treatments were studied: captopril and hydralazine, both ACE inhibitors, and the beta-blocker, propranolol. Use of captopril reduced the left ventricular weight in treated rats by 40%, associated with a lower baseline stroke volume than in untreated rats ($p < 0.05$). After dobutamine stress, the treated rats showed a dose-dependent increase ($r_2 = 0.95$, $p < 0.02$) in stroke volume, in contrast with no change in the untreated rats ($r_2 = 0.34$, $p < 0.05$). In hydralazine-treated rats, no regression of hypertrophy was observed, and there was no change in reserve after dobutamine stress. Propranolol treatment resulted in only partial regression and a slight, but not significant, change in stroke volume, very similar results to those of untreated rats. These data suggest that rats with LVH have a greater resting stroke volume, which does not increase with stress, and are thus limited in cardiac functional reserve. Regression of LVH using captopril was associated with a reduction of resting stroke volume but normalization of dynamic cardiac response to stress, whereas hydralazine and propranolol failed to cause a similar response. It is important to note that captopril would be a beneficial and better drug in treating hypertensive hypertrophy to obtain an improved cardiac functional reserve.

CONCLUSIONS

We have shown that during development of hypertrophy, both myosin and collagen and their isoforms change, especially during the transition of hypertrophy to heart failure. Myosin isoforms gradually change during development of hypertrophy, as well as in the chronic phase of hypertrophy and failure. On the other hand, collagen levels and proportions change only during the chronic phase of hypertrophy and change even more during the transition of hypertrophy to heart failure. During this transition, the heart contains almost 100% of the V_3 isoform and a significantly altered ratio of type I to type III collagen phenotypes. All these data suggest that the quality of both collagen and myosin is a critical factor in determining the degree of cardiac contractility and stiffness. Our data also show that the ACE inhibitor captopril is one of the most effective drugs not only for the regression of hypertrophy, but also in correcting the altered myosin and collagen phenotypes once the hypertrophy has regressed.

Studies have shown that various chemical factors and growth factors (including transforming growth factor and its family) are involved in changes in both collagen and myosin expression. Cell density, the extracellular matrix, and the extracellular environment have also been shown to influence collagen synthesis *in vitro*. This study demonstrates the unique new information that the quality of collagen and myosin is responsible for molecular changes that take place during the transition of hypertrophy to heart failure. Overall, our data suggest that hypertension plays a role in changes in the molecular structure of the myocardium during the chronic phase of hypertrophy and heart failure. This complex process cannot be explained by one factor but involves a combination of factors. However, the factors responsible for modulating each of the components that takes part in altering the myocardium's molecular structure and that results in transition of hypertrophy to heart failure have yet to be determined.

ACKNOWLEDGMENTS

The author gratefully acknowledges the technical assistance of David Young. Appreciation is extended to Dr. James Wong of the Department of Cardiology at the Cleveland Clinic for interpretation of the echocardiographic data and to the department for use of its facilities. Thanks, too, to JoAnne Holl and Christine Kassuba for preparing and editing this contribution.

REFERENCES

1. BARTOSOVA, D., M. CHVAPIL, B. KORECKY, O. POUPA, K. RAKUSAN, Z. TUREK & M. VISEK. 1969. The growth of the muscular and collagenous parts of the rat heart in various forms of cardiomegaly. J. Physiol. **200:** 285–295.
2. FANBURG, B.L. 1970. Experimental cardiac hypertrophy [Review]. N. Engl. J. Med. **282:** 723–732.
3. SKELTON, C.L. & E.H. SONNENBLICK. 1974. Heterogeneity of contractile function in cardiac hypertrophy [Review]. Circ. Res. **35**(Suppl II): 83–96.
4. GOODWIN, J.F. 1970. Congestive and hypertrophic cardiomyopathies. A decade of study. Lancet **1:** 732–739.
5. SEN, S., R.C. TARAZI, P.A. KHAIRALLAH & F.M. BUMPUS. 1974. Cardiac hypertrophy in spontaneously hypertensive rats. Circ. Res. **35:** 775–781.
6. SEN, S., R.C. TARAZI & F.M. BUMPUS. 1976. Biochemical changes associated with development and reversal of cardiac hypertrophy in spontaneously hypertensive rats. Cardiovasc. Res. **10:** 254–261.
7. SEN, S., R.C. TARAZI & F.M. BUMPUS. 1977. Cardiac hypertrophy and antihypertensive therapy. Cardiovasc. Res. **11:** 427–433.
8. TARAZI, R.C., C.M. FERRARIO & H.P. DUSTAN. 1998. *In* Hypertension: Physiopathology and Treatment. J. Genest & O. Kuchel, Eds.: 738–754. McGraw-Hill. New York, NY.
9. SEN, S. & D. YOUNG. 1991. Effect of sodium deprivation on cardiac hypertrophy in spontaneously hypertensive rats: influence of aging. J. Mol. Cell. Cardiol. **23:** 695–704.
10. BERGMAN, J. & R. LOXLEY. 1963. Two improved and simplified methods for the spectrophotometric determination of hydroxyproline. Anal. Chem. **35:** 1961–1965.
11. MAUGHAN, D., E. LOW, R. LITTEN, III, J. BRAYDEN & N. ALPERT. 1979. Calcium-activated muscle from hypertrophied rabbit hearts. Mechanical and correlated biochemical changes. Circ. Res. **44:** 279–287.
12. ALPERT, N.R., L.A. MULIERI & R.Z. LITTEN. 1979. Functional significance of altered myosin adenosine triphosphatase activity in enlarged hearts. Am. J. Cardiol. **44:** 946–953.
13. SCHWARTZ, K., Y. LECARPENTIER, J.L. MARTIN, A.M. LOMPRE, J.J. MERCADIER & B. SWYNGHEDAUW. 1981. Myosin isoenzymic distribution correlates with speed of myocardial contraction. J. Mol. Cell. Cardiol. **13:** 1071–1075.
14. MERCADIER, J.J., A.M. LOMPRE, C. WISNEWSKY, J.L. SAMUEL, J. BERCOVICI, B. SWYNGHEDAUW & K. SCHWARTZ. 1981. Myosin isoenzyme changes in several models of rat cardiac hypertrophy. Circ. Res. **49:** 525–532.
15. SINHA, A.M., P.K. UMEDA, C.J. KAVINSKY, C. RAJAMANICKAM, H.J. HSU, S. JAKOVCIC & M. RABINOWITZ. 1982. Molecular cloning of mRNA sequences for cardiac alpha- and beta-form myosin heavy chains: expression in ventricles of normal, hypothyroid, and thyrotoxic rabbits. Proc. Natl. Acad. Sci. USA **79:** 5847–5851.
16. MAHDAVI, V., A.P. CHAMBERS & B. NADAL-GINARD. 1984. Cardiac alpha- and beta-myosin heavy chain genes are organized in tandem. Proc. Natl. Acad. Sci. USA **81:** 2626–2630.
17. MUKHERJEE, D. & S. SEN. 1990. Collagen phenotypes during development and regression of myocardial hypertrophy in spontaneously hypertensive rats. Circ. Res. **67:** 1474–1480.
18. MUKHERJEE, D. & S. SEN. 1991. Alteration of collagen phenotypes in ischemic cardiomyopathy. J. Clin. Invest. **88:** 1141–1146.
19. YANG, C., K. KANDASWAMY, D. YOUNG & S. SEN. 1997. Changes in collagen phenotypes during progression and regression of cardiac hypertophy. Cardiovasc. Res. **36:** 236–245.

Oxidized LDL and Atherogenesis[a]

SEPPO YLÄ-HERTTUALA[b]

A.I. Virtanen Institute and Department of Medicine, University of Kuopio, P.O. Box 1627, FIN-70211 Kuopio, Finland

ABSTRACT: A brief review of recent findings regarding the role of oxidized low-density lipoproteins (Ox-LDL) in atherogenesis. Lipid peroxidation and oxidative damage to LDL make arteries susceptible to chronic inflammation, which is known to cause alterations in arterial gene expression and promote lesion development. Treatment protocols implementing antioxidants for preventing cardiovascular diseases are suggested.

INTRODUCTION

Atherosclerosis and cardiovascular diseases remain the major cause of mortality in the United States and Europe.[1] High plasma total cholesterol and low-density lipoprotein (LDL) values show significant positive relationship to the development of atherosclerosis and cardiovascular diseases.[2] Recent evidence suggests that oxidation (Ox) of LDL plays an important role in the pathogenesis of atherosclerosis.[2,3] The purpose of this article is to review recent findings regarding the role of oxidized LDL (Ox-LDL) in atherogenesis.

LDL OXIDATION

Peroxidation can damage LDL particles. Several reactive radical species can initiate lipid peroxidation. These include reactions involving lipoxygenases, superoxide anion, hydroxyl radical, peroxynitrate, heme proteins, ceruloplasmin, and myeloperoxidase. It has been demonstrated that 15-lipoxygenase, superoxide anion, peroxynitrate, and myeloperoxidase can oxidize LDL.[4] Peroxynitrate may be formed in the arterial wall from the reaction of superoxide anion with nitric oxide.[5] It is also possible that oxidized membrane lipids are transferred to LDL.

In addition to lipids, LDL oxidation also involves the modification of apoprotein B (ApoB). In Ox-LDL, ApoB is fragmented and contains covalently bound malondialdehyde and 4-hydroxynonenal conjugates.[2] These reactions change LDL properties so that it is metabolized through macrophage scavenger receptors.[6]

LDL antioxidant levels do not fully explain individual differences in the susceptibility of LDL to oxidative stress.[7] It is likely that other factors, such as fatty acid

[a]This work was supported by grants from Finnish Academy, Sigrid Juselius Foundation, and Finnish Heart Foundation and by research grant from the Finnish Insurance Companies.

[b]Address correspondence to: Seppo Ylä-Herttuala, M.D., Ph.D., A.I. Virtanen Institute and Department of Medicine, University of Kuopio, P.O. Box 1627, FIN-70211 Kuopio, Finland; Fax: 358-17-163030; E-mail: Seppo.YlaHerttuala@uku.fi

TABLE 1. Properties of minimally oxidized LDL and fully oxidized LDL

	Minimally Oxidized LDL	Oxidized LDL
Cellular lipid accumulation	No	Yes
Reactive aldehyde conjugates in ApoB	No	Yes
Metabolism through scavenger receptor	No	Yes
Metabolism through LDL receptor	Yes	No
Stimulates proinflammatory cytokines	Yes	No
Inhibits endothelial-derived relaxing factor	No	Yes
Immunogenic	No	Yes
Cytotoxic	No	Yes
Chemotactic for plasma monocytes	No	Yes

composition and LDL particle size, may also affect LDL oxidation. It has been shown that small, dense LDL particles are more susceptible to oxidation than larger LDL subfractions.[7] On the other hand, LDL particles enriched with monounsaturated fatty acids are less prone to oxidation than particles enriched with polyunsaturated fatty acids.[7]

ATHEROGENIC PROPERTIES OF OXIDIZED LDL

Ox-LDL can cause lipid accumulation in macrophages and foam cell formation.[2] Ox-LDL is also cytotoxic to many cell types and chemotactic for monocyte macrophages. In addition, Ox-LDL can inactivate endothelial cell–derived relaxing factor.[2]

It is becoming increasingly evident that the biological properties of minimally oxidized LDL (MM-LDL) are different from those of Ox-LDL.[8] TABLE 1 summarizes some of the properties of MM-LDL and Ox-LDL. MM-LDL seems to have several specific effects on gene expression.[8] It can stimulate monocyte chemotactic factor-1 and macrophage colony stimulating factor-1 expression and activate prothrombotic properties in the vascular wall.[8] However, MM-LDL can not cause lipid accumulation in arterial cells since it is not metabolized through scavenger receptors.[2] Ox-LDL appears to be immunogenic, causing autoantibody formation in humans and in experimental animals. According to preliminary results, presence of autoantibodies may predict the progression of atherosclerosis in human populations.[4,9]

EVIDENCE FOR THE PRESENCE OF OXIDIZED LDL IN ATHEROSCLEROTIC LESIONS

It has been clearly shown that Ox-LDL is present in atherosclerotic lesions: (1) LDL isolated from human atherosclerotic lesions, but not from normal arteries, resembles Ox-LDL[3]; (2) epitopes characteristic of Ox-LDL can be demonstrated in atherosclerotic lesions by immunocytochemistry[10]; (3) atherosclerotic lesions con-

TABLE 2. Evidence for the presence of oxidized LDL in atherosclerotic lesions

	References
LDL isolated from atherosclerotic lesions resembles Ox-LDL	3
Epitopes characteristic of Ox-LDL are present in atherosclerotic lesions	10
Atherosclerotic lesions contain immunoglobulins that recognize Ox-LDL	11
Serum contains autoantibodies against Ox-LDL	9, 10
Antioxidant treatment reduces atherogenesis in experimental animals	12

tain immunoglobulins that recognize Ox-LDL[11]; (4) serum contains autoantibodies to Ox-LDL[9]; and (5) antioxidant treatment reduces the rate of atherosclerotic lesion development in experimental animals (TABLE 2). Antioxidants shown to be effective in animal models include probucol,[12] α-tocopherol,[13] butylated hydroxytoluene,[14] and diphenylphenylenediamine.[15] It remains to be determined whether small quantities of Ox-LDL are present in plasma.[4]

CONCLUSIONS

Research has provided strong evidence that LDL oxidation plays an important role in the pathogenesis of atherosclerosis and cardiovascular diseases. There seems to be no doubt that lipid peroxidation and oxidative damage to LDL resemble chronic inflammation, which causes various alterations in arterial gene expression and promotes lesion development. Based on current knowledge about the role of Ox-LDL in atherogenesis, randomized placebo-controlled intervention trials using antioxidants are warranted to test the hypothesis that increased antioxidant protection could be useful in the prevention of cardiovascular diseases.

ACKNOWLEDGMENT

I thank Ms. Marja Poikolainen for typing the manuscript.

REFERENCES

1. TUOMILEHTO, J. & K. KUULASMAA. 1989. WHO Monica Project: Assessing CHD mortality and morbidity. Int. J. Epidemiol. **18**(3 Suppl 1): S38–45.
2. STEINBERG, D. 1997. Low density lipoprotein oxidation and its pathobiological significance. J. Biol. Chem. **272:** 20963–20966.
3. YLÄ-HERTTUALA, S., W. PALINSKI, M.E. ROSENFELD, S. PARTHASARATHY, T.E. CAREW, S. BUTLER, J.L. WITZTUM & D. STEINBERG. 1989. Evidence for the presence of oxidatively modified low density lipoprotein in atherosclerotic lesions of rabbit and man. J. Clin. Invest. **84:** 1086–1095.
4. YLÄ-HERTTUALA, S. 1998. Is oxidized low-density lipoprotein present in vivo? Curr. Opin. Lipidol. **9:** 337–344.
5. BECKMAN, J.S., T.W. BECKMAN, J. CHEN, P.A. MARSHALL & B.A. FREEMAN. 1990. Apparent hydroxyl radical production by peroxynitrite: implications for endothelial injury from nitric oxide and superoxide. Med. Sci. **87:** 1620–1624.

6. KODAMA, T., M. FREEMAN, L. ROHRER, J. ZABRECKY, P. MATSUDAIRA & M. KRIEGER. 1990. Type I macrophage scavenger receptor contains α-helical and collagen-like coiled coils. Nature **343:** 531–535.
7. ESTERBAUER, H., J. GEBICKI, H. PUHL & G. JURGENS. 1992. The role of lipid peroxidation and antioxidants in oxidative modification of LDL. Free Radical Biol. Med. **13:** 341–390.
8. BERLINER, J.A., M. NAVAB, A.M. FOGELMAN, J.S. FRANK, L.L. DEMER, P.A. EDWARDS *et al.* 1995. Atherosclerosis. Basic mechanisms: oxidation, inflammation, and genetics. Circulation **91:** 2488–2496.
9. SALONEN, J.T., S. YLÄ-HERTTUALA, R. YAMAMOTO, S. BUTLER, H. KORPELA, R. SALONEN, K. NYYSSÖNEN, W. PALINSKI & J.L. WITZTUM. 1992. Autoantibody against oxidised LDL and progression of carotid atherosclerosis. Lancet **339:** 883–887.
10. PALINSKI, W., M.E. ROSENFELD, S. YLÄ-HERTTUALA, G.C. GURTNER, S.S. SOCHER, S.W. BUTLER, S. PARTHASARATHY, T.E. CAREW, D. STEINBERG & J.L. WITZTUM. 1989. Low density lipoprotein undergoes oxidative modification *in vivo.* Proc. Natl. Acad. Sci. USA **86:** 1372–1376.
11. YLÄ-HERTTUALA, S., S. BUTLER, S. PICARD, W. PALINSKI, D. STEINBERG & J.L. WITZTUM. 1994. Rabbit and human atherosclerotic lesions contain IgG that recognizes epitopes of oxidized LDL. Arterioscler. Thromb. **14:** 32–40.
12. CAREW, T.E., D.C. SCHWENKE & D. STEINBERG. 1987. Antiatherogenic effect of probucol unrelated to its hypocholesterolemic effect: evidence that antioxidants in vivo can selectively inhibit low density lipoprotein degradation in macrophage-rich fatty streaks and slow the progression of atherosclerosis in the Watanabe heritable hyperlipidemic rabbit. Proc. Natl. Acad. Sci. USA **84:** 7725–7729.
13. VERLANGIERI, A.J. & M.J. BUSH. 1992. Effects of d-alpha-tocopherol supplementation on experimentally induced primate atherosclerosis. J. Am. Coll. Nutr. **11:** 131–138.
14. BJÖRKHEM, I., A. HENRIKSSON-FREYSCHUSS, O. BREUER, U. DICZFALUSY, L. BERGLUND & P. HENRIKSSON. 1991. The antioxidant butylated hydroxytoluene protects against atherosclerosis. Arterioscler. Thromb. **11:** 15–22.
15. SPARROW, C.P., T.W. DOEBBER, J. OLSZEWSKI, M.S. WU, J. VENTRE, K.A. STEVENS & Y.S. CHAO. 1992. Low density lipoprotein is protected from oxidation and the progression of atherosclerosis is slowed in cholesterol-fed rabbits by the antioxidant N,N′-diphenyl-phenylenediamine. J. Clin. Invest. **89:** 1885–1891.

Effect of Antioxidant Trace Elements on the Response of Cardiac Tissue to Oxidative Stress[a]

CHRISTINE BARANDIER, STÉPHANE TANGUY, SYLVIE PUCHEU, FRANCOIS BOUCHER, AND JOËL DE LEIRIS[b]

Groupe de Physiopathologie Cellulaire Cardiaque, ESA CNRS 5077, Université Joseph Fourier, Grenoble, France

ABSTRACT: It is now well established that several trace elements, because of their involvement in the catalytic activity and spatial conformation of antioxidant enzymes, may contribute to the prevention of oxidative stress such as occurs upon reperfusion of ischemic tissue. The aim of this paper is (1) to review the role of these trace elements (Cu, Mn, Se, and Zn) in antioxidant cellular defenses in the course of post-ischemic reperfusion of cardiac tissue, (2) to provide experimental data suggesting that variations in trace element dietary intake may modulate the vulnerability of cardiac tissue to ischemia-reperfusion, and (3) to discuss in more detail the effect of Mn ions, which seem to play a special protective role against reperfusion injury. Some results obtained from experiments in animal models of myocardial reperfusion have shown that the dietary intake of such trace elements can modulate cardiac activity of antioxidant enzymes and, consequently, the degree of reperfusion damage. In addition, experimental data on the protective effects of an acute treatment with Mn are presented. Finally, experimental evidence on the protective role of salen-Mn complexes, which exhibit catalytic SOD- and CAT-like activities against reperfusion injury, are described. These complexes should be of considerable interest in clinical conditions.

Ischemic heart disease (IHD) is the leading cause of death in most industrialized countries, causing more than 30% of deaths in the United States. In this context, trace elements may play a significant role as they appear to be associated with certain risk factors in the etiology and pathogenesis of ischemic heart disease, in the contractile function of cardiac cells, and in some types of arrhythmias.[1–3] Thus, in IHD patients, copper affects myocardial contractility whereas the level of magnesium (Mg), calcium (Ca), manganese (Mn), copper (Cu), and zinc (Zn) are closely related to cardiac rhythm disturbances. In experimental models of regional myocardial ischemia, Mn level decreased in the ischemic zone, whereas magnesium decreased in both the ischemic and non-ischemic myocardium. It is now well established that several trace elements are involved in the cellular defense potential against oxidative stress such as occurs upon reperfusion of ischemic tissue. The main

[a]This study was supported in part by a grant from Région Rhône-Alpes.

[b]Address correspondence to: Prof. Joël de Leiris, Groupe de Physiopathologie Cellulaire Cardiaque, ESA CNRS 5077, Université Joseph Fourier, BP53X, 38041 Grenoble Cedex, France; Fax and Telephone: (33) 4 76 51 26 59.

effect of these trace elements is to act as cofactors of various antioxidant enzymes, thus contributing to the prevention of oxidative stress.

The aim of this paper is (1) to review the role of trace elements in antioxidant cellular defenses in the course of post-ischemic reperfusion of cardiac tissue, (2) to provide experimental data suggesting that variations in trace element dietary intake may modulate the vulnerability of cardiac tissue to ischemia-reperfusion, and (3) to discuss in more detail the effect of Mn ions, which seem to play a special protective role against reperfusion injury.

ISCHEMIA-REPERFUSION: AN OXIDATIVE PATHOLOGY

It is now well established that early reperfusion by means of coronary bypass surgery, transluminal angioplasty, or thrombolytic therapy is an absolute prerequisite for the survival of ischemic myocardium. However, experimental studies designed to investigate the consequences of restoring blood flow to the ischemic myocardium have shown that reperfusion may by itself increase the apparent severity of tissue injury.[4,5] Indeed, there are at least three different unfavorable consequences of myocardial reperfusion: (1) reperfusion-induced arrhythmias; (2) a prolonged mechanical dysfunction which may last for several hours or even days, but is generally fully reversible (myocardial stunning); and (3) the killing of some myocytes that were still potentially viable at the time of reflow.

In 1978, Guarnieri and colleagues[6] reported that alpha-tocopherol (vitamin E), a major cellular lipid-soluble antioxidant, could reduce enzyme release and improve the recovery of contractile function and mitochondrial energy production in rabbit isolated heart preparations submitted to 30 minutes of hypoxia and then reoxygenated. They suggested that reoxygenation may lead to an increased production of reactive oxygen species (oxygen-derived free radicals) which could be partly responsible for the biochemical and functional deterioration associated with post-hypoxic reoxygenation. Since this pioneering work of Guarnieri, many other investigations from several laboratories support the view that reactive oxygen species (such as superoxide anions, hydrogen peroxide, and hydroxyl radicals) may contribute to the genesis of reperfusion-associated pathophysiological alterations. Although the production of reactive oxygen species has been shown to persist long into the reperfusion period, the consensus is in favor of a critical early burst, the intensity of which declines rapidly within a few minutes.[5,7] The suppression of this early burst of free radical generation by various pharmacological interventions is accompanied by an attenuation of myocardial stunning and arrhythmias, whereas suppression of free radical production after this burst (i.e., after the first 5–10 minutes of reflow) is not.[8]

During the early phase of post-ischemic reperfusion, reactive oxygen species can be produced at various intracellular and extracellular sites, by several routes. These include activation of the reaction catalyzed by xanthine oxidase, activation of the arachidonic acid cascade, autooxidation of catecholamines and other compounds, alterations of mitochondrial electron transfer chain, and activation of neutrophils infiltrating the previously ischemic region. Toxicity of partially reduced oxygen species arises from peroxidation of polyunsaturated acid moieties of membrane phospholipids which may cause membrane disintegration, mitochondrial dysfunction and calcium overload. Moreover, effects on lipid metabolism, especially arachidonic acid metabolism, can induce microcirculatory disturbances.

Until the late 1980s, the evidence for an involvement of free radicals in reperfusion injury was only based on indirect measurements (for instance, measurement of cardiac level of malondialdehydes, an end-product of lipid peroxidation). Since the early 1990s, the technique of electron spin resonance coupled with spin trapping procedures has allowed investigators to measure the production of radicals in either coronary effluent or myocardial tissue.[7,9–12] It is now well established that reperfusion-induced radical production is related to the duration or severity of the preceding period of ischemia and that it can be attenuated by various antioxidants.

ANTIOXIDANT CELLULAR DEFENSES: IMPLICATION OF TRACE ELEMENTS

According to the concept that reactive oxygen species play a major role in the pathophysiological manifestations of myocardial reperfusion, reintroduction of molecular oxygen into ischemic tissue upon reperfusion would lead to an excessive formation of partially reduced oxygen species, which overwhelm antioxidant tissue defense capacity and damage myocardial cells. There are both non-enzymatic and enzymatic defense mechanisms in the heart that protect myocardial tissue against the harmful effects of reactive oxygen species.[13] The former includes reduced glutathione (GSH), alpha-tocopherol, ascorbic acid, and beta-carotene, while the latter consists of superoxide dismutase (SOD), catalase (CAT), glutathione peroxidase (GPx), and glutathione reductase (GR).

The heart normally possesses sufficient activities of these antioxidant enzymes. However, its antioxidant defense system remains vital because the heart is a highly aerobic organ subjected to a delicate balance between prooxidant production and antioxidant defenses. Under conditions that weaken the cardiac antioxidant system, for instance during ischemia and postischemic reperfusion when the tissue is overexposed to reactive oxygen species,[14] the myocardium may be subjected to oxidative damage, the consequences of which have been described above. In most mammalian species, SOD and GPx appear to be the most active antioxidant enzymes in the myocardium. By dismutation of superoxide anions ($O_2^{\cdot -}$) and reduction of hydrogen peroxide (H_2O_2), these enzymes prevent Haber-Weiss reaction and thereby the formation of hydroxyl radical ($OH^{\cdot}$), one of the most reactive oxyradicals. However, recent experimental evidence suggests that CAT may also play a role in antioxidant defense mechanisms.

SOD catalyzes the dismutation of superoxide to oxygen and hydrogen peroxide with the fastest enzymatic rate constant ($2 \times 10^9\ M^{-1} \cdot s^{-1}$) actually known. All SODs are metalloproteins, and their metal center is essential for their catalytic function. There are two major classes of SODs in mammalian cells: Mn-centered (Mn-SOD) located in the mitochondria and Cu and Zn-centered (CuZn-SOD) in the cytosol.[15] Mn-SOD is one of the most important cellular primary defenses against oxygen-derived free radicals and is vital for maintaining a healthy balance between oxidants and antioxidants.[16] Its critical role in protecting against oxidative damage has been demonstrated both *in vivo* and *in vitro*.[17,18] GPx, located in the cytosol, is the main enzyme of defense against hydrogen peroxide. Selenium (Se), present in its active site, is essential for its catalytic activity.

One of the major roles of essential trace elements within the body is therefore to act as a cofactor of these key antioxidant enzymes in which they contribute to both catalytic activity and spatial conformation. In this regard, it has been suggested that any significant modification of trace element status would lead to changes in the activity of these enzymes and have important consequences on the susceptibility of the tissue to oxidative stress. Many investigations have suggested that diet may play a part in development of IHD. For many years, dietary studies have concentrated on the role of dietary lipids in the development of heart disease. Recently, several experimental and clinical studies have underlined a special role of dietary supply of metal salts[19,20] and there are now many direct and indirect studies showing that metals play an important role in the functioning of the normal heart, and that alterations in the body's supply of some metals may contribute to the development of IHD.[21]

Zinc

In addition to being a constituent of more than one hundred enzymes, Zn has several other functions, including a protective activity against oxidative stress,[22] as demonstrated by several *in vitro* and *in vivo* studies.[23–25] A positive correlation has been shown between cytosolic SOD activity and plasma Zn concentration,[23,26] and dietary Zn deficiency has been shown to cause a decrease in CuZn-SOD activity[23] and an increased susceptibility to oxidative damage. Thus, Zn depletion in rats is associated with an increase in free radical–induced lipid peroxidation both in plasma and organs[25] and an increase in lipoprotein oxidation.[27]

Selenium

Se, as an essential component of GPx, plays a critical role in protecting aerobic organisms from oxygen radical-initiated cell injury. Se deficiency has been known for decades to result in extensive oxidative damage in many tissues, including the myocardium.[28] Both epidemiological and etiological evidence indicate that Se deficiency can have several pathogenic consequences. Thus, Se is involved in nutritional myopathy (white muscle disease) and microangiopathy (mulberry disease) in livestock. Keshan disease, a widespread epidemic first reported in Northeast China, also provides evidence that heart deprived of Se is more vulnerable to functional damage.[29]

In animals and humans, Se is essential for the synthesis of Se-dependent GPx.[30] Furthermore, dietary Se deficiency significantly decreases GPx activity in rat myocardium,[31] thereby weakening cellular antioxidant defense. However, this GPx activity decrease appears more severe in cytosol than in mitochondria.[14] Moreover, Se is involved in the protection of cells against toxic agents, as well as in the prevention of hepatic heme decay, but none of these activities is mediated by GPx.[32] Clinical studies have shown a very low Se level in patients with myocardial infarction,[33–35] but the implication of Se in the development of cardiovascular diseases has not yet been clearly demonstrated. Moreover, isolated hearts of Se-deficient rats are more sensitive to hydrogen peroxide than hearts from control animals.[36] Finally, elevated concentrations of Se and Zn enhance plasma GPx and SOD activity in animals and man,[23,33] improve post-ischemic cardiac functional recovery, preserve high energy compounds, and reduce cardiac creatine kinase release and lactate production.[37]

Copper

Synthesis of CuZn-SOD and its activity depend on Cu status[38] and has also been shown to vary as a function of Cu intake. Studies of the influence of Cu on cardiac susceptibility to ischemia and reperfusion showed conflicting results. Allen and Saari[39] reported an improvement of post-ischemic function of *in vitro* cardiac preparations isolated from Cu-deficient rats, whereas other studies have shown that Cu deficiency enhanced oxidative stress in various tissues.[40,41] On the basis of animal experiments, it has also been suggested that Cu deficiency or an imbalance of Cu and Zn in the diet might be a risk factor for IHD.[42,43]

Manganese

Mn is an essential trace element and is important for several key enzymes. Furthermore, *Lactobacillus plantarum*, which is aerotolerant but devoid of SOD, was seen to accumulate high intracellular concentrations of Mn salts as a functional replacement for SOD.[44] This substitution indicates that low molecular weight Mn complexes can provide functional replacements for SOD and are very well tolerated within at least certain types of cells. Singh and colleagues[17] reported on the effectiveness of Mn as an intravenous superoxide scavenger in mammals, suggesting a direct antioxidant role of Mn. Mn deficiency causes damage to mitochondrial membranes in mice and rats, which could be due to decreased Mn-SOD activity resulting in increased lipid peroxidation and reduced antioxidant potential.[45] Rats fed Mn-deficient diet showed decreased Mn-SOD activity,[46] which was due to negative pretranscriptional regulation of Mn-SOD.[45] Davis and Greger[47] reported that Mn supplementation resulted in significant increases in human lymphocyte Mn-SOD activity. It has been shown that chronic *in vivo* exposure to Mn significantly increased the Mn-SOD activity in selected brain regions.[48] The mechanism by which the activity of Mn-SOD is increased has not yet been explained. Induction of Mn-SOD mRNA has never been shown.

INFLUENCE OF DIETARY TRACE ELEMENTS ON CARDIAC SUSCEPTIBILITY TO ISCHEMIA AND REPERFUSION

We have studied the influence of Cu, Zn, Mn, and Se, on the antioxidant status of cardiac tissue and on the susceptibility of the myocardium to ischemia-reperfusion.[49] We first investigated whether or not a dietary deficiency in one of these four trace elements could modify functional and structural myocardial susceptibility to ischemia-reperfusion.

In our experiments, rats received diets deficient in one given element (Zn, Cu, Se, or Mn) for a period of ten weeks (in mg metal/kg diet, Zn deficient = 2 versus control = 90; Cu deficient = 1 versus control = 20; Se deficient = 0 versus control = 0.15; Mn deficient = 0 versus control = 60). At the end of this period, rats were anesthetized; hearts were isolated and perfused through the aorta for 30 min under control nor-

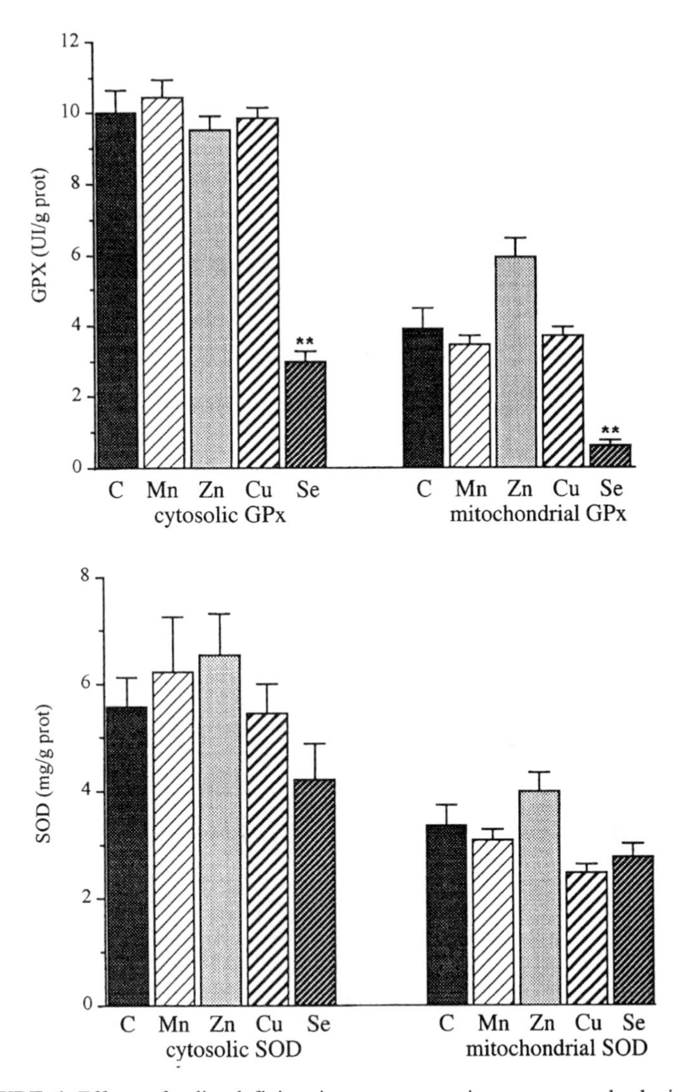

FIGURE 1. Effects of a diet deficient in manganese, zinc, copper, and selenium compared to a control diet on cytosolic and mitochondrial GPx and SOD activities. $^{**}p < 0.01$ versus control (C).

moxic conditions, then submitted to 15 min of normothermic global total ischemia followed by 30 min of reperfusion. Trace element assays indicated effective plasma deficiencies. In cardiac tissue, significant Mn, Se, and Cu deficiencies were observed, whereas the Zn level did not appear significantly decreased.

None of the single deficiencies modified post-ischemic functional recovery except for the Cu-deficient diet, which significantly decreased functional recovery of developed pressure (Cu deficient 7.5 ± 2.3% of pre-ischemic value versus control

31.3 ± 7.6% after 10-min reperfusion; $p < 0.01$), heart rate (Cu deficient 62.5% of pre-ischemic value versus control 87.5% after 10-min reperfusion; $p < 0.05$), or [heart rate × pressure] product (Cu deficient 7.8 ± 1.7% of pre-ischemic value versus control 23.1 ± 3.8% after 10-min reperfusion; $p < 0.01$).

Electron microscopic analysis of ventricular myocyte ultrastructure at the end of the perfusion protocol showed extensive damage to mitochondria and sarcomeres in control hearts. Nuclear chromatin accumulated along nuclear membranes, mitochondria were swollen or showed extensive damage, and sarcomeres were contracted and often ruptured. The extent of damage appeared slightly greater in Mn- and Zn-deficient hearts and was much more evident in Cu- and Se-deficient hearts. The proportion of normal sarcomeres and mitochondria was lower in deficient groups and mitochondrial edema was significantly more extensive in the Cu-deficient group versus control group.

Cu, Zn, or Mn deficiencies increased the susceptibility to reperfusion injury, as attested by functional parameters and ultrastructural observations, but did not modify either cytosolic or mitochondrial SOD activities, whereas Se deficiency significantly decreased cytosolic (Se deficient 2.99 ± 0.27 IU/g protein versus control 9.15 ± 0.76 IU/g protein; $p < 0.01$) and mitochondrial (Se deficient 0.64 ± 0.12 IU/g protein versus control 3.19 ± 0.38 IU/g protein; $p < 0.01$) GPx activity (FIG. 1).

In the second part of our study, we used rats fed with a diet supplemented in the four elements (Cu, Zn, Mn, and Se) simultaneously. We evaluated cardiac susceptibility to ischemia-reperfusion and antioxidant status of rats submitted during ten weeks to a standard diet [Control (mg/kg): Zn 98; Mn 68; Cu 26; Se 0.24] or a diet supplemented with the four elements [Supplemented (mg/kg): Zn 214; Mn 272; Cu 52.2; Se 2.4]. Isolated hearts were submitted to the same perfusion protocol as described above.

Dietary trace element supplementation of Cu, Zn, Mn, and Se enhanced functional post-ischemic recovery in terms of developed pressure (after 30-min reperfusion: supplemented group 77.1 ± 6.3% of preischemic value versus control 70.9 ± 3.3%; $p < 0.01$), dP/dt (after 30-min reperfusion: supplemented group 71.7 ± 2.4% of preischemic value versus control 53.3 ± 3.1%; $p < 0.01$) and [heart rate × pressure] product (after 30-min reperfusion: supplemented group 70.4 ± 2.6% of preischemic value versus control 51.7 ± 1.4%; $p < 0.01$) (TABLE 1). In addition, ventricular ultrastructure was protected by the supplementation, with a marked limitation of mitochondrial edema and sarcomere contracture (TABLE 2). Only Mn-SOD activity was significantly enhanced in supplemented hearts.

TABLE 1. Functional recovery measured after 30 min of reperfusion in control and trace element supplemented groups

	Control	Supplemented
% recovery of developed pressure	70.9 ± 3.3	77.1 ± 6.3[a]
% recovery of dP/dt	53.3 ± 3.1	71.7 ± 2.4[a]
% recovery of [heart rate × left ventricular systolic pressure]	51.7 ± 1.4	70.4 ± 2.6[a]

[a] $p < 0.01$ versus control.

TABLE 2. Mitochondria and sarcomeres were analyzed by electron microscopy in a blinded manner

	Mitochondria (%)			Sarcomeres (%)	
	Type A	Type B	Type C	Type A	Type B
Control	31.1	16.8	52.1	49.1	50.9
Supplemented	39.7[a]	11.0[b]	49.3	59.2[a]	40.8[a]

NOTATION: Type A mitochondria, normal; Type B mitochondria, swollen, with an intact membrane and a thinner matrix; Type C mitochondria, ruptured membranes. Type A sarcomeres, normal; Type B sarcomeres, presence of contraction bands and/or necrosis.

[a] $p < 0.01$, supplemented versus control group.

[b] $p < 0.05$, supplemented versus control group.

Our results suggest that an oral supplementation of the four trace elements implicated in antioxidant enzyme activity can modulate the Mn-SOD activity and simultaneously reduce functional and structural post-ischemic damage.

ACUTE TREATMENT WITH ANTIOXIDANT TRACE ELEMENTS: THE EXAMPLE OF MANGANESE

Another strategy to protect myocardium against reperfusion injury might consist in an acute administration of high doses of antioxidant trace elements. In this kind of treatment, there are two main approaches to limit oxidative damage: prevention of initiation and prevention of propagation. Ideally, preventing the formation of an initiating radical, such as superoxide, is the best approach. Limiting superoxide formation or facilitating its removal is an attractive option because it is required for hydroxyl radical production. This prevention can be obtained by enhancing superoxide anion dismutation. Various studies have reported protective effects of SOD against stunning in animal models of myocardial ischemia.[50,51] However, because SOD does not enter readily into cells, has a short half-life, and must be administered parenterally, its clinical use has been often disappointing.[51] For these reasons, there is an increasing interest in developing synthetic SOD mimics that should present more favorable pharmacological properties than native SOD. Among these molecules, a great number of Mn complexes have been designed.

Mn is a constituent of connective tissue as well as of many enzymes, particularly mitochondrial SOD. Furthermore, it is able to activate more than 50 different enzymatic systems. Its ionic radius being close to that of calcium, Mn interferes with calcium transport, causing derangements in cardiac electrophysiological processes. It has been shown to exert a negative inotropic effect through its calcium antagonistic properties. Although manganese is a naturally occurring trace element within the body, much attention must be paid to its possible interference with cardiac function. Despite this possible unfavorable effect, manganese offers potentially interesting properties.

It has been shown *in vitro*[44] that superoxide anions oxidize divalent manganese to the trivalent state in the presence of proton donors, with concomitant production of hydrogen peroxide. Trivalent Mn is then reduced to the divalent state by a second superoxide anion. Moreover, hydrogen peroxide reacts rapidly with trivalent Mn to

TABLE 3. Functional variables after 60-min reperfusion

	Control	Mn10	Mn60
N	11	11	6
Coronary flow (ml/min)	5.20 ± 0.47	5.82 ± 0.43	$2.83 \pm 0.40^{a,b}$
Left ventricular end-diastolic pressure (mm Hg)	69.60 ± 3.63	71.00 ± 2.14	69.00 ± 3.38
Systolic pressure (mm Hg)	92.80 ± 3.71	101.42 ± 2.30	84.33 ± 1.71^{b}
Recovery of developed pressure (%)	18.09 ± 3.26	26.60 ± 4.41	12.98 ± 2.33
–dP/dt (mm Hg/s)	1012.50 ± 123.05	1187.50 ± 144.88	$395.83 \pm 109.19^{a,c}$
+dP/dt (mm Hg/s)	1300.00 ± 153.30	2041.70 ± 201.54^{a}	1229.17 ± 198.64^{c}

NOTATION: Control = 60-min perfusion without manganese; Mn10 = received 10^{-4} M $MnCl_2$ only during the first 10 min of reperfusion; Mn60 = received 10^{-4} M $MnCl_2$ throughout reperfusion.

$^{a}p < 0.01$ versus Control. $^{b}p < 0.01$ versus Mn10. $^{c}p < 0.05$ versus Mn10.

form oxygen. Recent studies have reported antioxidant properties of Mn both *in vitro*[52] and *in vivo.*[53] Negative inotropic and chronotropic effects under conditions of normoxic perfusion have been observed.[54,55] But to our knowledge, no study has examined the effects of Mn on rat isolated hearts submitted to ischemia-reperfusion.

Mn, primarily as an antioxidant trace element but possibly also as a calcium antagonist, might exert protective effects upon reperfusion of ischemic myocardium. We recently studied this potential protection in rat isolated hearts submitted to 30 minutes of normothermic global total ischemia followed by 60 minutes of reperfusion. The protection of post-ischemic myocardium was investigated in terms of functional and metabolic recovery. Mn, as a simple inorganic salt $MnCl_2$ (10^{-4} M), was administered either throughout reperfusion or only during the first ten minutes of reperfusion.[56]

$MnCl_2$ administered during the first 10 minutes, i.e., when the oxidative burst occurs, enhanced recovery of developed pressure, whereas Mn treatment throughout reperfusion reduced coronary flow and recovery of developed pressure (TABLE 3). In both treated groups, Mn improved the recovery of energy metabolism (TABLE 4).

TABLE 4. The effect of manganese on the recovery of energy metabolism

	Control	Mn10	Mn60
ATP (μmol/g prot)	6.44 ± 0.79	9.26 ± 0.79^{a}	9.51 ± 0.61^{a}
ATP+ADP+AMP (μmol/g prot)	15.40 ± 1.28	19.77 ± 1.54	$26.96 \pm 1.91^{b,c}$
PCr+creatine (μmol/g prot)	26.83 ± 1.15	38.77 ± 3.35^{b}	51.84 ± 5.45^{b}

NOTATION: Effects of 60-min reperfusion on tissue ATP, ATP+ADP+AMP, and PCr+creatine contents measured in hearts reperfused without $MnCl_2$ (Control); with 10^{-4} M $MnCl_2$ during the first 10 min of reperfusion (Mn10); or with 10^{-4} M $MnCl_2$ throughout the reperfusion (Mn60).

$^{a}p < 0.05$ versus Contol. $^{b}p < 0.01$ versus Control. $^{c}p < 0.05$ versus Mn10.

Calcium antagonism appears unlikely to be the explanation for the protective effect of Mn in our experimental conditions since it was administered only during reperfusion, i.e., when administration of calcium antagonists fails to protect myocardial cells and improve functional recovery. Mn seems to exert its protective effect on post-ischemic myocardium essentially by protecting cardiomyocyte membranes against oxidative stress, thereby limiting loss of adenyl nucleotides. This would result in the protection of metabolism, which in turn would favor a better functional recovery.

Mn also seems to enhance ATP turnover. It can be proposed that Mn, by retarding calcium uptake in mitochondria upon reperfusion, might antagonize adverse effects of calcium overload, such as inhibition of NAD^+-linked oxidations,[57] uncoupling of oxidative phosphorylation, inhibition of ATP synthesis,[58] and swelling of mitochondria. The protection of metabolic status might also be explained by the interaction of Mn with key mitochondrial enzymes.

ANTIOXIDANT TRACE ELEMENT COMPLEXES

As previously noticed, low molecular weight SOD mimics should be useful pharmaceutical agents in conditions of oxidative stress. The catalytic abilities of certain transition metal cations encouraged the view that such mimics could be found. These synthetic antioxidants generally retain a functional group chemistry analogous to that of natural cellular antioxidants and introduce new chemical groups that enhance their range of cellular action or make them available to cell sites hitherto restricted. Since one of the main limitations remains the possible toxicity of such synthetic mimics in living systems, such compounds, and any dissociation or metabolic products, should present minimal or no toxicity.

Synthetic Copper Complexes

The first low molecular weight SOD mimics were Cu complexes that showed antitumor-promoting activity in mice.[59,60] High stability of Cu complexes is imperative to their possible use as therapeutic antioxidant agents because free Cu^{2+} is likely to have harmful effects, promoting oxygen radical damage to lipids, DNA, and proteins. One of the most effective Cu complexes seems to be Cu-3,5-diisopropylsalicylate, which has been shown to limit ischemia-reperfusion injury.[61] Many other Cu-based SOD mimics have been synthesized and studied.[62] While their *in vitro* SOD activities are high, they have provided mixed results *in vivo*, mainly due to the fact that Cu complexes often have dual activities as anti-oxidant and pro-oxidant.[63] Furthermore, some Cu complexes initially recognized as SOD mimics[64] have recently been shown to exert cytotoxic effects toward human fibroblasts.[65]

Synthetic Manganese Complexes

Mn complexes are of particular interest because, unlike Cu, Mn (MnII), should it be liberated from the complex, does not participate in Fenton reaction. Fridovich and colleagues[66,67] originally described *in vitro* studies with SOD mimics, which were complexes of desferrioxamine and MnO_2. Other low molecular weight Mn macrocyclic ligand complexes have been studied as SOD mimics[68,69] and have been shown to provide some degree of protection against ischemia-reperfusion injury in the rabbit isolated heart.[70] A porphyrin Mn(III) complex has been shown to protect SOD-competent *E. coli*[71] and mammalian cell lines against paraquat toxicity. Another group of SOD mimics, cyclic polyamine complexes of Mn(III), catalyzes the dismutation of superoxide at approximately 1% of the rate exhibited by SOD and could protect endothelial cells against superoxide anion–induced damage generated by activated neutrophils or by the xanthine oxidase reaction.[72]

In vivo studies using Mn macrocyclic compounds suggest a protective effect against myocardial ischemia-reperfusion injury.[70] At the same time, Mn porphyrins were shown to mimic SOD and to substitute for it both *in vitro* and *in vivo.*[71]

Salen-Manganese Complexes

EUK-8: A Prototype Molecule

Salen-manganese (salen = *N,N'*-bis-salicyden aminoethane) complexes are stable complexes that contain Mn III at rest as well as oxygen binding sites. These complexes have been shown to possess both SOD-[73] and CAT-like activities.[74,75] They act catalytically, presumably enhancing their efficiency over noncatalytic low molecular weight radical scavengers. Furthermore, their ability to scavenge both superoxide anion and hydrogen peroxide should enhance their protective effect in various oxidative pathologies implicating multiple reactive oxygen species.

EUK-8 (Eukarion Inc., Bedford, MA) is considered the prototype molecule of a new family of antioxidant compounds and is now the most widely studied of these synthetic catalytic antioxidant complexes (FIG. 2). It is stable in solution (half-life > 15 h at pH 1.5) and has a low molecular weight (355 g/mol). The Mn III present at the center of the molecule gives it solubility in water, whereas its aromatic rings make it a rather lipophilic molecule that may easily enter through cellular membranes. This structure is in some way similar to that of mitochondrial Mn-SOD, in which Mn is associated with four ligands, three of which are imidazole rings. The SOD-like activity of EUK-8 has been demonstrated using a coupled indirect assay method in which it effectively suppressed the rate of reduction of the indicator molecule nitroblue tetrazolium.[73] This activity was not due to a direct inhibition of xanthine oxidase and was shown to be of catalytic nature. EUK-8 also exhibits CAT-like activity, based on its ability to generate oxygen in the presence of hydrogen peroxide, as well as peroxidase activity.[77,78] The ability of EUK-8 to suppress cellular lipid peroxidation was first demonstrated by measuring levels of malondialdehyde in a model of isolated hippocampal slices submitted to lactic acidosis–induced oxidative stress.[79] An electrophysi-

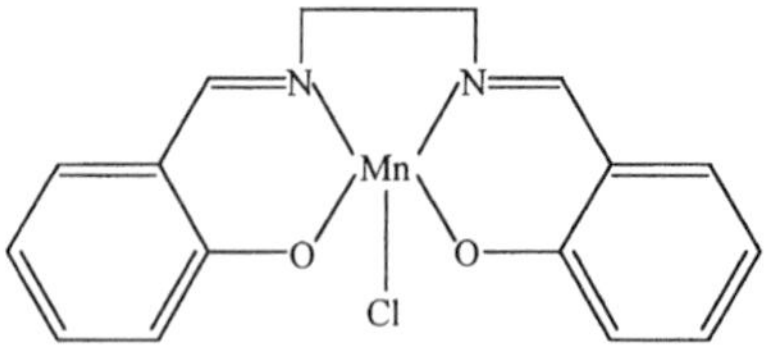

FIGURE 2. Structure of EUK-8.

ological study of excitatory post-synaptic potentials of rat hippocampal slices subjected to anoxia-reoxygenation sequences attested to the functional protection afforded by EUK-8.[79] Studies on the effects of EUK-8 in experimental models of disease were reviewed by Doctrow and colleagues.[80] EUK-8 was evaluated in a porcine model for sepsis-induced adult respiratory distress syndrome. Intravenously administered EUK-8 reduced pulmonary hypertension, arterial hypoxemia, and loss of dynamic pulmonary compliance and also abrogated pulmonary edema.[75] Because of the susceptibility of the brain to oxidative damage, as well as the profound lack of effective treatment for oxidative neurological disorders, such as Parkinson's and Alzheimer's diseases, several studies have focused on the potential protective effects of EUK-8. This complex protects organotypic hippocampal slices from neurotoxicity induced by beta-amyloid peptide.[81] EUK-8, administered intraperitoneally or orally, also exhibits protection against neurotoxin (6-hydroxydopamine and MPTP)-induced damages.

EUK-8 and Myocardial Reperfusion Injury

We have demonstrated that EUK-8 (5×10^{-5} M) present in perfusion fluid reduces the severity of reperfusion-induced arrhythmias of rat isolated hearts submitted to 10-min regional ischemia induced by left coronary ligation.[82] Using *in vitro* rat heart preparations, isolated from iron-overloaded animals, we have also studied the effects of EUK-8 on post-ischemic structural and functional damage. Indeed, in a previous study,[83] we reported that iron overload obtained by intramuscular injections of an iron-dextran solution every third day during a 5-week period, by enhancing Fenton and Haber-Weiss reactions, increased the sensitivity of cardiac tissue to ischemia-reperfusion damage.

TABLE 5. Functional parameters before and after ischemia and reperfusion in untreated and EUK-8–treated hearts

	Heart Rate (beats/min)	Systolic Pressure (mm Hg)	Diastolic Pressure (mm Hg)	Heart Rate × Left Ventricular Developed Pressure (10^{-3})	Frequency 24of Ventricular Fibrillations
Control Group					
Before Ischemia	276 ± 11	78 ± 7	6.3 ± 0.3	19.6 ± 1.6	
1-min Reperfusion	96 ± 0	40 ± 6	26.5 ± 6.0	4.2 ± 1.7	5/7
15-min Reperfusion	232 ± 15	62 ± 10	13.6 ± 4.2	12.6 ± 2.3	
EUK-8–Treated Group					
Before Ischemia	278 ± 7	90 ± 2	5.4 ± 0.3	23.5 ± 0.9	
1-min Reperfusion	130 ± 13[b]	72 ± 8[a]	5.8 ± 0.5[a]	9.9 ± 0.8[a]	2/8
15-min Reperfusion	241 ± 15	92 ± 15	8.3 ± 0.6	21.7 ± 3.4	

NOTATION: Functional parameters measured at the end of the 15-min equilibration period (before ischemia), and 1 and 15 min following reperfusion after a 15-min ischemic period in untreated hearts (control group) and in EUK-8–treated hearts.

[a] $p < 0.05$, EUK-8–treated versus control group.

[b] $p < 0.01$, EUK-8–treated versus control group.

TABLE 6. Effect of EUK-8 on mitochondria and sarcomeres

	Mitochondria (%)			Sarcomeres (%)	
	Type A	Type B	Type C	Type A	Type B
Normoxia	38.0	5.1	56.9	75.0	25.0
Ischemia-reperfusion					
Control group	10.4	21.0	68.5	21.3	78.7
EUK-8–treated group	31.0[a]	15.2[a]	53.8[a]	60.6[a]	39.4[a]

NOTATION: Mitochondria and sarcomeres were analyzed by electron microscopy in a blinded manner. Type A mitochondria, normal; Type B mitochondria, swollen, with an intact membrane and a thinner matrix; Type C mitochondria, ruptured membranes. Type A sarcomeres, normal; Type B sarcomeres, presence of contraction bands and/or necrosis.

[a] $p < 0.01$, EUK-8–treated versus control group.

When isolated hearts were submitted to 15-min normothermic global total ischemia followed by 15-min reperfusion, functional parameters (systolic and diastolic pressures, and oxygen consumption as estimated by the product of heart rate and left ventricular systolic pressure) appeared severely impaired after reperfusion. In the presence of EUK-8 (5×10^{-5} M) in the perfusion medium, cardiac function almost fully recovered to pre-ischemic values (TABLE 5). Electron microscopic analysis of heart tissue after 15-min reperfusion showed extensive damage to mitochondria and sarcomeres in untreated hearts, while the extent of damage was significantly reduced in EUK-8–treated hearts (FIG. 3, TABLE 6).

These beneficial effects have been attributed to the catalytic antioxidant properties of EUK-8. However, it should be noted that a recent study on isolated aortic rings has shown that EUK-8 exerts a dose-dependent vasorelaxant effect independent of its antioxidant properties,[84] which could play a role in its protective effect against ischemia-reperfusion damage. These results suggest that such Mn complexes may have some therapeutic potential. Indeed, under pathophysiological conditions, such as ischemia and post-ischemic reperfusion, a molecule able to exert both an antioxidant and a vasodilatory effect would be extremely interesting as it would improve circulatory function while protecting the vascular system, which is the first target of oxygen free radicals in such situations.

CONCLUSION

The hypothesis that reactive oxygen species mediate cellular damage produced upon reperfusion of ischemic myocardium has gained considerable support during the past ten years. The results of several experimental studies indicate that the administration of antioxidant enzymes or antioxidants offers a significant degree of protection against post-ischemic reperfusion damage, improving functional recovery and reducing morphological alterations to cardiomyocytes. In this respect, several trace elements (Cu, Zn, Mn, Se), because they are involved in the catalytic activity and spatial conformation of antioxidant enzymes such as SOD and GPx, might play an important role in the antioxidant defense capacity of cardiac tissue. Some results from animal experiments have shown that the dietary intake of such trace elements can modulate the degree of reperfusion damage. Recently, Mn-SOD

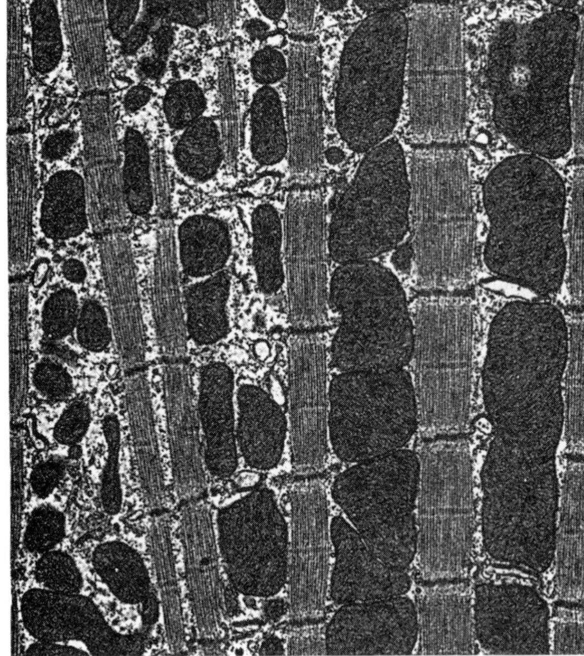

FIGURE 3. Electron micrographs of left ventricular tissue from hearts subjected to 15-min of ischemia followed by 15-min of reperfusion. **(top)** Untreated hearts. **(bottom)** Hearts treated with EUK-8. Enlargement is 11,300×.

has been suggested to play a special role in this functional improvement. For this reason, a new family of compounds, salen-Mn complexes, has been developed. These agents exhibit catalytic SOD- and CAT-like activities and may therefore be of considerable interest in clinical conditions. However, well-designed, randomized, placebo-controlled experimental and clinical trials of such compounds should be performed to determine the possible therapeutic potential efficiency of such agents.

ACKNOWLEDGMENT

The authors thank Dr. Michèle Bernier for critical reading of the manuscript and useful comments.

REFERENCES

1. Perry, H.M. *et al.* 1991. Concentration of trace metals (Cd, Zn, Se, Cu, Cr and Fe) in organs (heart, kidney and liver) of subjects with myocardial infarction or hypertension. WHO/IAEA Myocardial Infarction and Hypertension Autopsy Study. J. Trace Elem. Exp. Med. **4:** 109–128.
2. Pucheu, S. *et al.* 1995. Time-course of changes in plasma levels of trace elements after thrombolysis during the acute phase of myocardial infarction in humans. Biol. Trace Elem. Res. **47:** 171–182.
3. Kusleikaite, M. & R. Masironi. 1996. Trace elements in prognosis of myocardial infarction and sudden coronary death. J. Trace Elem. Exp. Med. **9:** 57–62.
4. Bolli, R. 1991. Oxygen-derived free radicals and myocardial reperfusion injury: an overview. Cardiovasc. Drugs Ther. **5:** 249–268.
5. Hearse, D.J. 1992. Stunning: a radical review. *In* Stunning, Hibernation, and Calcium in Myocardial Ischemia and Reperfusion. L.H. Opie, Eds: 10–55. Kluwer Academic Publishers. Boston, MA.
6. Guarnieri, C. *et al.* 1996. Alpha-tocopherol pretreatment improves endothelium-dependent vasodilation in aortic strips of young and aging rats exposed to oxidative stress. Mol. Cell. Biochem. **157:** 223–228.
7. Garlick, P.B. *et al.* 1987. Direct detection of free radicals in the reperfused rat heart using electron spin resonance spectroscopy. Circ. Res. **61:** 757–760.
8. Bolli, R. *et al.* 1989. Marked reduction of free radical generation and contractile dysfunction by antioxidant therapy begun at the time of reperfusion. Evidence that myocardial stunning is a manifestation of reperfusion injury. Circ. Res. **65:** 607–622.
9. Arroyo, C.M. *et al.* 1987. Identification of free radicals in myocardial ischemia/reperfusion by spin trapping with nitrone DMPO. FEBS Lett. **221:** 101–104.
10. Baker, J.E. *et al.* 1988. Myocardial ischemia and reperfusion: direct evidence for free radical generation by electron spin resonance spectroscopy. Proc. Natl. Acad. Sci. USA **85:** 2786–2789.
11. Charlon, V. & J. De Leiris. 1988. Ability of N-tert-butyl alpha phenylnitrone (PBN) to be used in isolated perfused rat heart spin trapping experiments: preliminary studies. Basic Res. Cardiol. **83:** 306–313.
12. Boucher, F. *et al.* 1992. Evidence of cytosolic iron release during post-ischaemic reperfusion of isolated rat hearts. Influence of spin-trapping experiments with DMPO. FEBS Lett. **302:** 261–264.
13. Yu, B.P. 1994. Cellular defenses against damage from reactive oxygen species. Physiol. Rev. **74:** 139–162.
14. Ji, L.L. *et al.* 1992. Antioxidant enzyme response to selenium deficiencies in rat myocardium. J. Am. Coll. Nutr. **11:** 79–86.
15. Fridovich, I. 1995. Superoxide radical and superoxide dismutases. Annu. Rev. Biochem. **64:** 97–112.

16. Flores, S.C. *et al.* 1993. Tat protein of human immunodeficiency virus type 1 represses expression of manganese superoxide dismutase in HeLa cells. Proc. Natl. Acad. Sci. USA **90:** 7632–7636.
17. Singh, R.K. *et al.* 1992. Potential use of simple manganese salts as antioxidant drugs in horses. Am. J. Vet. Res. **53:** 1822–1829.
18. Coassin, M. *et al.* 1992. Antioxidant effect of manganese. Arch. Biochem. Biophys. **299:** 330–333.
19. Chipperfield, B. 1978. Dietary factors in the development of ischaemic heart disease. Chest **3:** 3–9.
20. Mertz, W. 1982. Trace minerals and atherosclerosis. Fed. Proc. **41:** 2807–2812.
21. Chipperfield, B. 1986. Metals and ischemic heart disease. Rev. Environ. Health **6:** 209–250.
22. Bray, T.M. & W.J. Bettger. 1990. The physiological role of zinc as an antioxidant. Free Radical Biol. Med. **8:** 281–291.
23. Coudray, C. *et al.* 1992. Superoxide dismutase activity and zinc status: a study in animals and man. J. Nutr. Med. **3:** 13–26.
24. Searle, A.J.F. & A. Tomasi. 1982. Hydroxyl free radical production in iron-cystein solutions and protection by zinc. J. Inorg. Biochem. **17:** 161–166.
25. Coudray, C. *et al.* 1993. Effect of zinc deficiency on lipid peroxidation status and infarct size in rat hearts. Int. J. Cardiol. **41:** 109–113.
26. Jain, V.K. & G. Mohan. 1991. Serum zinc and copper in myocardial infarction with particular reference to prognosis. Biol. Trace Elem. Res. **31:** 317–322.
27. Faure, P. *et al.* 1991. Effect of an acute zinc depletion on rat lipoproteine and peroxidation. Biol. Trace Elem. Res. **28:** 135–146.
28. Burk, R.F. 1989. Recent developments in trace element metabolism and function: newer roles of selenium in nutrition. J. Nutr. **119:** 1051–1054.
29. Whanger, P.D. 1989. China, a country with both selenium deficiency and toxicity: some thoughts and impressions. J. Nutr. **119:** 1236–1239.
30. Rotruck, J.T. *et al.* 1973. Selenium: biochemical role as component of glutathione peroxidase. Science **179:** 588–590.
31. Nouguchi, T. *et al.* 1973. Mode of action of selenium and Vit. E in prevention of exudative diathesis in chicks. J. Nutr. **103:** 1502–1511.
32. Mercurio, F.D. 1986. Selenium-dependent glutathione peroxidase inhibitors increase toxicity of pro-oxidant compounds. J. Nutr. **116:** 1726–1734.
33. Kok, F. *et al.* 1989. Decreased selenium levels in acute myocardial infarction. J. Am. Med. Assoc. **261:** 1161–1164.
34. Beaglehole, R. *et al.* 1990. Decreased blood selenium and risk of myocardial infarction. Int. J. Epidemiol. **19:** 918–922.
35. Suadicani, P. *et al.* 1992. Serum selenium concentration and risk of ischaemic heart disease in a prospective cohort study of 3000 males. Atherosclerosis **96:** 33–42.
36. Konz, K.H. *et al.* 1991. Selenium as a protector of diastolic function during oxidant stress. J. Trace Elem. Elect. H. **5:** 87–93.
37. Poltronieri, R. *et al.* 1992. Protective effect of selenium in cardiac ischemia and reperfusion. Cardioscience **3:** 155–160.
38. Hassan, H.M. 1988. Biosynthesis and regulation of superoxide dismutases. Free Radical Biol. Med. **5:** 377–385.
39. Allen, C.B. & J.T. Saari. 1993. Isolated hearts from copper-deficient rats exhibit improved postischemic contractile performance. J. Nutr. **123:** 1794–1800.
40. Fields, M. *et al.* 1991. The severity of copper deficiency can be ameliorated by deferoxamine. Metabolism **40:** 105–109.
41. Chao, P.Y. & K.G. Allen. 1992. Glutathione production in copper-deficient isolated rat hepatocytes. Free Radical Biol. Med. **12:** 145–150.
42. Klevay, L.M. & E.K. Viestenz. 1981. Abnormal electrocardiograms in rats deficient in copper. Am. J. Physiol. **240:** H185–189.
43. Kopp, S.J. *et al.* 1983. Physiological and metabolic characterization of a cardiomyopathy induced by chronic copper deficiency. Am. J. Physiol. **245:** H855–856.
44. Archibald, F.S. & I. Fridovich. 1982. The scavenging of superoxide radical by manganese complexes: *in vitro*. Arch. Biochem. Biophys. **214:** 452–463.

45. Borello, S. *et al.* 1992. Transcriptional regulation of MnSOD by manganese in the liver of manganese deficient mice and during rat development. Biochemistry Int. **28:** 595–601.
46. Paynter, D.I. 1980. Changes in activity of the manganese superoxide dismutase enzyme in tissue of the rat with changes in dietary manganese. J. Nutr. **110:** 437–447.
47. Davis, C.D. & J.L. Greger. 1992. Longitudinal changes of manganese-dependent superoxide dismutase and other indexes of manganese and iron status in women. Am. J. Clin. Nutr. **55:** 747–752.
48. Hussain, S. *et al.* 1997. The effects of chronic exposure of manganese on antioxidant enzymes in different regions of rat brain. Neurosci. Res. Commun. **21:** 135–144.
49. Pucheu, S. 1994. Contribution à l'étude des manifestations physiopathologiques liées au stress oxydatif intervenant lors de la reperfusion du myocarde ischémique: rôle des oligoéléments et essais de protection par des molécules antioxydantes. Ph.D. thesis, Joseph Fourier University, Grenoble, France.
50. Przylenk, K. & R.A. Kloner. 1986. Superoxide dismutase plus catalase improve contractile function in the canine model of the "stunned myocardium." Circ. Res. **58:** 148–156.
51. Bolli, R. 1991. Superoxide dismutase 10 years later: A drug in search of use. J. Am. Coll. Cardiol. **18:** 231–233.
52. Stadtman, E.R. *et al.* 1990. Manganese-dependent disproportionation of hydrogen peroxide in bicarbonate buffer. Proc. Natl. Acad. Sci. USA **87:** 384-388.
53. Varani, J. *et al.* 1991. Hydrogen peroxide-induced cell and tissue injury: protective effect of Mn. Inflammation **15:** 291–301.
54. Brurok, H. *et al.* 1995. Effects of manganese dipyridoxyl diphosphate, dipyridoxyl diphosphate, and manganese chloride on cardiac function. Invest. Radiol. **30:** 159–167.
55. Brurok, H. *et al.* 1997. Manganese and the heart: acute cardiodepression and myocardial accumulation of manganese. Acta Physiol. Scand. **159:** 33–40.
56. Barandier, C.E. *et al.* 1998. Manganese reduces myocardial reperfusion injury on isolated rat heart. J. Mol. Cell. Cardiol. **30:** 837–847.
57. Lindberg, O. & L. Ernster. 1954. Manganese, as a co-factor of oxidative phosphorylation. Nature **173:** 1038–1039.
58. Hillered, L. *et al.* 1983. Mn^{2+} prevents the Ca^{2+}-induced inhibition of ATP synthesis in brain mitochondria. FEBS Lett. **154:** 247–250.
59. Kensler, T.W. *et al.* 1983. Inhibition of tumor promotion by a biomimetic SOD. Science **221:** 75–77.
60. Yamamoto, S. *et al.* 1990. Anti-tumor promoting action of phthalic acid mono-n-butyl ester cupric salt. Carcinogenesis **11:** 749–754.
61. Hernandez, L.A. *et al.* 1987. Effects of Cu-DIPS on ischemia-reperfusion injury. *In* Biology of Copper Complexes. J.R.J. Sorenson, Ed.: 201–214. Humana Press. Clifton, NJ
62. Sorenson, J.R.J. 1989. Copper complexes offer a physiological approach to treatment of chronic diseases. Prog. Med. Chem. **26:** 437–568.
63. Nagele, A. *et al.* 1993. Induction of oxidative stress and protection against hydrogen peroxide-mediated cytotoxicity by the superoxide dismutase-mimetic complex copper-putrescine-pyridine. Biochem. Pharmacol. **47:** 555–562.
64. Brigelius, R. *et al.* 1974. Superoxide dismutase activity of low molecular weight Cu^{2+}-chelates studied by pulse radiolysis. FEBS Lett. **47:** 72–75.
65. Arena, G. *et al.* 1993. Cytotoxic and cytostatic activity of copper(II) complexes. Importance of the speciation for the correct interpretation of the *in vitro* biological results. J. Inorg. Biochem. **50:** 31–45.
66. Beyer, W. & I. Fridovich. 1989. Characterisation of a superoxide dismutase mimic prepared from desferrioxamine and MnO_2. Arch. Biochem. Biophys. **271:** 149–156.
67. Darr, D. *et al.* 1987. A mimic of superoxide dismutase activity based upon desferrioxamine B and manganese (IV). Arch. Biochem. Biophys. **258:** 351–355.

68. RILEY, D.P. & R.H. WEISS. 1994. Manganese macrocyclic ligand complexes as mimics of superoxide dismutase. J. Am. Chem. Soc. **116:** 387–388.
69. WEISS, R.H. *et al.* 1993. Evaluation of activity of putative superoxide dismutase mimics: direct analysis by stopped-flow kinetics. J. Biol. Chem. **268:** 23049–23054.
70. KILGORE, K.S. *et al.* 1994. Protective effects of the SOD-mimetic SC-52608 against ischemia-reperfusion damage in the rabbit isolated heart. J. Mol. Cell. Cardiol. **26:** 995–1006.
71. FAULKNER, K.M. *et al.* 1994. Stable Mn (II) porphyrins mimic superoxide dismutase *in vitro* and substitute for it *in vivo*. J. Biol. Chem. **269:** 23471–23476.
72. HARDY, M.M. *et al.* 1994. Superoxide dismutase mimetics inhibit neutrophil-mediated human aortic endothelial cell injury *in vitro*. J. Biol. Chem. **269:** 18535–18540.
73. BAUDRY, M. *et al.* 1993. Salen-manganese complexes are superoxide dismutase-mimics. Biochem. Biophys. Res. Commun. **192:** 964–968.
74. MALFROY-CAMINE, B. & M. BAUDRY. 1995. Synthetic catalytic free radical scavengers useful as antioxidants for prevention and therapy of disease. U.S. Patent #5,403,834. April, 4.
75. GONZALEZ, P.K. *et al.* 1995. EUK-8, a synthetic superoxide dismutase and catalase mimetic, ameliorates acute lung injury in endotoxemic swine. J. Pharmacol. Exp. Ther. **275:** 798–806.
76. MCCORD, J.M. *et al.* 1973. Superoxide and superoxide dismutase. *In* Oxidases and Related Redox Systems. University Press. Baltimore, MD
77. PUCHEU, S. *et al.* 1995. Protective effect of superoxide scavenger EUK8 against ultrastructural alterations induced by ischemia and reperfusion in isolated rat hearts. Nutrition **11:** 582–584.
78. PUCHEU, S. *et al.* 1996. A synthetic catalytic scavenger of reactive oxygen species protects isolated iron-overloaded rat heart from functional and structural damage induced by ischemia/reperfusion. Cardiovasc. Drugs Ther. **10:** 331–339.
79. MUSLEH, W. *et al.* 1994. Effects of EUK-8, a synthetic catalytic scavenger on hypoxia and acidosis induced damage in hippocampal slices. Neuropharmacology **33:** 929–934.
80. DOCTROW, S.R. *et al.* 1997. Salen-manganese complexes: combined superoxide dismutase/catalase mimics with broad pharmacological efficacy. Adv. Pharmacol. **38:** 247–269.
81. BRUCE, A. *et al.* 1996. Beta-amyloid toxicity in organotypic hippocampal cultures: protection by EUK-8, a synthetic catalytic free radical scavenger. Proc. Natl. Acad. Sci. USA **93:** 2312–2316.
82. TANGUY, S. *et al.* 1997. Free radicals in reperfusion-induced arrhythmias: a study with EUK8 a novel non protein catalytic antioxidant. Free Radical Biol. Med. **21:** 945–954.
83. PUCHEU, S., *et al.* 1993. Effect of iron overload in the isolated ischemic and reperfused rat heart. Cardiovasc. Drugs Ther. **7:** 701–711.
84. BARANDIER, C. *et al.* 1997. Vasodilatory effects of a salen-manganese complex with potent oxyradical scavenger activities. J. Vasc. Res. **34:** 49–57.

Apoptosis in Isolated Adult Cardiomyocytes Exposed to Adriamycin[a]

DINENDER KUMAR, LORRIE KIRSHENBAUM, TIMAO LI, IGOR DANELISEN, AND PAWAN SINGAL[b]

Institute of Cardiovascular Sciences, St. Boniface General Hospital Research Centre Department of Physiology, Faculty of Medicine, University of Manitoba, Winnipeg, R2H 2A6, Canada

ABSTRACT: Adriamycin (doxorubicin) is a highly potent antineoplastic agent, but its use is limited by the risk of developing cardiomyopathy and congestive heart failure. Available evidence suggests that adriamycin-induced congestive heart failure is mediated by oxidative stress. We examined the possibility of adriamycin-induced apoptosis in isolated adult rat cardiomyocytes and its inhibition by trolox, a water-soluble antioxidant. Cardiomyocytes isolated from rat hearts were exposed to 20 μM adriamycin for 1 h and examined at different post-treatment durations (0–23 h). Adriamycin caused a significant decrease in rod-shaped cells and an increase in round cells. Both Hoechst 33258 staining and TUNEL assay revealed a significantly increased number of apoptotic myocytes and nucleosomal fragmentation upon exposure to adriamycin. In agarose gel electrophoresis, DNA laddering was found to be more intense in adriamycin-exposed myocytes. A bright smear at the leading edge of the gels suggested indiscriminate fragmentation of DNA and myocyte necrosis by adriamycin. Both types of DNA degradations due to adriamycin were significantly reduced by trolox. We suggest that adriamycin-induced cell death involves both apoptosis and necrosis and these may be mediated by oxidative stress.

INTRODUCTION

Adriamycin (doxorubicin) is an effective antineoplastic agent used for the treatment of a variety of tumors. However, its use is limited because of the serious cardiotoxic side effects.[1,2] Current evidence suggests that increased oxidative stress plays an important role in mediating adriamycin cardiotoxicity.[3–5] Drugs with antioxidant properties have been found to improve the myocardial antioxidant reserve as well as prevent adriamycin-induced cardiomyopathy and congestive heart failure in animal models.[5,6]

Apoptosis, also known as programmed cell death, has been suggested recently to play a role in the pathogenesis of cardiac dysfunction under a variety of experimental

[a]This study was supported by a grant from the Manitoba Heart and Stroke Foundation. Dr. Kirshenbaum was supported by a scholarship from the Heart and Stroke Foundation of Canada and Dr. Singal by a salary award from the Medical Research Council of Canada.

[b]Address correspondence to: Dr. Pawan K. Singal, Ph.D., D.Sc., F.A.C.C., Institute of Cardiovascular Sciences, St. Boniface General Hospital Research Centre, 351 Tache Avenue, Room R3022, Winnipeg, Manitoba R2H 2A6 Canada; Telephone: (204) 235-3416; Fax: (204) 233-6723; E-mail: psingal@sbrc.umanitoba.ca

and clinical conditions.[7–11] Adriamycin has been shown to cause apoptosis in a variety of tissues including kidney, hair follicles, and intestine, as well as in a variety of cell lines.[12–15] Although adriamycin is reported to cause apoptosis in the heart, the phenomenon is suggested to be limited to the interstitial dendritic cells and macrophages.[15] However, it is important to note that morphological features of adriamycin-induced cardiomyopathy[6] suggest that the process may be a regulated event and may occur in a defined fashion. In this regard, adriamycin cardiomyopathy in a variety of animal models is accompanied by morphological changes, including dilatation of the sarcoplasmic reticulum, loss of myofibrils, and ultimately emptying of the myocyte with a minimal immune response.[6,16] Daunorubicin, an analogue of adriamycin, has been reported to cause apoptotic cell death in neonatal rat cardiomyocytes.[17] Thus the occurrence as well as the role of apoptosis in adriamycin cardiomyopathy is still controversial.

Since apoptosis in myocardial infarction has been reported to be an early event,[18] previous reports about the lack of apoptosis in adriamycin cardiomyopathy could be due to a mistiming of the post-treatment duration examined. The dosage of the drug used in these experiments may also have influenced the study outcome as it has been shown that adriamycin-induced death in certain cells depends upon the concentration of the drug used.[19] In order to resolve this issue, we studied adriamycin-induced apoptosis in isolated adult rat cardiomyocytes exposed to different concentrations of adriamycin and examined at different post-treatment durations. Since antioxidants have been shown to be protective in adriamycin cardiomyopathy,[6] the protective effects of trolox, a water-soluble antioxidant and an analogue of vitamin E, were also studied.

MATERIALS AND METHODS

Isolation of Rat Cardiomyocytes

Adult rat ventricular myocytes were isolated by a procedure described earlier.[20,21] Male Sprague-Dawley rats (250–300 g) were injected with sodium heparin and killed after one hour. Thoracotomy was performed, hearts were exposed, and the ascending aorta was cannulated to initiate coronary perfusion *in situ*. Hearts were then excised and mounted on a modified Langerdorff perfusion apparatus that allowed for switching between single-pass and recirculating perfusions at 37°C. The perfusate contained a modified Joklik's minimum essential medium (calcium free) supplemented with 60 mM taurine, 8 mM glutamate, 3.4 mM magnesium chloride, 15 mM glucose, and 0.1% bovine serum albumin with a low fatty acid content (pH 7.4). The perfusion system was switched to the recirculating mode with the Joklik buffer containing 25 μM calcium, 0.1% collagenase, and 0.1% hyaluronidase for 20 min. The hearts were removed from the apparatus, cut into smaller pieces, and incubated in the same buffer for 20 min to facilitate disaggregation. Following incubation, the suspension was gently triturated through pipettes with progressively smaller tip diameters. The suspension was filtered through a nylon mesh (200 μm size) and resuspended in buffer containing 30 mM KCl and 2% albumin and centrifuged at $30 \times g$ for two to three times. Finally, the cell pellet was resuspended in Medium 199 (GIBCO BRL, Gaithersburg, MD) with Hank's salts 1.4 mM $CaCl_2$,

0.68 mM glutamine, 1 μg/ml insulin, 5 μg/ml transferrin, 1 nM LiCl, 1 nM Na_2SeO_4, 25 ng/ml ascorbic acid, 1 nM T_3, 100 U/ml penicillin, and 100 μg/ml streptomycin.

Primary Cell Culture and Drug Treatments

Adult rat myocytes were maintained in a primary cell culture by previously described method.[22,23] Briefly, before cell plating in 35-mm plastic dishes, these dishes were coated with 20 μg/ml laminin at 37°C for 24 h. Cells were pre-plated for 24 h at a density of about 1×10^5 cells per dish in a serum-free medium supplemented with 5 mM carnitine, 5 mM taurine, 5 mM creatine, and 0.2% bovine serum albumin. Cell morphology was examined by bright field and fluorescence microscopy.

After 24 h primary culture, the myocytes were exposed to different concentrations of adriamycin (10–40 μM) in a serum-free medium for 1 h and were observed for up to 23 h following treatment. For a study of the role of oxidative stress, cardiomyocytes were pre-treated with an antioxidant (trolox, 20 μM) for 30 min and then incubated with adriamycin for 1 h.

Analysis of Apoptosis

Hoechst Staining

Myocytes were examined for the occurrence of apoptosis at 0 h, 1 h, and 23 h post-treatment by monitoring for nucleosomal DNA fragmentation. For this, myocytes were fixed with 70% ethanol for 20–30 min, washed in PBS for 10 min, and incubated with bisbenzimide 33258 (1 μg/ml) for 10 min. Myocytes were washed in PBS and mounted on glass slides with antifade medium (0.1% phenylenediamine in 1:9, PBS:glycerol), and examined using epifluorescence microscopy. For quantitative analysis, percent positive cells were calculated by counting fragmented nuclei/100.

TUNEL Assay

After adriamycin treatment, myocytes were fixed in 4% paraformaldehyde for 30 min and washed twice in PBS. Myocytes were incubated with 0.3% H_2O_2 for 30 min to minimize background peroxidase activity and were washed and permeabilized with 0.1% Triton X-100 in 0.1% sodium citrate. For the detection of apoptotic cells by nick-end labeling method, a commercially available kit (Boehringer Mannheim) was used. Reaction was developed with a substrate solution containing diaminobenzidine (DAB) and H_2O_2 for 5 min at room temperature. After three washings, glass coverslips were mounted on glass slides and examined by light microscopy.

DNA Laddering

To characterize the extent of DNA fragmentation by agarose gel electrophoresis following adriamycin treatment, we followed the method of Hirt[24] with some modifications. Myocytes, either treated or untreated, were suspended in 200 μl of lysis buffer (10 mM Tris HCl, pH 8.0; 5 mM EDTA; 100 mM NaCl) supplemented with proteinase K (1 mg/ml) and 20% SDS and digested for 5 h at 37°C. Following digestion, 5 M NaCl was added to the cell suspension and incubated overnight at 4°C. The suspension was centrifuged for 30 min at 12,000 rpm. Supernatant was mixed with 3 μl of RNase and DNA was extracted using phenol:chloroform and ethanol precipitation. The DNA was resuspended in sterile water and analyzed in 0.8% agarose gels stained with ethidium bromide. The gels were visualized under UV light and photographed.

RESULTS

Cell Morphology

Based on the morphological appearance and criteria described before,[21] cells were characterized and counted as rod, round, or intermediate-shaped. Rod-shaped cells are considered viable and are able to contract and relax, whereas round cells stayed contracted and could no longer relax.[21] In a preliminary study, using morphological analysis, we examined myocyte loss at different drug concentrations (10–40 μM) as well as post-treatment durations (0–23 h). Adriamycin at a concentration of 40 μM caused a significant loss of cells and at 23 h post-treatment there were few recognizable rod-shaped cells present. The converse was true at 10 μM of adriamycin, in that the percent of cell loss at 23 h was indistinguishable from that seen in controls. An intermediate dose of 20 μM of adriamycin was found to be optimal with respect to a gradual induction of morphological injury. Thus all experiments in this study were done using 20 μM of adriamycin and 1 h of drug-exposure time followed by 0 to 23 h of post-treatment duration. Although adriamycin was removed from the medium after 1-h exposure, some of the drug may still be present in the myocytes due to its lipophilicity as well as its DNA binding property. A fluorescence microscopy assay was done to confirm that the cardiomyocytes exposed to adriamycin did take up the drug and it was mostly concentrated in the nuclei (FIG. 1). The fluorescence due to adriamycin was not influenced by trolox, suggesting that the latter drug did not interfere with the uptake of adriamycin.

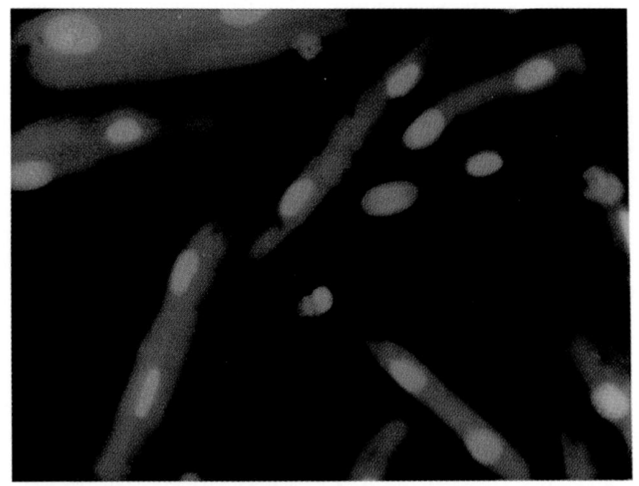

FIGURE 1. Cardiomyocytes exposed to adriamycin. The drug appears in the nuclei and gives a pinkish-orange fluorescence. 400×.

TABLE 1. Effects of adriamycin and trolox on cell morphology and cell viability

Post-Treatment Duration	Cell Morphology		
	Rod	Round	Intermediate
0 h			
CTL	69.8 ± 5.1	24.1 ± 4.8	6.1 ± 2.4
ADR	36.7 ± 4.0[a]	51.7 ± 5.3[a]	11.6 ± 2.9[a]
ADR + TLX	59.1 ± 2.7	33.1 ± 2.8	7.1 ± 2.0
1 h			
CTL	61.8 ± 2.6	28.0 ± 2.9	10.2 ± 1.8
ADR	29.5 ± 5.3[a]	58.7 ± 5.4[a]	12.0 ± 2.2
ADR + TLX	57.0 ± 6.3	32.1 ± 4.6	10.9 ± 3.9
23 h			
CTL	53.4 ± 17.5	40.4 ± 14.9	4.6 ± 1.6
ADR	17.0 ± 6.4[a]	69.5 ± 10.6[a]	13.5 ± 4.5
ADR + TLX	40.3 ± 7.7	39.6 ± 7.4	20.0 ± 4.1

NOTATION: CTL, control; ADR, adriamycin; ADR + TLX, adriamcyin + trolox. Rod, rod-shaped cardiomyocytes; Round, round-shaped cardiomyocytes; and Intermediate, intermediate-shaped cardiomyocytes. The time points of 0 h, 1 h, and 23 h are post-treatment duration. Data are percentage of total cells examined and expressed as mean ± S.E. of five different experiments. For each experiment, cardiomyocytes were freshly prepared from five adult rats. [a]$p < 0.05$, significantly different from other groups.

The zero hour of post-treatment duration in this study is defined as 24 + 1 h following primary culture. The control dish at 0 h had 69.8 ± 5.1% of the rod-shaped myocytes; 24.1 ± 4.8% round-shaped; and 6.1 ± 2.4% intermediate type of myocytes (TABLE 1). Following additional time in culture, the number of rod-shaped myocytes decreased by 11.5% and 23.4% at 1 and 23 h, respectively. During this period, there was a significant increase in the round-shaped myocytes but the number of intermediate-type myocytes fluctuated in the range of 4–10%. Cardiac myocytes exposed to 20 μM adriamycin for 1 h showed a significant decrease ($p < 0.05$) in rod-shaped cells at 0, 1, and 23 h of post-treatment duration, whereas round- and intermediate-type myocytes increased in number (TABLE 1). Exposure to trolox for 30 min before the addition of adriamycin reduced the incidence of cell death and resulted in the maintenance of the number of rod cells near control levels (TABLE 1).

Nuclear Fragmentation

Myocytes were also examined using Hoechst 33258 staining. In control rod-shaped myocytes, the majority of the nuclei had a normal oblong appearance and stained blue (FIG. 2A). Adriamycin exposure resulted in nuclear fragmentation (FIG. 2B). Although nuclear fragmentation was more common in cells that showed shape change, it was not a consistent finding. In the myocytes exposed to trolox before the

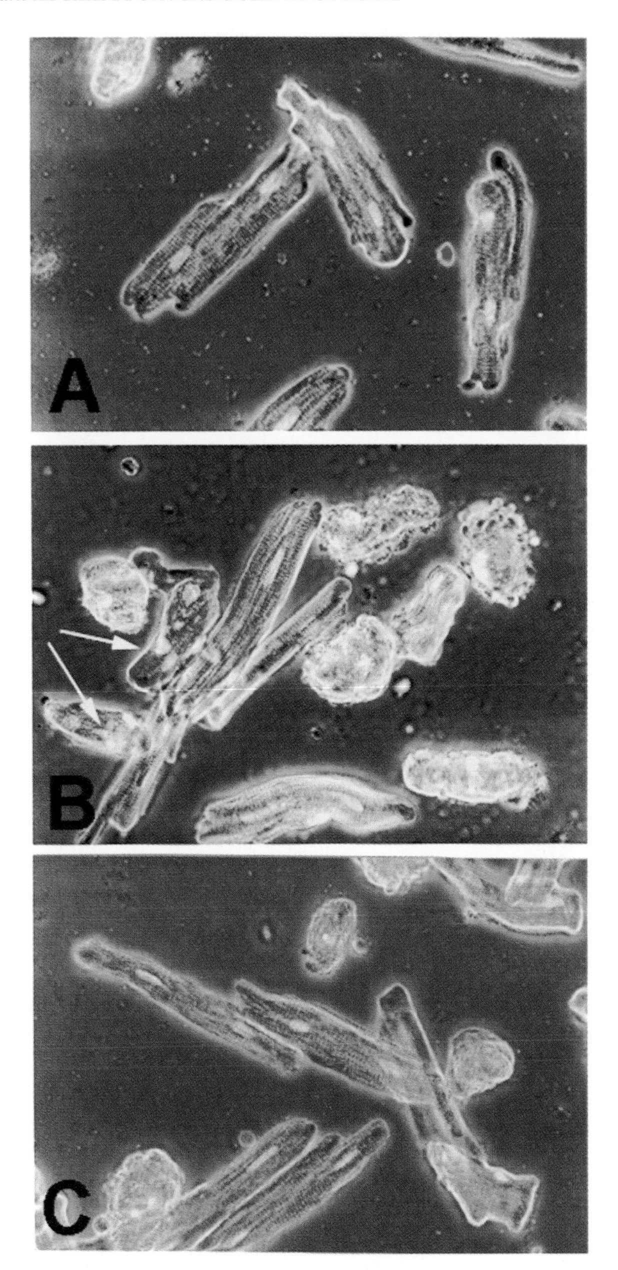

FIGURE 2. Hoechst staining. (**A**) Control myocytes; (**B**) nuclear fragmentation due to adriamycin is shown by arrows; and (**C**) This effect is significantly mitigated by trolox. 1,000×.

adriamycin treatment, the extent of nuclear fragmentation was significantly reduced and comparable to control levels (FIG. 2C).

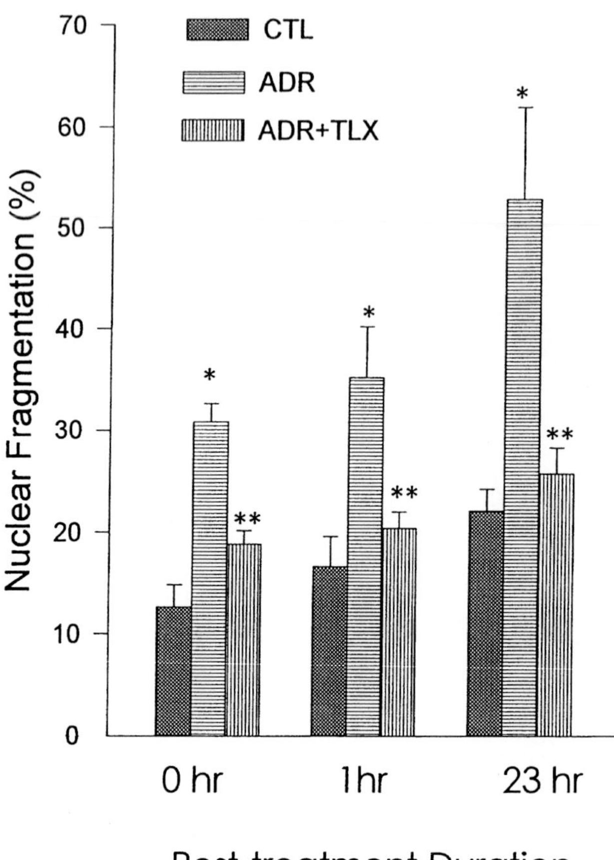

FIGURE 3. Quantitative analysis of the nuclear fragmentation in adult rat cardiomyocytes at 0, 1, and 23 h after exposure to adriamycin (ADR) for 1 h using Hoechst 33258 staining. CTL, control myocytes incubated in the medium for 1, 2, and 24 h labeled here as 0, 1, and 23 h, respectively. ADR + TLX, cells exposed to trolox for 30 min were removed at 0, 1, 23 h ADR post-exposure. Data expressed as mean ± S.E. of five different experiments. *Significantly different ($p < 0.05$) from control and ADR + TLX at the same time point. **Significantly different ($p < 0.05$) from the ADR group.

Quantitative assessment of nuclear fragmentation and apoptosis is shown in FIGURE 3. The number of apoptotic myocytes after exposure to adriamycin for 1 h increased to 31%, 35%, and 52% at 0 h, 1 h, and 23 h of post-treatment durations, respectively, and in the presence of trolox these values were reduced to 19%, 20%, and 25%, respectively. There was a small, insignificant increase in DNA fragmentation in control myocytes after 23 h, which is considered due to ageing in culture as well as serum deprivations.[25]

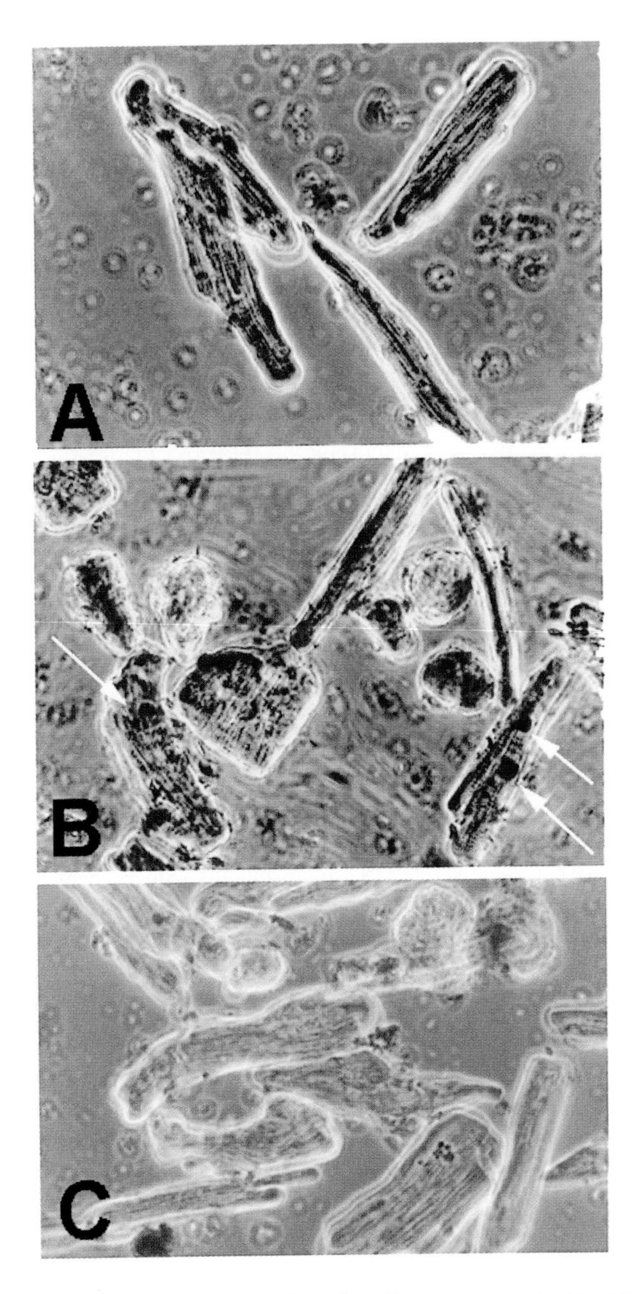

FIGURE 4. Nuclear DNA fragmentation of cardiomyocytes, stained by TUNEL assay using peroxidase. (**A**) Control; (**B**) Adriamycin; and (**C**) Adriamycin + Trolox. TUNEL positive nuclei in the adriamycin group are shown (*arrow*). 1,000×.

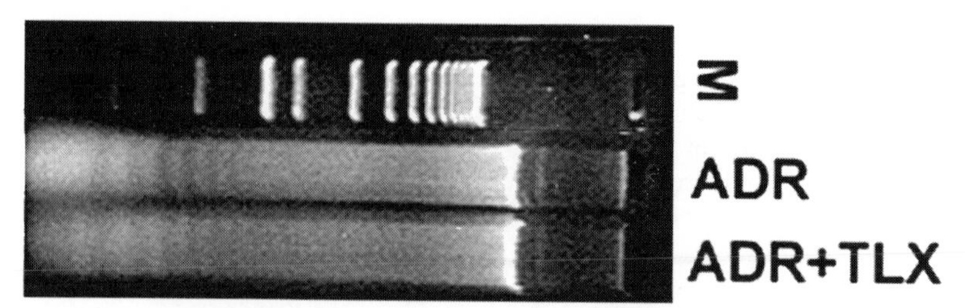

FIGURE 5. Electrophoresis pattern of DNA isolated from cardiomyocytes exposed to adriamycin (ADR), and Adriamycin + Trolox (ADR + TLX). DNA isolation was done 23 h after the exposure. M, molecular weight markers.[7]

In order to further analyze nuclear fragmentation in cardiomyocytes, TUNEL assay with peroxidase staining was done (FIG. 4). A significant increase in the number of apoptotic nuclei, positive with TUNEL assay, was apparent in adriamycin-exposed myocytes (FIG. 4B) compared to controls (FIG. 4A). Pre-treatment with trolox modulated these effects (FIG. 4C).

DNA Laddering

DNA fragmentation was further examined using agarose gel electrophoresis. DNA was extracted from myocytes at 0 h, 1 h, and 23 h post-treatment durations. At 0 h and 1 h post-treatment durations, there was no significant difference in DNA laddering as compared to untreated controls (data not shown). Although there was some evidence of DNA laddering in control myocytes at the 23 h time-point, adriamycin caused a significant increase in DNA laddering as compared to controls. The adriamycin-treated myocytes showed higher intensity bands of low molecular weight DNA, indicative of apoptosis. Interestingly, a bright DNA smear at the leading end of the gel was observed in the adriamycin-treated group and indicated cell necrosis (FIG. 5). Pre-treatment of myocytes with trolox significantly inhibited the adriamycin-induced low molecular weight DNA fragmentation with a concomitant decrease in the DNA smear intensity at the leading edge (FIG. 5).

DISCUSSION

Apoptosis has been reported in a variety of non-dividing cells including cardiomyocytes.[7,26] Data obtained in this study, clearly show that adriamycin is taken up by myocytes and causes apoptosis in a time- and dose-dependent manner. Two previous studies from another laboratory did not observe adriamycin-induced apoptosis of the cardiomyocytes in spontaneously hypertensive rats, which were examined at 7 days to weeks after the first injection.[15,27] It is possible that apoptosis in the heart occurs rapidly after the adriamycin administration as has been reported for other cell types including cardiac myocytes.[18] This narrow time window of detecting apoptosis may have been missed in these two studies as has also been pointed out by these authors.[15,27] The occurrence of apoptosis in isolated myocytes in the present study was confirmed by three different independent procedures including Hoechst staining,

TUNEL assay, and agarose gel electrophoresis. A characteristic chronology of morphological changes during adriamycin cardiomyopathy includes loss of myofibrils and dilation of the sarcotubular system[6] and provides strong evidence that there is systematic progression of cell injury—a form of programmed cell death or apoptosis. More recently, anthracyclines have been reported to induce apoptosis in neonatal rat cardiomyocytes and the process was inhibited by superoxide mimetic agents.[17] Apoptosis in H9C2 cardiac muscle cells exposed to adriamycin has also been reported and it is suggested to be due to the induction of Bax and caspase 3.[25]

Although the precise mechanism responsible for the induction of apoptosis is not known, increased oxidative stress has been suggested to be involved in this process. Physiological events as well as chemical agents that induce apoptosis are also shown to produce free radicals. In this regard, direct evidence supportive of the role of oxidative stress in this process was provided by the demonstration of apoptosis induced by H_2O_2.[28] Adriamycin and many other agents, such as cisplatin, UV irradiation, and TNF-α, have also been reported to produce free radicals and cause apoptosis in various cell lines.[25,29] Inhibition of apoptosis by antioxidants, such as catalase, SOD, thioredoxin, vitamin E, and trolox,[30–35] further suggests the involvement of oxidative stress in apoptosis. Adriamycin-induced cardiomyopathy is also thought to be mediated by oxidative stress.[2] In the present study, induction of apoptosis in adult cardiomyocytes by adriamycin and its prevention by trolox, an antioxidant, provide a strong evidence for the role of oxidative stress in apoptosis.

Trolox, being more hydrophilic than vitamin E, can easily be administered to the cells directly.[36] It has been reported that trolox is a potent cytoprotector against oxygen free radical damage in isolated human ventricle myocytes, erythrocytes, and hepatocytes.[37] Trolox has a potent activity in scavenging oxyradical both *in vivo* and *in vitro*.[38–40] In this regard, trolox has been shown to reduce oxidative stress injury induced by ischemia-reperfusion in post-ischemic rat livers,[41,42] dog myocardium,[43] and rabbit myocardium.[44] The upregulation of genes associated with programmed cell death in cardiomyocytes appears to occur within a short period following adriamycin treatment. In the present investigation, we exposed cardiomyocytes to trolox for 30 min before adriamycin treatment, which resulted in a significant decrease in the occurrence of apoptosis. Similar findings have been reported in hearts subjected to ischemia-reperfusion and trolox offered significant protection when administered 10 min before ischemia.[45] There are many other examples where oxidative stress has been shown to cause apoptosis and its prevention by trolox.[30,46] Thus, the mechanism by which trolox inhibits adriamycin-induced apoptosis in cardiomyocytes appears to involve a decrease in oxidative stress. The possibility that trolox may interfere with adriamycin uptake was ruled out by fluorescence studies.

It has been shown that redox cycling of adriamycin and its DNA-iron complex promote the formation of free radicals.[5,47–49] Increased oxidative stress due to adriamycin in a variety of cell culture systems as well as in *in vivo* experiments has been reported.[6] Importantly, increased oxidative stress has also been suggested to cause apoptosis.[29] Free radical generation as well as different antitumor agents have been shown to indiscriminately degrade DNA and cause cell necrosis.[6,50–52] The presence of a bright smear in agarose gel electrophoresis at the leading edge of the gel may in fact be an indication of this type of DNA fragmentation and myocyte necrosis. It is likely that myocardial cell death due to adriamycin may involve two components, *vis á vis* apoptotic and necrotic, and both may be mediated by oxidative stress. The cytoprotective effect of trolox appears to be related to its antioxidant property, which may modulate both programmed and necrotic cell death by decreasing oxidative stress.

REFERENCES

1. LEFRAK, E.A., J. PITHA, S. ROSENHEIM & T. GOTTLIEB. 1973. A clinicopathologic analysis of adriamycin cardiotoxicity. Cancer **32:** 302–314.
2. SINGAL, P.K. & N. ILISKOVIC. 1998. Adriamycin cardiomyopathy. N. Eng. J. Med. **339:** 900–905.
3. MYERS, C.E., W.P. MCGUIRE, R. H. LISS, I. IFRIM, K. GROTZINGER & R.C. YOUNG. 1977. Adriamycin: the role of lipid peroxidation in cardiac toxicity and tumor response. Science **19:** 165–167.
4. SINGAL, P.K., C.M.R. DEALLY & L.E. WEINBERG. 1987. Subcellular effects of adriamycin in the heart: A concise review. J. Mol. Cell. Cardiol. **19:** 817–828.
5. SINGAL, P.K., N. ILISKOVIC, T. LI & D. KUMAR. 1997. Adriamycin cardiomyopathy: pathophysiology and prevention. FASEB J. **11:** 931–936.
6. SINGAL, P.K., N. SIVESKI-ILISKOVIC, T. LI & C. SENEVIRATNE. 1995. Cardiomyopathie due a l'adriamycine et sa prevention. L'information Cardiologique **XIX:** 298–302.
7. NARULA, J., N. HAIDER, R. VIRMANI *et al.* 1996. Apoptosis in myocytes in end-stage heart failure. N. Engl. J. Med. **335:** 1182–1189.
8. SARASTE, A., K. PULKKI, M. KALLAJOKI, K. HENRIKSEN, M. PARVINEN & L.-M. VOIPIO-PULKKI. 1997. Apoptosis in human acute myocardial infarction. Circulation **95:** 320–323.
9. SHAROV, V.G., H.N. SABBAH, H. SHIMOYAMA, A.V. GOUSSEV, M. LESCH & S. GOLDSTEIN. 1996. Evidence of cardiocyte apoptosis in myocardium of dogs with chronic heart failure. Am. J. Pathol. **148:** 141–149.
10. MALLAT, Z., A. TEDGUI, F. FONTALIRAN, R. FRANK, M. DURIGON & G. FONTAIN. 1996. Evidence of apoptosis in arrhythmogenic right ventricular dysplasia. N. Engl. J. Med. **335:** 1190–1196.
11. OLIVETTI, G., R. ABBI, F. QUAINI, J. KAJSTURA, W. CHENG, J.A. NITAHARA, E. QUAINI, C. DI LORETO, C.A. BELTRAMI, S. KRAJEWSKI, J.C. REED & P. ANVERSA. 1997. Apoptosis in the failing human heart. N. Engl. J. Med. **336:** 1131–1141.
12. LING, Y.H., W. PRIEBE & R. PEREZ-SOLER. 1993. Apoptosis induced by anthracycline antibiotics in P388 parent and multidrug-resistant cells. Cancer Res. **53:** 1845–1852.
13. THAKKAR, N.S. & C.S. POTTEN. 1993. Inhibition of doxorubicin-induced apoptosis *in vivo* by 2-deoxy-D-glucose. Cancer Res. **53:** 2057–2060.
14. CECE, R., S. CAZZANIGA, D. MORELLI, L. SFONDRINI, M. BIGNOTTO, S. MENARD, M.I. COLNAGHI & A. BALSARI. 1996. Apoptosis of hair follicle cells during doxorubicin-induced alopecia in rats. Lab. Invest. **75:** 601–609.
15. ZHANG, J., J.R. CLARK, JR., E.H. HERMAN & V.J. FERRANS. 1996. Doxorubicin-induced apoptosis in spontaneously hypertensive rats: differential effects in heart, kidney and intestine, and inhibition by ICRF-187. J. Mol. Cell. Cardiol. **28:** 1931–1943.
16. FERRANS, V.J. 1983. Anthracycline cardiotoxicity. Adv. Exp. Med. Biol. **161:** 519–532.
17. AMIN, J.K., D.R. PIMENTEL, D.L. CHANG, J. WANG, W.S. COLUCCI & D.B. SAWYER. 1998. Preconditioning inhibits anthracycline induced apoptosis in neonatal rat ventricular myocytes [abstract]. FASEB J. **12:** A70, 407.
18. VEINOT, J.P., D.A. GATTINER & H. FLISS. 1997. Early apoptosis in human myocardial infarcts. Hum. Pathol. **28:** 485–492.
19. ZALESKIS, G., E. BERLETH, S. VERSTOVSEK, M.J. EHRKE & E. MIHICH. 1994. Doxorubicin-induced DNA degradation in murine thymocytes. Mol. Pharmacol. **46:** 901-908.
20. BIHLER, I., K. HO & P.C. SAWH. 1984. Isolation of calcium-tolerant myocytes from adult rat heart. Can. J. Physiol. Pharmacol. **62:** 581–588.
21. KIRSHENBAUM, L.A., T.P. THOMAS, A.K. RANDHAWA & P.K. SINGAL. 1992. Time-course of cardiac myocyte injury due to oxidative stress. Mol. Cell. Biochem. **111:** 25–31.

22. PIPER, H.M., S.L. JACOBSON & P. SCHWARTZ. 1988. Determinants of cardiomyocyte development in long-term primary culture. J. Mol. Cell. Cardiol. **20:** 825–835.
23. KIRSHENBAUM, L.A., W.R. MACLELLAN, W. MAZUR, B.A. FRENCH & M.D. SCHNEIDER. 1993. Highly efficient gene transfer into adult ventricular myocytes by recombinant adenovirus. J. Clin. Invest. **92:** 381–387.
24. HIRT, B. 1967. Selective extraction of polyoma DNA from infected mouse cultures. J. Mol. Biol. **26:** 365–369.
25. WANG, L., W. MA, R. MARKOVICH, W.L. LEE & P.H. WANG. 1998. Insulin-like growth factor I modulates induction of apoptotic signaling in H9C2 cardiac muscle cells. Endocrinology **139:** 1354–1360.
26. KAJSTURA, J., W. CHENG, K. REISS, W.A. CLARK, E.H. SONNENBLICK, S. KRAJEWSKI, J.C. REED, G. OLIVETTI & P. ANVERSA. 1996. Apoptotic and necrotic myocyte cell deaths are independent contributing variables of infarct size in rats. Lab. Invest. **74:** 86–107.
27. HERMAN, E.H., J. ZHANG, B.B. HASINOFF, J.R. CLARK, JR. & V. J. FERRANS. 1997. Comparison of the structural changes induced by doxorubicin and mitoxantrone in the heart, kidney and intestine and characterization of the Fe(III)-mitoxantrone complex. J. Mol. Cell. Cardiol. **29:** 2415–2430.
28. HOCKENBERY, D.M., Z.N. OLTVAI, X.-M. YIN, C.L. MILLIMAN & S.J. KORSMEYER. 1993. Bcl-2 functions in an antioxidant pathway to prevent apoptosis. Cell **75:** 241–251.
29. BUTTKE, T.M. & P.A. SANDSTROM. 1994. Oxidative stress as a mediator of apoptosis. Immunol. Today **15:** 7–10.
30. FORREST, V.J., Y.H. KANG, D.E. MCCLAIN, D.H. ROBINSON & N. RAMAKRISHNAN. 1994. Oxidative stress-induced apoptosis prevented by trolox. Free Radical Biol. Med. **16:** 675–684.
31. SANDSTROM, P.A. & T.M. BUTTKE. 1993. Autocrine production of extracellular catalase prevents apoptosis of the human CEM T-cell line in serum-free medium. Proc. Natl. Acad. Sci. USA **90:** 4708–4712.
32. SANDSTROM, P.A., M.D. MANNIE & T.M. BUTTKE. 1994. Inhibition of activation-induced death in T cell hybridomas by thiol antioxidants: oxidative stress as a mediator of apoptosis. J. Leukoc. Biol. **55:** 221–226.
33. DIMMELER, S., J. HAENDELER, J. GALLE & A.M. ZEIHER. 1997. Oxidized low-density lipoprotein induces apoptosis of human endothelial cells by activation of CPP32-like proteases. A mechanistic clue to the "response to injury" hypothesis. Circulation **95:** 1760–1763.
34. MATSUDA, M., H. MASUTANI, H. NAKAMURA, S. MIYAJIMA, A. YAMAUCHI, S. YONEHARA, A. UCHIDA, K. IRIMAJIRI, A. HORIUCHI & J. YODOI. 1991. Protective activity of adult T cell leukemia-derived factor (ADF) against tumor necrosis factor-dependent cytotoxicity on U937 cells. J. Immunol. **147:** 3837–3841.
35. HIROSE, K., D.L. LONGO, J.J. OPPENHEIM & K. MATSUSHIMA. 1993. Overexpression of mitochondrial manganese superoxide dismutase promotes the survival of tumor cells exposed to interleukin-1, tumor necrosis factor, selected anticancer drugs, and ionizing radiation. FASEB J. **7:** 361–368.
36. ZIELENSKI, J., T.-W. WU, K.-P. FUNG, L.-H. ZENG, R.-K. LI, D.A.G. MICKLE & J. WU. 1993. Chemical syntheses of trolox conjugates which protect human ventricular myocytes against *in situ*-generated oxyradicals. Eur. J. Pharmacol. **248:** 313–318.
37. WU, T.-W., N. HASHIMOTO, J. WU, D. CAREY, R.-K. LI, D.A.G. MICKLE & R.D. WEISEL. 1990. The cytoprotective effect of trolox demonstrated with three types of human cells. Biochem. Cell. Biol. **68:** 1189–1194.
38. DEAN, R.T., J.V. HUN, A.J. GRANT, Y. YAMAMOTO & E. NIKI. 1991. Free radical damage to proteins: the influence of the relative localization of radical generation, antioxidants, and target proteins. Free Radical Biol. Med. **11:** 161–168.
39. THIRIOT, C., P. DURAND, M.P. JASSERSON, J.F. KERGONOU & R. DUCOUSSO. 1987. Radiosensitive antioxidant membrane-bound factors in rat liver microsomes: I. The roles of glutathione and vitamin E. Biochemistry **14:** 9–14.
40. RUBINSTEIN, J.D., E.J. LESNEFSKY, R.M. BYLER, P.V. FENNESSEY & L.D. HORWITZ. 1992. Trolox C, a lipid-soluble membrane protective agent, attenuates myocardial injury from ischemia and reperfusion. Free Radical Biol. Med. **13:** 627–634.

41. ZENG, L.H., J. WU, D. CAREY & T.W. WU. 1991. Trolox and ascorbate: are they synergistic in protecting liver cell in vitro and in vivo? Biochem. Cell. Biol. **69:** 198–201.
42. WU, T.W., N. HASHIMOTO, J.X. AU, J. WU, D.A.G. MICKLE & D. CAREY. 1991. Trolox protects rat hepatocytes against oxyradical damage and the ischemic rat liver from reperfusion injury. Hepatology **13:** 575–580.
43. MICKLE, D.A.G., R.-K. LI, R.D. WEISEL, P.L. BIRNBAUM, T.-W. WU, G. JACKOWSKI, M.M. MADONIK, G.W. BURTON & K.U. INGOLD. 1989. Myocardial salvage with trolox and ascorbic acid for an evolving infarction. Ann. Thorac. Surg. **47:** 553–557.
44. WU, T.-W., J. WU, L.H. ZENG, H. SUGIYAMA, D.A. MICKLE & J.X. AU. 1993. Reduction of experimental myocardial infarct size by infusion of lactosylphenyl trolox. Cardiovasc. Res. **27:** 73–739.
45. PETTY, M., J.M. GRISAR, J. DOW & W. DE JONG. 1998. Effects of an alpha-tocopherol analogue on myocardial reperfusion injury in rats. Eur. J. Pharmacol. **179:** 241–242.
46. MCCLAIN, D.E., J.F. KALINICH & N. RAMAKRISHNAN. 1995. Trolox inhibits apoptosis in irradiated MOLT-4 lymphocytes. FASEB J. **9:** 1345–1354.
47. KEIZER, H.G., H.M. PINEDO, G.J. SCHUURHUIS & H. JOFNJE. 1990. Doxorubicin (adriamycin): a critical review of free radical-dependent mechanisms of cytotoxicity. Pharmac. Ther. **47:** 219–231.
48. SINHA, B.K. & J.L. GREGORY. 1981. Role of one-electron and two-electron reduction products of adriamycin and daunomycin in deoxynucleic acid binding. Biochem. Pharmacol. **30:** 2626–2629.
49. BACHUR, N.R., M.V. GEE & R.D. FRIEDMAN. 1982. Nuclear catalyzed antibiotic free radical formation. Cancer Res. **42:** 1078–1081.
50. FEINSTEIN, E., E. CANAANI & L.M. WEINER. 1993. Dependence of nucleic acid degradation on *in situ* free-radical production by adriamycin. Biochemistry **13:** 13156–13161.
51. GONG, J., X. LI & Z. DARZYNKIEWICZ. 1993. Different patterns of apoptosis of HL-60 cells induced by cycloheximide and camptothecin. J. Cell. Physiol. **157:** 263–270.
52. GUPTA, M. & P.K. SINGAL. 1989. Time course of structure, function, and metabolic changes due to an exogenous source of oxygen metabolites in rat heart. Can. J. Physiol. Pharmacol. **67:** 1549–1559.

Physical Exercise and Antioxidant Defenses in the Heart[a]

MUSTAFA ATALAY[b] AND CHANDAN K. SEN[b,c,d]

[b]*Department of Physiology, University of Kuopio, 70211 Kuopio, Finland*
[c] *Biological Technologies Section, Environmental Energies Technologies Division, Lawrence Berkeley National Laboratory, Berkeley, California 94720-3200, USA*

ABSTRACT: Cardiac muscle relies highly on aerobic metabolism. Heart muscle has a high oxygen uptake at resting conditions, which increases many fold during exhaustive physical exercise. Such a high rate of oxidative metabolism is often associated with enhanced production of reactive oxygen metabolites. A single bout of strenuous exercise has been demonstrated to induce oxidative damage in heart. Such oxidant insult may lead to adaptive responses and strengthen antioxidant defenses in the heart tissue. Endurance exercise training has indeed been shown to upregulate heart tissue antioxidant defenses. Recently, we have observed that even predominantly anaerobic sprint training regimens may enhance cardiac antioxidant defenses. Regular physical exercise may beneficially influence cardiac antioxidant defenses and promote overall cardiac function.

INTRODUCTION

Cardiac muscle has unique aerobic metabolism characteristics. The ability to provide energy through anaerobic glycolysis is limited in this tissue. At rest, oxygen uptake per gram of heart muscle is more than the oxygen consumption of skeletal muscle during heavy physical exercise. During physical exercise coronary blood flow increases up to fourfold and heart muscle has remarkable ability to extract oxygen from blood.[1] While oxygen is essential for aerobic metabolism in the heart tissue, a heavy load of oxygen metabolism in the heart during physical exercise has been shown to be associated with enhanced production of partially reduced forms of oxygen and their reactive derivatives, collectively known as reactive oxygen species. Elevated levels of oxidative damage markers, which may be caused by various mechanisms as listed in TABLE 1, have been shown in the post-exercise heart tissue.[2–5]

[a]This work was supported by research grants from the Finnish Ministry of Education and the Juho Vainio Foundation of Helsinki to CKS.
[d]Address correspondence to: Chandan K. Sen, Ph.D., Life Sciences Addition, Building 20A, Room 251C, Mail Stop 3200, University of California, Berkeley, California 94720-3200; Telephone: (510) 642-4445; Fax: (510) 644-2341; E-mail: cksen@socrates.berkeley.edu

TABLE 1. Possible mechanisms inducing oxidative stress in the exercising heart

Organelle/Tissue	Process/Site	Mechanism	Reference
Mitochondria	electron transport chain	univalent reduction of oxygen	32
Mitochondria/cystosol	xanthine oxidase	O_2 acts as an electron acceptor	41
Activated neutrophils	NADPH oxidase/ phagosomes	oxidative burst, myeloperoxidase	33
Endothelial cells Cardiac muscle Macrophages Neuromuscular junction	nitric oxide synthesis	peroxynitrate formation	34
Cardiac muscle	myoglobin	metmyoglobin production	35
Cardiac muscle Erythrocytes	any site hosting Fe/Cu	transition metals Fenton reaction	36

ACUTE EXERCISE

Acute physical exercise increases cardiac contractility and heart rate. Strenuous exercise may be associated with a fourfold increase in blood flow through and oxygen consumption by the myocardium.[1] A single bout of exhaustive treadmill running has been shown to decrease total glutathione levels in the heart without causing significant increase of lipid peroxidation and glutathione oxidation (TABLE 2). In contrast, Ohkuwa and colleagues[6] reported increased cardiac levels of reduced glutathione after one short bout of exercise in young rats. This increase in heart glutathione level was thought to be caused by enhanced hepatic glutathione efflux during exercise.[6] In this study hydroxyl radical formation, however, markedly increased in the heart of young physically active rats despite the elevated cardiac glutathione content.[6] Benderitter and colleagues[7] reported that swim exercise until exhaustion did not increase lipid peroxidation, but decreased vitamin E levels in heart tissue of rats swim-trained for 9 weeks. In a comparable study Frankiewicz-Jozko and colleagues[3] reported a significant increase of levels of thiobarbituric acid–reactive substances in heart tissue of untrained rats 3 h after exhaustive treadmill exercise, but no change of post-exercise thiobarbituric acid–reactive substances content was detected in animals treadmill-trained for 4 weeks. These studies suggest that training and the acute exercise may cause oxidative damage to lipids in the heart. Levels of 8-hydroxydeoxyguanosine (8-OH-dG), a DNA oxidative damage marker, have been shown to be increased following both spontaneous and forced exercise in rats. 8-OH-dG levels were twofold higher in forced-exercise groups than in spontaneous-exercise groups, indicating the importance of exercise intensity on oxidative DNA damage in the heart tissue.[5]

Somani and colleagues[8] studied the response of cardiac antioxidant enzymes in untrained rats and in rats endurance-trained for 10 weeks. Acute exercise induced activities of Mn-superoxide dismutase, catalase, and glutathione peroxidase in untrained rats. The potential protective role of glutathione against exercise-induced oxidative stress has been tested using a glutathione-deficient rat model.[9,10] In con-

TABLE 2. Effects of acute exercise on heart antioxidant defenses and lipid peroxidation

Investigator/ Reference	Model	Type of Exercise	Effect
Benderitter *et al.*[7]	Swim-trained rats	Exhaustive swim	MDA→
			Vit E↓
Frankiewicz *et al.*[3]	Untrained rats	Exhaustive run	MDA ↑(3 h after ex)
	Treadmill-trained rats		MDA →(0–48 h after ex)
Ji [38]	Untrained rats	Exhaustive run	SOD ↑(immediately after)
			CAT →
			GSHPx C
			GRD→
			SOD →(30 min after)
			CAT →
			GSHPx →
			GRD →
Leeuwenburgh *et al.*[11]	Untrained mice	Exhaustive swim	GSH ↓, GSSG ↓
			GSH/GSSG →
			SOD ↑, GGT →, CAT →
			GSHPx →, GRD →, GST →
Ohkuwa *et al.*[6]	Young, physically active rats	Short run	GSH ↑, GSSG →
			GSH/TGSH ↑
			$OH^{\cdot}$ formation ↑
	Old, physically active rats		GSH ↓, GSSG ↓
			GSH/TGSH ↑
			$OH^{\cdot -}$ formation ↑
Sen *et al.* [9]	Untrained rats	Exhaustive run	TGSH ↓
			GSSG/TGSH →
			MDA →
Somani *et al.*[8]	Untrained rats	Exhaustive run	Mn-SOD ↑↑
			CAT ↑↑
			GSHPx ↑↑
	Endurance-trained rats		Mn-SOD ↑
			CAT ↑
			GSHPx ↑
Venditti & Di Meo[4]	Untrained rats	Exhaustive swim	MDA ↑
			LHP ↑
	Trained rats		MDA ↑
			LHP ↑

NOTATION: ↑, increased; ↓, decreased; →, no change; SOD, total superoxide dismutase activity; CAT, catalase activity; GSHPx, glutathione peroxidase activity; GRD, glutathione disulfide reductase activity; GST, glutathione S-transferases activity; GGT, γ-glutamyl transpeptidase, activity; GCS, γ-glutamylcysteine synthetase activity; TGSH, total glutathione content; GSH, reduced glutathione; GSSG, oxidized glutathione; MDA, malondialdehyde; LHP, lipid hydroperoxide; Vit E, vitamin E content; T. antioxidant capacity, total antioxidant capacity; EPR, electron paramagnetic resonance spectroscopy; C, cytosolic; M, mitochondrial; I-R, ischemia-reperfusion.

trast to the response in the glutathione-adequate control group, exercise did not cause any further significant decrease of cardiac total glutathione levels, but increased significantly oxidized glutathione/total glutathione ratio in the heart of glutathione-deficient rats.[9] Glutathione deficiency also increased basal lipid peroxidation levels.[9] Leeuwenburgh and colleagues[11] also tested the effects of endogenous glutathione in glutathione-deficient mice subjected to swim exercise. In this study, which had a different exercise regimen, acute exercise did not influence oxidized glutathione/total glutathione ratio in heart.[11] The role of exogenous glutathione as well as N-acetyl-L-cysteine, a pro-glutathione drug, in cardiac antioxidant defenses at rest and after exercise has been also tested. Supplemented glutathione was observed to be not readily available to the heart.[9] In another supplementation study Kumar and colleagues[12] reported that swim training for 2 months resulted in elevated levels of lipid peroxidation byproducts in the heart. Vitamin E supplementation was effective in decreasing training-induced lipid peroxidation perhaps by inhibiting lipoxygenase activity. In a more recent study we observed that 8 weeks of α-lipoic acid supplementation (150 mg/kg/day) protected against exercise-induced GSH depletion in heart tissue in rats.[13] Furthermore, compared to non-supplemented control rats, α-lipoic acid supplementation markedly decreased overall heart lipid peroxidation measured as thiobarbituric acid–reactive substances.[13]

TRAINING

Most studies investigating the influence of physical training on tissue antioxidant status have tested the effect of endurance training, which enhances oxidative capacity of several tissues (TABLE 3).[14–18] Information on the effect of sprint training, which relies primarily on anaerobic metabolism, on tissue antioxidant defenses is limited.[19] We have recently observed that a predominantly anaerobic 6-wk sprint training program upregulates the activities of redox cycle enzymes, such as glutathione peroxidase and glutathione disulfide reductase, in rat heart tissue.[20] However sprint training did not affect the activities of glutathione S-transferases and total glutathione content in rat heart tissue.[20] Sprint-type exercise utilizes anaerobic energy pathways followed by oxidative metabolism during the recovery phase. In many ways the situation may be considered to be analogous to ischemia-reperfusion and has been shown to activate the xanthine oxidase pathway for superoxide production.[21]

Endurance-exercise training may provide added antioxidant protection to the heart tissue. Ji and colleagues[22] have shown that post-training hypertrophied myocardium is more resistant to ischemia-reperfusion–induced glutathione depletion and hemodynamic dysfunction. Consistently, Somani and colleagues[8] reported increased levels of cytosolic GSH levels in the myocardium of 10-wk endurance-trained rats. Leichtweis and colleagues[23] studied the protective effect of 8–9 wk of vigorous swimming on the hearts of rats subjected to ischemia-reperfusion. Training decreased cytosolic reduced glutathione and oxidized glutathione/total glutathione ratio but increased the ability of the tissue to import extracellular glutathione by increasing the activity of γ-glutamyl transpeptidase. This study also showed that vigorous exercise training regimens might have detrimental effects on the heart by depressing mitochondrial function and downregulating tissue antioxidant defenses.

TABLE 3. Effects of chronic exercise on cardiac antioxidant defenses and exercise performance

Investigator	Model	Type of Training	Effect
Atalay *et al.*[20]	Rats	Spint run 6 wk	SOD →
			GSHPx ↑
			GRD ↑
			TGSH →
Gohil *et al.*[37]	Rats	Run 12 wk	Ubiquinone →
			Vit E →
			Cytochrome *c* reductase→
Higuchi *et al.*[31]	Rats	Run 3 months	Cu,Zn SOD →
			Mn SOD →
Hong & Johnson[27]	Normo/hypertensive rats	Run + 10 wk + Detraining 1 wk	CAT ↓ GSHPx ↓
Husain & Somani[24]	Rats	Training 6.5 wk	SOD ↑
			GSHPx ↑
			GSH ↑
Ji [38]	Rats	Run 12 wk	Cu,Zn SOD →
			Mn SOD →
			CAT →
			GSHPx (C-M) →
			GST →
Kanter *et al.*[30]	Mice	Swim 7 wk	SOD →
			CAT →
			GSHPx →
		Swim 21 wk	SOD →
			CAT ↑
			GSHPx →
Kihlstrom *et al.*[15]	Rats	Swim 3 months	CAT ↓
			Cu,ZnSOD ↓
			Thioredoxin reductase ↓
			GRD ↓
			Vit E ↓
Kim *et al.*[26]	Rats	Run 18.5 months	CAT ↑
			MDA ↓
Kumar *et al.*[12]	Rats	Swim 2 months	SOD ↑, xanthine oxidase ↑
		+ Vit E suppl.	Catalase ↓, GSHPx ↓, GST ↑
			MDA ↑, EPR signals ↑
			MDA ↓, EPR signals ↓
Leeuwenburgh *et al.*[18]	Rats	Run 10 wk	GSH / GSSG ↓
			SOD →, Mn-SOD →
			GSHPx → , GRD →
			GST ↓, GGT →, GCS →

(*Continued*)

TABLE 3. Effects of chronic exercise on cardiac antioxidant defenses and exercise performance

Investigator	Model	Type of Training	Effect
Leichtweis *et al.*[23]	Rats	Vigorous swim 8–9 wk + I-R	GSH →(mitochondrial)
			TGSH→, GSSG →
			GSH ↓, (cytosolic)
			GSSG /TGSH ↓
			GGT ↑
			MDA ↓
Lew & Quintanilha[16]	Rats	Run 10 wk	CAT ↑
			GSHPx↑
			GRD →
Powers *et al.*[17]	Rats	Run 10 wk/30, 60, 90 min	
		Low intensity	SOD → ↑, CAT →, GSHPx →
		Moderate intensity	SOD →↑, CAT →, GSHPx →
		High intensity	SOD ↑ ↑, CAT →, GSHPx →
Reznick *et al.*[39]	6-month-old mice	Run 5 wk	SOD ↑
	22-month-old mice		SOD →
	27-month-old mice		SOD ↓
Somani *et al.*[8]	Rats	Run 10 wk	Cytosolic GSH ↑
Tiidus & Houston[40]	Rats	Run 8 wk	SOD →
		Vit E suppl.	CAT →
		Vit E deprivation	GSHPx →
Venditti & Di Meo[4]	52-week-old rats	Swim 10 wk	GSHPx ↑
			GRD ↑
			T. antioxidant capacity ↑
			Mitochondrial integrity →

[a]See TABLE 2 footnote for abbreviations.

Several studies have examined the influence of exercise training on the activity of specific antioxidant enzymes. Because of the variations in experimental design, model, and analytical procedures, much of these studies may not be directly compared to each other. Overall, the results show that endurance training may enhance the activity of certain antioxidant enzymes in the heart. Lew and Quintanilha[16] reported that 10-wk treadmill training may enhance catalase and glutathione peroxidase activities in rat heart without affecting glutathione disulfide reductase activity. Husain and Somani[24] reported a significant increase of cardiac superoxide dismutase and glutathione peroxidase activities and glutathione content of 6.5-wk treadmill-trained rats. Somani and colleagues[8] showed that exercise-induced increases in the activities of Mn-superoxide dismutase, Cu,Zn-superoxide dismutase, catalase, and glutathione peroxidase were higher than respective increases in mRNA content of the respective enzymes. These results suggest that upregulation of enzyme activity may not be wholly accounted for by increased protein expression and that other factors contributing to the catalytic activity of these proteins may have been influenced by exercise.

One of the most comprehensive studies investigating the role of exercise training in regulating endogenous cardiac antioxidant defenses was reported by Powers and colleagues.[17] In this work, rats were treadmill-trained for 10 weeks at three different durations of daily run time (30, 60, and 90 min). Also, three different relative intensities of daily exercise (low, moderate, and high) were studied. None of these nine training groups showed any effects in cardiac citrate synthase, catalase, or glutathione peroxidase activities. In all duration groups of moderate and high intensity–trained animals, right ventricular superoxide dismutase activity increased in response to training. Left ventricular superoxide dismutase activity also increased after short-duration intensive training and long-duration training with low or moderate intensities. These data show that daily exercise intensity may influence training-dependent upregulation of the activity of cardiac antioxidant enzymes. Studies from our and Ji's laboratories have shown that endurance training does not affect rat skeletal muscle and heart glutathione S-transferases activities.[14,20,25] In other studies, endurance-type treadmill training was observed to decrease glutathione S-transferases activity in the heart.[18]

Endurance training of rats on treadmill enhances the ability to perform endurance exercise.[3] Despite longer exercise-duration in trained animals, exercise-induced elevation of tissue thiobarbituric acid–reactive substances levels was higher in the liver but not in heart suggesting that the trained heart was able to cope more efficiently with exercise-induced oxidative stress.[3] These results are consistent with the finding of another study by Kim and colleagues.[26] Direct evidence showing that indeed exercise training may strengthen cardiac antioxidant defenses was also obtained in a 10-wk swim-training study. Exercise training enhanced glutathione peroxidase, glutathione reductase enzyme activities, and total antioxidant scavenging capacity without changing mitochondrial integrity and resting lipid peroxidation in rats.[4] Hong and Johnson[27] have studied the effects of 10-wk treadmill training and 1-wk detraining on antioxidant enzyme activity in normotensive and hypertensive rats. Sedentary hypertensive rats had higher glutathione peroxidase activity in the left ventricles. Exercise training, however, decreased left ventricular glutathione peroxidase activity both in normotensive as well as in hypertensive rats. Another potential source of oxidative stress in the heart is a diet rich in fish oil.[28,29] We observed that a regimen of 8 weeks of 1 g/kg body weight/day fish oil supplementation increases cardiac glutathione peroxidase activity, which was normalized in the rats that were co-supplemented with fish oil and 500 mg/kg/day vitamin E (Atalay and colleagues, unpublished results).

Some other studies investigating the efficacy of endurance exercise training programs to enhance cardiac antioxidant defenses have shown mixed results. Kanter and colleagues[30] have tested the effects of 7-wk and 21-wk swim-training program on superoxide dismutase, catalase, and glutathione peroxidase enzyme activities in mice. After 21 weeks of training only catalase activity was upregulated in the heart tissue while activities of other antioxidant enzymes were increased only in blood and liver.[30] Similarly, Higuchi and colleagues[31] did not observe any increase of Cu,Zn-superoxide dismutase and Mn-superoxide dismutase activity in the heart after 3-month treadmill training. In another study, 3-month swim-training decreased the activities of catalase, Cu,Zn-superoxide dismutase, thioredoxin reductase, glutathione reductase, and vitamin E content mainly in the right ventricle and subendomyocardium, despite significant increase in the cardiac weight.[15]

In summary, an acute bout of strenuous physical exercise may pose oxidant insult to the heart. Despite some discrepancies in the literature, there is a general trend showing that chronic regular physical exercise may beneficially influence cardiac antioxidant defenses and promote overall cardiac function.

REFERENCES

1. ANDERSON, K.L. 1968. The cardiovascular system in exercise. *In* Exercise Physiology. H. B. Falls, Ed.: 62–84. Academic Press. New York.
2. JI, L.L. 1994. Exercise-induced oxidative stress in the heart. *In* Exercise and Oxygen Toxicity. C.K. Sen, L. Packer & O. Hänninen, Eds.: 249–267. Elsevier Science, B.V. Amsterdam.
3. FRANKIEWICZ-JOZKO, A., J. FAFF & B. SIERADZAN-GABELSKA. 1996. Changes in concentrations of tissue free radical marker and serum creatine kinase during the post-exercise period in rats. Eur. J. Appl. Physiol. **74:** 470–474.
4. VENDITTI, P. & S. DI MEO. 1996. Antioxidants, tissue damage, and endurance in trained and untrained young male rats. Arch. Biochem. Biophys. **331:** 63–68.
5. ASAMI, S., T. HIRANO, R. YAMAGUCHI, Y. TSURUDOME, H. ITOH & H. KASAI. 1998. Effects of forced and spontaneous exercise on 8-hydroxydeoxyguanosine levels in rat organs. Biochem. Biophys. Res. Commun. **243:** 678–682.
6. OHKUWA, T., Y. SATO & N.M. NAOI. 1997. Glutathione status and reactive oxygen generation in tissues of young and old exercised rats. Acta Physiol. Scand. **159:** 237–244.
7. BENDERITTER, M., F. HADJ-SAAD, M. LHUISSIER, V. MAUPOIL, J.C. GUILLAND & L. ROCHETTE. 1996. Effects of exhaustive exercise and vitamin B6 deficiency on free radical oxidative process in male trained rats. Free Radic. Biol. Med. **21:** 541–549.
8. SOMANI, S.M., S. FRANK & L.P. RYBAK. 1995. Responses of antioxidant system to acute and trained exercise in rat heart subcellular fractions. Pharmacol. Biochem. Behav. **51:** 627–634.
9. SEN, C.K., M. ATALAY & O. HANNINEN. 1994. Exercise-induced oxidative stress: glutathione supplementation and deficiency. J. Appl. Physiol. **77:** 2177–2187.
10. ATALAY, M., P. MARNILA, E. M. LILIUS, O. HANNINEN & C.K. SEN. 1996. Glutathione-dependent modulation of exhausting exercise-induced changes in neutrophil function of rats. Eur. J. Appl. Physiol. **174:** 342–347.
11. LEEUWENBURGH, C., S. LEICHTWEIS, J. HOLLANDER, R. FIEBIG, M. GORE & L.L. JI. 1996. Effect of acute exercise on glutathione deficient heart. Mol. Cell. Biochem. **156:** 17–24.
12. KUMAR, C.T., V.K. REDDY, M. PRASAD, K. THYAGARAJU & P. REDDANNA. 1992. Dietary supplementation of vitamin E protects heart tissue from exercise-induced oxidant stress. Mol. Cell. Biochem. **111:** 109–115.
13. KHANNA, S., M. ATALAY, D.E. LAAKSONEN, M. GUL, S. ROY & C.K. SEN. 1999. α-Lipoic acid supplementation: tissue homeostasis at rest and following exercise. J. Appl. Physiol. **86:** 1257–1262.
14. JI, L.L., F.W. STRATMAN & H.A. LARDY. 1988. Enzymatic down regulation with exercise in rat skeletal muscle. Arch. Biochem. Biophys. **263:** 137–149.
15. KIHLSTROM, M., J. OJALA & A. SALMINEN. 1989. Decreased level of cardiac antioxidants in endurance-trained rats. Acta Physiol. Scand. **135:** 549–554.
16. LEW, H. & A. QUINTANILHA. 1991. Effects of endurance training and exercise on tissue antioxidative capacity and acetaminophen detoxification. Eur. J. Drug Metab. Pharmacokinet. **16:** 59–68.
17. POWERS, S.K., D. CRISWELL, J. LAWLER, D. MARTIN, F.K. LIEU, L.L. JI & R.A. HERB. 1993. Rigorous exercise training increases superoxide dismutase activity in ventricular myocardium. Am. J. Physiol. **265:** H2094–H2098.
18. LEEUWENBURGH, C., J. HOLLANDER, S. LEICHTWEIS, M. GRIFFITHS, M. GORE & L.L. JI. 1997. Adaptations of glutathione antioxidant system to endurance training are tissue and muscle fiber specific. Am. J. Physiol. **272:** R363–P369.
19. SEN, C.K. 1995. Oxidants and antioxidants in exercise. J. Appl. Physiol. **79:** 675–686.

20. ATALAY, M., T. SEENE, O. HANNINEN & C.K. SEN. 1996. Skeletal muscle and heart antioxidant defences in response to sprint training. Acta Physiol. Scand. **158:** 129–134.
21. HELLSTEN-WESTING, Y., L. KAIJSER, B. EKBLOM & B. SJODIN. 1994. Exchange of purines in human liver and skeletal muscle with short-term exhaustive exercise. Am. J. Physiol. **266:** R81–R86.
22. JI, L.L., R.G. FU, E.W. MITCHELL, M. GRIFFITHS, T.G. WALDROP & H.M. SWARTZ. 1994. Cardiac hypertrophy alters myocardial response to ischaemia and reperfusion in vivo. Acta Physiol. Scand. **151:** 279–290.
23. LEICHTWEIS, SB., C. LEEUWENBURGH, D.J. PARMELEE, R. FIEBIG & L.L. JI. 1997. Rigorous swim training impairs mitochondrial function in post-ischaemic rat heart. Acta Physiol. Scand. **160:** 139–148.
24. HUSAIN, K. & S. M. SOMANI. 1997. Response of cardiac antioxidant system to alcohol and exercise training in the rat. Alcohol **14:** 301–307.
25. SEN, C.K., E. MARIN, M. KRETZSCHMAR & O. HANNINEN. 1992. Skeletal muscle and liver glutathione homeostasis in response to training, exercise, and immobilization. J. Appl. Physiol. **73:** 1265–1272.
26. KIM, J.D., B.P. YU, R.J. MCCARTER, S.Y. LEE & J.T. HERLIHY. 1996. Exercise and diet modulate cardiac lipid peroxidation and antioxidant defenses. Free Radic. Biol. Med. **20:** 83–88.
27. HONG, H. & P. JOHNSON. 1995. Antioxidant enzyme activities and lipid peroxidation levels in exercised and hypertensive rat tissues. Int. J. Biochem. Cell Biol. **27:** 923–931.
28. NALBONE, G., J. LEONARDI, E. TERMINE, H. PORTUGAL, P. LECHENE, A.M. PAULI & H. LAFONT. 1989. Effects of fish oil, corn oil and lard diets on lipid peroxidation status and glutathione peroxidase activities in rat heart. Lipids **24:** 179–186.
29. LEIBOVITZ, B.E., M.L. HU & A.L. TAPPEL. 1990. Lipid peroxidation in rat tissue slices: effect of dietary vitamin E, corn oil-lard and menhaden oil. Lipids **25:** 125–129.
30. KANTER, M.M., R.L. HAMLIN, D.V. UNVERFERTH, H.W. DAVIS & A.J. MEROLA. 1985. Effect of exercise training on antioxidant enzymes and cardiotoxicity of doxorubicin. J. Appl. Physiol. **59:** 1298–1303.
31. HIGUCHI, M., L. J. CARTIER, M. CHEN & J.O. HOLLOSZY. 1985. Superoxide dismutase and catalase in skeletal muscle: adaptive response to exercise. J. Gerontol. **40:** 281–286.
32. BOVERIS, A., E. CADENAS & A.O. STOPPANI. 1976. Role of ubiquinone in the mitochondrial generation of hydrogen peroxide. Biochem. J. **156:** 435–444.
33. CANNON, J.G. & J.B. BLUMBERG. 1994. Acute phase immune response in exercise. *In* Exercise and Oxygen Toxicity. C.K. Sen, L. Packer & O. Hänninen, Eds.: 447–462. Elsevier Science, B.V. Amsterdam.
34. LIPTON, S.A., Y.B. CHOI, Z.H. PAN, S.Z. LEI, H.S. CHEN, N.J. SUCHER, J. LOSCALZO, D. J. SINGEL & J.S. STAMLER. 1993. A redox-based mechanism for the neuroprotective and neurodestructive effects of nitric oxide and related nitroso-compounds. Nature (Aug 12) **364:** 626–632.
35. TAJIMA, G. & K. SHIKAMA. 1987. Autoxidation of oxymyoglobin. An overall stoichiometry including subsequent side reactions. J. Biol. Chem. **262:** 12603–12606.
36. JENKINS, R.R. & B. HALLIWELL. 1994. Metal bindings agents: possible role in exercise. *In* Exercise and Oxygen Toxicity. C.K. Sen, L. Packer & O. Hänninen, Eds.: 59–76. Elsevier Science, B.V. Amsterdam.
37. GOHIL, K., L. ROTHFUSS, J. LANG & L. PACKER. 1987. Effect of exercise training on tissue vitamin E and ubiquinone content. J. Appl. Physiol. **63:** 1638–1641.
38. JI, L.L. 1993. Antioxidant enzyme response to exercise and aging. Med. Sci. Sports Exer. **25:** 225–231.
39. REZNICK, A.Z., E. STEINHAGEN-THIESSEN & D. GERSHON. 1982. The effect of exercise on enzyme activities in cardiac muscles of mice of various ages. Biochem. Med. **28:** 347–352.
40. TIIDUS, P.M. & M.E. HOUSTON. 1994. Antioxidant and oxidative enzyme adaptations to vitamin E deprivation and training. Med. Sci. Sports Exer. **26:** 354–359.
41. DELLA-CORTE, E. & F. STIRPE. 1968. The regulation of rat-liver xanthine oxidase: activation by proteolytic enzymes. FEBS Lett. **2:** 83–84.

New Insights into Cardioprotection by Ischemic Preconditioning and Other Forms of Stress[a]

SANDRA DE ZEEUW, MIRELLA A. VAN DEN DOEL, DIRK J. DUNCKER, AND PIETER D. VERDOUW[b]

Experimental Cardiology, Thoraxcenter, Erasmus University Rotterdam, (Cardiovascular Research Institute COEUR), Rotterdam, The Netherlands

ABSTRACT: Ischemic preconditioning has not only received wide attention in heart research, but has also been a topic of extensive studies involving other organs. In several of these studies, it has been shown that in spite of differences in the endpoints used to assess protection, the same mediators as in myocardial ischemic preconditioning may be involved. However, several of the putative mediators do not require ischemia to become activated. This has guided us and others to investigate whether the myocardium can also be protected by brief ischemia in other organs and whether other non-pharmacological forms of stress, which do not produce ischemia but are capable of activating these potential mediators, are also cardioprotective.

INTRODUCTION

In the past, numerous attempts involving pharmacological agents have been undertaken to limit myocardial infarct size after a coronary artery occlusion. Although several compounds showed some initial promise, in the long run the results have been rather disappointing. In 1985, Murry and colleagues[1] revived interest in cardioprotection when they showed that after four days of reperfusion, myocardial infarcts in dogs produced by a 45-min coronary artery occlusion were 75% smaller (29% versus 7%) when this 45-min coronary occlusion was preceded by four sequences of a 5-min coronary artery occlusion and a 5-min reperfusion. This phenomenon of protecting myocardium against irreversible damage during a period of sustained ischemia by preceding periods of brief ischemia has been termed ischemic preconditioning. The smaller infarct size observed after such an extended period of reperfusion was most encouraging as in most of the earlier studies the infarct size

[a]This study has been supported by grants NHS 95.103 and D96.024 of the Netherlands Heart Foundation. Dr. Duncker's research has been made possible by a Research Fellowship of the Royal Netherlands Academy of Arts and Sciences.

[b]Address correspondence to: P.D. Verdouw, Ph.D., Experimental Cardiology, Thoraxcenter, Erasmus University Rotterdam, P.O. Box 1738, 3000 DR Rotterdam, The Netherlands; Telephone: 31 10 4088029; Fax: 31 10 4089494; E-mail: verdouw@tch.fgg.eur.nl

limitation proved only to be a delay in the development of infarct size and ultimate infarct size was not affected. Subsequent studies not only confirmed the occurrence of ischemic preconditioning in a large number of animal species, but also revealed that the time course of protection exhibited (at least in some species) a biphasic pattern.[2,3] Thus, while in all animal species studied, ischemic preconditioning triggered an early phase of cardioprotection lasting up to two hours, it could be shown that in some species there was a second window of protection 24 hours later that usually lasted a few days. This second window of protection against infarct size has remained controversial, however, as several groups of investigators failed to show its existence.[4,5] Reasons may be numerous and could include such factors as the intensity and the duration of the preconditioning stimulus, the duration of the infarct-producing coronary artery occlusion, the time interval between the preconditioning stimulus and the sustained coronary artery occlusion, the area at risk, the surgical preparation, and the anesthetic regimen employed. When demonstrated, the protection during the second window usually proved to be considerably less than during the early phase and this smaller magnitude of protection could have contributed to the failure to observe a significant infarct size limitation in some of the negative studies. Furthermore, in a recent study Miki and colleagues[6] subjected instrumented conscious rabbits to a 30-min coronary artery occlusion and determined infarct size by either triphenyltetrazolium chloride (TTC) staining after 3 h of reperfusion or by histology after 72 h of reperfusion. Using TTC staining, they found that four cycles of 5-min coronary artery occlusion and 10-min reperfusion preceding the 30-min coronary artery occlusion by 24 h resulted in smaller infarct sizes (33% of the risk zone compared to 45% in control animals), whereas the infarct sizes of the preconditioned animals and the control animals were almost identical (57% versus 59%) when they were determined with histology. The authors hypothesized that increased levels of myocardial superoxide dismutase, which have been implicated in the mechanism of the second window of protection (not in the early protection), may cause necrotic tissue to be seen as viable tissue when TTC staining is performed.[6] They therefore conclude that the existence of a second window of protection might be based on the failure of TTC staining to measure total infarct size.

Despite numerous efforts, the mechanisms underlying the protection by both early (classical) and delayed (second window) ischemic preconditioning are still incompletely understood. Nevertheless a large number of potential mediators, such as adenosine receptors, norepinephrine, and activation of (isoenzymes of) protein kinase C, which all ultimately lead to activation of ATP-sensitive potassium channels, have been suggested to be involved in both phases of protection.[7–13]

Ischemic preconditioning has not only received wide attention in heart research, but has also been a topic of extensive studies involving other organs such as brain,[14–16] kidney,[17,18] skeletal muscle,[19] and liver.[20] In several of these studies, it has been shown that despite differences in the endpoint used to assess protection the same mediators as in myocardial ischemic preconditioning may be involved. However, several of the putative mediators do not require ischemia to become activated. This has guided us and others to investigate whether the myocardium can also be protected by brief ischemia in other organs and whether other (not pharmacological) forms of stress that do not produce ischemia but are capable of activating these potential mediators are also cardioprotective.

CARDIOPROTECTION BY NON-ISCHEMIC STRESS

The first to describe that regional myocardium can become preconditioned without prior local ischemia were Przyklenk and colleagues[21] when they determined infarct size in anesthetized dogs subjected to a 60-min occlusion of the left anterior descending coronary artery (LAD). They observed that when the LAD occlusion was preceded by four episodes of 5-min left circumflex coronary artery (LCX) occlusion and 5-min reperfusion, infarct sizes were limited to the same extent as after local ischemic preconditioning. An explanation for this finding was not given but the authors suggested that this could involve factors that were produced or activated during ischemia and/or reperfusion and transported throughout the heart. If true, this could also imply that ischemia in other organs might produce or activate the same factors that could then be transported to the heart and thereby protect the myocardium. Conversely, it is also feasible that myocardial ischemia could precondition other organs, an option that to our knowledge has not yet been investigated. In a subsequent study of the same group,[22] it was shown that in the same canine model stretch produced by left atrial infusion of saline also limited infarct size in dogs subjected to a 60-min coronary artery occlusion. Volume loading was chosen such that it caused a 10–15% increase in end-diastolic segment length, which is similar to that observed in the study by Przyklenk and colleagues[21] in which the LAD distribution area was preconditioned by brief periods of left circumflex coronary artery occlusion. Because stretch activates ion channels located in the sarcolemma,[23] which appear to be selective for cations but are rather non-selective for K^+, Na^+, or Ca^{2+}, and because these channels can be blocked by gadolinium,[24] Ovize and colleagues[22] investigated whether this compound affected the protection by stretch. They proved that pretreatment with gadolinium blocked the protection by stretch and attenuated the protection by ischemic preconditioning. Unfortunately, the investigators did not study the effect of gadolinium on the protection of the remote myocardium observed in the study of Przyklenk and colleagues,[21] as this might have led to an insight into the mechanism by which ischemia in the left circumflex coronary artery–perfused myocardium protected the adjacent virgin myocardium of the LAD distribution territory. In a follow-up study, Gysembergh and colleagues[25] not only showed that volume loading was also as effective as ischemic preconditioning in protecting myocardium in anesthetized rabbits, but more importantly, showed that pretreatment with glibenclamide also abolished the protection by stretch, thereby suggesting that stretch ultimately protects the myocardium through activation of K^+_{ATP} channels. Although these studies suggest a common mechanism for the protection by stretch and by early ischemic preconditioning, there have been no studies investigating whether there is also a second window of protection by stretch. It is equally unknown if the time course of the protection of the remote myocardium in the study by Przyklenk and colleagues shows a biphasic pattern.[21]

Adenosine has been repeatedly found to play a major role in the mechanism underlying ischemic preconditioning. There are, however, several maneuvers that do not produce ischemia, but cause adenosine levels to increase. Thus Saito and colleagues[26] observed increased myocardial adenosine concentrations during exercise, while Watkinson and colleagues[27] found that adenosine concentrations in the pericardial fluid increased with increasing workloads during treadmill exercise in dogs, and finally Hall and colleagues[28] have reported that in pigs an increase in workload in the absence of ischemia was accompanied by an increase in interstitial adenosine concentrations. Nevertheless, Marber and colleagues[29] failed to show a protective effect of a single 5-min period of rapid atrial pacing against myocardial infarction in the rabbit heart. On the other hand, transient rapid ventricular pacing has been reported to protect against the occurrence of ventricular arrhythmias (a still controversial endpoint in ischemic preconditioning studies) during a subsequent coronary artery occlusion. However, the authors concluded that based on the ST-segment changes occurring during the pacing period, the pacing-induced protection was secondary to ischemia.[30] We have reported that in anesthetized pigs, infarct size after a 60-min coronary artery occlusion was less when the occlusion was preceded by 30-min ventricular pacing at a rate of 200 beats/min.[31] Assessment of ventricular performance during and after pacing by a number of metabolic, perfusion, and functional parameters, such as myocardial ATP and phosphocreatine levels, energy charge, and regional wall function data, revealed that pacing at this rate did *not* lead to ischemia. In that study, as with ischemic preconditioning, protection by ventricular pacing was abolished after pretreatment with the non-selective ATP-sensitive potassium channel blocker glibenclamide. Surprisingly, however, administration of glibenclamide during the intermittent period of normal sinus rhythm between the period of ventricular pacing and the 60-min coronary artery occlusion did not abolish the protection by ventricular pacing. In a more recent study, Domenech and colleagues[32] reported on a series of similar experiments performed in anesthetized dogs. In that study arterial blood pressure was controlled at 80–90 mm Hg to avoid effects of changes in hemodynamics during the five sequences of ventricular tachycardia at 213±12 cycles/min and the subsequent infarct-producing coronary artery occlusion. Based on the coronary flow reserve during the pacing period, it was also excluded that the period of tachycardia caused myocardial ischemia. Ventricular pacing again protected the myocardium, but this protection was abolished by treatment with the non-selective adenosine blocker 8-phenyltheophylline (8PT), independent of whether its administration occurred before or after the periods of tachycardia, suggesting a mechanism that is similar to ischemic preconditioning. Using microdialysis, the authors also showed that the tachycardia stimulus indeed increased interstitial adenosine concentrations twofold and that in the preconditioned animals concentrations continued to rise during the first 40 min of ischemia, but started to decline during the last 20 min of ischemia, and returned to baseline during the first hour of reperfusion. Because dialysis data were not obtained in the other series of experiments, it is unknown how treatment with 8PT, either before or after the intermittent pacing periods, affected the interstitial adenosine concentrations during and after the coronary artery occlusion. It is also of interest that Domenech and colleagues[32] did not find any changes in cytosolic or particulate protein kinase C (PKC) activity of translocation of the α, β, ε, and ζ-protein kinase C isoenzymes, suggesting that (isoenzyme) protein kinase C activity or translocation does not play a role in the tachycardia-induced protection. These data on activity and translocation of isoenzymes of PKC are in agreement with unpublished studies from our laboratory, in which we also could not show any changes in the activity or translocation of the α- and ε-isoenzymes.

Although both studies[31,32] suggest that similar mechanisms appear to underlie the cardioprotection by ventricular tachycardia and ischemic preconditioning, the degree of protection by ventricular tachycardia was in both studies found to be less than with ischemic preconditioning. If only activation of adenosine receptors is involved in the mechanism underlying the protection by ischemic preconditioning these observations are difficult to explain, as the increase in the interstitial adenosine concentrations during ventricular tachycardia observed in the study by Domenech and colleagues[32] should be sufficient to maximally activate adenosine A_1 receptors.[33]

Another difference in the protection by ventricular pacing and ischemic preconditioning relates to the time course of protection, as the protection by ventricular pacing appears to be more ephemeral than the first window of protection by ischemic preconditioning. Furthermore, while a second window of protection against the occurrence of ventricular arrhythmias has been demonstrated after ventricular pacing,[34,35] no study has so far addressed whether ventricular pacing also produces a second window of protection against infarction.

The conclusions regarding the magnitude of protection and the mechanisms by which ventricular pacing and ischemic preconditioning protect the myocardium in both *in vivo* studies[31,32] have been challenged by Hearse and colleagues[36] employing isolated blood-perfused, paced rat hearts. In this model ischemic preconditioning and rapid pacing produced, in contrast with the *in vivo* studies, a similar improvement of postischemic function at 40 min of reperfusion after 35-min ischemia as assessed by left ventricular developed pressure. The duration of the ischemic period and the time point of the postischemic measurements raise the question of whether the results may have been the consequence of a mixture of stunning and irreversible damage. Hearse and colleagues[36] concluded that the mechanisms of protection are different because rapid pacing did not, but ischemic preconditioning did, decrease tissue levels of high energy phosphates. This conclusion is premature, however, in view of the involvement of K^+_{ATP} channels in protection by ischemic preconditioning and pacing in our studies.[31,37]

MYOCARDIAL INFARCT SIZE LIMITATION BY ISCHEMIC STRESS IN OTHER ORGANS

The first to report that brief ischemia in organs other than the heart itself could protect the heart during a coronary artery occlusion were McClanahan and colleagues,[38] who showed that a brief renal artery occlusion followed by reperfusion preceding a 45-min coronary artery occlusion limited myocardial infarct size in rabbits. These preliminary data led us to investigate in detail whether a 15-min occlusion of either renal artery or the mesenteric artery applied 10 min before a 60-min coronary artery occlusion also limited myocardial infarct size in anesthetized rats.[39,40] Since body temperature may influence infarct size and interventions may be protective only in combination with hypothermia, we studied animals under normothermic (36.5°C–37.5°C) and mild hypothermic (30°C–31°C) conditions. TABLE 1 shows that a 15-min mesenteric artery occlusion 10 min before the 60-min coronary artery occlusion limited myocardial infarct size in both temperature ranges, while brief renal ischemia was only effective in the hypothermic range. Pretreatment with the ganglion blocker hexamethonium abolished the protection by the transient mesenteric artery occlusion, but the protection by classical ischemic preconditioning was not affected. When the 60-min coronary artery occlusion was repeated in the presence of a permanent mesenteric artery occlusion, in-

TABLE 1. Effect of remote organ ischemia on infarct size produced by 60-min coronary artery occlusion in rats

	AR (%LV_{mass})		IA/AR (%)	
	36.5–37.5°C	30–31°C	36.5–37.5°C	30–31°C
Protocol I				
(Ganglion intact)				
Sham + 60-min CAO	31 ± 4 (*N* = 11)	36 ± 4 (*N* = 11)	68 ± 2	67 ± 3
15-min CAO + 10 min Rep + 60 min CAO	47 ± 4 (*N* = 9)	40 ± 5 (*N* = 8)	50 ± 3[a]	22 ± 3[a,b]
15-min MAO + 10-min Rep + 60-min CAO	42 ± 4 (*N* = 10)	41 ± 3 (*N* = 11)	50 ± 3[a]	44 ± 5[a]
15-min RAO + 10-min Rep + 60-min CAO	35 ± 8 (*N* = 8)	37 ± 2 (*N* = 9)	72 ± 5	46 ± 6[a,b]
Protocol II				
(After ganglion blockade)				
Sham + 60-min CAO	37 ± 5 (*N* = 7)	35 ± 3 (*N* = 7)	68 ± 3	67 ± 3
15-min CAO + 10-min Rep + 60-min CAO	45 ± 3 (*N* = 7)	35 ± 2 (*N* = 7)	54 ± 3[a]	18 ± 4[a,b]
15-min MAO + 10-min Rep + 60-min CAO	40 ± 3 (*N* = 7)	37 ± 3 (*N* = 7)	74 ± 2	69 ± 3
Protocol III				
Permanent MAO + 60-min CAO	36 ± 4 (*N* = 6)	34 ± 2 (*N* = 8)	70 ± 3	63 ± 3

Sham, control group undergoing 60-min CAO without stimulus; CAO, coronary artery occlusion; MAO, mesenteric artery occlusion; RAO, renal artery occlusion; Rep, reperfusion. Permanent MAO started 25 min before the onset of 60-min CAO and was maintained until the end of the 3-h reperfusion period. Data are mean ± SEM. [a]$p < 0.05$ versus Control; [b]$p < 0.05$ versus corresponding 36.5–37.5°C group. (After Gho *et al.*[40])

farct size was not different from the control group, strongly suggesting that a mediator released upon reperfusion of the mesenteric artery may be involved. The reason we failed to observe protection by the renal artery occlusion at normothermia is unclear. Other groups of investigators have also found positive results with brief renal ischemia in rabbits and suggest the involvement of adenosine in the protection.[41,42] Preliminary data by Pell and colleagues[42] obtained in rabbits preconditioned with a 10-min renal artery occlusion and 10-min reperfusion before a 30-min coronary artery occlusion suggest that brief renal ischemia and preconditioning by local myocardial ischemia protect the myocardium by similar mechanisms, as pretreatment with both the non-selective adenosine blocker 8-(*p*-sulphophenyl)theophylline and the ATP-sensitive K^+ channel blocker 5-hydroxydecanoate abolished the protection by either mode of protection.

Since ischemia produced by a partial coronary artery occlusion and can also precondition the myocardium,[43–46] Birnbaum and colleagues[47] investigated whether a 55–65% reduction in femoral artery blood flow for 30 min and a 30-min stimulation of the gastrocnemius muscle (at a rate of one pulse per second for 20 msec with a stimulus of 9 V) could also limit infarct size produced by a 30-min coronary artery occlusion. The results revealed that if performed alone, neither of these two interventions limited myocardial infarct size when compared to the infarct size of a group of control animals (26 ± 3%). However, when both maneuvers were combined, infarct size was limited to 9 ± 2%. At variance with abrupt brief renal and mesenteric artery occlusion and reperfusion, the combination of flow restriction in the femoral artery and stimulation of the gastrocnemius muscle may have a clinical analog in patients with peripheral vascular disease. This investigation therefore emphasizes the need for further studies exploring the possibilities of how the myocardium can be preconditioned by transient ischemia outside the heart.

In this respect the influence of cerebral ischemia on the heart may be of special interest. This topic has already been the subject of many studies because donor hearts for transplantation are often obtained from patients with brain death. In several of these studies it has been noted that brain death leads to severe impairment in myocardial contractility and even to irreversible myocardial damage.[48,49] In the experimental animal, cell damage is usually produced by increasing intracranial pressure (ICP). Shivalkar and colleagues[50] have shown that rapid, rather than gradual, increases in ICP (producing a 1,000–fold and a 200–fold increase in epinephrine levels, respectively) cause irreversible myocardial damage. In recent studies, the same group of investigators has shown that sympathetic withdrawal rather than myocardial damage, if present at all, is responsible for the changes in hemodynamic profile after brain death in rats.[51,52] In contrast to the influence of prolonged cerebral ischemia on myocardial function and structure, the effect of brief cerebral ischemia on the former has not been studied. It is of interest, however, that the brain can be preconditioned by brief cerebral ischemia, but in contrast to the heart, the protection is observed only 2–5 days after the preconditioning stimulus, a time interval that resembles that of the second window of protection in myocardial ischemic preconditioning.[16]

HYPOTHERMIA

The effect of body temperature on the development of infarction after a coronary artery occlusion has been the topic of several investigations in recent years. For instance, Chien and colleagues[53] reported a steep relation between body core temperature in the range of 35°C–42°C and infarct size after a 30-min coronary artery occlusion for rabbits. Thus a decrease in temperature of 1°C resulted in 12% less infarction of the area at risk, with no infarction occurring at a body core temperature of 34.5°C. An even more temperature sensitive relation was found by Duncker and colleagues[54] when they subjected anesthetized pigs to a 45-min coronary artery occlusion. Similarly, Schwartz and colleagues[55] also observed that in dog hearts the infarct size after a 60-min coronary artery occlusion was modulated by epicardial temperature. Because we did not observe a difference in infarct size when we subjected anesthetized rats to a 60-min coronary artery occlusion at body temperature of 31°C and 37°C, we determined in anesthetized rats infarct size after coronary artery occlusions of different duration.[56] FIGURE 1 shows that in rats infarct sizes are smaller at lower body temperatures, provided that the coronary artery is occluded for

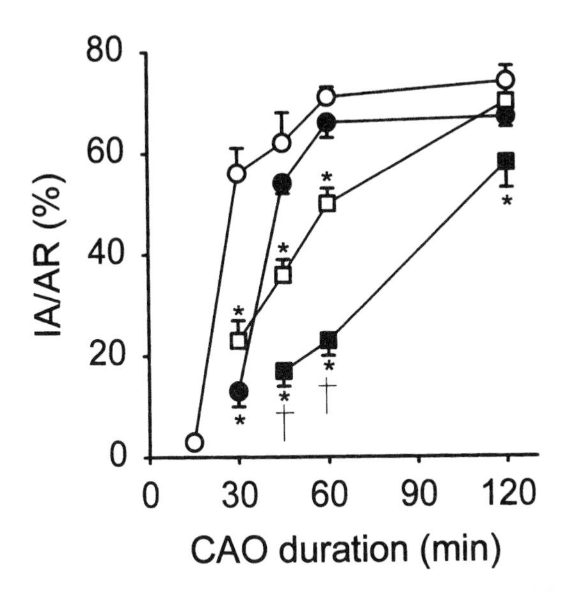

FIGURE 1. Effect of mild hypothermia and ischemic preconditioning alone and in combination on infarct size (expressed as percentage of area at risk, IA/AR) produced by coronary artery occlusions of different duration. Notice that the slopes of the relation between infarct size (IA/AR) and the duration of the coronary artery occlusion (CAO) is less steep and linear (over the CAO range tested) in the preconditioned animals and that combined hypothermia and ischemic preconditioning were also protective for CAO's of 120 min. ○ = normothermia (36.5–37.5°C); ● = hypothermia (30–31°C); □ = preconditioning at normothermia; ■ = preconditioning at hypothermia; IA = infarcted area; AR = area at risk. Data are mean ± SEM. *$p < 0.05$ versus ○ at corresponding CAO duration. ($p < 0.05$ versus □ at corresponding CAO duration. (Reproduced with permission of *Cardiovascular Research.*)

less than 60 minutes. For coronary artery occlusions exceeding 60 minutes, infarct size development was complete at both body temperatures and no beneficial effect of hypothermia was noticeable. In all the aforementioned studies the total body was cooled and cooling was started before the coronary artery occlusion. In order to assess whether regional myocardial hypothermia also affected infarct size and the importance of the timing of the onset of regional cooling, Hale and colleagues[57,58] studied infarct sizes in rabbits in which the entire anterior portion of the heart was cooled using a bag containing ice and water. This procedure permitted a local temperature reduction of approximately 6°C within 5 minutes. These studies showed that regional cooling can be protective even when started 10 min after the onset of ischemia and that changes in hemodynamic parameters are not responsible for the protection. As in man, infarct size development is slower than in rabbits, it could very well be that the delay in the onset of cooling with respect to the onset of the development of infarction may be longer than 10 minutes. This approach of regional cooling may therefore have therapeutic value if the procedure can be done safely and without surgical intervention in patients developing an infarction.

To investigate whether the protection by ischemic preconditioning also depends on body temperature, we determined infarct sizes after 3 hours of reperfusion following coronary artery occlusions varying from 15 min to 120 min which were preceded by an ischemic preconditioning stimulus consisting of a 15-min coronary artery occlusion and 10-min reperfusion.[56] FIGURE 1 shows that ischemic preconditioning had a protective effect at both temperatures. Furthermore, the steep parts of the sigmoid curves describing the relation between infarct size and coronary artery occlusion are less steep for the preconditioned animals (at 37°C) than for the hypothermic animals, suggesting a different mechanism of action for ischemic preconditioning and lowering of temperature. FIGURE 1 also shows that the hypothermic animals still benefit from ischemic preconditioning and that the duration of the coronary artery occlusion at which there is still infarct limitation can be expanded to 120 minutes when hypothermia and ischemic preconditioning are combined.

Hypothermia and ischemic preconditioning have also been combined in an isolated perfused rat heart model by Lu and colleagues.[59] After preconditioning with a single 5-min period of ischemia and 10-min reperfusion, hearts were arrested by a 4°C St. Thomas Hospital cardioplegic solution for 3 hours and then reperfused by a 37°C Krebs-Henseleit buffer solution for 45 min. The authors observed that creatine kinase activity in the effluent was higher when preconditioning was performed at 31°C than at 37°C and therefore concluded that hypothermia during preconditioning attenuated the myocardial protection of preconditioning. However control groups for either the hypothermic and normothermic preconditioning experiments were lacking in this study. Furthermore, the reperfusion period lasted only 45 min and it can therefore not be excluded that the lesser recovery in the hypothermic group reflected only a delay of recovery. Nevertheless, the data by Lu and colleagues[59] are of interest as they point toward a potential temperature-dependent effect of the ischemic preconditioning stimulus. Such an effect is also supported by the observations of Dote and colleagues[60] who reported that an ischemic preconditioning stimulus at 25°C was less effective than an ischemic preconditioning stimulus at 38°C in protecting against infarction produced by a 45-min coronary artery occlusion at 38°C. These findings suggest that in our study[56] an ischemic preconditioning stimulus at 37°C could have protected the myocardium more during the 60-min coronary artery occlusion at 31°C than the preconditioning stimulus at 31°C.

CAN PATHOLOGICAL HEARTS BE PRECONDITIONED?

In all ischemic preconditioning studies, but also in all studies employing stimuli which do not lead to ischemia, infarct-size limitation had been investigated in animals with normal healthy hearts, until Speechly-Dirk and colleagues[61] reported that ischemic preconditioning also occurred in hypertrophied rabbit hearts.

It is also of interest that Ferdinandy and colleagues[62] have shown that the protection by ventricular pacing could not be demonstrated in rats that had been fed a high cholesterol diet for 24 weeks. One should also keep in mind that the authors evaluated their preconditioning protocol with rapid ventricular pacing in a setting of a 10-min coronary artery occlusion in an isolated rat heart preparation and that evaluation was therefore based on recovery of performance rather than infarct size. A major reason for the failure to observe a protective effect in the hypercholesterolemic animals may be that an improved recovery of the evaluated parameters involves myocardial production of nitric oxide.[62] Because that same group of investigators also showed that ischemic preconditioning was lost in rabbits fed a high cholesterol diet,[63] such data strongly suggest that the capability of the myocardium to adapt to several forms of stress may be impaired under pathological conditions.

In contrast to the negative studies,[62–64] Iliodromitis and colleagues[65] have recently shown that ischemic preconditioning with one cycle of 5-min ischemia and 10-min reperfusion was equally effective in normocholesterolemic as in hypercholesterolemic (0.2% cholesterol rich diet for 8 weeks caused cholesterol increase from 58 ± 9 mg% to 1,402 ± 125 mg%) rabbits in limiting infarct size produced by 30-min ischemia. Similarly, Cokkinos and colleagues[66] reported that in isolated hearts obtained from hyperthyroid rats (L-thyroxine administration for 2 weeks causing an increase in left ventricular mass of 15%), recovery of left ventricular developed pressure was similar (38%) in control and hyperthyroid hearts after 20-min ischemia and 45-min reperfusion. After preconditioning with two periods of no flow ischemia, recovery of function improved in both animals to the same extent (59% and 69%, respectively). The currently available data must, however, be interpreted with caution as it can not yet be excluded that in the negative studies only the time course of protection may be shifted or that more intense stress or stress of a longer duration is still capable of eliciting a cardioprotective response. It is, however, equally possible that under certain pathological conditions more severe stress or stress of the longer duration preceding a sustained coronary artery occlusion may prove to be deleterious rather than protective.

CONCLUSIONS

The evidence that myocardium can be protected against the development of irreversible damage is increasing. Local ischemic myocardial preconditioning is the most potent endogenous stimulus, but transient ischemia in remote organs and non-pharmacological stimuli that do not lead to ischemia have also been proven to be cardioprotective. A major question remains whether cardioprotection can still be shown in models that mimic more closely the pathological conditions in man. Major efforts should therefore be directed to the study of ischemic and non-ischemic preconditioning in more pathological models. In earlier studies we have shown that partial coronary artery occlusions are capable of preconditioning normal myocardium without an intermittent reperfusion period between the partial and complete occlusion,[45,46] analogous to the two-stage Harris model.[67] In these studies we used complete reperfusion after release of the infarct producing 60-min coronary artery occlusion. Kapadia and colleagues[68] have extended these studies by showing that myocardium can also be preconditioned in the presence of a permanent stenosis, which is thus also present during the reperfusion period. Studies in hypercholesterolemic animals, in particular when they have moderate to severe coronary artery lesions, and in animals with hypertrophied and failing hearts are another step forward in assessing whether ischemic preconditioning or other stimuli may be protective in man. A major reason for undertaking such studies is that we believe that the definitive proof of ischemic preconditioning in man cannot be achieved[69,70] because of the numerous uncontrolled and confounding factors. If the human myocardium can protect itself against the development of irreversible damage, one must also realize that this could be a confounding factor when one wants to evaluate the salvaging effects of therapeutic interventions such as thrombolysis.

REFERENCES

1. MURRY, C.E., R.B. JENNINGS & K.A. REIMER. 1986. Preconditioning with ischemia: a delay of lethal cell injury in ischemic myocardium. Circulation **74:** 1124–1136.
2. KUZUYA, T., S. HOSHIDA, N. YAMASHITA, H. FUJI, H. OE, M. HORI, T. KAMADA & M. TADA. 1993. Delayed effects of sublethal ischemia on the acquisition of tolerance to ischemia. Circ. Res. **72:** 1293–1299.
3. MARBER, M.S., D.S. LATCHMAN, J.M. WALKER & D.M. YELLON. 1993. Cardiac stress protein elevation 24 hours after brief ischemia or heat stress is associated with resistance to myocardial infarction. Circulation **88:** 1264–1272.
4. QUI, Y., X.L. TANG, S.W. PARK, J.Z. SUN, A. KALYA & R. BOLLI. 1997. The early and late phases of ischemic preconditioning. A comparative analysis of their effects on infarct size, myocardial stunning and arrhythmias in conscious pigs undergoing a 40-minute coronary occlusion. Circ. Res. **80:** 730–742.
5. TANAKA, M., H. FUJIWARA, K. YAMASAKI, M. MIYAMAE, R. YOKOTA, K. HASEGAWA, T. FUJIWARA & S. SASAYAMA. 1994. Ischemic preconditioning elevates cardiac stress protein but does not limit infarct size 24 or 48 hours later in rabbits. Am. J. Physiol. **267:** H1476–H1482.
6. MIKI, T., A.N. SWAFFORD, M.V. COHEN & J.M. DOWNEY. 1998. Second window of protection in conscious rabbits: real or artifactual. J. Mol. Cell. Cardiol. **30:** 285 (Abstract).
7. YELLON, D.M. & G.F. BAXTER. 1995. A "second window of protection" or delayed preconditioning phenomenon: future horizons for myocardial protection? J. Mol. Cell. Cardiol. **27:** 1023–1034.
8. MENG, X., J.M. BROWN, A. BANERJEE & A.H. HARKEN. 1996. Norepinephrine induces cardiac shock protein and delayed cardioprotection in the rat through α_1-adrenoceptors. Cardiovasc. Res. **32:** 374–383.
9. LIGHT, P.E., A.A. SABIR, B.G. ALLEN, M.P. WALSH & R.J. FRENCH. 1996. Protein kinase C–induced changes in the stoichiometry of ATP binding activate ATP-sensitive K^+ channels: A possible mechanistic link to ischemic preconditioning. Circ. Res. **79:** 399–406.
10. BAXTER, G.F., F.M. GOMA & D.M. YELLON. 1995. Involvement of protein kinase C in the delayed cytoprotection following sublethal ischaemia in rabbit myocardium. Br. J. Pharmacol. **115:** 222–224.
11. LAWSON, C.S. & J.M. DOWNEY. 1993. Preconditioning: state of the art myocardial protection. Cardiovasc. Res. **27:** 542–550.
12. BROOKS, G. & D.J. HEARSE. 1996. Role of protein kinase C in ischemic preconditioning: player or spectator? Circ. Res. **79:** 627–630.
13. GHO, B.C.G., Y.E.G. ESKILDSEN-HELMOND, S. DE ZEEUW, J.M.J. LAMERS & P.D. VERDOUW. 1996. Does protein kinase C play a pivotal role in the mechanisms of ischemic preconditioning? Cardiovasc. Drugs. Ther. **10:** 775–786.
14. KITAGAWA, K., M. MATSUMOTO, M. TAGAYA, R. HTA, H. UEDA, M. NIINOBE, N. HANDA, R. FUKUNAGA, K. KIMURA, K. MIKOSHIBA & T. KAMADA. 1990. "Ischemic tolerance" phenomenon found in the brain. Brain Res. **582:** 21–24.
15. KAWAI, K., T. NAGAGOMI, T. KIRINO, A. TAMURA & N. KAWAI. 1998. Preconditioning *in vivo* ischemia inhibits anoxic long-term potentation and functionally protects CA1 neurons in the gerbil. J. Cerebr. Blood Flow Metab. **18:** 288–296.
16. CHEN, J. & R. SIMON. 1997. Ischemic tolerance in the brain. Neurology **48:** 306–311.
17. ZAGER, R.A., L.A. BALTES, H.M. SHARMA & M.S. JURKOWITHZ. 1984. Responses of the ischemic acute renal failure kidney to additional ischemic events. Kidney Int. **26:** 689–700.

18. ISLAM, C.F., R.T. MATHIE, M.D. DINNEEN, E.A. KIELY, A.M. PETERS & P.A. GRACE. 1997. Ischaemia-reperfusion injury in the rat kidney: the effect of preconditioning. Br. J. Urol. **79:** 842–847.
19. PANCY, C.Y., P. NELIGAN, A. ZONG, W. HE, H. XU & C.R. FORREST. 1997. Effector mechanism of adenosine in acute ischemic preconditioning of skeletal muscle against infarction. Am. J. Physiol. **273:** R887–R895.
20. PERALTA, C., D. CLOSA, G. HOLTER, E. GELPI, N. PRATS & J. ROSELLO-CATAFAU. 1996. Liver ischemic preconditioning is mediated by the inhibitory action of nitric oxide on endothelin. Biochem. Biophys. Res. Commun. **229:** 264–270.
21. PRZYKLENK, K., B. BAUER, M. OVIZE, R.A. KLONER & P. WHITTAKER. 1993. Regional ischemic "preconditioning" protects remote virgin myocardium from subsequent sustained coronary occlusion. Circulation **87:** 893–899.
22. OVIZE, M., R.A. KLONER & K. PRZYKLENK. 1994. Stretch preconditions canine myocardium. Am. J. Physiol. **266:** H137–H146.
23. GUHARAY, F. & F. SACHS. 1984. Stretch-activated single ion channel currents in tissue-cultured embryonic chick skeletal muscle. J. Physiol. (London) **352:** 685–701.
24. YANG, X. & F. SACHS. 1989. Block of stretch-activated ion channels in *Xenopus* oocytes by gadolinium and calcium ions. Science **243:** 1068–1071.
25. GYSEMBURGH, A., H. MARGONARI, J. LOUFOUA, A. OVIZE, X. ANDRÉ-FOUËT, Y. MINAIRE & M. OVIZE. 1998. Stretch-induced protection shares a common mechanism with ischemic preconditioning in rabbit heart. Am. J. Physiol. **274:** H955–H964.
26. SAITO, D., D.G. NIXON, R.B. VOMACKA & R.A. OLSSON. 1980. Relationship of cardiac oxygen usage, adenosine content, and coronary resistance in dogs. Circ. Res. **47:** 875–880.
27. WATKINSON, W.P., D.H. FOLEY, R. RUBIO & R.M. BERNE. 1979. Myocardial adenosine formation with increased cardiac performance in the dog. Am. J. Physiol. **236:** H13–H21.
28. HALL, J.L., D.G.L. VAN WYLEN, R.D. PIZURRO, C.D. HAMILTON, C.M. REILING & W.C. STANLEY. 1995. Myocardial interstitial purine metabolites and lactate with increased work in swine. Cardiovasc. Res. **30:** 351–356.
29. MARBER, M.S., D.M. WALKER, D.J. EVESON, J.M. WALKER & D.M. YELLON. 1993. A single five-minute period of rapid atrial pacing fails to limit infarct size in the *in situ* rabbit heart. Cardiovasc. Res. **27:** 597–601.
30. VEGH, A., L. SZEKERES & J.R. PARRATT. 1991. Transient ischaemia induced by rapid cardiac pacing results in myocardial preconditioning Cardiovasc. Res. **25:** 1051–1053.
31. KONING, M.M.G., B.C.G. GHO, E. VAN KLAARWATER, R.L.J. OPSTAL, D.J. DUNCKER & P.D. VERDOUW. 1996. Rapid ventricular pacing produces myocardial protection by nonischemic activation of ATP potassium channels. Circulation **93:** 178–186.
32. DOMENECH, R.J., P. MACHO, D. VÉLEZ, G. SÁNCHEZ, X. LIU & N. DHALLA. 1998. Tachycardia preconditions infarct size in dogs: role of adenosine in protein kinase C. Circulation **97:** 786–794.
33. LONDOS, C., D.M.F. COOPER, W. SCHEGEL & M. RODBELL. 1978. Adenosine analogs inhibit adipocyte adenylate cyclase by a GTP-dependent process: basis for actions of adenosine and methylxanthines on cyclic AMP production and lipolysis. Proc. Natl. Acad. Sci. USA **75:** 5362–5366.
34. VEGH, A., J.G. PAPP & J.R. PARRATT. 1994. Dexamethasone prevents the marked antiarrhythmic effects of preconditioning induced 20 hours after rapid cardiac pacing. Br. J. Pharmacol. **113:** 1081–1083.
35. KASZALA, K., A. VEGH, J.G. PAPP & J.R. PARRATT. 1996. Time course of the protection against ischaemia and reperfusion-induced ventricular arrhythmias resulting from brief periods of cardiac pacing. J. Mol. Cell. Cardiol. **28:** 2085–2095.
36. HEARSE, D.J., R. FERRARI & F.J. SUTHERLAND. 1998. Preconditioning by ischemia, rapid pacing and ventricular fibrillation: studies of catecholamines and high energy phosphates. J. Mol. Cell. Cardiol. **30:** A16 (Abstract).
37. ROHMANN, S., H. WEYGANDT, P. SCHELLING, L.K. SOEI, P.D. VERDOUW & I. LUES. 1994. Involvement of ATP-sensitive potassium channels in preconditioning protection. Basic. Res. Cardiol. **89:** 563–576.
38. MCCLANAHAN T.B., B.S. NAO, L.J. WOLKE, B.J. MARTIN, T.E. METZ & K.P. GAL-

LAGHER. 1993. Brief renal occlusion and reperfusion reduces myocardial infarct size in rabbits. FASEB Lett. **7:** A118 (Abstract).
39. VERDOUW, P.D., B.C.G. GHO, M.M.G. KONING, R.G. SCHOEMAKER & D.J. DUNCKER. 1996. Cardioprotection by ischemic and nonischemic myocardial stress and ischemia in remote organs. Ann. N. Y. Acad. Sci. **793:** 27–42.
40. GHO, B.C.G., R.G. SCHOEMAKER, M.A. VAN DEN DOEL, D.J. DUNCKER & P.D. VERDOUW. 1996. Myocardial protection by brief ischemia in noncardiac tissue. Circulation **94:** 2193–2200.
41. TAKAOKA, A., I. NAKAE, K. MITSUNAMI, T. YABE, S. MORIKAWA, T. INUBUSHI & M. KINOSHITA. 1999. Renal ischemia/reperfusion remotely improves myocardial energy metabolism during myocardial ischemia via adenosine receptors in rabbits: Effects of "remote" preconditioning. J. Am. Coll. Cardiol. **33:** 556–564.
42. PELL, T.J., G.F. BAXTER, D.M. YELLON & G.M. DREW. 1998. Renal ischemia preconditions myocardium: Role of adenosine receptors and ATP-sensitive potassium channels. Am. J. Physiol. **275:** H1542–H1547.
43. OVIZE, M., R.A. KLONER, S.L. HALE & K. PRZYKLENK. 1992. Coronary cyclic flow variations "precondition" the ischemic myocardium. Circulation **85:** 779–789.
44. IWAMOTO, T., X.J. BAI & H.F. DOWNEY. 1993. Preconditioning with supply-demand imbalance limits infarct size in dog hearts. Cardiovasc. Res. **27:** 2071–2076.
45. KONING, M.M.G., L.A.J. SIMONIS, S. DE ZEEUW, S. NIEUKOOP, S. POST & P.D. VERDOUW. 1994. Ischaemic preconditioning by partial occlusion without intermittent reperfusion. Cardiovasc. Res. **28:** 1146–1151.
46. KONING, M.M.G., B.C.G. GHO, E. VAN KLAARWATER, D.J. DUNCKER & P.D. VERDOUW. 1995. Endocardial and epicardial infarct size after preconditioning by a partial coronary artery occlusion without intervening reperfusion: importance of the degree and duration of flow reduction. Cardiovasc. Res. **30:** 1017–1027.
47. BIRNBAUM, Y., S.L. HALE & R.A. KLONER. 1997. Ischemic preconditioning at a distance: Reduction of myocardial infarct size by partial reduction of blood supply combined with rapid stimulation of the gastrocnemius muscles in the rabbit. Circulation **96:** 1641–1646.
48. GALIÑANES, M. & D.J. HEARSE. 1992. Brain death-induced impairment of cardiac contractile performance can be reversed by explantation and may not preclude the use of hearts for transplantation. Circ. Res. **71:** 1213–1219.
49. SHANLIN, R.J., M.J. SOLE, M. RAHIMIFAR, C.H. TATOR & S.M. FACTOR. 1988. Increased intracranial pressure elicits hypertension, increased sympathetic activity, electrocardiographic abnormalities and myocardial damage in rats. J. Am. Coll. Cardiol. **12:** 727–736.
50. SHIVALKAR, B., J. VAN LOON, W. WIELAND, T.B. TJANDRA-MAGA, M. BORGERS, C. PLETS & W. FLAMENG. 1993. Variable effects of explosive or gradual increase of intracranial pressure on myocardial structure and function. Circulation **87:** 230–239.
51. HERIJGERS, P., M. BORGERS & W. FLAMENG. 1998. The effect of brain death on cardiovascular function in rats. Part I. Is the heart damaged? Cardiovasc. Res. **38:** 98–106.
52. HERIJGERS, P. & W. FLAMENG. 1998. The effect of brain death on cardiovascular function in rats. Part II. The cause of the *in vivo* haemodynamic changes. Cardiovasc. Res. **38:** 107–115.
53. CHIEN, G.L., R.A. WOLFF, R.F. DAVIS & D.M. VAN WINKLE. 1994. "Normothermic range" temperature affects myocardial infarct size. Cardiovasc. Res. **8:** 1014–1017.
54. DUNCKER, D.J., C.L. KLASSEN, S.H. HERRLINGER, T.J. PAVEK, Y. ISHIBASHI & R.J. BACHE. 1996. Effect of temperature on myocardial infarction in swine. Am. J. Physiol. **270:** H1189–H1199.
55. SCHWARTZ, L.M., S.G. VERBINSKI, R.S. VAN DER HEIDE & K.A. REIMER. 1997. Epicardial temperature is a major predictor of myocardial infarct size in dogs. J. Mol. Cell. Cardiol. **29:** 1577–1583.
56. VAN DEN DOEL, M.A., B.C.G. GHO, S.Y. DUVAL, R.G. SCHOEMAKER, D.J. DUNCKER & P.D. VERDOUW. 1998. Hypothermia extends the cardioprotection by ischaemic preconditioning to coronary artery occlusions of longer duration. Cardiovasc. Res. **37:** 76–81.

57. HALE, S.L. & R.A. KLONER. 1997. Myocardial temperature in acute myocardial infarction: protection with mild regional hypothermia. Am. J. Physiol. **273:** H220–H227.
58. HALE, S.L., R.H. DAVE & R.A. KLONER. 1997. Regional hypothermia reduces myocardial necrosis even when instituted after the onset of ischemia. Basic Res. Cardiol. **92:** 351–357.
59. LU, E.X., G.L. YING & X. GUO. 1997. Hypothermia during preconditioned ischemia reperfusion attenuates the myocardial protection of preconditioning. J. Thorac. Cardiovasc. Surg. **72:** 514–515.
60. DOTE, K., R.A. WOLFF & D.M. VAN WINKLE. 1996. Hypothermia during transient antecedent ischemia attenuates preconditioning. FASEB J. **10:** A36.
61. SPEECHLY-DIRK, M.E., G.F. BAXTER & D.M. YELLON. 1994. Ischaemic preconditioning protects hypertrophied myocardium. Cardiovasc. Res. **28:** 1025–1029.
62. FERDINANDY, P., Z. SZILVASSY, L.I. HORVATH, T. CSONT, C. CSONKA, E. NAGY, R. SZENTGYÖRGYI, I. NAGY, M. KOLTAI & L. DUX. 1997. Loss of pacing-induced preconditioning in rat hearts: Role of nitric oxide and cholesterol-enriched diet. J. Mol. Cell. Cardiol. **29:** 3321–3333.
63. SZILVASSY, Z., P. FERDINANDY, J. SZILVASSY, I. NAGY, S. KARCSU, J. LONOVICS, L. DUX & M. KOLTAI. 1995. The loss of pacing-induced preconditioning in atherosclerotic rabbits: role of hypercholesterolemia. J. Mol. Cell. Cardiol. **27:** 2559–2569.
64. FERDINANDY, P., T. CSONT, Z. SZILVASSY, A. TOSAKI & L. DUX. 1998. Inhibition of HMG-CoA reductase, similarly to hypercholesterolemia, inhibits preconditioning in rat hearts. J. Mol. Cell. Cardiol. **30:** A77 (Abstract).
65. ILIODROMITIS, E.K., E. BOFILIS, L. KAKLAMANIS, A. PAPALOIS & D.T. KREMASTINOS. 1998. Preconditioning in hypercholesterolemic rabbits *in vivo*. J. Mol. Cell. Cardiol. **30:** A76 (Abstract).
66. COKKINOS, D.D., C. PANTOS, S. TZEIS, V. MALLIOPOULOU, C. KARAGEORGIOU, C. DAVOS, D. VARONOS & D.V. COKKINOS. 1998. Ischemic preconditioning protects against myocardial dysfunction caused by ischaemia in isolated thyroxine induced hypertrophied rat hearts. J. Mol. Cell. Cardiol. **30:** A76 (Abstract).
67. HARRIS, A.S. 1950. Delayed development of ventricular ectopic rhythms following experimental coronary occlusion. Circulation **1:** 1318–1328.
68. KAPADIA, S.J., J.S TERLATO & A.S. MOST. 1997. Presence of a critical coronary artery stenosis does not abolish the protective effect of ischemic preconditioning. Circulation **95:** 1286–1292.
69. VERDOUW, P.D., M.A. VAN DEN DOEL, S. DE ZEEUW & D.J. DUNCKER. 1997. On the relevance of ischemic preconditioning in humans. Basic Res. Cardiol. **92:** 51–53.
70. VERDOUW, P.D., B.C.G. GHO & D.J. DUNCKER. 1995. Ischemic precondtioning: is it clinically relevant? Eur. Heart J. **16:** 1169–1176.

Cellular Mechanisms of Infarct Size Reduction with Ischemic Preconditioning

Role of Calcium?

KARIN PRZYKLENK,[a,b] BORIS Z. SIMKHOVICH,[a] BARBARA BAUER,[a,c] KATSUYA HATA,[a,c] LIN ZHAO,[c,d] GARY T. ELLIOTT, [d] AND ROBERT A. KLONER[a]

[a]*Heart Institute, Good Samaritan Hospital and Department of Medicine, Section of Cardiology, University of Southern California, Los Angeles, California 90017, USA*

[d]*RIBI Immunochem Research, Inc., Hamilton, Montana 59840, USA*

ABSTRACT: Brief episodes of ischemia protect or "precondition" the heart and reduce infarct size caused by a subsequent sustained ischemic insult. Despite a decade of intensive investigation, the cellular mechanism(s) responsible for this paradoxical protection remain poorly understood. In this review, we focus on the emerging concept that alterations in intracellular calcium homeostasis may participate in either triggering and/or mediating infarct size reduction with preconditioning.

There is no doubt that coronary artery occlusion initiates a deleterious sequence of events, including the rapid cessation of active contraction and conversion from aerobic to anaerobic metabolism, progressive depletion of myocardial high energy phosphate stores, and, within ~15–20 minutes, the onset of myocyte necrosis. However, in 1986, Murry and colleagues[1] revealed an intriguing paradox: canine myocardium subjected to brief, transient episodes of coronary artery occlusion—too brief in themselves to result in myocyte death—exhibited an increased resistance to infarction caused by a subsequent, more sustained ischemic insult. In the ensuing years, this seminal observation of "preconditioning with ischemia" has been confirmed by countless investigators in virtually all species and experimental models evaluated to date.[2–6] Moreover, although not conclusive,[7,8] there is reason for cautious optimism that brief antecedent ischemia may also protect or "precondition" the human heart (FIG. 1).[9–12,13]

The obvious question arising from these studies is: what are the cellular mechanism(s) responsible for the increased resistance to ischemia and smaller infarct sizes in preconditioned hearts versus time-matched controls? Many potential factors and mediators,[13] ranging from favorable changes in myocardial energy metabolism[14,15] to

[b]Address correspondence to: Karin Przyklenk, Ph.D., Heart Institute/Research, Good Samaritan Hospital, 1225 Wilshire Boulevard, Los Angeles, California 90017-2395; Telephone: 213-977-4050; Fax: 213-977-4107; E-mail: Karinp@dnamail.com

[c]Current affiliations: Barbara Bauer, Deegenbergklinik, Bad Kissingen, Germany; Katsuya Hata, First Department of Internal Medicine, Kobe University School of Medicine, Kobe, Japan; Lin Zhao, Abbott Laboratories, Abbott Park, Illinois.

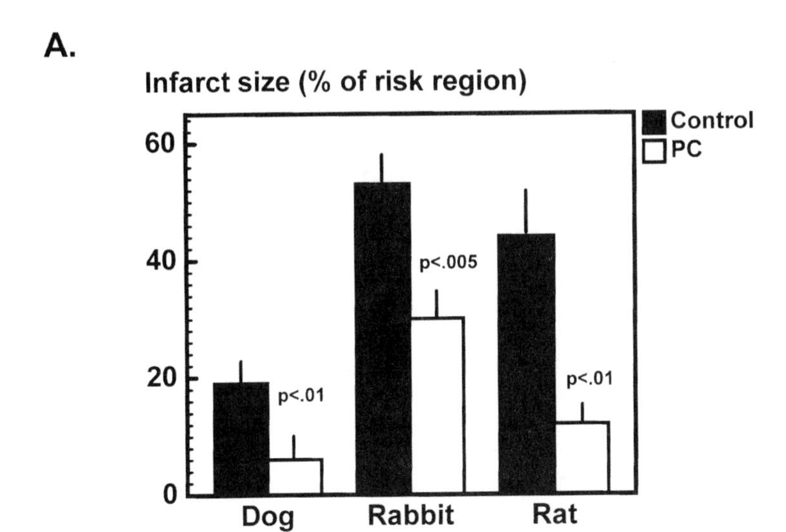

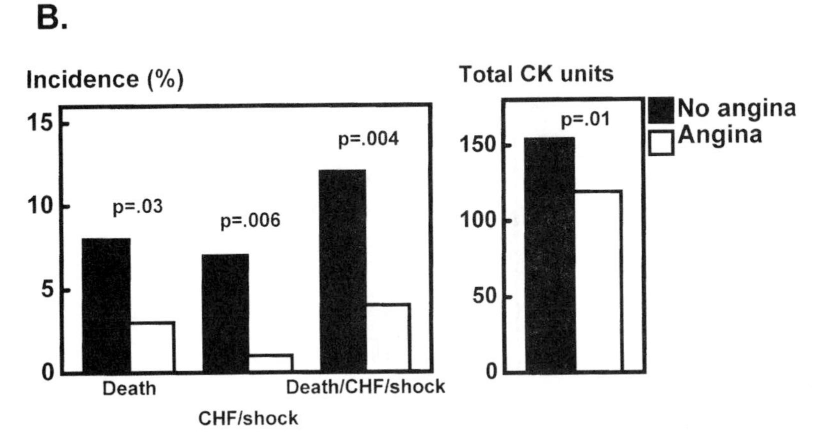

FIGURE 1. (**A**) Examples of infarct size reduction with preconditioning in the *in vivo* dog, rabbit, and rat models. In each case, infarct size (expressed as a % of the myocardium at risk) was significantly reduced in cohorts that first received brief episodes of preconditioning ischemia when compared with time-matched controls that underwent the test occlusion alone.[3–5] (**B**) Clinical evidence of preinfarct angina as a preconditioning stimulus. Retrospective analysis of data from the Thrombolysis in Myocardial Infarction (TIMI)-4 trial revealed that in-hospital outcome (assessed by the incidence of death, congestive heart failure (CHF), and/or shock) was significantly improved and infarct size (i.e., median total creatine kinase (CK) release) was significantly reduced in patients who experienced angina (i.e., brief antecedent ischemia) prior to myocardial infarction versus those with no preinfarct angina.[12] (*Reproduced from Przyklenk & Kloner*[13] *with permission.*)

complex alterations in the subcellular activity of multiple kinases and phosphatases,[5,16–22] have been implicated. In this review, we focus on the emerging concept that alterations in intracellular calcium homeostasis may participate in either triggering and/or mediating infarct size reduction with preconditioning.

CALCIUM DURING ANTECEDENT ISCHEMIA AS A "TRIGGER" FOR CARDIOPROTECTION

Rationale and First Evidence

Considerable evidence derived from direct measurements of intracellular free calcium ($[Ca^{2+}]_i$) in intact isolated hearts indicates that brief (3–5 min), nonlethal episodes of transient ischemia (i.e., well-recognized to serve as effective preconditioning stimuli[23,24]) elicit a short-lived, approximately two- to fourfold increase in $[Ca^{2+}]_i$.[25,26] This observation, together with the established role of calcium as a ubiquitous second messenger in a host of signal transduction pathways,[27,28] makes increased $[Ca^{2+}]_i$ during antecedent ischemia an attractive candidate for possible "trigger" of the initiation of preconditioning-induced cardioprotection.

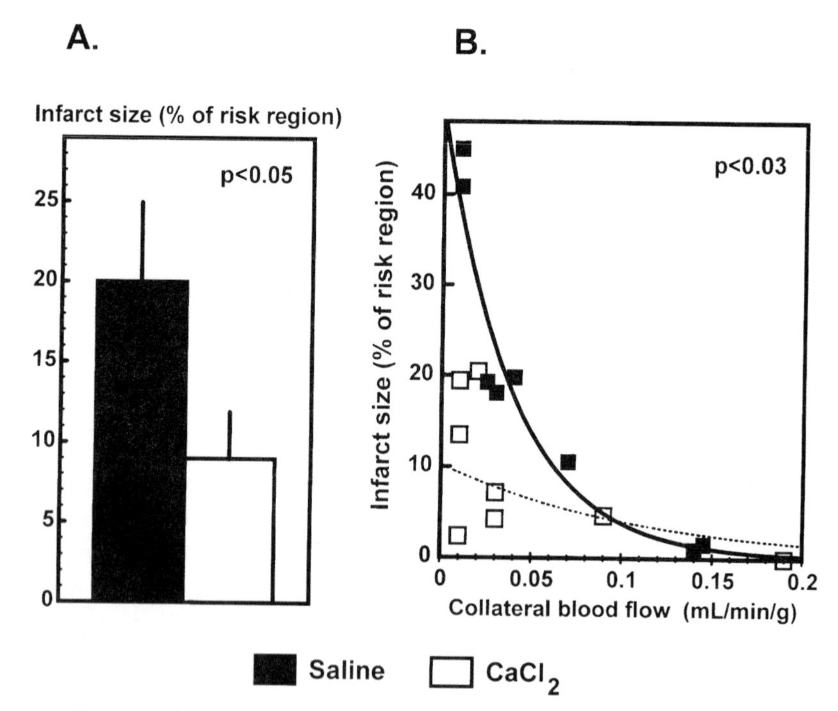

FIGURE 2. Infarct size (expressed as a % of the myocardium at risk) was reduced in dogs that received a 15-min intracoronary infusion of $CaCl_2$ before a 1-h sustained period of coronary artery occlusion when compared with controls that received a matched infusion of saline. Significant cardioprotection by brief infusion of $CaCl_2$ was documented both by comparison of mean values of infarct size (**A**), and by incorporating collateral blood flow to the ischemic subendocardium as a covariate in the analysis (**B**). (*Adapted from Przyklenk* et al.[29])

In apparent support of this concept, recent studies have revealed that brief exogenous infusion of $CaCl_2$ or calcium gluconate—presumably augmenting $[Ca^{2+}]_i$ either directly and/or as a secondary consequence of Ca^{2+}-induced Ca^{2+} release from internal stores, influx of extracellular calcium via voltage-dependent Ca^{2+} channels, or influx of calcium via Na^+-Ca^{2+} exchange—effectively renders the myocardium resistant to a subsequent prolonged ischemic insult.[29–36] For example, we found that infarct size in dogs randomized to receive a 15-min intracoronary infusion of 20 mM $CaCl_2$ before 1-h sustained coronary artery occlusion averaged only 9% of the myocardium at risk, significantly smaller than the 20% observed in the control cohort that received a matched, antecedent intracoronary infusion of saline[29] (FIG. 2). This observation is not restricted to *in vivo* models employing infarct size as the endpoint[29–31]: corroborating results that assess enzyme release and recovery of left ventricular developed pressure as indices of cellular injury have been obtained using (1) isolated buffer-perfused rat hearts[32–35] and explanted human papillary muscle preparations[36] exposed to exogenous calcium, and (2) rat hearts subjected to brief infusion of ryanodine, thereby eliciting transient release of endogenous calcium from the sarcoplasmic reticulum.[37] Similarly, in rat, rabbit, and canine models, brief infusion of exogenous catecholamines in lieu of brief antecedent ischemia has been shown by many investigators to limit infarct size.[13] Importantly, however, these results do not, in themselves, establish whether infarct size reduction with brief antecedent exposure to calcium has any relevance to cardioprotection with brief transient ischemia. That is, the critical question that must be addressed is: can the concept of increased $[Ca^{2+}]_i$ as a trigger be rationally integrated with our current knowledge (and working hypotheses) of the cellular mechanisms for infarct size reduction with preconditioning?

The Current Theory: G Protein–Coupled Signaling and Activation of Protein Kinase C

There is a general consensus among investigators that infarct size reduction with preconditioning is a receptor-mediated phenomenon, initiated, in all likelihood, by stimulation of G protein–coupled receptors (including adenosine A_1 and/or A_3, muscarinic M_2, α_1-adrenergic, angiotensin II, bradykinin B_2, δ-opioid, etc.) during brief preconditioning ischemia.[13] Although G protein–coupled receptors are involved in multiple signal transduction pathways, the currently favored hypothesis, pioneered by Downey and colleagues,[16] is that brief antecedent ischemia initiates, via this receptor stimulation, activation of phospholipase C and/or D,[38,39] production of the second messenger diacylglycerol (DAG), and the resultant activation and subcellular redistribution of one or more of the 12 known isoforms of protein kinase C (PKC). Specific translocation of PKC from the cytosol to the myocyte membranes, manifest at the onset of the sustained test occlusion,[17] potentially triggers a kinase cascade (purportedly involving activation of tyrosine and MAP kinases[18–21,40]) that ultimately culminates in the phosphorylation of an as-yet unidentified membrane-bound end-effector (possibly sarcolemmal or mitochondrial ATP-sensitive potassium (K_{ATP}) channels[41,42]) in order to achieve the well-documented, preconditioning-induced reduction in infarct size.

Support for the critical involvement of PKC in preconditioning has largely been deduced from indirect pharmacologic evidence obtained in the rat and rabbit models.

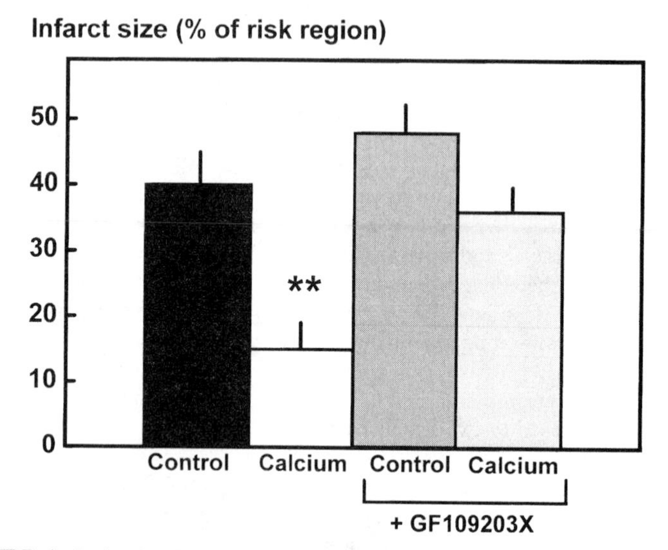

FIGURE 3. Reduction in infarct size (expressed as a % of the myocardium at risk) achieved by brief intracoronary infusion of $CaCl_2$ in the *in vivo* canine model was abrogated by coadministration of the GF109203X, an inhibitor of protein kinase C. $**p < 0.005$ versus Control. (*Adapted Node* et al.[30])

Many investigators have reported that brief administration of PKC agonists (i.e., DAG analogues and phorbol esters) substituted for the brief antecedent ischemia mimic the benefits of preconditioning. Conversely, PKC inhibitors (including polymyxin B, staurosporine, chelerythrine, calphostin C, etc.) partially or completely abrogate preconditioning-induced protection.[13,43] Moreover (and, arguably, more importantly), a handful of studies have provided direct evidence of a subcellular redistribution of PKC (most notably the isoforms PKC ε and δ) from the cytosol to the particulate fraction in response to brief preconditioning ischemia.[43–48]

If activation and translocation of PKC is indeed a pivotal step in preconditioning-induced cardioprotection, how might changes in $[Ca^{2+}]_i$ during the preconditioning stimulus be involved? The most obvious connection between the two hypotheses is that activation of one subgroup of the PKC family is critically dependent upon both lipids (i.e., DAG) and calcium.[43] Indeed, this was the underlying rationale for most of the protocols investigating the potential protective effects of brief, nonischemic exposure of the heart to calcium.[30,32–37] In support of this argument, brief infusion of exogenous $CaCl_2$ or ryanodine was associated with an increase in total membrane-associated PKC activity[30] and, more specifically, translocation of PKC isoforms α, δ, and/or ζ, to the myocyte membranes.[32–35] In addition, coadministration of the PKC inhibitors chelerythrine, bisindolylmaleimide, and GF109203X blocked the cardioprotection achieved with calcium administration (FIG. 3).[30,32–37]

There is, however, an overt inconsistency in this line of reasoning: the PKC isoforms implicated in most studies to play a role in ischemia-induced preconditioning, ε and δ, are members of the novel, calcium-independent PKC subfamily which, in contrast to the conventional isoforms (α, β_1, β_2, and γ), require lipids, but not calcium, for activation.[43] The reasons for this apparent incongruity are speculative. Although it has been suggested that translocation of one or more isoforms may simply be coincidental,[31] an alternative explanation is that an increase in $[Ca^{2+}]_i$ may indirectly activate novel calcium-independent PKC isozymes via G protein–mediated upregulation of phospholipase C and a resultant increase in DAG.[30,34,37] This does not, however, appear compatible with recent evidence implicating phospholipase D, rather than phospholipase C, as the predominant cellular source of DAG in the setting of brief ischemia.[38,39,49] Interestingly, one laboratory has obtained internally consistent results with regard to ischemic preconditioning, calcium infusion, and PKC. Using the canine model, Kitakaze and colleagues have reported selective subcellular redistribution of the calcium-dependent PKC α (with no changes in the novel isoforms ε and δ) in response to brief antecedent ischemia,[50] cardioprotection together with an increased total membrane activity of calcium-dependent PKC in response to brief intracoronary infusion of $CaCl_2$,[30] and loss of calcium-induced protection by administration of a PKC antagonist.[30] This, however, conflicts with the fundamental observation by our group and others that calcium-independent isoforms[43] (in particular, the novel isoform ε and atypical isoform ζ[51]) are predominant and expression of calcium-dependent PKC isoforms is absent (or negligible) in adult canine myocardium. Resolution of these conceptual inconsistencies will clearly require further study.

"No One Thing Does Only One Thing": PKC Agonists/Antagonists Modulate L-Type Calcium Channels

As aptly emphasized by Brooks and Hearse,[52] an important caveat in interpreting the outcome of any study employing pharmacologic agents is that "no one thing does only one thing." In this regard, it is interesting to note that phorbol esters, DAG analogues, and calphostin C have all recently been reported to have potent and PKC-independent effects on the activity of cardiac L-type calcium channels.[53–55] Does this imply that results obtained with PKC agonists/antagonists in the setting of ischemic preconditioning can be explained in part by altered calcium influx via calcium channels rather than modulation of PKC activity per se? Results obtained by Wallbridge and colleagues[56] seemingly argue against this possibility: the L-type calcium channel antagonist nisoldipine, administered throughout antecedent brief ischemia and the subsequent test occlusion, had no effect on infarct size reduction achieved with preconditioning in the porcine model. This potentially confounding issue has not, however, been rigorously investigated.

G Protein–Coupled Signaling and Activation of Inositol(1,4,5)-Trisphosphate: An Alternative Hypothesis?

Despite the considerable support for the "PKC theory" of preconditioning, the evidence is by no means conclusive.[13,43,52] For example, PKC inhibitors have, in some studies, reportedly failed to block infarct size reduction with preconditioning, [5,57,58] yielded intermediate results,[59,60] or, in marked contrast to the PKC hypothesis, have reduced infarct size in control hearts rather than abrogated preconditioning-induced protection.[61,62] In fact, there are data—albeit obtained in a rat neuronal, rather than cardiac, model of preconditioning—to suggest that, paradoxically, both activation and inhibition of PKC protected against a subsequent episode of ischemia-reperfusion.[63] These discrepant results, while not invalidating the potential involvement of PKC in ischemic preconditioning, have lead most investigators to the reasonable conclusion that, at the very least, other cellular mediators must undoubtedly also play a role.[18–22]

It is well-known from the cell biology literature that stimulation of G protein–coupled receptors results not only in the generation of DAG (the substrate for PKC activation), but also initiates the "parallel" production of the second messenger inositol (1,4,5)-trisphosphate (IP_3) via activation of phosphatidylinositol-specific phospholipase C and hydrolysis of phosphatidylinositol 4,5-bisphosphate.[27,28,64–66] Recent attention has focused on the concept that a release of IP_3 following relief of prolonged (> 20 min) ischemia may contribute to the generation of reperfusion-induced arrhythmias and lethal myocyte injury.[67,68] Interestingly, preconditioning with three 5-min cycles of brief ischemia was shown to block this postischemic burst of IP_3 in isolated rat heart.[69] It has been demonstrated that a brief cycle of myocyte stretch, virtually as effective as brief antecedent ischemia in rendering the dog and rabbit heart resistant to infarction,[70–72] is a potent stimulus for IP_3 production.[73] However, in contrast to the considerable investigative effort devoted to PKC, the possibility that release of IP_3 during brief antecedent ischemia may act as a cellular mediator of infarct size reduction has, with the exception of recent studies from our laboratory,[66,74] been essentially unexplored.

Using an isolated rabbit heart model of regional ischemia, we found that one 5-min episode of coronary artery occlusion did indeed result in a significant, approximately twofold increase in myocardial IP_3 content: IP_3 (quantified by competitive binding assay) averaged 0.69 pmol/mg tissue following brief ischemia versus only 0.34 pmol/mg in nonischemic sham-operated controls.[66] Activation of IP_3 in response to brief ischemia does not appear to be unique to the rabbit model. Preliminary analysis of repeated myocardial biopsy samples obtained in the *in vivo* canine model has revealed that IP_3 levels at 5 min into coronary artery occlusion were ~75% higher than the corresponding baseline values (FIG. 4A). Finally, we further observed that neomycin (an aminoglycoside antibiotic that inhibits production of IP_3 by binding to its precursor, phosphatidylinositol 4,5-bisphosphate[67,75,76]) both abrogated the release of IP_3 seen with brief ischemia and, when administered during the preconditioning stimulus, abolished the reduction in infarct size achieved with preconditioning (FIG. 4B).[66] Although the admonition of "no one thing does only one thing" must also be applied to neomycin, these results, taken together, may be interpreted as initial, indirect evidence consistent with the concept that IP_3 may contribute to preconditioning-induced cardioprotection.

The established cellular role of IP_3 is to mobilize the release of calcium from intracellular stores via binding to IP_3 receptors on the endoplasmic reticulum.[27,28,65,66,77] Interestingly, function of the IP_3 receptor is regulated both by IP_3 binding and by phosphorylation of the channel by protein tyrosine kinases,[77] mediators which are also implicated in preconditioning.[18–21] Thus, the observation of increased myocardial concentrations of IP_3 during brief ischemia is, in theory, readily integrated with the concept of $[Ca^{2+}]_i$ as a trigger for preconditioning, However, it remains to be determined whether a relatively modest "spike" of calcium[65,78] specifically released by IP_3 signaling occurs during brief antecedent ischemia, and

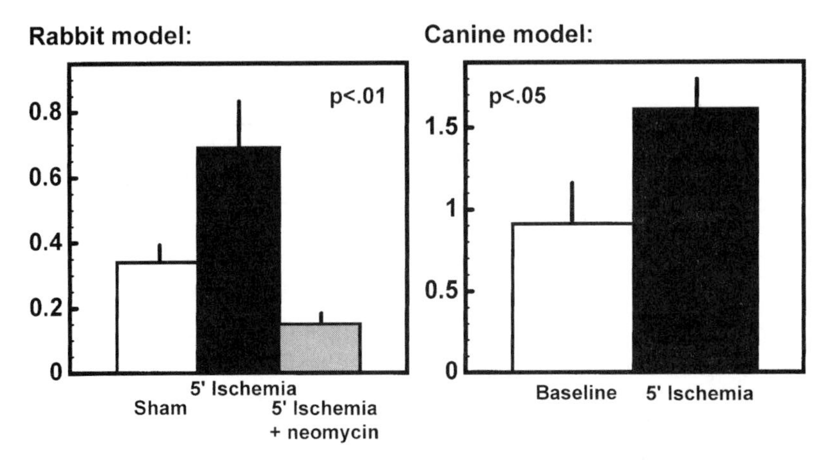

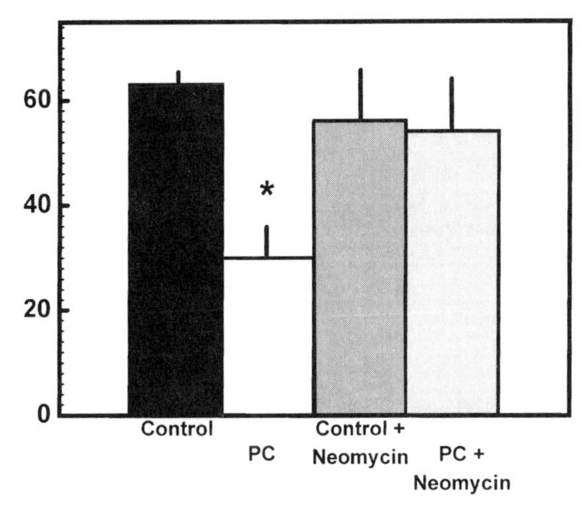

FIGURE 4. (**A**) Myocardial concentrations of inositol (1,4,5)-trisphosphate (IP_3) were significantly increased following a brief, 5-min coronary artery occlusion in both isolated regionally ischemic rabbit hearts versus sham-operated controls[66] (*left*), and in *in vivo* canine myocardium versus matched samples obtained at baseline (*right*). Administration of neomycin, an agent that binds to the precursor of IP_3, blocked the release of IP_3 seen with brief ischemia in rabbit heart. (*Left panel reproduced with permission from Bauer* et al.[66]) (**B**) Reduction of infarct size (expressed as a % of the myocardium at risk) obtained with preconditioning (PC) in the isolated rabbit heart model of regional ischemia was prevented by coadministration of neomycin. $*p < 0.01$ versus Control. (*Adapted from Bauer* et al.[66])

whether this, in turn, contributes to an increased resistance to infarction. These issues are the focus of ongoing investigation in our laboratory. A second and related concept is that IP_3 signaling may further modulate $[Ca^{2+}]_i$ by activating Na^+-Ca^{2+} exchange.[65,67] Increased Na^+-H^+ exchanger activity (presumably resulting in calcium influx via subsequent Na^+-Ca^{2+} exchange) has, in fact, been reported in response to a brief preconditioning stimulus in isolated rat hearts,[79] while Na^+-H^+ exchange inhibitors amiloride[80] and dimethylamiloride,[28] administered exclusively during brief antecedent ischemia, have been found to render preconditioning ineffective in protecting the rat[80] and dog heart[28] from subsequent sustained ischemia. This latter explanation is, however, controversial. Rigorous assessment by Shipolini and colleagues using the more selective Na^+-H^+ exchange inhibitor HOE 642 revealed no evidence for increased Na^+-H^+ exchange activity during preconditioning ischemia in isolated globally ischemic rat hearts.[81]

Calcium and the "End-Effector": The K_{ATP} Channel

While most studies employing exogenous antecedent calcium administration in lieu of brief ischemia have sought to establish a connection between $[Ca^{2+}]_i$ and PKC,[30,32–37] Kouchi and colleagues pursued the possibility that reduction of infarct size with calcium exposure involves opening of the K_{ATP} channel,[31] implicated as a candidate for the final, membrane-bound end-effector in ischemic preconditioning.[13,41] Using the *in vivo* rabbit model, they reported that cardioprotection achieved with both conventional ischemic preconditioning and brief antecedent infusion of calcium gluconate was indeed blunted by pretreatment with the K_{ATP} channel antagonist glibenclamide.[31] Opening of K_{ATP} channels and the resultant membrane hyperpolarization and shortening of the action potential duration have been associated with a reduction in calcium influx via voltage-gated calcium channels.[13,41,82] However, other than postulating PKC as an intermediary,[31] no explanation has, to date, been provided as to how brief preischemic exposure to calcium might specifically modulate the K_{ATP} channel. Thus, as with PKC and IP_3, the interrelationships among K_{ATP} channel activation, increased $[Ca^{2+}]_i$ (via exogenous administration or as a consequence of brief ischemia), and cardioprotection with preconditioning await definitive resolution.

CALCIUM DURING SUSTAINED OCCLUSION AS A "MEDIATOR" OF CARDIOPROTECTION

In contrast to the relatively novel concept that a brief, transient, and reversible increase in $[Ca^{2+}]_i$ during brief nonlethal ischemia may paradoxically initiate cardioprotection, it has long been recognized that the failure of ischemic-reperfused myocytes to maintain ionic homeostasis—most notably manifest as a massive increase in cell calcium content—is a harbinger of their death.[83] In fact, well before the current preoccupation with ischemic preconditioning, a host of experimental studies sought to limit infarct size by the administration of calcium channel antagonists.[84] A considerable body of evidence, obtained largely from isolated rat heart models, has revealed an apparent adaptation in calcium regulation, characterized by lower values of $[Ca^{2+}]_i$ with repeated episodes of brief ischemia,[85] and reduced $[Ca^{2+}]_i$ during the sustained test ischemia in preconditioned hearts versus controls.[86–88] These pieces of information give rise to three obvious (albeit complex and related) questions: (1) How is this improved regulation of $[Ca^{2+}]_i$ achieved? (2) Is the reduction in $[Ca^{2+}]_i$ during sustained ischemia precipitated by the modest increase in $[Ca^{2+}]_i$ during the preceding brief ischemia? (3) Are favorable alterations in calcium homeostasis during sustained occlusion a cellular mechanism for (rather than simply an epiphenomenon of) infarct size reduction with preconditioning?

Preconditioning and Release of Intracellular Calcium

Two lines of evidence suggest that an "internal" source of calcium, in particular the ryanodine channel on the sarcoplasmic reticulum, may be modified by brief preconditioning ischemia. Specifically, Zucchi and colleagues[89] reported that three 3-min cycles of global ischemia in isolated rat hearts resulted in both a decrease in the density of ryanodine binding sites and a slowing in the rate of Ca^{2+}-induced Ca^{2+} release, presumably facilitating a delay or slowing in the accumulation of $[Ca^{2+}]_i$ during imposition of a subsequent sustained ischemic insult. They further demonstrated a temporal correlation, suggestive of "cause and effect," with cardioprotection: favorable changes in ryanodine channels were manifest and reduction of infarct size was elicited at 5 min, 1, 2, and 3 h after repeated brief ischemia, while, with 4 h of intervening reflow, ryanodine binding normalized and protection waned.[89]

Tani and colleagues[90,91] further addressed this issue, again in the isolated rat heart, by measuring oxalate-supported $^{45}Ca^{2+}$ uptake by the sarcoplasmic reticulum at the end of sustained global ischemia and 30 min after reflow in control and preconditioned cohorts. When the assay was conducted in the presence of high concentrations of ryanodine to close the calcium release channel,[92] control hearts exhibited an increase in $^{45}Ca^{2+}$ uptake whereas preconditioned hearts did not (FIG. 5A).[90] Moreover, sarcoplasmic reticular $^{45}Ca^{2+}$ release, defined as the difference in $^{45}Ca^{2+}$ uptake in the presence and absence of ryanodine,[92] was significantly attenuated, both during occlusion and following reflow, in the preconditioned group versus controls (FIG. 5B).[90]

These results suggest that, in the isolated rat heart, preconditioning blunts an inappropriate release of calcium from the sarcoplasmic reticulum during sustained ischemia-reperfusion. This may, however, be a species- or model-specific phenomenon: using the *in vivo* canine model, we found no difference in oxalate-supported $^{45}Ca^{2+}$ uptake by the sarcoplasmic reticulum at 20 min into sustained occlusion (i.e., the crucial time at which myocyte death begins in the dog) between control versus preconditioned groups. Moreover, at 4 h after reperfusion, there was evidence of exacerbated (rather than attenuated) $^{45}Ca^{2+}$ uptake and $^{45}Ca^{2+}$ release in the viable subepicardium of preconditioned canine hearts (FIG. 5C and D). The reasons for this apparent discrepancy are not known, but methodologic differences (i.e., concentrations of calcium, potassium oxalate, and ryanodine used in the reaction media; the presence of variable amounts of necrotic versus viable myocardium in control and preconditioned rat hearts; and analysis of fresh[90] versus frozen myocardial samples in our protocol) and apparent variations among species in the importance of calcium overload via ryanodine channels[92] may all play a role. Although no definitive conclusions can as yet be made, one interpretation of these differences between the rat and dog may be that favorable changes in ryanodine channels during sustained occlusion are not a prerequisite for cardioprotection with preconditioning.

Even less information is available concerning potential changes in calcium release via IP_3. Analysis of myocardial biopsies obtained from isolated rabbit hearts subjected to regional ischemia revealed that myocardial concentrations of IP_3 are ap-

A. Calcium uptake with ryanodine: rat model

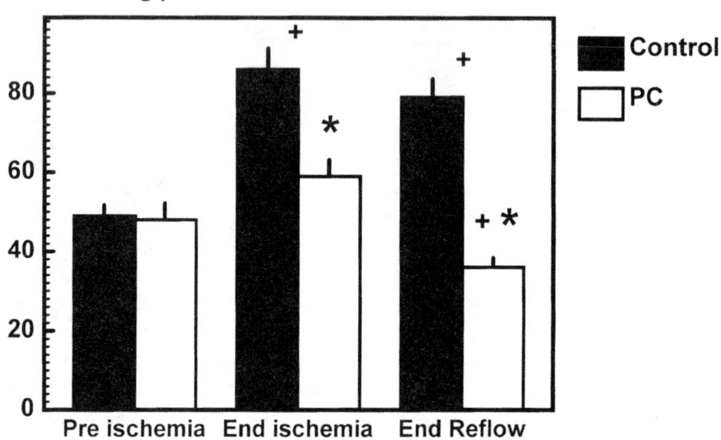

B. Calcium release: rat model

nmol/min/mg protein

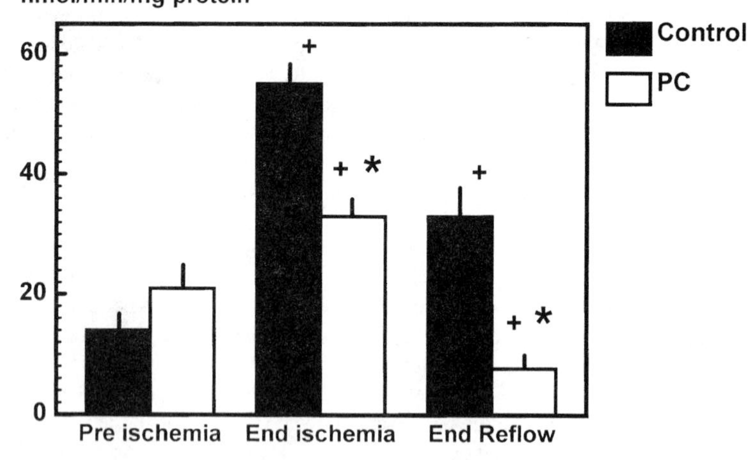

FIGURE 5. Oxalate-supported ^{45}Ca uptake by the sarcoplasmic reticulum measured in the presence of ryanodine (**A**) and ^{45}Ca release (the difference between ^{45}Ca uptake measured with versus without ryanodine) (**B**) assessed in the isolated rat heart model of regional ischemia.[90] Both the increase in calcium uptake and inappropriate release of calcium from the sarcoplasmic reticulum seen in control hearts at the end of 25-min sustained global ischemia and at 30 min after reperfusion were not manifest in hearts first preconditioned (PC) with brief ischemia. $^{+}p < 0.05$ versus corresponding values obtained before sustained ischemia; $*p < 0.05$ versus corresponding control. (*Adapted from Tani* et al.[90]).

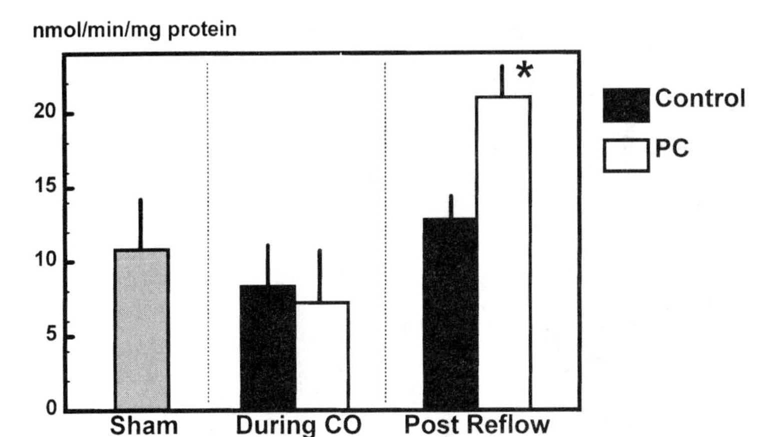

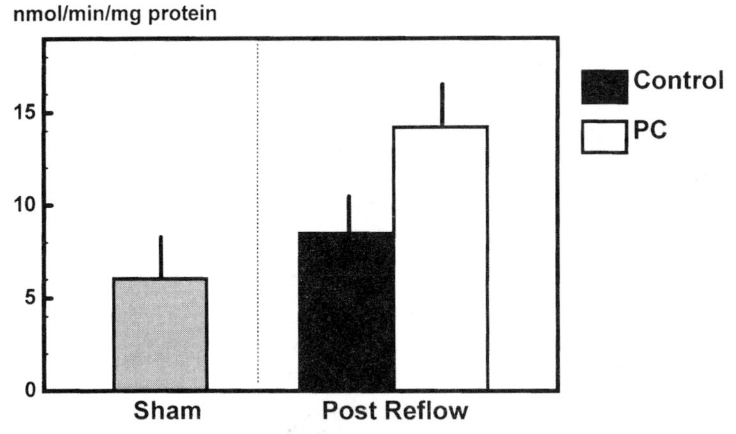

FIGURE 5 (*Continued*). Oxalate-supported ^{45}Ca uptake by the sarcoplasmic reticulum measured in the presence of ryanodine (**C**), and ^{45}Ca release (the difference between ^{45}Ca uptake measured with versus without ryanodine) (**D**) assessed in the *in vivo* canine model. There was no difference in calcium uptake in the ischemic subendocardium at 20 min into sustained coronary occlusion (CO: the crucial time and location at which myocyte death commences in this model) between control and preconditioned (PC) groups. Four hours after reperfusion, both calcium uptake and calcium release in the viable subepicardium were increased in preconditioned hearts versus controls ($*p < 0.05$ and $p = 0.08$ [ns], respectively).

parently reduced during the early minutes of sustained occlusion in preconditioned hearts versus controls (FIG. 6).[74] Whether this is manifest in other models and species, whether this represents an active downregulation versus passive decrease (perhaps due to depletion of substrates) in IP_3 signaling, whether this is accompanied by

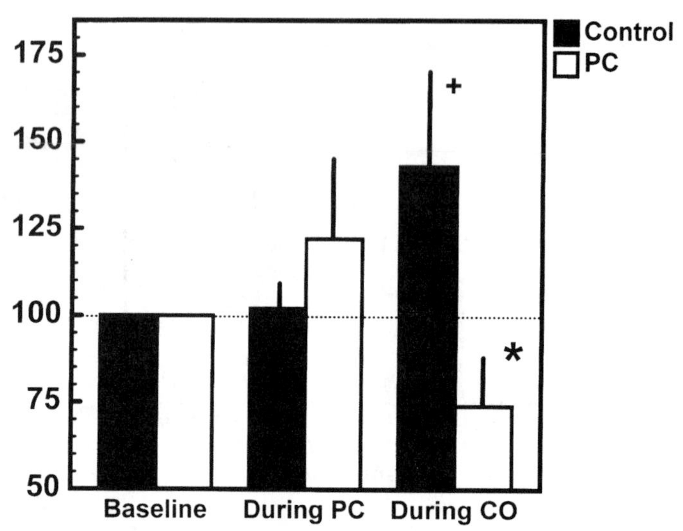

FIGURE 6. Repeated measurements of myocardial inositol (1,4,5)-trisphosphate (IP_3) content obtained at baseline, ~midway during 5 min of antecedent preconditioning (PC) ischemia/no intervention, and at ~3–5 minutes after the onset of sustained coronary occlusion (CO) in isolated regionally ischemic rabbit myocardium. The first exposure of the heart to ischemia (i.e., during brief ischemia in the PC group; early during CO in controls) was associated with an increase in IP_3 content. However, in the PC group, IP_3 during the initial minutes of the sustained test occlusion was significantly decreased versus controls. $^*p < 0.05$ versus Control; $^+p < 0.05$ versus baseline. Data published in abstract form in Simkhovich *et al.*[74]

changes in the number or function of IP_3 receptors on the sarcoplasmic reticulum, whether this translates into physiologically relevant alterations in IP_3-mediated calcium release, and, most importantly, whether this contributes in any way to the reduction in infarct size seen with preconditioning all remain to be determined.

Preconditioning and Influx of Extracellular Calcium

It is perhaps surprising, given the long-standing historical interest in calcium channel antagonists in the setting of myocardial ischemia and infarction,[84] that the role of altered calcium influx via L-type calcium channels during sustained coronary occlusion has received little attention as a mechanism of infarct size reduction with preconditioning. The limited amount of available data does, however, appear to refute this possibility—no differences were detected in the density or binding characteristics of L-type calcium channels in preconditioned porcine myocardium versus controls[93] and, as mentioned previously, administration of the calcium channel antagonist nisoldipine had no effect on preconditioning-induced infarct size reduction in the pig.[56] However, this does not exclude the as-yet unexplored possibility that calcium influx via other channels (i.e., T-type) may be involved.

The paucity of studies focusing on L-type calcium channels may reflect the more recent emphasis on Na^+-H^+ exchange inhibitors as a new, promising therapeutic approach to protect the heart against sustained ischemia-reperfusion. Timely administration of amiloride and its derivatives, as well as the newer and more selective agents such as HOE 694 and HOE 642 (cariporide), has consistently been reported to limit infarct size in a variety of models,[81,94–99] presumably by inhibiting Ca^{2+} influx secondary to intracellular acidosis, the resultant activation of Na^+-H^+ exchange and influx of Na^+, and the subsequent increase in Na^+-Ca^{2+} exchange. This, together with observations that the lower values of $[Ca^{2+}]_i$ seen in preconditioned hearts during sustained ischemia are accompanied by an attenuated acidosis and a reduced Na^+ gain,[86–88,100] have prompted investigators to question whether reduced Na^+-H^+ exchange during the sustained test ischemia might be involved in the cardioprotection seen with preconditioning. Studies employing the isolated rat heart model have described additive protection in preconditioned hearts treated with ethylisopropyl amiloride and HOE 642 at the onset of sustained ischemia.[81,97] In contrast, in the rabbit, others found no evidence of synergism between the two protective strategies, but noted that pharmacologic antagonists effective in blocking infarct size reduction with preconditioning (i.e., polymyxin B and glibenclamide) did not alter the benefits achieved with the Na^+-H^+ inhibitors.[98,99] The common conclusion drawn by all investigators is that ischemic preconditioning and Na^+-H^+ exchange inhibitors given before and during sustained occlusion may both protect the heart against infarction, but apparently via divergent cellular mechanisms.

WEIGHING THE EVIDENCE

The concept that increases in $[Ca^{2+}]_i$ may be both "good" (i.e., if present briefly and in moderation, may initiate cardioprotection) and "bad" (if out of control, will kill the myocyte) represents an intriguing intellectual parallel to the paradox of ischemic preconditioning. A growing body of evidence indicates that brief antecedent exposure of the heart to exogenous calcium can, indeed, render the myocardium resistant to infarction. Moreover, rational arguments can be made in support of a theoretical link between modest increases in $[Ca^{2+}]_i$ and signal transduction pathways implicated to be involved in preconditioning-induced cardioprotection. However, the specific nature of the detailed relationships between increased $[Ca^{2+}]_i$ during brief antecedent ischemia, activation of PKC and/or generation of IP_3, and cardioprotection remain to be elucidated. The second facet of the paradox—that attenuation of calcium overload during sustained ischemia may represent a mechanism for infarct size reduction with preconditioning—has received even less attention. Favorable regulation of intracellular calcium-release channels (ryanodine and/or IP_3 receptors on the sarcoplasmic reticulum) in preconditioned myocardium versus controls provides a compelling, but as-yet unsubstantiated hypothetical scenario by which this might be achieved. In contrast to the concerted effort aimed at defining the contributions of G protein–coupled receptors, PKC, and the K_{ATP} channel, the study of calcium as a mediator of preconditioning is in its infancy and further prospective investigation is clearly warranted.

REFERENCES

1. MURRY, C.E., R.B. JENNINGS & K.A. REIMER. 1986. Preconditioning with ischemia: a delay of lethal cell injury in ischemic myocardium. Circulation **74:** 1124–1136.
2. LIU, G.S., J. THORNTON, D.M. VAN WINKLE *et al.* 1991. Protection against infarction afforded by preconditioning is mediated by A_1 adenosine receptors in rabbit heart. Circulation **84:** 350–356.
3. HALE, S.L. & R.A. KLONER. 1992. Effect of ischemic preconditioning on regional myocardial blood flow in the rabbit heart. Coronary Artery Dis **3:** 133–140.
4. LI, Y., P. WHITTAKER & R.A. KLONER. 1992. The transient nature of the effect of ischemic preconditioning on myocardial infarct size and ventricular arrhythmia. Am. Heart J. **123:** 346–353.
5. PRZYKLENK, K., M.A. SUSSMAN, B.Z. SIMKHOVICH *et al.* 1995. Does ischemic preconditioning trigger translocation of protein kinase C in the canine model? Circulation **92:** 1546–1557.
6. SCHOTT, R.J., S. ROHMAN, E.R. BRAUN *et al.* 1990. Ischemic preconditioning reduces infarct size in swine myocardium. Circ. Res. **66:** 133–144.
7. DUPOUY, P., H. GESCHWIND, G. PELLE *et al.* 1996. Repeated coronary artery occlusions during routine balloon angioplasty do not induce myocardial preconditioning in humans. J. Am. Coll. Cardiol. **27:** 1374–1380.
8. BEHAR, S., H. REICHER-REISS, E. ABINADER *et al.* 1992. The prognostic significance of angina pectoris before first acute myocardial infarction. Am. Heart J. **123:** 1481–1486.
9. IKONOMIDIS, J.S., L.C. TUMAITI, R.D. WEISEL *et al.* 1994. Preconditioning human ventricular cardiomyocytes with brief periods of simulated ischemia. Cardiovasc. Res. **28:** 1285–1291.
10. DEUTSCH, E., M. BERGER, W.G. KUSSMAUL *et al.* 1990. Adaptation to ischemia during percutaneous transluminal angioplasty: clinical, hemodynamic and metabolic features. Circulation **82:** 2044–2051.
11. MAYBAUM, S., M. ILAN, J. MOGILEVSKY *et al.* 1996. Improvement in ischemic parameters during repeated exercise testing: a possible model for myocardial preconditioning. Am. J. Cardiol. **78:** 1087–1091.
12. KLONER, R.A., T. SHOOK, K. PRZYKLENK *et al.* 1995. Previous angina alters in-hospital outcome in TIMI-4: a clinical correlate to preconditioning? Circulation **91:** 37–47.
13. PRZYKLENK, K. & R.A. KLONER. 1998. Ischemic preconditioning: exploring the paradox. Prog. Cardiovasc. Dis. **40:** 517–547.
14. MURRY, C.E., V.J. RICHARD, K.A. REIMER *et al.* 1990. Ischemic preconditioning slows energy metabolism and delays ultrastructural damage during a sustained ischemic episode. Circ. Res. **66:** 913–931.
15. WOLFE, C.L., R.E. SIEVERS, F.L.J. VISSEREN *et al.* 1993. Loss of myocardial protection after preconditioning correlates with the time course of glycogen recovery within the preconditioned segment. Circulation **87:** 881–892.
16. YTREHUS, K., Y. LIU, J.M. DOWNEY. 1994. Preconditioning protects ischemic rabbit hearts by protein kinase C activation. Am. J. Physiol. **266:** H1145–H1152.
17. YANG, X.M., H. SATO, J.M. DOWNEY *et al.* 1997. Protection of ischemic preconditioning is dependent upon a critical timing sequence of protein kinase C activation. J. Mol. Cell. Cardiol. **29:** 991–999.
18. WEINBRENNER, C., G.S. LIU, M.V. COHEN *et al.* 1997. Phosphorylation of tyrosine 182 of p38 mitogen activated protein kinase correlates with the protection of preconditioning in the rabbit heart. J. Mol. Cell. Cardiol. **29:** 2382–2391.
19. BAINES, C.P., L. WANG, M.V. COHEN *et al.* 1998. Protein tyrosine kinase is downstream of protein kinase C for ischemic preconditioning's anti-infarct effect in the rabbit heart. J. Mol. Cell. Cardiol. **30:** 383–392.
20. VAHLHAUS, C., R. SCHULZ, H. POST *et al.* 1998. Prevention of ischemic preconditioning only by combined inhibition of protein kinase C and protein tyrosine kinase in pigs. J. Mol. Cell. Cardiol. **30:** 197–209.

21. MAULIK, N., M. WATANABE, Y.L. ZU *et al.* 1996. Ischemic preconditioning triggers the activation of MAP kinases and MAPKAP kinase 2 in rat hearts. FEBS Lett. **396:** 233–237.
22. ARMSTRONG, S.C., W. GAO, J.R. LANE *et al.* 1998. Protein phosphatase inhibitors calyculin A and fostreicin protect rabbit cardiomyocytes in late ischemia. J. Mol. Cell Cardiol. **30:** 61–73.
23. VAN WINKLE, D.M., J. THORNTON, J.M. DOWNEY *et al.* 1991. The natural history of preconditioning: cardioprotection depends on duration of transient ischemia and the time to subsequent ischemia. Coronary Artery Dis. **2:** 613–619.
24. BANERJEE, A., C. LOCKE-WINTER, K.B. ROGERS *et al.* 1993. Preconditioning against myocardial dysfunction after ischemia and reperfusion by an α_1-adrenergic mechanism. Circ. Res. **73:** 656–670.
25. AMENDE, I., L.A. BENTIVEGNA, A.J. ZEIND *et al.* 1992. Intracellular calcium and ventricular function: effects of nisoldipine on global ischemia in the isovolumic, coronary-perfused heart. J. Clin. Invest. **89:** 2060–2065.
26. SMITH, G.B., T. STEFENELLI, S.T. WU *et al.* 1996. Rapid adaptation of myocardial calcium homeostasis to short episodes of ischemia in isolated rat hearts. Am. Heart J. **131:** 1106–1112.
27. BERRIDGE, M.J. 1997. Elementary and global aspects of calcium signaling. J. Physiol. **499:** 291– 306.
28. POTTER, B.V.L. & D. LAMPE. 1995. Chemistry of inositol lipid mediated cellular signaling. Angew. Chem. Int. Ed. Engl. **1995:** 1933–1972.
29. PRZYKLENK, K., K. HATA & R.A. KLONER. 1997. Is calcium a mediator of infarct size reduction with preconditioning in canine myocardium? Circulation **96:** 1305–1312.
30. NODE, K., M. KITAKAZE, H. SATO *et al.* 1997. Role of intracellular Ca^{2+} in activation of protein kinase C during ischemic preconditioning. Circulation **96:** 1257–1265.
31. KOUCHI, I., T. MURAKAMI, R. NAWADA *et al.* 1998. K_{ATP} channels are common mediators of ischemic and calcium preconditioning in rabbits. Am. J. Physiol. **274:** H1106–H1112.
32. MELDRUM, D.R., J.C. CLEVELAND, B.C. SHERIDAN *et al.* 1996. Cardiac protection with calcium: clinically accessible myocardial protection. J. Thorac. Cardiovasc. Surg. **112:** 778–786.
33. MIYAWAKI, H., X. ZHOU & M. ASHRAF. 1996. Calcium preconditioning elicits strong protection against ischemic injury via protein kinase C signaling pathway. Circ. Res. **79:** 137–146.
34. MIYAWAKI, H. & M. ASHRAF. 1997. Ca^{2+} as a mediator of ischemic preconditioning. Circ. Res. **80:** 790–799.
35. MIYAWAKI, H. & M. ASHRAF. 1997. Isoproterenol mimics calcium preconditioning-induced protection against ischemia. Am. J. Physiol. **272:** H927–H936.
36. CAIN, B.S., D.R. MELDRUM, X. MENG *et al.* 1998. Calcium preconditioning in human myocardium. Ann. Thorac. Surg. **65:** 1065–1070.
37. MELDRUM, D.R., J.C. CLEVELAND, M.B. MITCHELL *et al.* 1996. Protein kinase C mediates Ca^{2+}-induced cardioadaptation to ischemia-reperfusion injury. Am. J. Physiol. **271:** R718–R726.
38. COHEN, M.V., Y. LIU, G.S. LIU *et al.* 1996. Phospholipase D plays a role in ischemic preconditioning in rabbit heart. Circulation **94:** 1713–1718.
39. TOSAKI, A., N. MAULIK, G. CORDIS *et al.* 1997. Ischemic preconditioning triggers phospholipase D signaling in rat heart. Am. J. Physiol. **273:** H1860–H1866.
40. BOGOYEVITCH, M.A., J. GILLESPIE-BROWN, A. J. KETTERMAN *et al.* 1996. Stimulation of the stress-activated mitogen-activated kinase subfamilies in perfused heart: p38/RK mitogen-activated protein kinases and c-Jun N-terminal kinases are activated by ischemia/reperfusion. Circ. Res. **79:** 162–173.
41. GROSS, G.J. & J.A. AUCHAMPACH. 1992. Blockade of ATP-sensitive potassium channels prevents myocardial preconditioning in dogs. Circ. Res. **70:** 223–233.
42. GARLID, K.D., P. PAUCEK, V. YAROV-YAROVOY *et al.* 1997. Cardioprotective effects of diazoxide and its interaction with mitochondrial ATP-sensitive K^+ channels. Possible mechanism of cardioprotection. Circ. Res. **81:** 1072–1082.

43. SIMKHOVICH, B.Z., K. PRZYKLENK & R.A. KLONER. 1999. Role of protein kinase C as a cellular mediator of ischemic preconditioning: a critical review. Cardiovasc. Res. **40:** 9–22.
44. MITCHELL, M.B., X. MENG, I. AO *et al.* 1995. Preconditioning of isolated rat heart is mediated by protein kinase C. Circ. Res. **76:** 73–81.
45. BOGOYEVITCH, M.A., P.A. PARKER & P.H. SUGDEN. 1993. Characterization of protein kinase C isoenzyme expression in adult rat heart: protein kinase C-ε is the major isotype present, and is activated by phorbol esters, epinephrine and endothelin. Circ. Res. **72:** 757–767.
46. ARMSTRONG, S. & C.E. GANOTE. 1994. Preconditioning of isolated rabbit cardiomyocytes: effects of glycolytic blockade, phorbol esters and ischemia. Cardiovasc. Res. **28:** 1700–1706.
47. PING, P., J. ZHANG, X.T. TANG *et al.* 1997. Ischemic preconditioning induces selective translocation of protein kinase C isoforms ε and η in the heart of conscious rabbits without subcellular redistribution of total protein kinase C activity. Circ. Res. **81:** 404–414.
48. GRAY, M.O., J.S. KARLINER & D. MOCHLY-ROSEN. 1997. A selective ε-protein kinase C antagonist inhibits protection of cardiac myocytes from hypoxia-induced cell death. J. Biol. Chem. **272:** 30945–30951.
49. OVIZE, M., L. MEUNIER, S. EL AWAB *et al.* 1997. Preferential hydrolysis of phosphatidylcholine during ischemia in preconditioned rabbit heart [abstract]. Circulation **96** (Suppl I)**:** I–574.
50. KITAKAZE, K., H. FUNAYA, T. MINAMINO *et al.* 1997. Role of protein kinase C-α in activation of ecto-5′-nucleotidase in the preconditioned canine myocardium. Biochem. Biophys. Res. Comm. **239:** 171–175.
51. STEINBERG, S.F., M. GOLDBERG & V.O. RYBIN. 1995. Protein kinase C isoform diversity in the heart. J. Mol. Cell. Cardiol. **27:** 141–143.
52. BROOKS, G. & D.J. HEARSE. 1996. Role of protein kinase C in ischemic preconditioning: player or spectator? Circ. Res. **79:** 627–630.
53. ASAI, T., L.M. SHUBA, D.J. PELZER *et al.* 1996. PKC-independent inhibition of cardiac L-type Ca^{2+} channel current by phorbol esters. Am. J. Physiol. **270:** H620–H627.
54. SCHREUR, K.D. & S. LIU. 1996. 1,2-Dictanoyl-*sn*-glycerol depresses cardiac L-type Ca^{2+} current: independent of protein kinase C activation. Am. J. Physiol. **270:** C655–C662.
55. HARTZELL, H.C. & A. RINDERKNECHT. 1996. Calphostin C, a widely used protein kinase C inhibitor, directly and potently blocks L-type Ca channels. Am. J. Physiol. **270:** C1293–C1299.
56. WALLBRIDGE, D.R., R. SCHULZ, C. BRAUN *et al.* 1996. No attenuation of ischaemic preconditioning by the calcium antagonist nisoldipine. J. Mol. Cell. Cardiol. **28:** 1801–1810.
57. MOOLMAN, J.A., S. GENADE, E. TROMP *et al.* 1996. No evidence for mediation of ischemic preconditioning by α_1 adrenergic signal transduction pathway or protein kinase C in isolated rabbit heart. Cardiovasc. Drugs Ther. **10:** 125–136.
58. VAHLHAUS, C., R. SCHULZ, H. POST *et al.* 1996. No prevention of ischemic preconditioning by the protein kinase C inhibitor staurosporine in swine. Circ. Res. **79:** 407–414.
59. BUGGE, E. & K. YTREHUS. 1995. Ischaemic preconditioning is protein kinase C dependent but not through stimulation of α–adrenergic or adenosine receptors in the isolated rat heart. Cardiovasc. Res. **29:** 401–406.
60. SANDHU, R., R.J. DIAZ, G.D. MAO *et al.* 1997. Ischemic preconditioning: differences in protection and susceptibility to blockade with single cycle versus multicycle transient ischemia. Circulation **96:** 984–995.
61. VOGT, A.M., P. HTUN, M. ARRAS *et al.* 1996. Intramyocardial infusion of tool drugs for the study of molecular mechanisms of ischemic preconditioning. Basic Res. Cardiol. **91:** 389–400.
62. LASLEY, R.D., M.A. NOBLE & R.M. MENTZER. 1997. Effects of protein kinase C

inhibitors in *in situ* and isolated ischemic rabbit myocardium. J. Mol. Cell. Cardiol. **29:** 3345–3356.
63. RESHEF, A., O. SPERLING & E. ZOREF-SHANI. 1997. Activation and inhibition of protein kinase C protect rat neuronal cultures against ischemia-reperfusion insult. Neurosci. Lett. **238:** 37–40.
64. NISHIZUKA, Y. 1992. Intracellular signaling by hydrolysis of phospholipids and activation of protein kinase C. Science **258:** 607–614.
65. DE JONGE, H.W., H.A.A. VAN HEUGTEN & J.M.J. LAMERS. 1995. Signal transduction by the phosphatidylinositol cycle in myocardium. J. Mol. Cell. Cardiol. **27:** 93–106.
66. BAUER, B., B.Z. SIMKHOVICH, R.A. KLONER *et al.* 1999. Preconditioning-induced cardioprotection and release of the second messenger inositol (1,4,5)-trisphosphate are both abolished by neomycin in rabbit heart. Basic Res. Cardiol. **94:** 31–40.
67. DU, X.J., K.E. ANDERSON, A. JACOBSEN *et al.* 1995. Suppression of ventricular arrhythmias during ischemia-reperfusion by agents inhibiting Ins(1,4,5)P_3 release. Circulation **91:** 2712–2716.
68. OTANI, H., R. PRASAD, R.M. ENGELMAN *et al.* 1988. Enhanced phosphodiesteratic breakdown and turnover of phosphoinositides during reperfusion of ischemic rat heart. Circ. Res. **63:** 930–936.
69. ANDERSON, K.E. & E.A. WOODCOCK. 1995. Preconditioning of perfused rat heart inhibits reperfusion-induced release of inositol (1,4,5)-trisphosphate. J. Mol. Cell. Cardiol. **27:** 2421–2431.
70. PRZYKLENK, K., B. BAUER, M. OVIZE *et al.* 1993. Regional ischemic preconditioning protects remote virgin myocardium from subsequent sustained coronary occlusion. Circulation **87:** 893–899.
71. OVIZE, M., R.A. KLONER & K. PRZYKLENK. 1994. Stretch preconditions the canine myocardium. Am. J. Physiol. **266:** H137–H146.
72. GYSEMBERGH, A., H. MARGONARI, J. LOUFOUA *et al.* 1998. Stretch-induced protection shares a common mechanism with ischemic preconditioning in rabbit heart. Am. J. Physiol. **274:** H955–H964.
73. DASSOULI, A., J.C. SULPICE, S. ROUX *et al.* 1993. Stretch-induced inositol trisphosphate and tetrakisphosphate production in rat cardiomyocytes. J. Mol. Cell. Cardiol. **25:** 973–982.
74. SIMKHOVICH, B.Z., R.A. KLONER & K. PRZYKLENK. 1997. Preconditioning alters tissue levels of the second messenger inositol trisphosphate in rabbit heart [abstract]. Circulation **96** (Suppl I)**:** I-575.
75. GABEV, E., J. KASIANOWICS, T. ABBOTT *et al.* 1989. Binding of neomycin to phosphoinositol 4,5-bisphosphate (PIP_2). Biochim. Biophys. Acta **979:** 105–112.
76. SLIVKA, S.R., K.E. MEIER & P.A. INSEL. 1988. Alpha 1-adrenergic receptors promote phosphatidylcholine hydrolysis in MDCK-D1 cells. A mechanism for rapid activation of protein kinase C. J. Biol. Chem. **263:** 12242–12246.
77. MARCKS, A.R. 1997. Intracellular calcium-release channels: regulators of cell life and death. Am. J. Physiol. **272:** H597–H605.
78. SEGHIERI, P., C. DUSSERT, J. PALMARI *et al.* 1997. A minimal model for calcium signal generated by tyrosine kinase and G protein linked receptors: a stochastic computer simulation with CALSIM. Int. J. Medical Informatics **46:** 53–65.
79. RAMASAMY, R., H. LIU, S. ANDERSON *et al.* 1995. Ischemic preconditioning stimulates sodium and proton transport in isolated rat hearts. J. Clin. Invest. **96:** 1464–1472.
80. KAUR, H., V. PARIKH, A. SHARMA *et al.* 1997. Effect of amiloride, a Na^+/H^+ exchange inhibitor, on cardioprotective effect of ischaemic preconditioning: possible involvement of resident cardiac mast cells. Pharmacol. Res. **36:** 95–102.
81. SHIPOLINI, A.R., H. YOKOYAMA, M. GALIÑANES *et al.* 1997. Na^+/H^+ exchanger activity does not contribute to protection by ischemic preconditioning in the isolated rat heart. Circulation **96:** 3617– 3625.
82. NOMA, A. 1983. ATP-regulated K^+ channels in cardiac myocytes. Nature **305:** 147–148.

83. SHEN, A.C. & R.B. JENNINGS. 1972. Kinetics of calcium accumulation in acute myocardial ischemic injury. Am. J. Pathol. **67:** 441–452.
84. KLONER, R.A. & E. BRAUNWALD. 1987. Effects of calcium antagonists on infarcting myocardium. Am. J. Cardiol. **59:** 84B–94B.
85. SMITH, G.B., T. STEFENELLI, S.T. WU *et al.* 1996. Rapid adaptation of myocardial calcium homeostasis to short episodes of ischemia in isolated rat hearts. Am. Heart J. **131:** 1106–1112.
86. STEENBERGEN, C., T.A. FRALIX, E. MURPHY. 1993. Mechanisms of preconditioning: ionic alterations. Circ. Res. **72:** 112–125.
87. MURPHY, E., W. GLASGOW, T. FRALIX *et al.* 1995. Role of lipoxygenase metabolites in ischemic preconditioning. Circ. Res. **76:** 457–467.
88. TOSAKI, A., G.A. CORDIS, P. SZERDAHELYI *et al.* 1994. Effects of preconditioning on reperfusion arrhythmias, myocardial function, formation of free radicals and ion shifts in isolated ischemic/reperfused rat hearts. J. Cardiovasc. Pharmacol. **23:** 365–373.
89. ZUCCHI, R., S. RONCA-TESTONI, G. YU *et al.* 1995. Postischemic changes in cardiac sarcoplasmic reticulum Ca^{2+} channels: a possible mechanism of ischemic preconditioning. Circ. Res. **76:** 1049–1056.
90. TANI, M., Y. ASAKURA, H. HASEGAWA *et al.* 1996. Effect of preconditioning on ryanodine-sensitive Ca^{2+} release from sarcoplasmic reticulum from rat heart. Am. J. Physiol. **271:** H876–H881.
91. TANI, M., Y. SUGANUMA, H. HASEGAWA *et al.* 1997. Changes in ischemic tolerance and effects of ischemic preconditioning in middle-aged rat hearts. Circulation **95:** 2559–2566.
92. MUBAGWA, K., P. KAPLAN & W. FLAMENG. 1997. The effects of ryanodine on calcium uptake by the sarcoplasmic reticulum of ischemic and reperfused rat myocardium. Fundam. Clin. Pharmacol. **11:** 315–321.
93. STOKKE, M., G. AKSNES, K. LANDE *et al.* 1994. Density of L-type calcium channels in ischaemically preconditioned porcine myocardium. Acta Physiol. Scand. **150:** 425–430.
94. MENG, H.P. & G.N. PIERCE. 1990. Protective effects of 5-(*N,N*-dimethy)amiloride on ischemia- reperfusion injury in hearts. Am. J. Physiol. **258:** H1615–H1619.
95. KLEIN, H.H., S. PICH, R.M. BOHLE *et al.* 1995. Myocardial protection by Na^+-H^+ exchange inhibition in ischemic, reperfused porcine hearts. Circulation **92:** 912–917.
96. ROHMAN, S., H. WEYGANDT & K.O. MINCK. 1995. Preischaemic as well as postischaemic application of a Na^+/H^+ exchange inhibitor reduces infarct size in pigs. Cardiovasc. Res. **30:** 945–951.
97. BUGGE, E. & K. YTREHUS. 1995. Inhibition of sodium-hydrogen exchange reduces infarct size in the isolated rat heart: a protective additive to ischaemic preconditioning. Cardiovasc. Res. **29:** 269–274.
98. MIURA, T., T. OGAWA, K. SUZUKI *et al.* 1997. Infarct size limitation by a new Na^+-H^+ exchange inhibitor HOE 642: difference from preconditioning in the role of protein kinase C. J. Am. Coll. Cardiol. **29:** 693–701.
99. SATO, H., T. MIKI, R.P. VALLABHAPURAPU *et al.* 1997. The mechanism of protection from 5 (*N*-ethyl-*N*-isopropyl)amiloride differs from that of ischemic preconditioning in rabbit heart. Basic Res. Cardiol. **92:** 339–350.
100. ASIMAKIS, G.K., K. INNERS-MCBRIDE, G. MEDELLIN *et al.* 1992. Ischemic preconditioning attenuates acidosis and postischemic dysfunction in isolated rat heart. Am. J. Physiol. **263:** H887–H894.

Role of K_{ATP} Channel in Heat Shock and Pharmacological Preconditioning[a]

RAKESH C. KUKREJA[b]

Division of Cardiology, Medical College of Virginia, Virginia Commonwealth University, Richmond, Virginia 23298, USA

ABSTRACT: Heat shock (HS) and 4-monophosphoryl lipid A (MLA, a non-toxic analogue of endotoxin) protects the myocardium against ischemia-reperfusion injury. We studied the involvement of ATP-sensitive potassium channel (K_{ATP} channel) in ischemic protection induced by these stimuli. Anesthetized rabbits were preconditioned with either HS (by raising temperature to 42°C for 15 min) or intravenous pretreatment with MLA (35 μg/kg). After 24 h, animals were re-anesthetized and subjected to 30-min regional ischemia followed by 180-min reperfusion (I/R). K_{ATP} channel blockers glibenclamide and/or 5-hydroxydecanoate (5-HD) were used to inhibit channel function. The 72 kD heat shock protein (HSP-72) was measured by Western blots. HS produced a marked reduction in infarct size (39.4 ± 8.1% to 14.3 ± 2.5%, $p < 0.05$) that was abolished by glibenclamide (42.3 ± 3.2%) and 5-HD (33.7 ± 4.8%) when given before I/R. These drugs failed to block HS protection when given before HS. Expression of HSP-72 was increased in all HS groups as compared to non-HS groups in both glibenclamide and 5-HD–treated rabbits. Similarly, pretreatment with MLA reduced infarct size from 40 ± 8.6% to 15.1 ± 1.5% ($p < 0.05$). The infarct size increased to 51.9 ± 5.8 with 5-HD in MLA-treated rabbits. 5-HD did not alter infarct size significantly when given in vehicle-treated control rabbits. These data suggest that HS and MLA exert their anti-ischemic effect through activation of K_{ATP} channel.

INTRODUCTION

Sublethal ischemia or nonlethal whole body heat stress (HS) activates a powerful endogenous protective mechanism that has been shown to significantly improve myocardial salvage following prolonged ischemia in *in vivo* and *in vitro* models.[1,2] Heat stress has been shown to enhance the delayed post-ischemic contractile function *in vitro*[3] and reduce infarct size *in vivo*.[1,4] The stress response is commonly associated with a rapid overexpression of a family of heat shock proteins (HSPs). Induction of HSPs following whole body hyperthermia or sublethal ischemia has been suggested as the mechanism of myocardial protection against ischemia-reperfusion injury. Exposure of rats to elevated temperature, with subsequent induction of 72 kD HSP (HSP 72) resulted in an improved recovery of contractile function and reduced cre-

[a]This work was supported in part by grants HL 51045 and HL 59469 from the National Institutes of Health.

[b]Address correspondence to: Rakesh C. Kukreja, Ph.D, Associate Professor, Eric Lipman Laboratories of Molecular and Cellular Cardiology, Division of Cardiology, Medical College of Virginia, Virginia Commonwealth University, Richmond, Virginia 23298; Telephone: 804-828-0389; Fax: 804-828-8700; E-mail: rakesh@email.hsc.vcu.edu

atine kinase release after subsequent ischemia and reperfusion.[5,6] In addition to ischemia or HS, certain pharmacological agents, such as 4-monophosphoryl lipid A (MLA), induce delayed ischemic preconditioning *in vivo*[7–11] and in isolated perfused mouse heart.[12] MLA, an analogue of endotoxin, retains several of the immunostimulatory properties of the parent molecule without associated toxicity.[13] The selective reduction of the toxicity of lipid A has been achieved by the removal of the phosphate group from the reducing end of glucosamine disaccharide.[14] Similar to metabolic and and heat-shock preconditioning,[15] higher concentrations of MLA (200 ng/ml) have been shown to induce HSP 72 *in vitro* in cultured myocytes[16] although a low protective dose (35 μg/kg) of the drug failed to synthesize this protein *in vivo*.[8]

Evidence that HSP 72 is directly protective *in vivo* is mostly correlative and a direct cause and effect relationship of this protein in ischemic protection requires further investigation. Recent studies from our laboratory suggest that mere quantitative accumulation of these proteins following ischemia or heat shock may not be the determining factor in protection.[17,18] Whether these proteins activate some other unknown "effector" of protection or must undergo post-translational modifications/translocation before they can exert protection remains to be determined. In our quest for this "unknown" effector of HS-induced protection, we considered the opening of ATP-sensitive potassium channel as a possible mediator of HS-induced protection. Recent studies suggest that K_{ATP} channel plays an important role in myocardial protection following ischemic preconditioning.[19,20] Pretreatment with K_{ATP} channel blockers, such as glibenclamide and sodium 5-hydroxydecanoate (5-HD, an ischemia-selective K_{ATP} channel antagonist), prevented the beneficial effects of preconditioning as well as K_{ATP} channel openers. Gross and Auchampach[19] found that intravenous administration of glibenclamide 10 minutes before or immediately after ischemic preconditioning completely abolished the beneficial effect of preconditioning. Similarly, 5-HD blocked ischemic preconditioning without affecting infarct size in non-preconditioned dogs[21] and rats.[22] In the isolated buffer-perfused rat hearts, the K_{ATP} channel opener nicorandil duplicated the effects of ischemic preconditioning, improving contractility and reducing contracture during reperfusion, and these beneficial effects were blocked by the prior infusion of glibenclamide.[23]

Despite the overwhelming evidence for the role of K_{ATP} channel in early preconditioning, limited work has been done to investigate the existence of a similar pathway in delayed preconditioning induced by HS or pharmacological agents.[24–27] Some of our work on the role of K_{ATP} channel in delayed preconditioning is summarized in this paper.

SURGICAL PREPARATION

Male New Zealand White rabbits, weighing 2.0–3.8 kg, were anesthetized with intramuscular ketamine HCl (35 mg/kg) and xylazine (5 mg/kg). A rectal thermometer was placed in the animals and core body temperature was raised to 42°C with heating pads for 15 min, 24 h before ischemia-reperfusion (I/R). Saline was administered intraperitoneally to maintain hydration and ice was placed on the head to prevent brain damage. Animals were allowed to recover for 24 h at room temperature. Rabbits were re-anesthetized, tracheotomy was performed, and the rabbits were ventilated by positive pressure with room air, supplemented with 100% oxygen if needed to maintain blood gases in physiological range. The rate and volume of respiration were also adjusted during the experiment to maintain pH, pCO_2, and pO_2 in normal range. Catheters were placed in the left carotid artery and jugular vein for measuring blood pressure and arterial blood gas or administering drugs and fluids. A left thoracotomy was performed between the fourth and fifth ribs and the pericardium was opened to expose the heart. A 5-0 silk thread was passed around the left anterior descending artery with a taper needle and the ends of the tie were threaded through a small vinyl tube to form a snare. The coronary artery was ligated by pulling the snare tight and securing with a hemostat. Myocardial ischemia was determined by S-T segment elevation and the appearance of regional cyanosis. Reperfusion was documented by observation of hyperemia and resumption of contractions in the area below the snare upon release. Following completion of the experimental protocol, the ligature around the LAD was re-tightened and approximately 4 ml 10% Evans blue dye was injected into the jugular vein until the eyes turned blue. The rabbits were sacrificed and their hearts harvested and cut into six transverse slices of equal thickness. The area at risk was determined by negative staining. The slices were stained by incubation for 15 min in 1% triphenyl tetrazolium chloride (TTC) in isotonic pH 7.4 phosphate buffer. After staining, the sections were placed in formalin for preservation. Measurements of risk area, infarct area, and left ventricle were made using Bioquant imaging software for computer-aided morphometry. From each section, the ischemic risk area (unstained by blue dye) and the infarcted area (unstained by TTC) were outlined and measured by planimetry. The area from each region was averaged from the slices. Infarct size was expressed both as a percentage of total LV and as a percentage of the ischemic risk area.

WHOLE-BODY HYPERTHERMIA AND EXPERIMENTAL GROUPS

Rabbits were anesthetized with intramuscular ketamine HCl (35 mg/kg) and xylazine (5 mg/kg). A rectal thermometer was placed in the animals, and core body temperature was raised to 42°C with heating pads for 15 min, 24 h before ischemia-reperfusion (I/R). Saline was administered intraperitoneally to maintain hydration and ice was placed on the head to prevent brain damage. Animals were allowed to recover for 24 h at room temperature. Eight groups of rabbits were subjected to ischemia-reperfusion (I/R). Group I: control (I/R), 30-min ischemia followed by 3-h reperfusion; Group II: glibenclamide control, rabbits treated with glibenclamide (0.3 mg/kg intraperitoneally) 30 min before I/R; Group III: HS only, rabbits subjected to whole-body hyperthermia by raising temperature to 42°C for 15 min followed by I/R 24 h later; Group IV: HS-glibenclamide, rabbits treated with glibenclamide 30 min before I/R; Group V: glibenclamide-HS, rabbits given glibenclamide (0.3 mg/kg intraperitoneally) 30 min before whole-body hyperthermia followed by I/R 24 h later; Group VI: 5-HD control, rabbits treated with 5-HD (5 mg/kg) 10 min before I/R; Group VII: 5HD-HS, rabbits treated with 5-HD 10 min before I/R; Group VIII: 5HD-HS, animals treated with 5-HD 10 min before HS followed by I/R 24 h later. HSP 72 was measured by Western blotting in a separate set of animals from each group. The only difference was that the ventricular samples were collected from these animals without ischemia-reperfusion.

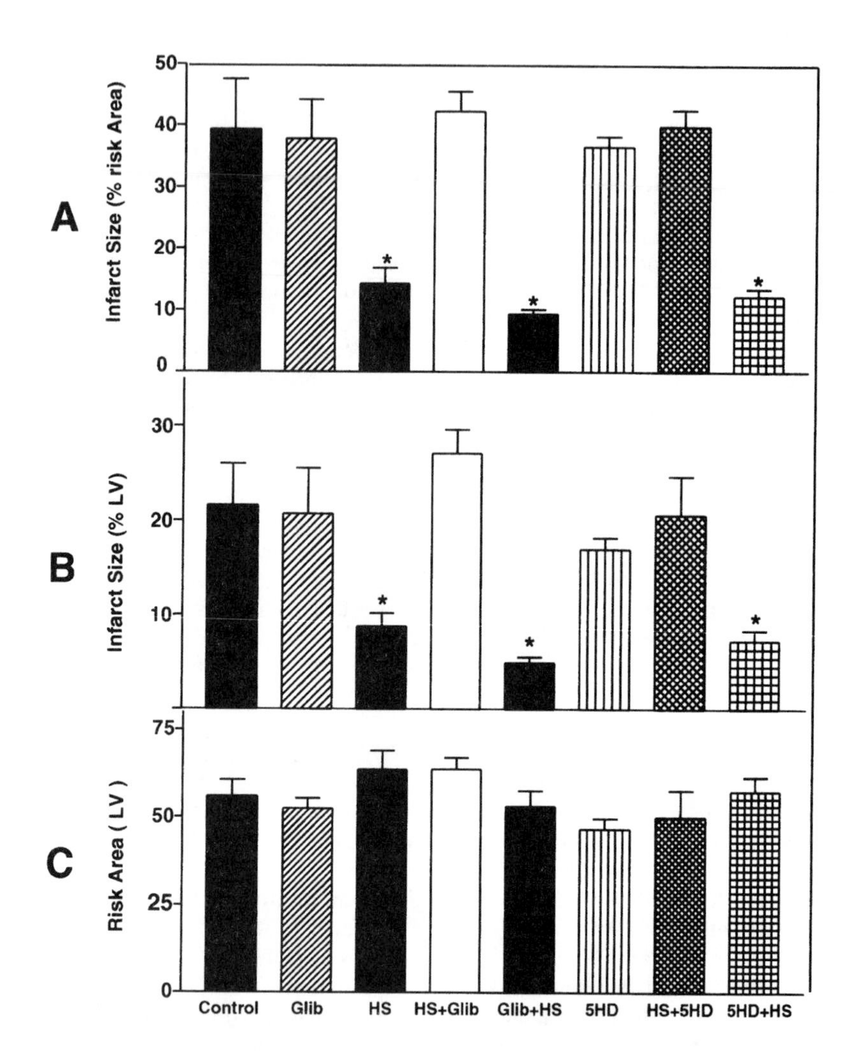

FIGURE 1. **(A)** Diagram showing infarct size expressed as percentage of area at risk. In the HS-preconditioned rabbits, infarct size was reduced. The beneficial effect of HS preconditioning was lost by glibenclamide as well as 5-HD when these agents were administered before ischemia-reperfusion in HS rabbits (groups HS-Glib and HS-5-HD). Glibenclamide and 5-HD failed to block the protective effect of HS when these agents were given before HS (groups Glib-HS and 5-HD-HS). Glibenclamide and 5-HD did not change infarct size significantly (as compared to control I/R, $p > 0.05$) in non-HS control animals subjected to ischemia-reperfusion only (groups Glib-I/R and 5-HD-I/R). Each bar represents mean ± SE of 6–7 animals. **(B)** Diagram showing infarct size (expressed as % LV) in six groups. (**C**) Diagram showing area at risk expressed as % LV. *$p < 0.05$ from control, Glib, HS + Glib, 5-HD, and HS + 5-HD. (*Reprinted from Hoag* et al.[25] *with permission.*)

TABLE 1. Experimental results[a]

Experimental Group	Risk Area (% Left Ventricle)	Infarct Size (% Risk Area)
MLA-Vehicle	53.3 ± 4.3	40.5 ± 8.6
MLA (35 μg/kg)	50.0 ± 4.3	15.1 ± 1.5
MLA (35 μg/kg) + 5-HD (5 mg/kg)	45.1 ± 4.6	51.9 ± 5.8
MLA Vehicle + 5-HD (5 mg/kg)	46.7 ± 3.1	36.5 ± 1.7

Myocardial infarct size 24 h after treatment with MLA-Vehicle or MLA with or without 5-HD administered 15 min before ischemia. There is a significant reduction of infarct size with MLA as compared to MLA-Vehicle, MLA + 5-HD, and 5-HD.

PHARMACOLOGICAL PRECONDITIONING AND EXPERIMENTAL GROUPS

Animals were randomly divided into four groups. Group I (MLA-Vehicle): rabbits treated with 0.35 ml vehicle (40% propylene glycol, 10% ethanol in water); Group II (MLA): rabbits treated with MLA (35 μg/kg intravenously) 24 h before ischemia-reperfusion. Group III (MLA-5-HD): rabbits treated with MLA as in group II and 24 h later given 5-HD (5 mg/kg) 15 min before ischemia. Group IV (5-HD Controls): rabbits treated with 5-HD 15 min before ischemia-reperfusion. All animals were subjected to ischemia by occlusion of coronary artery for 30 min and reperfusion for 3 hours.

HEAT SHOCK PRECONDITIONING AND K_{ATP} CHANNEL

FIGURE 1 (A) shows the infarct size expressed as percentage of anatomic area at risk in eight groups. Infarct size was 39.4 ± 8.1% in the control group; decreased significantly to 14.3 ± 2.5% HS rabbits, a 64% reduction from control hearts ($p < 0.01$). Treatment with glibenclamide and 5-HD in HS rabbits resulted in a significant increase in the infarct size to 37.8 ± 6.4% and 33.7 ± 4.8%, respectively ($p < 0.01$). Also, non-HS control rabbits treated with glibenclamide or 5-HD had a infarct size of 42.3 ± 3.2% and 39.9 ± 2.7%, respectively, which were not significantly different when compared to untreated control I/R hearts, i.e., 39.4 ± 8.1%, $p > 0.01$. FIGURE 1 (B) shows infarct size expressed as percentage of left ventricle. A similar trend in the infarct size was observed when expressed as percentage of left ventricle. The mean value of infarct size was 21.6 ± 4.4% in the control group; reduced significantly to 8.8 ± 1.4% in HS rabbits ($p < 0.02$). Again, both glibenclamide and 5-HD significantly blocked heat shock–induced protection without having significant effect in non-HS rabbits. FIGURE 1 (C) shows the area at risk in eight groups. The areas at risk ranged from 50–64% with no significant differences between all the groups (p>0.05). These data suggested that changes in the size of infarcts observed between various groups were not related to the percentage of area of left ventricle occluded by our technique. No significant differences in the baseline levels of heart rate, mean arterial blood pressure, and rate pressure product were observed between each

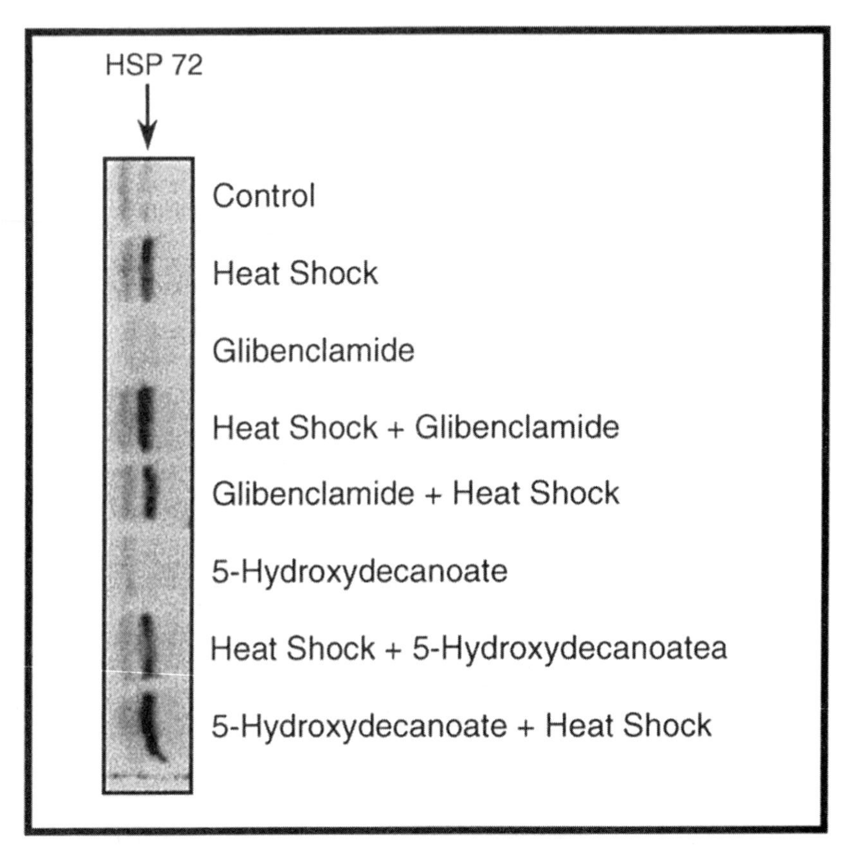

FIGURE 2. Western blot analysis showing expression of HSP 72 in the left ventricle. (*Reprinted from Hoag* et al.[25] *with permission.*)

group. The hemodynamics did not alter significantly throughout the reperfusion period although it decreased gradually at most of the data points in all the groups (not shown).

FIGURE 2 shows the expression of HSP 72 in eight groups. A large increase in the expression of HSP 72 in the left ventricle was observed in HS rabbits, whereas non-HS control as well drugs-treated control (non-HS) demonstrated minimal expression of HSP 72. Furthermore, except for some variations, treatment with the glibenclamide and 5-HD before or after whole-body hyperthermia did not decrease the expression of HSP 72.

"PHARMACOLOGICAL" PRECONDITIONING AND K_{ATP} CHANNEL

The rabbits that received MLA-Vehicle, 24 h before the 30-min coronary artery occlusion and 180-min reperfusion, had a 40.5 ± 8.5% necrosis in the area at risk.

This was not significantly different from the infarct size measured in rabbits receiving 5-HD 15 min before sustained ischemia-reperfusion. MLA administered 24 h before ischemia-reperfusion resulted in significant reduction in the infarct size to 15.1 ± 1.4% ($p < 0.05$), as compared to the animals treated with either MLA-Vehicle or 5-HD. However, 5-HD completely abolished the myocardial protective effect of MLA with the infarct size of 51.8 ± 5.8% ($p < 0.05$ from MLA group). The percent of myocardium at risk was comparable in all groups. MLA administration 24 h before ischemia-reperfusion failed to induce HSP 72 in the heart.[8]

POSSIBLE MECHANISMS OF K_{ATP} CHANNEL ACTIVATION

K_{ATP} channels are activated when intracellular ATP levels drop. Within 1–3 min of acute coronary occlusion there is a pronounced decline in action potential duration secondary to the activation of K_{ATP} channels.[28] There is mounting evidence supporting the involvement of the K_{ATP} channels in the mechanism of preconditioning. Gross and Auchampach[19] demonstrated that blockade of the K_{ATP} channels with glibenclamide prevented the development of myocardial ischemic preconditioning.[29,30] We do not know the mechanism by which HS may have opened K_{ATP} channels, although we can speculate several possibilities. Recent studies by Hu and colleagues[31] have demonstrated that protein kinase C (PKC) activated K_{ATP} channels in rabbit and human ventricular myocytes by reducing channel sensitivity to intracellular ATP. Phorbol 12,13-didecanoate–induced activation of the K_{ATP} channel was blocked by highly selective PKC inhibitor in these studies. Direct evidence of the activation of PKC with heat shock is currently lacking although a recent study from our laboratory demonstrated blockade of heat shock–induced cardiac protection in rat heart by chelerythrine, a specific PKC antagonist.[32] The mechanism by which heat shock activates PKC remains unclear. One plausible hypothesis is that heat shock transiently increased intracellular calcium, which may trigger signal transduction cascade leading to the activation of PKC, phosphorylation of K_{ATP} channel directly or via another unknown effector protein, possibly HSP 72. Although no direct evidence is available to support this theory, a recent study by Saad and Hahn[33] reported activation of voltage-dependent K^+ channels after heating in radiation-induced fibrosarcoma cell line. These currents were blocked by tetraethylammonium cations as well modification of extracellular K^+ currents. Negulyaev and colleagues[34] demonstrated that exogenous HSP 70 caused an activation of outward currents through potassium-selective channels. These studies do not necessarily mean that a similar activation of K_{ATP} channels may have occurred by heat shock or HSPs. However such a possibility cannot be ruled out and further studies showing the cause-and-effect relationship of HSP 72 with the opening of K_{ATP} channel in cardiac myocytes are warranted.

Exactly how MLA preconditioning opens K_{ATP} channel during delayed preconditioning is not clear, although several mechanisms have been proposed. For example, bacterial endotoxin, which incorporates lipid A in its molecule, has been demonstrated to increase free radical production in different models.[35] MLA could also induce the generation of non-toxic, beneficial concentrations of reduced oxygen intermediates,[36] which could potentially induce changes in cellular redox status leading to the activation of transcription factor NF-κB. Alternatively, LPS-mediated activation of NF-κB can be regulated by phosphorylation as suggested by Ishikawa and colleagues.[37] NF-κB has been shown to regulate the inducible nitric oxide synthase (iNOS) gene in rodent cells stimulated by TNFα, IL-1, and LPS. Many cytokines whose transcription is induced by endotoxin during sepsis are thought to be regulated by NF-κB.[38] On stimulation, NF-κB has been shown to promote transcription of a large family of genes. The promoter of the murine gene encoding the iNOS gene contains an NF-κB site. Induction of this gene leads to the production of NO in LPS-treated cells.[39] The activity of the iNOS and thereby production of NO is tightly controlled by NF-κB at the transcriptional level.[40] Treatment with conventional endotoxin and MLA is known to increase the *de novo* synthesis of iNOS.[41,42] NO has been shown to open K_{ATP} channels in blood vessels[43] as well as in ventricular myocytes.[44] Therefore, increased NO generation following MLA treatment may possibly be responsible for increased activity of K_{ATP} channel. Alternatively, non-toxic levels of reduced oxygen intermediates (generated as a result of MLA-induced oxidative stress in myocytes) may protect via direct activation of K_{ATP} channel.[45,46] Tokube and colleagues[45] showed that free radicals significantly increased the open probability of the channel at a narrow range of ATP (0.2–2 mM) and this effect was enhanced in the presence of ADP (0.1 mM) and abolished by free radical scavengers or glibenclamide.

CONCLUSIONS

These results show that heat shock and MLA induce significantly delayed cardioprotective effect in the heart. Since the first description of the role of K_{ATP} channel in acute ischemic preconditioning by Gross and coworkers[19] it appears that this channel also acts as the "end effector" of delayed preconditioning induced by heat shock or MLA. However, it is not clear whether the sarcolemmal or mitochondrial K_{ATP} channels, or both, contribute to the delayed cardioprotective effect of these stimuli. Future studies are necessary to address these issues.

REFERENCES

1. HUTTER, M.W., R.E. SIEVERS, V. BARBOSA & C.L. WOLFE. 1994. Heat-shock protein induction in rat hearts: a direct correlation between the amount of heat-shock protein induced and the degree of myocardial protection. Circulation **89:** 355–360.
2. MURRY, C.E., R.B. JENNINGS & K.A. REIMER. 1986. Preconditioning with ischemia: a delay of lethal cell injury in ischemic myocardium. Circulation **74:** 1124–1136.
3. CURRIE, R.W. & M. KARMAZYN. 1990. Improved post-ischemic ventricular recovery in the absence of changes in energy metabolism in working rat hearts following heat-shock. J. Mol. Cell. Cardiol. **22:** 631–636.
4. CURRIE, R.W., R.M. TANGUAY & J.G. KINGMA, JR. 1993. Heat-shock response and limitation of tissue necrosis during occlusion/reperfusion in rabbit hearts. Circulation **87:** 963–971.
5. CURRIE, R.W., B.M. ROSS & T.A. DAVID. 1990. Induction of the heat shock response in rats modulate heart rate, creatine kinase and protein synthesis after subsequent hyperthermic treatment. Cardiovasc. Res. **14:** 87–93.
6. KONTOS, M.C., J.S. SHIPLEY & R.C. KUKREJA. 1996. Heat stress improves functional recovery and induces synthesis of 27- and 70-kDa heat shock proteins without pre-

serving sarcoplasmic reticulum function in the ischemic rat heart. J. Mol. Cell. Cardiol. **28:** 1885–1894.
7. YAO, Z., J.L. RASMUSSEN, J.L. HIRT, D.A. MEI, G.M. PIEPER & G.J. GROSS. 1993. Effects of monophosphoryl lipid A on myocardial ischemia/reperfusion injury in dogs. J. Cardiovasc. Pharmacol. **22:** 653–663.
8. YOSHIDA, K.I., M.M. MAAIEH, J.B. SHIPLEY, M. DOLORESCO, N.L. BERNARDO, Y.Z. QIAN, G.T. ELLIOTT & R.C. KUKREJA. 1996. Monophosphoryl lipid A induces pharmacologic "preconditioning" in rabbit hearts without concomitant expression of 70-kDa heat shock protein. Mol. Cell. Biochem. **159:** 73–80.
9. BAXTER, G.F., R.W. GOODWIN, M.J. WRIGHT, M. KERAC, R.J. HEADS & D.M. YELLON. 1996. Myocardial protection after monophosphoryl lipid A: studies of delayed anti-ischemic properties in rabbit heart. Br. J. Pharmacol. **117**: 1685–1692.
10. PRZYKLENK, K., L. ZHAO, R.A. KLONER & G.T. ELLIOTT. 1996. Cardioprotection with ischemic preconditioning and MLA: Role of adenosine-regulating enzymes? Am. J. Physiol. **271:** H1004–H1014
11. TOSAKI, A., N. MAULIK, G.T. ELLIOTT, R.M. ENGELMAN & D.K. DAS. 1998. Preconditioning of rat heart with monophosphoryl lipid A: a role of nitric oxide. J. Pharmacol. Exp. Ther. **285:** 1274–1279.
12. JARRETT, N.C., L. XI, M.L. HESS & R.C. KUKREJA. 1998. Monophosphoryl lipid A induces delayed protection against ischemia/reperfusion injury in the mouse heart. J. Mol. Cell. Cardiol. **30:** A262(Abstract).
13. RIBI, E. 1984. Beneficial modification of the endotoxin molecule. J. Biol. Resp. Modif. **3:** 1–9.
14. QURESHI, N., K. TAKAYAMA & E. RIBI. 1982. Purification and structural determination of nontoxin lipid A obtained from lipopolysaccharide of *Salmonella tuphimurium*. J. Biol. Chem. **257:** 11808–11815.
15. NAYEEM, M.A., G.T. ELLIOTT, M.R. SHAH, S.L. HASTILLO-HESS & R.C. KUKREJA. 1997. Monophosphoryl lipid A protects adult rat cardiac myocytes with induction of the 72-kD heat shock protein. A cellular model of pharmacologic preconditioning. J. Mol. Cell. Cardiol. **29:** 2305–2310.
16. NAYEEM, M.A., M.L. HESS, Y.-Z. QIAN, K.E. LOESSER & R.C. KUKREJA. 1997. Delayed preconditioning of cultured adult rat cardiac myocytes. Role of 70 and 90 kD heat stress proteins in protection against lethal cellular injury. Am. J. Physiol. **42:** H861–H868
17. QIAN, Y.-Z., J.S. SHIPLEY, J.E. LEVASSEUR & R.C. KUKREJA. 1998. Dissociation of the expresion of 72 and 27 kDa heat shock proteins with ischemic tolerance following heat shock in rat heart. J. Mol. Cell. Cardiol. **30:** 1163–1172.
18. QIAN, Y.-Z., N.L. BERNARDO, M.A. NAYEEM, J. CHELLIAH & R.C. KUKREJA. 1999. Induction of 72 kilodalton heat shock protein does not produce second window of ischemic preconditioning in rat heart. Am J. Physiol. **276:** H224–H234.
19. GROSS, G.J. & J.A. AUCHAMPACH. 1992. Blockade of ATP-sensitive potassium channels prevents myocardial preconditioning in dogs. Circ. Res. **70:** 223–233.
20. QIAN, Y.Z., J.E. LEVASSEUR, K.I. YOSHIDA & R.C. KUKREJA. 1996. K_{ATP} channels in rat heart: Blockade of ischemic and acetylcholine-mediated preconditioning by glibenclamide. Am. J. Physiol. **271:** H23–H28.
21. AUCHAMPACH, J.A., G.J. GROVER & G.J. GROSS. 1992. Blockade of ischaemic preconditioning in dogs by the novel ATP dependent potassium channel antagonist sodium 5-hydroxydecanoate. Cardiovasc. Res. **26:** 1054–1062.
22. SCHULTZ, J.E.J., Y.-Z. QIAN, G.J. GROSS & R.C. KUKREJA. 1997. Specific ATP-sensitive potassium channel antagonist 5-hydroxydecanoate blocks ischemic preconditioning in the rat heart. J. Mol. Cell. Cardiol. **29:** 1055–1060.
23. MENASCHE, P., E. KEVELAITIS, C. MOUAS, C. GROUSSET, A. PIWNICA & G. BLOCH. 1995. Preconditioning with potassium channel openers. A new concept for enhancing cardioplegic protection? J. Thorac. Cardiovasc. Surg. **110:** 1606–1614.
24. ELLIOTT, G.T., M.L. COMERFORD, J.R. SMITH & L. ZHAO. 1996. Myocardial ischemia/reperfusion protection using monophosphoryl lipid A is abrogated by the ATP-sensitive potassium channel blocker, glibenclamide. Cardiovasc. Res. **32:** 1071–1080.
25. HOAG, J.B., Y.-Z. QIAN, M.A. NAYEEM, M. D'ANGELO & R.C. KUKREJA. 1997. ATP-

sensitive potassium channel mediates delayed ischemic protection by heat stress in rabbit heart. Am. J. Physiol. **42:** H861–H868

26. PELL, T.J., D.M. YELLON, R.W. GOODWIN & G.F. BAXTER. 1997. Myocardial ischemic tolerance following heat stress is abolished by ATP-sensitive potassium channel blockade. Cardiovasc. Drugs Ther. **11:** 679–686.
27. JANIN, Y., Y.-Z. QIAN, J. HOAG, G.T. ELLIOTT & R.C. KUKREJA. 1999. Pharmacologic preconditioning with monophosphoryl lipid A is abolished by 5-hydroxydecanoate, a specific inhibitor of the K_{ATP} channel. J. Cardiovasc. Pharmacol. **32:** 337–342.
28. COLE, W.C., C.D. MCPHERSON & D. SONTAG. 1991. ATP-regulated K^+ channels protect the myocardium against ischemia/reperfusion damage. Circ. Res. **69:** 571–581.
29. TAN, H.L., P. MAZON, H.J. VERBERNE, M.E. SLEESWIJK, R. CORONEL, T. OPTHOF & M.J. JANSE. 1993. Ischaemic preconditioning delays ischaemia induced cellular electrical uncoupling in rabbit myocardium by activation of ATP sensitive potassium channels. Cardiovasc. Res. **27:** 644–651.
30. TOOMBS, C.F., T.L. MOORE & R.J. SHEBUSKI. 1993. Limitation of infarct size in the rabbit by ischaemic preconditioning is reversible with glibenclamide. Cardiovasc. Res. **27:** 617–622.
31. HU, K.L., D.Y. DUAN, G.R. LI & S. NATTEL. 1996. Protein kinase C activates ATP-sensitive K^+ current in human and rabbit ventricular myocytes. Circ. Res. **78:** 492–498.
32. KUKREJA, R.C., Y.-Z. QIAN & E.E. FLAHERTY. 1999. Protein kinase C is involved in heat stress-induced protection of the heart. Mol. Cell. Biochem. In press.
33. SAAD, A.H. & G.M. HAHN. 1992. Activation of potassium channels: relationship to the heat shock response. Proc. Natl. Acad. Sci. USA **89:** 9396–9399.
34. NEGULYAEV, Y.A., E.A. VEDERNIKOVA, A.V. KINEV & A.P. VORONIN. 1996. Exogenous heat shock protein hsp70 activates potassium channels in U937 cells. Biochim. Biophys. Acta **1282:** 156–162.
35. SIEGFRIED, M.R., X.L. MA & A.M. LEFER. 1992. Splanchnic vascular endothelial dysfunction in rat endotoxemia: role of superoxide radicals. Eur. J. Pharmacol. **212:** 171–176.
36. MAULIK, N., M. WATANABE, D.T. ENGELMAN, M. ENGELMAN & D.K. DAS. 1995. Oxidative stress adaptation improves postischemic ventricular recovery. Mol. Cell Biochem. **144:** 67–74.
37. ISHIKAWA, Y., N. MUKAIDA, K. KUNO, N. RICE, S. OKAMOTO & K. MATSUSHIMA. 1995. Establishment of lipopolysaccharide-dependent nuclear factor kappa B activation in a cell-free system. J. Biol. Chem. **270:** 4158–4164.
38. BLACKWELL, T.S., E.P. HOLDEN, T.R. BLACKWELL, J.E. DELARCO & J.W. CHRISTMAN. 1994. Cytokine-induced neutrophil chemoattractant mediates neutrophilic alveolitis in rats: association with nuclear factor kappa B activation. [published erratum appears in Am. J. Respir. Cell Mol. Biol. 1994. Dec.11(6):following 765.] Am. J. Respir. Cell Mol. Biol. **11:** 464–472.
39. XIE, Q.W., Y. KASHIWABARA & C. NATHAN. 1994. Role of transcription factor NF-kappa B/Rel in induction of nitric oxide synthase. J. Biol. Chem. **269:** 4705–4708.
40. NAKAYAMA, D.K., D.A. GELLER, C.J. LOWENSTEIN, H.D. CHERN, P. DAVIES, B.R. PITT, R.L. SIMMONS & T.R. BILLIAR. 1992. Cytokines and lipopolysaccharide induce nitric oxide synthase in cultured rat pulmonary artery smooth muscle. [published erratum appears in Am. J. Respir. Cell Mol. Biol. 1993. Aug.9 (2):following 229.] Am. J. Respir. Cell Mol. Biol. **7:** 471–476.
41. KNOWLES, R.G., M. MERRETT, M. SALTER & S. MONCADA. 1990. Differential induction of brain, lung and liver nitric oxide synthase by endotoxin in the rat. Biochem. J. **270:** 833–836.
42. ZHAO, L., P.A. WEBER, J.R. SMITH, M.L. COMERFORD & G.T. ELLIOTT. 1997. Role of inducible nitric oxide synthase in pharmacological "preconditioning" with monophosphoryl lipid A. J. Mol. Cell. Cardiol. **29:** 1567–1576.
43. MURPHY, M.E. & J.E. BRAYDEN. 1995. Nitric oxide hyperpolarizes rabbit mesenteric arteries via ATP-sensitive potassium channels. J. Physiol. (Lond) **486:** 47–58.
44. CAMERON, J.S., K.K.A. KIBLER, H. BERRY, D.N. BARRON, V.H. SODDER & F. BARIN. 1996. Nitric oxide activates ATP-sensitive potassium channels in hypertrophied ventricular myocytes. FASEB J. **10:** A65(Abstract).

45. Tokube, K., T. Kiyosue & M. Arita. 1996. Openings of cardiac KATP channel by oxygen free radicals produced by xanthine oxidase reaction. Am. J. Physiol. **271:** H478–489.
46. Filipovic, D.M. & W.B. Reeves.1997. Hydrogen peroxide activates glibenclamide-sensitive K^+ channels in LLC-PK1 cells. Am. J. Physiol. **272:** C737–743.

Pharmacologic Enhancement of Tolerance to Ischemic Cardiac Stress Using Monophosphoryl Lipid A

A Comparison with Antecedent Ischemia

LIN ZHAO[a] AND GARY T. ELLIOTT[b]

[a]*Department of Integrative Pharmacology, Pharmaceuticals Products Division, Abbott Laboratories, Abbott Park, Illinois 60064, USA*

[b]*Pharmaceutical Development Division, Ribi ImmunoChem Research, Inc., 553 Old Corvallis Road, Hamilton, Montana 59840, USA*

ABSTRACT: In comparison with ischemic preconditioning, MLA-mediated cardioprotection seems to show numerous common features. Like ischemia, MLA induces a first and second window (biphasic profile) of heightened tolerance to ischemia. As with delayed ischemic preconditioning, MLA protects against infarction, stunning, and arrhythmias associated with ischemia-reperfusion. In contrast with acute ischemic preconditioning, MLA reduces infarction and stunning. A role has been demonstrated for nitric oxide synthase and K_{ATP} channel activation in the mechanism of delayed preconditioning induced by ischemia and by MLA. Regarding acute preconditioning, kinase and K_{ATP} channel activation have been implicated as involved in the mechanism of ischemic preconditioning and also in MLA cardioprotection. Use of MLA or related compounds as cardioprotectants may represent a method for inducing acute tolerance to ischemia-reperfusion injury manifested as infarction or stunning, with the added benefit of a sustained delayed cardioprotective state being achieved.

INTRODUCTION

The damage caused by myocardial ischemia and reperfusion (MI/R) is responsible for the most common cause of death, ischemic heart disease. It occurs in coronary artery disease, angina, angioplasty, cardiac bypass surgery, and heart transplantation. The manifestations associated with this injury are arrhythmias, cardiomyocyte death (infarction), and stunning.

The depletion of ATP, overproduction of oxygen-derived free radicals, intracellular calcium overload, and neutrophil infiltration have been proposed to be involved in such injury.[1,2] Much effort has been devoted to find treatments for MI/R. However, most protective agents were found to be not very successful until ischemic preconditioning (IP) was discovered in 1986 by Murry and coworkers.[3] In a regional MI/R canine model, using infarct size as endpoint, Murry and coworkers found that myocardial tissue could develop resistance to ischemia-reperfusion injury following brief cycles of ischemia before the onset of the prolonged ischemic stress. This IP phenomenon has so far been proven to be the most effective method described for delaying MI/R injury and has been demonstrated to be protective in a wide range of animal species, including humans.[4]

BIPHASIC CARDIOPROTECTION WITH BRIEF ISCHEMIA-INDUCED PRECONDITIONING

Since the first observation by Murry and colleagues, IP was believed for almost seven years to be short lived, lasting only 1–2 h after its induction.[5] In 1993, a second window of protection (SWOP), reappearing 12 to 24 h following IP, was reported in the literature.[6–8]

The acute phase of IP protects the myocardium against infarction[3,9,10] and arrhythmia.[11] However, controversial results have been reported regarding the acute antiarrhythmic activity of IP.[12] With regard to myocardial stunning, most researchers agree that early IP does not protect.[13] Experiments documenting the cardioprotective activities with SWOP have shown that it can reduce all forms of MI/R injury, including stunning, infarction, and arrhythmia.[7,14,15] However, when comparing the degree of protection against infarction given by the early and late phases of IP in same animal models, various labs have found that the late protective effects are less efficacious than the early protective effects.[6,16]

MECHANISMS OF ACTION FOR ISCHEMIA-INDUCED PRECONDITIONING

Since the first window of IP was initially discovered, more is known about the mechanism of action for the early phase of IP. There is much evidence that endogenous adenosine released from ischemic myocardium as a product of ATP degradation plays an important role in this phenomenon.[10] In a rabbit myocardial infarct model, the adenosine receptor antagonist 8-(*p*-sulfophenyl)-theophylline completely blocked the ability of IP to salvage myocardium, while administration of adenosine could mimic IP-mediated protection. Subsequent studies indicated that adenosine may mediate protection by coupling to phospholipase C (PLC) and/or phospholipase D (PLD), which led to activation of protein kinase C (PKC) via a Gi protein–coupled signal transduction pathway.[17] In addition to adenosine receptor activation, stimulation of other Gi-coupled receptors, including catecholamine, bradykinin, and opioid receptors, has also been proposed in various species to be involved in or mimic the early phase of IP.[18–21] Protein kinase C (PKC) activation or translocation has been proposed as the common downstream signal transduction element of these receptors in cardiomyocytes.[22] Free radicals, such as nitric oxide, generated during IP may also play key roles in mediating cardioprotection.[22,23] Nitric oxide and other free radical species have been noted to trigger PKC activation in the cell, which explains their role in IP signaling.[24] Other kinases such as protein tyrosine kinase (PTK), MAP kinase, and MAPKAP kinase 2 have also been shown to be stimulated by IP.[25] Using an isolated working rat heart model, Maulik and colleagues have demonstrated that the PTK inhibitor, genistin, would not only completely block the beneficial effects of IP, but also inhibit downstream activation of PKC, MAP kinase, and MAPKAP kinase by IP, indicating that PTK activation may occur relatively early in the signal transduction pathway. If PKC serves as the common signal transduction pathway for IP, what remains to be determined is the end effector that PKC acts on to elicit the final cardioprotective effects. Results from many studies have suggested that the ATP-dependent potassium channel (K_{ATP}) may be the end effector. Gross and Auchampach have shown that channel closure with glibenclamide could block the protection of IP and that opening K_{ATP} channel pharmacologically could mimic the effects of IP.[9] Cardioprotective adenosine, opioid, and bradykinin receptor agonists have also been shown to activate K_{ATP} channel.[17,20] Moreover, the cardioprotective effects of the abovementioned pharmacologic preconditioning agents can also be eliminated by K_{ATP} channel blockers.[26]

With regard to the mechanisms responsible for IP-delayed cardioprotection, new protein synthesis triggered during the short preconditioning ischemia has been proposed in the literature to be involved. Induction of cytoprotective heat shock protein (e.g., HSP70), antioxidant enzymes (e.g., MnSOD), and possibly inducible NO synthase (iNOS) has been proposed to mediate SWOP.[27] Bolli and colleagues found that they could not induce SWOP in the iNOS knockout mouse while they could with the analogous wild-type strain (personal communication, Dr. Robert Bolli, University of Louisville, Louisville, KY). Adenosine receptor stimulation, formation of oxygen-derived free radicals, and NO burst during or shortly after the brief ischemia have all been suggested to play roles as triggers of SWOP. Adenosine receptor blockers, free radical scavengers, and NOS inhibitors given right before or during the brief ischemia could abolish protection by SWOP.[15,28,29] Activation of gene transcription by these mediators through NFκB may work through the same signal transduction pathway (e.g., activation of PKC) as suggested for the induction of acute PC.[30] As with acute IP, Bernardo and colleagues have shown that the activity of K_{ATP} channels is also required by SWOP, which suggests that acute and delayed IP may share a common end effector.[31]

Attendant with the observation and investigation of the ischemia-mediated stress adaptation response has been an effort to develop pharmacologic methods to enhance myocardial ischemic tolerance. Evaluations of extensive clinical databases suggest that myocardial infarction stunning and arrhythmias frequently occur in association with ischemia and reperfusion inherent in procedures requiring aortic cross clamping or cardiopulmonary bypass.[32,33] The occurrence of these complications has been correlated with increased incidence of morbidity, mortality, and prolonged hospitalization in cardiac surgery patients.[34]

ENDOTOXIN: AN INDUCER OF DELAYED ISCHEMIC TOLERANCE

Numerous pharmacologic cardioprotectants have been evaluated in preclinical models; one such agent is endotoxin. In a rabbit infarction model, within the narrow dose range of 5 to 10 μg/kg, endotoxin reduced infarct size when administered 24 h before ischemia.[35] Protection was associated with HSP 72, but not catalase, induction. Others demonstrated improved global contractility and aortic flow in isolated working rat hearts subjected to global ischemia-reperfusion 24 h following intravenous administration of 500 μg/kg endotoxin.[36] Cardioprotection was associated with oxidative stress acutely following endotoxin dosing and enhanced antioxidant reserves the day after dosing. In spite of these and other intriguing reports, the narrow therapeutic index of endotoxin precludes its serious consideration as a cardioprotective compound for inducing delayed ischemic tolerance.

Monophosphoryl lipid A (MLA) is an amphipathic polyesterified diglucosamine monophosphate derivative of lipid A; the latter being the minimal substructural pharmacophore of endotoxin.[37] MLA is apparently devoid of endotoxin's undesirable ability to cause diffuse intravascular coagulation, neutrophil activation, and multiorgan failure. Pyrogenicity and ability to promote release of proinflammatory cytokines is also significantly lower with MLA.[38] It has been demonstrated that MLA can be safely administered to humans at doses up to at least 20 μg/kg.[39] Investigations were therefore undertaken to determine if MLA displayed cardioprotective activity against ischemia-reperfusion injury in preclinical and clinical settings.

PRETREATMENT WITH MONOPHOSPHORYL LIPID A ENHANCES MYOCARDIAL ISCHEMIC TOLERANCE IN A BIPHASIC FASHION

Single intravenous bolus dosing with MLA in the rabbit model of *in situ* regional ischemia has been demonstrated to reduce infarct size following 3 or 48 h of reperfu-

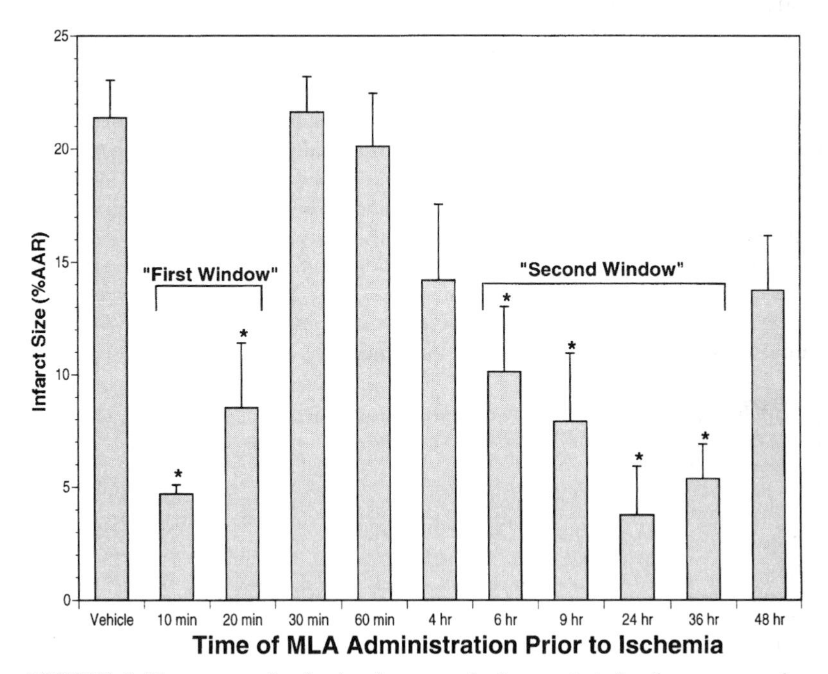

FIGURE 1. Time course for the development of tolerance to infarction, expressed as a percent of area at risk (%AAR), following regional myocardial ischemia-reperfusion in rabbits administered a single 35 μg/kg bolus dose of MLA at various times before ischemia. A biphasic pharmacodynamic profile of cardioprotection is apparent. *$p < 0.05$ versus vehicle control. All values are mean ± SEM.

sion.[40,41] Interestingly, a biphasic profile of cardioprotective activity has been reported, with ischemic tolerance observed in the rabbit 10–20 min following dosing and with protection reappearing 6–36 h following administration of a single 35 μg/kg dose of MLA (FIG. 1). This observation of an acute and delayed window of protection with MLA is similar to that reported following ischemic preconditioning[7] or adenosine A_1 receptor agonist administration.[42] Presently, more is now known about the manifestations of protection and mechanism of action of the delayed cardioprotective effect of MLA than about the first window of protection. Consequently, this review will first focus on MLA's delayed cardioprotective effect.

DELAYED CARDIOPROTECTIVE ACTIVITY OF MONOPHOSPHORYL LIPID A

In addition to the rabbit, dog models have demonstrated that MLA doses of 10–100 μg/kg reduce infarct size following regional *in situ* myocardial ischemia in dogs 24 h but not 1 h following bolus administration.[43] In a porcine model of regional *in situ* ischemia followed by global normothermic ischemia during cardiopulmonary bypass, infarct size reduction was also observed 24 h following pretreatment with MLA.[44] In a murine Langendorff model of global ischemia, a 24-h single dose (350 μg/kg) pretreatment with MLA reduces infarct size.[45]

Following repetitive cycles of transient *in situ* ischemia, administration of MLA 24 h but not 1 h before ischemia reduces myocardial stunning immediately following ischemia and improves recovery of regional contractility during reperfusion (FIG. 2).[46] Improvement in left ventricular global function has also been observed in a rabbit model of prolonged *in situ* regional ischemia and reperfusion.[47] In a rabbit rapid pacing model, improvement in left ventricular end diastolic pressure, maintenance of mean arterial pressure following pacing, and reversal of ECG ST segment abnormalities during pacing were observed in MLA-pretreated animals.[48]

In the chloralose-urethane anesthetized dog, pretreatment with a single dose of MLA (10–100 μg/kg) was associated with dose-responsive reduction in the incidence and/or frequency of premature ventricular contractions and ventricular tachycardia during occlusion and in the incidence of fibrillation during reperfusion,

TABLE 1. Antiarrhythmic effect of MLA pretreatment after 25 minutes LAD occlusion and sudden reperfusion in dogs

	Ischemia				Reperfusion	
Treatment	PVCs	Incidence VT	Episodes of VT	Incidence VF	Incidence VF	Survival
Vehicle Control	260 ± 77	63%	12 ± 5	44	81%	19%
MLA 10 μg/kg	89 ± 60[a]	25%[a]	1.1 ± 1.1[a]	13[a]	75%	25%
MLA 100 μg/kg	28 ± 26[a]	25%	1.6 ± 1.5[a]	12[a]	50%	50%[a]

NOTATION: PVC, premature ventricular contraction; VT, ventricular tachycardia; VF, ventricular fibrillation.

[a] $p < 0.05$ versus control.

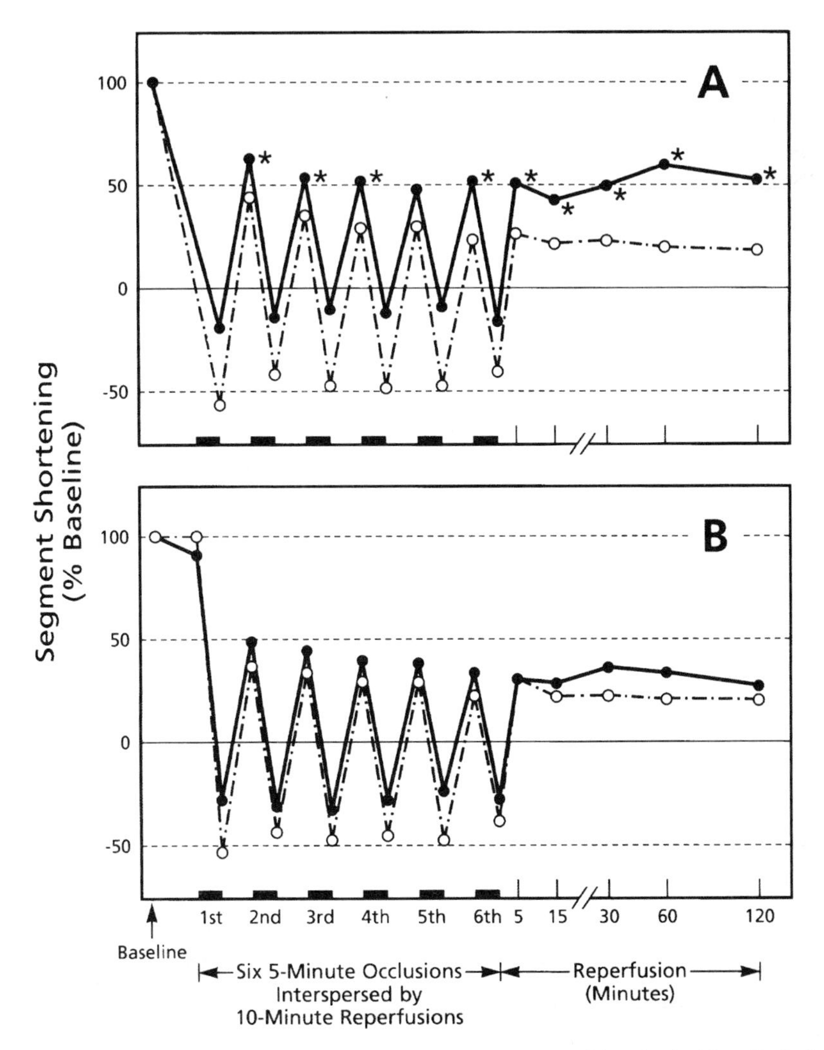

FIGURE 2. Ability of a 1-h (**A**) or 24-h (**B**) pretreatment with a single 35 μg/kg bolus dose of MLA (●) to improve recovery of regional ventricular contractility in dogs (segment shortening as % of baseline) versus vehicle control (○). *$p < 0.05$ versus vehicle control.

resulting in a significant improvement in survival at the higher MLA dose (TABLE 1).[49,50]

Incubation of primary rat cardiomyocyte cultures with MLA (200 ng/ml) for 4 h followed by washout and subsequent incubation for 20 h in drug-free media is associated with protection from cell death upon "simulated ischemic" challenge.[51] Release of LDH and CK was reduced when drug-treated cells were incubated in media containing 10 mM 2-deoxy-D-glucose and 2 mM lactic acid for 2 hours.

Pretreatment with MLA 6–24 h before myocardial ischemia has been demonstrated in various animal models to enhance tolerance to ischemia-reperfusion injury. Demonstration with MLA pretreatment of a delayed time course for the development of ischemic tolerance as well as observation of protection against infarction, myocardial stunning, and ventricular arrhythmias is reminiscent of features of the SWOP observed following ischemic preconditioning.

MONOPHOSPHORYL LIPID A MECHANISM FOR INDUCTION OF DELAYED ISCHEMIC TOLERANCE

A considerable number of investigations have been undertaken to illustrate potential mechanisms by which MLA induces delayed tolerance to ischemia-reperfusion injury. A recent review inclusively summarizes most published investigations.[52] Classic pharmacologic antagonism studies have been conducted with the ATP-sensitive potassium (K_{ATP}) channel blockers glibenclamide and 5-hydroxydecanonate (5-HD). In these experiments MLA is "administered" to rabbits, dogs, or isolated rat cardiomyocytes 24 h before "ischemia," and the K_{ATP} channel blocker within 1 h of "ischemic" challenge. In the dog, glibenclamide and 5-HD blocked MLA-mediated infarct size reduction,[53] an observation also reported in the rabbit (FIG. 3).[54,55] Glibenclamide blocks the ability of MLA pretreatment to improve regional ventricular

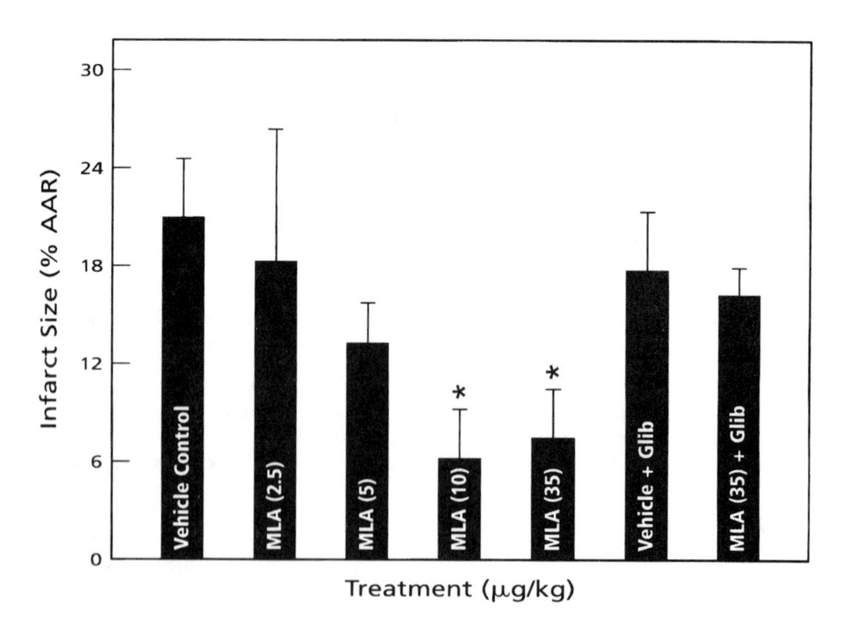

FIGURE 3. Ability of a single dose (2.5, 5, 10, or 35 μg/kg) of MLA administered 24 h before regional myocardial ischemia to reduce infarct size (IF) expressed as a percent of the area at risk (AAR) in the rabbit. Glibenclamide (GLB, 0.3 mg/kg) given 15 min before ischemia completely blocked MLA cardioprotection. *$p < 0.05$ versus vehicle controls. All values are mean ± SEM.

contractility (percent segment shortening) following repetitive brief cycles of ischemia-reperfusion.[56] The cytoprotective activity against LDH release of an *in vitro* 24-h pretreatment of adult rat cardiomyocytes with MLA can also be blocked by incubation of cells in glibenclamide or 5-HD during "simulated ischemia."[57]

Insight into a rationale for how MLA could in a delayed fashion induce tolerance to ischemia-reperfusion through a mechanism dependent on activation of myocardial K_{ATP} channels came as a result of investigations into nitric oxide metabolism. In the rabbit infarct model, it was demonstrated that cardioprotection associated with a 24-h MLA pretreatment could be blocked via the administration of the inducible nitric oxide synthase (iNOS) selective inhibitor aminoguanidine.[58] It was further reported that giving cardioprotective doses of MLA to rabbits was associated with significant activation of myocardial iNOS enzyme activity upon ischemic challenge. These observations were subsequently supported by studies conducted in the isolated working rat heart and intact porcine and dog infarct models.[44,59] In both the rat and porcine models, augmentation of myocardial iNOS mRNA as detected by Northern blot analysis was observed 4-8 h following administration to animals of cardioprotective doses of MLA. In the pig infarct model, a dose-responsive induction of

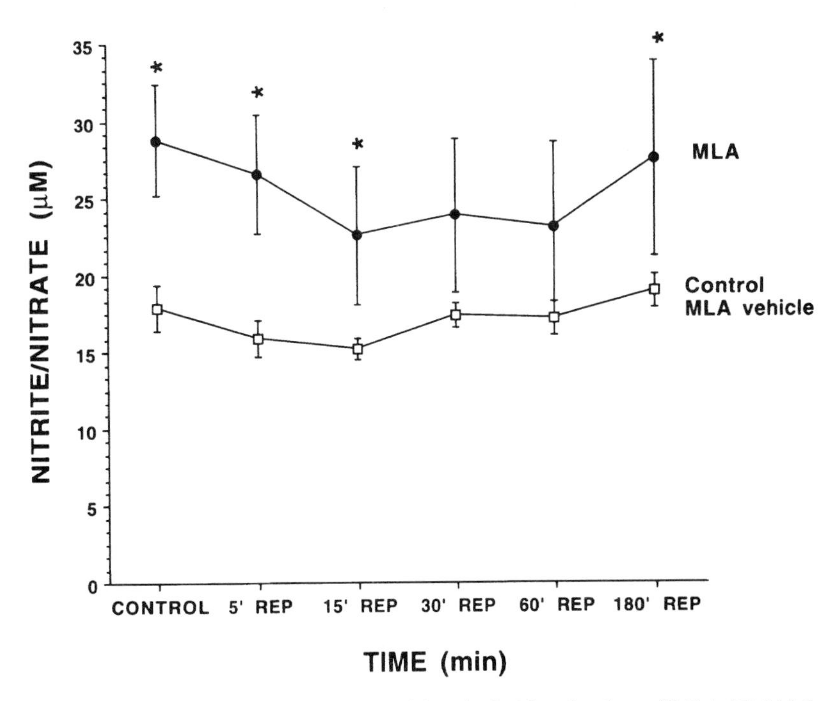

FIGURE 4. The effect of pretreatment with a single 35 μg/kg dose of MLA (●) 24 h before regional myocardial ischemia in dogs to increase plasma coronary venous nitrate concentration (μM) compared with controls (□). Measurements were made before ischemia and at 5, 15, 30, 60, and 180 min of reperfusion (REP). All values are mean ± SEM. *$p < 0.05$ versus vehicle control.

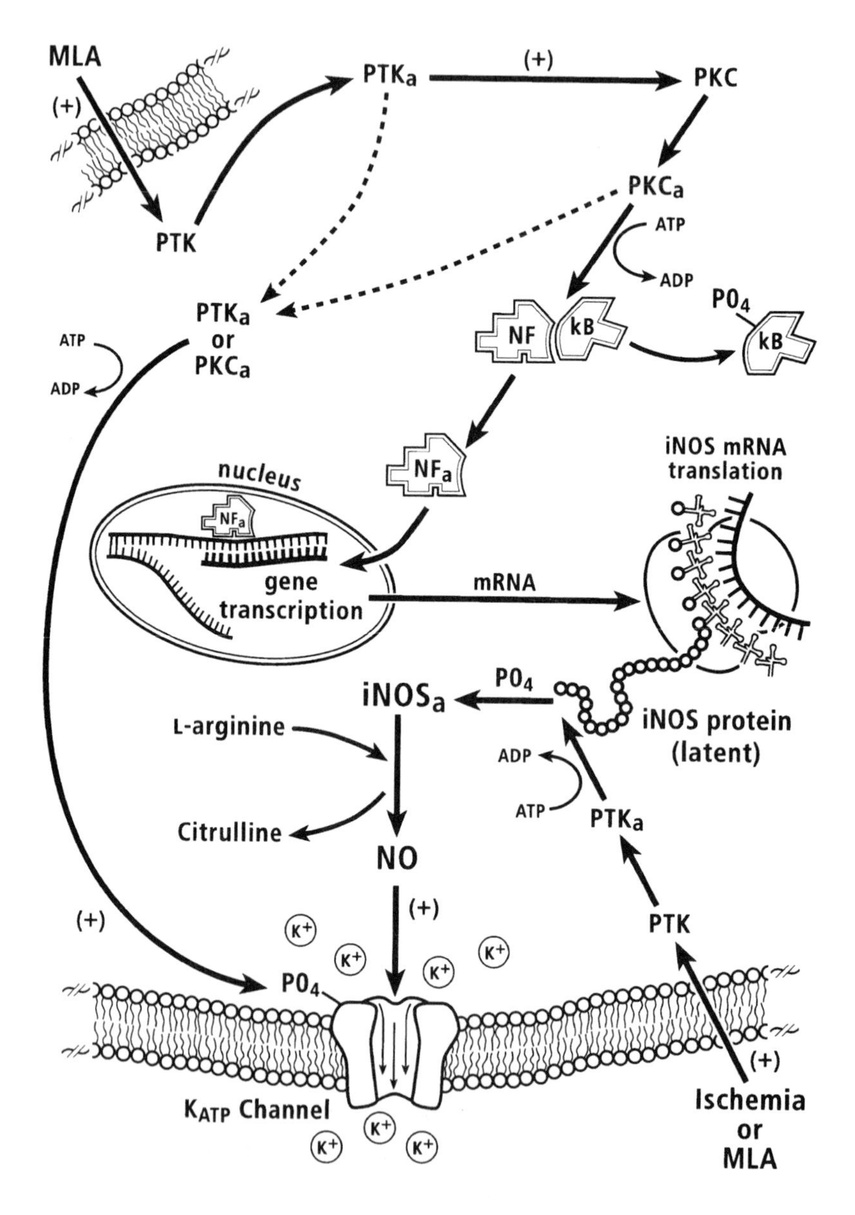

FIGURE 5. Schematic for the proposed mechanism of MLA-induced delayed and acute cardioprotective activity. Delayed cardioprotection appears to require myocardial iNOS protein synthesis with nitric oxide signaling during ischemia coupling to K_{ATP} channels in cardiomyocytes. Acute cardioprotection also ultimately requires K_{ATP} channel activation, possibly as a result of phosphorylation and activation of constitute pools of NOS or via direct phosphorylation of K_{ATP} channels.

iNOS mRNA signaling was noted with the more cardioprotective 35 μg/kg dose generating a stronger iNOS signal than the less efficacious dose of 10 μg/kg. Additionally, in the isolated working rat heart the nonselective inhibitor of nitric oxide synthase, L-nitro-arginine-methyl ester (L-NAME) blocked the ability of MLA to sustain left ventricular function in the face of ischemia-reperfusion. In the canine myocardial infarct model, administration of cardioprotective doses of MLA was associated with elevated concentrations of plasma nitrite/nitrate in coronary vein (FIG. 4). An investigation to evaluate the ability of MLA to reduce infarct size in a murine Langendorff model of infarction using iNOS knockout and wild-type strains of mice has confirmed the importance of iNOS in MLA-delayed cardioprotection.[45]

It has been reported that post-translational regulation of iNOS activity by endotoxin may be modulated by a tyrosine kinase–dependent mechanism.[60] We previously demonstrated that the ability of lipid A analogs such as MLA to induce cytokine elaborations from monocytic cell lines is a tyrosine kinase–dependent process. Administration of the tyrosine kinase inhibitor genistin just prior to ischemia blocked delayed MLA cardioprotection in the rabbit infarct model and correspondingly prevented MLA-dependent activation of myocardial iNOS during ischemia, thought to be important in causing MLA ischemic tolerance.[61]

A link between nitric oxide and K_{ATP} channel activation is also suggested by Cameron and colleagues.[62] Nitric oxide donors have been demonstrated *in vitro* to increase ventricular myocyte K_{ATP} channel open-state probability, as measured by patch clamp. It is possible that MLA induces synthesis of myocardial iNOS; possibly in a latent form in the rabbit, if not so in the dog. Subsequent ischemic challenge may result in tyrosine kinase–dependent phosphorylation and activation of this MLA-induced iNOS pool, resulting in augmented nitric oxide–dependent activation of myocardial K_{ATP} channel. This signaling pathway may at least in part explain the mechanism by which MLA induces delayed tolerance to ischemia-reperfusion injury.

MECHANISM OF MONOPHOSPHORYL LIPID A INDUCED ACUTE CARDIOPROTECTION

Considerably less is presently understood regarding the mechanism by which MLA acutely causes ischemic tolerance. It has been demonstrated in the rabbit infarct model that administration of glibenclamide immediately before ischemia blocks the ability of a simultaneously administered dose of MLA to reduce infarct size.[63] These results suggest that, as with delayed cardioprotection, the acute protective activity of MLA involves activation of K_{ATP} channel. Work is presently underway to investigate the potential role of nitric oxide in acute ischemic tolerance induction with MLA. A schematic illustration of a hypothesis for the mechanism of MLA acute and delayed cardioprotection is depicted in FIGURE 5. Regarding acute cardioprotection, it is proposed that MLA's known ability to rapidly activate kinases of the PTK and PKC class may lead to downstream phosphorylation of K_{ATP} channel. Phosphorylation of myocardial K_{ATP} channel appears to promote opening of the channel, possibly in response to G protein–coupled receptor agonists such as adenosine.[64,65] Alternatively, MLA may cause acute cardioprotection via phosphorylation of constitutive pools of nitric oxide synthase, as has been reported for endotoxin,[60] ultimately resulting in nitric oxide–mediated K_{ATP} channel activation.

CONCLUSIONS

In comparison with ischemic preconditioning, MLA-mediated cardioprotection seems to show numerous common features. Like ischemia, MLA induces a first and second window (biphasic profile) of heightened tolerance to ischemia. As with delayed ischemic preconditioning, MLA protects against infarction, stunning, and arrhythmias associated with ischemia-reperfusion. In contrast with acute ischemic preconditioning where protection against infarction and possibly arrhythmias but not against stunning have been reported, MLA reduces infarction and stunning. A role has been demonstrated for nitric oxide synthase and K_{ATP} channel activation in the mechanism of delayed preconditioning induced by ischemia and by MLA. Finally, regarding acute preconditioning, kinase and K_{ATP} channel activation have been implicated as involved in the mechanism of ischemic preconditioning and also in MLA cardioprotection.

Use of MLA or related compounds as cardioprotectants may represent a method for inducing acute tolerance to ischemia-reperfusion injury manifested as infarction or stunning, with the added benefit of a sustained delayed cardioprotective state being achieved.

REFERENCES

1. BRAUNWALD, E. & R.A. KLONER. 1985. Myocardial reperfusion: a double-edged sword? J. Clin. Invest. **75:** 1713–1719.
2. GRACE, P.A. 1994. Ischaemia-reperfusion injury. Br. J. Surg. **81:** 637–647.
3. MURRY, C.E., R.B. JENNINGS & K.A. REIMER. 1986. Preconditioning with ischemia: a delay of lethal cell injury in ischemic myocardium. Circulation **74**(5)**:** 1124–1136.
4. KLONER, R.A. & D.M. YELLON. 1994. Does ischemic preconditioning occur in patients? J. Am. Coll. Cardiol. **24:** 1133–1142.
5. VAN WINKLE, D.M., J.D. THORTON, J.M. DOWNEY & D.M. DOWNEY. 1991. The natural history of preconditioning: cardioprotection depends on duration of transient ischemia and time to subsequent ischemia. Coronary Artery Dis. **2:** 613–619.
6. KUZUYA, T., S. HOSHIDA, N. YAMASHITA, H. FUJI, H. OE, M. HORI, T. KAMADA & M. TADA. 1993. Delayed effects of sublethal ischemia on the acquisition of tolerance to ischemia. Circ. Res. **72:** 1293–1299.
7. MARBER, M.S., D.S. LATCHMAN, J.M. WALKER & D.M. YELLON. 1993. Cardiac stress protein elevation 24 hours after brief ischemia or heat stress is associated with resistance to myocardial infarction. Circulation **88:** 1264–1272.
8. SZEKERES, L., J.G. PAPP, Z. SZILVASSY, E. UDVARY & A. VEGH. 1993. Moderate stress by cardiac pacing may induce both short term and long term cardioprotection. Cardiovasc. Res. **27**(4)**:** 593–596.
9. GROSS, G.J. & J.A. AUCHAMPACH. 1992. Blockade of ATP-sensitive potassium channels prevents myocardial preconditioning in dogs. Circ. Res. **70**(2)**:** 223–233.
10. LIU, G.S., J. THORNTON, D.M. VAN WINKLE, A. W.H. STANLEY, R.A. OLSSON & J.M. DOWNEY. 1991. Protection against infarction afforded by preconditioning is mediated by A1 adenosine receptors in rabbit heart. Circulation **84**(4)**:** 350–356.
11. VEGH, A., L. SZEKERES & J.R. PARRATT. 1990. Protective effects of preconditioning of the ischaemic myocardium involve cyclo-oxygenase products. Cardiovasc Res. **24:** 1020–1023.
12. PRZYKLENK, K. & R.A. KLONER. 1995. Preconditioning: a balanced perspective [editorial]. Br. Heart J. **74**(6)**:** 575–577.
13. OVIZE, M., K. PRZYKLENK, S.L. HALE & R.A. KLONER. 1992. Preconditioning does not attenuate myocardial stunning. Circulation **85**(6)**:** 2247–2254.

14. YANG, X.-M., G.F. BAXTER, R.J. HEADS, D.M. YELLON, J.M. DOWNEY & M.V. COHEN. 1996. Infarct limitation of the second window of protection in a conscious rabbit model. Cardiovasc. Res. **31:** 777–783.
15. BOLLI, R., Z.A. BHATTI, X.L. TANG, Y. QIU, Q. ZHANG, Y. GUO & A.K. JADOON. 1997. Evidence that late preconditioning against myocardial stunning in conscious rabbits is triggered by the generation of nitric oxide. Circ. Res. **81**(1)**:** 42–52.
16. QIU, Y., X.L. TANG, S.W. PARK, J.Z. SUN, A. KALYA & R. BOLLI. 1997. The early and late phases of ischemic preconditioning: a comparative analysis of their effects on infarct size, myocardial stunning, and arrhythmias in conscious pigs undergoing a 40-minute coronary occlusion. Circ. Res. **80**(5)**:** 730–742.
17. DOWNEY, J.M. & M.V. COHEN. 1995. Signal transduction in ischemic preconditioning. Z. Kardiol. **84**(Suppl 4)**:** 77–86.
18. GOTO, M., Y. LIU, X.M. YANG, J.L. ARDELL, M.V. COHEN & J.M. DOWNEY. 1995. Role of bradykinin in protection of ischemic preconditioning in rabbit hearts. Circ. Res. **77**(3)**:** 611–621.
19. RONGEN, G.A., P. SMITS, T. THIEN, C.F. TOOMBS & A.L. WILTSE. 1994. Role of norepinephrine in ischemic preconditioning in rabbit myocardium and reply. Circulation **89**(5)**:** 2460–2461.
20. SCHULTZ, J.E., E. ROSE, Z. YAO & G.J. GROSS. 1995. Evidence for involvement of opioid receptors in ischemic preconditioning in rat hearts. Am. J. Physiol. **268**(5 Pt 2)**:** H2157–H2161.
21. SCHULTZ, J.E., A.K. HSU, H. NAGASE & G.J. GROSS. 1998. TAN-67, a delta 1-opioid receptor agonist, reduces infarct size via activation of Gi/o proteins and KATP channels. Am. J. Physiol. **274**(3 Pt 2)**:** H909–H914.
22. DOWNEY, J.M. & M.V. COHEN. 1997. Signal transduction in ischemic preconditioning. Adv. Exp. Med. Biol. **430:** 39–55.
23. HARTMAN, J.C., H. HOUSHYAR, S.C. LEVA & T.M. WALL. 1995. A role of nitric oxide in myocardial ischemic preconditioning. [Abstract] Circulation **92**(8)**:** I–716.
24. GOPALAKRISHNA, R. & W.B. ANDERSON. 1989. Ca^{2+}- and phospholipid-independent activation of protein kinase C by selective oxidative modification of the regulatory domain. Proc. Natl. Acad. Sci. USA **86**(17)**:** 6758–6762.
25. MAULIK, N., M. WATANABE, Y.L. ZU, C.K. HUANG, G.A. CORDIS, J.A. SCHLEY & D.K. DAS. 1996. Ischemic preconditioning triggers the activation of MAP kinases and MAPKAP kinase 2 in rat hearts. FEBS Lett. **396**(2-3)**:** 233–237.
26. GROSS, G.J. 1995. Do ATP-sensitive potassium channels play a role in myocardial stunning? Basic Res. Cardiol. **90**(4)**:** 266–268.
27. YELLON, D.M. & G.F. BAXTER. 1995. A "second window of protection" or delayed preconditioning phenomenon: future horizons for myocardial protection? J. Mol. Cell Cardiol. **27**(4)**:** 1023–1034.
28. SUN, J.Z., X.L. TANG, S.W. PARK, Y.M. QIU, J.F. TURRENS & R. BOLLI. 1996. Evidence for an essential role of reactive oxygen species in the genesis of late preconditioning against myocardial stunning in conscious pigs. J. Clin. Invest. **97**(2)**:** 562–576.
29. BAXTER, G.F., M.S. MARBE, V.C. PATEL & D.M. YELLON. 1993. A "second window of protection" 24 hours after ischemic preconditioning may be dependent upon adenosine receptor activation. [Abstract] Circulation **88:** I-101.
30. BAXTER, G.F., F.M. GOMA & D.M. YELLON. 1994. Possible involvement of protein kinase C signalling in the "second window of protection" following ischemic preconditioning. Circulation **90**(4Pt2)**:** I-647, #3482.
31. BERNARDO, N.L., M. D'ANGELO, P.V. DESAI, J.E. LEVASSEUR & R.C. KUKREJA. 1997. ATP-sensitive potassium (KATP) channel is involved in the second window of ischemic preconditioning in rabbit. [Abstract] J. Mol. Cell Cardiol. **29:** A228.
32. MANGANO, D.T. 1995. Cardiovascular morbidity and CABG surgery—a perspective: epidemiology, costs, and potential therapeutic solutions. J. Card. Surg. **10**(4)**:** 366–368.
33. LEUNG, J.M., B. O'KELLY, W.S. BROWNER, J. TUBAU, M. HOLLENBERG & D.T. MANGANO. 1989. Prognostic importance of postbypass regional wall-motion abnormali-

ties in patients undergoing coronary artery bypass graft surgery. SPI Research Group. Anesthesiology **71**(1): 16–25.
34. Lazar, H.L., C. Fitzgerald, S. Gross, T. Heeren, G.S. Aldea & R.J. Shemin. 1995. Determinants of length of stay after coronary artery bypass graft surgery. Circulation **92**(Suppl): II20–II24.
35. Rowland, R.T., J.C. Cleveland, X. Meng, L. Ao, A.H. Harken & J.M. Brown. 1996. A single endotoxin challenge induces delayed myocardial protection against infarction. J. Surg. Res. **63**(1): 193–198.
36. Maulik, N., M. Watanabe, D. Engelman, R.M. Engelman, V.E. Kagan, E. Kisin, V. Tyurin, G.A. Cordis & D.K. Das. 1995. Myocardial adaptation to ischemia by oxidative stress induced by endotoxin. Am. J. Physiol. **269:** C907–C916.
37. Ribi, E. 1984. Beneficial modification of the endotoxin molecule. J. Biol. Resp. Modif. **3:** 1–9.
38. Myers, K., A. Truchot & J. Ward. 1990. A critical determinant of lipid A endotoxic activity. *In* Cellular and Molecular Aspects of Endotoxin. A. Nowotny, J. Spitzer & E. Ziegler, Eds.: 145–156. Elsevier. Amsterdam.
39. Astiz, M.E., E.C. Rackow, J.G. Still, S.T. Howell, A. Cato, K.B. Von Eschen, J. T. Ulrich, J.A. Rudbach, G. McMahon, R. Vargas & W. Stern. 1995. Pretreatment of normal humans with monophosphoryl lipid A induces tolerance to endotoxin: A prospective, double-blind, randomized, controlled trial. Crit. Care Med. **23**(1): 9–17.
40. Weber, P., M. Smart, M. Comerford, J. Smith, L. Zhao & G. Elliott. 1997. Monophosphoryl lipid A mimics both first and second window of ischemic preconditioning and preserves myocardial sarcoplasmic reticular calcium pump. [Abstract] J. Mol. Cell Cardiol. **29**(6): A233.
41. Cluff, C., M. Heindel & G.T. Elliott. 1998. Protection from cardiac ischemia/reperfusion injury after treatment of rabbits with monophosphoryl lipid A is durable. J. Mol. Cell Cardiol. **30**(6): A80.
42. Baxter, G.F. & D.M. Yellon. 1997. Time course of delayed myocardial protection after transient adenosine A1-receptor activation in the rabbit. J. Cardiovasc. Pharmacol. **29**(5): 631–638.
43. Yao, Z., J.L. Rasmussen, J.L. Hirt, D.A. Mei, G.M. Pieper & G.J. Gross. 1993. Effects of monophosphoryl lipid A on myocardial ischemia/reperfusion injury in dogs. J. Cardiovasc. Pharmacol. **22:** 653–663.
44. Yoshida, T., J.A. Rousou, J.E.I. Flack, M.G. Barot, G.T. Elliott, N. Maulik, D. Das & R.M. Engelman. 1997. Induction of iNOS expression by monophosphoryl lipid A: a pharmacological approach of ischemic preconditioning of swine hearts undergoing open heart surgery. [Abstract] Circulation **96**(8): I–620.
45. Xi, L., N.C. Jarrett, M.L. Hess & R.C. Kukreja. 1999. Role of inducible nitric oxide synthase (iNOS) in MLA-induced late cardioprotection: evidence from pharmacological inhibition and gene knockout mice. Circulation. In press.
46. Yao, Z., G.T. Elliott & G.J. Gross. 1995. Monophosphoryl lipid A preserves myocardial contractile function following multiple, brief periods of coronary occlusion in dogs. Pharmacology **51:** 152–159.
47. Zhao, L., C. Kirsch, S.R. Hagen & G.T. Elliott. 1996. Preservation of global cardiac function in the rabbit following protracted ischemia/reperfusion using monophosphoryl lipid A (MLA). J. Mol. Cell Cardiol. **28:** 197–208.
48. Szilvássy, Z., P. Ferdinandy, C.W. Cluff & G.T. Elliott. 1998. Anti-ischaemic effect of monophosphoryl lipid A in conscious rabbits with hypercholesterolaemia and atherosclerosis. J. Cardiovasc. Pharmacol. **32**(2): 206–212.
49. Vegh, A., K. Gyorgyi, J.G. Papp, G.T. Elliott & J.R. Parratt. 1997. Delayed protection against ventricular arrhythmias by monophosphoryl lipid-A in a canine model of ischaemia and reperfusion. Eur. J. Pharmacol. In press.
50. Vegh, A., J.G. Papp, G.T. Elliott & J.R. Parratt. 1996. Pretreatment with monophosphoryl lipid A reduces ischemia reperfusion-induced arrhythmias in dogs. [Abstract] J. Mol. Cell Cardiol. **28:** A56.
51. Nayeem, M.A., G.T. Elliott, M.R. Shah, S.L. Hastillo-Hess & R.C. Kukreja. 1997. Monophosphoryl lipid A protects adult rat cardiac myocytes with induction

of the 72-kD heat shock protein: a cellular model of pharmacologic preconditioning. J. Mol. Cell Cardiol. **29**(8): 2305–2310.
52. ELLIOTT, G.T. 1998. Monophosphoryl lipid A induces delayed preconditioning against cardiac ischemia-reperfusion injury [In Process Citation]. J. Mol. Cell Cardiol. **30**(1): 3–17.
53. MEI, D.A., G.T. ELLIOTT & G.J. GROSS. 1996. K_{ATP} channels mediate late preconditioning against infarction produced by monophosphoryl lipid A. Am. J. Physiol. **271**(40): H2723–H2729.
54. ELLIOTT, G.T., M.L. COMERFORD, J.R. SMITH & L. ZHAO. 1996. Myocardial ischemia/reperfusion protection using monophosphoryl lipid A is abrogated by the ATP-sensitive potassium channel blocker glibenclamide. Cardiovasc. Res. **32:** 1071–1080.
55. JANIN, Y., Y.-Z. QIAN, J.B. HOAG, G.T. ELLIOTT & R.C. KUKREJA. 1998. Pharmacologic preconditioning with monophosphoryl lipid A is abolished by 5-hydroxydecanoate, a specific inhibitor of the K_{ATP} channel. J. Cardiovasc. Res. **32**(3): 337–342.
56. GROSS, G.J., G.T. ELLIOTT & D.A. MEI. 1997. Late preconditioning (PC) against myocardial stunning produced by monophosphoryl lipid A (MLA) is mediated via the K_{ATP} channel. [Abstract] J. Mol. Cell Cardiol. A229.
57. NAYEEM, M.A., N.L. BERNARDO, G.T. ELLIOTT & R.C. KUKREJA. 1997. Delayed preconditioning by heat shock or monophosphoryl lipid A in cultured myocytes is mediated by K_{ATP} channel. [Abstract] J. Mol. Cell Cardiol. **29:** I231.
58. ZHAO, L., P.A. WEBER, J.R. SMITH, M.L. COMERFORD & G.T. ELLIOTT. 1997. Role of inducible nitric oxide synthase in pharmacological "preconditioning" with monophosphoryl lipid A. J. Mol. Cell Cardiol. **29:** 1567–1576.
59. TOSAKI, A., N. MAULIK, G.T. ELLIOTT, R.M. ENGELMAN & D.K. DAS. 1998. Preconditioning of rat heart with monophosphoryl lipid A: A role for nitric oxide. J. Pharmacol. Exp. Ther. **285**(3): 1274–1279.
60. PAN, J., K.L. BURGHER, A.M. SZCZEPANIK & G.E. RINGHEIM. 1996. Tyrosine phosphorylation of inducible nitric oxide synthase: implications for potential post-translational regulation. Biochem. J. **314**(Pt 3): 889–894.
61. ZHAO, L., P.A. WEBER, M.L. COMERFORD & G.T. ELLIOTT. 1997. Potential role of tyrosine phosphorylation of myocardial inducible nitric oxide synthase in delayed preconditioning by monophosphoryl lipid A (MLA). [Abstract] Circulation **96**(8): I-256.
62. CAMERON, J.S., K.K.A. KIBLER, H. BERRY, D.N. BARRON & V.H. SODDER. Nitric oxide activates ATP-sensitive potassium channels in hypertrophied ventricular myocytes. [Abstract] FASEB J. A65.
63. WEBER, P., M. COMERFORD, J. SMITH & G.T. ELLIOTT. 1998. Monophosphoryl lipid A (MLA) induces "first window" preconditioning which is blocked by glibenclamide. J. Mol. Cell Cardiol. **30**(6): A18.
64. HU, K., D. DUAN, G.-R. LI & S. NATTEL. 1996. Protein kinase C activates ATP-sensitive K^+ current in human and rabbit ventricular myocytes. Circ. Res. **78:** 492–498.
65. LIU, Y., W.D. GAO, B. O'ROURKE & E. MARBAN. 1996. Synergistic modulation of ATP-sensitive K^+ currents by protein kinase C and adenosine. Implications for ischemic preconditioning. Circ. Res. **78**(3): 443–454.

Adaptation to Chronic Hypoxia Confers Tolerance to Subsequent Myocardial Ischemia by Increased Nitric Oxide Production

JOHN E. BAKER,[a-d] PATRICIA HOLMAN,[a] B. KALYANARAMAN,[e] OWEN W. GRIFFITH,[c] AND KIRKWOOD A. PRITCHARD, JR.[f]

Departments of [a]Cardiothoracic Surgery, [c]Biochemistry, [e]Biophysics Institute, [f]Pathology, Medical College of Wisconsin, Milwaukee, Wisconsin 53226, USA
[b]Department of Cardiovascular Surgery, Children's Hospital of Wisconsin, Milwaukee, Wisconsin 53226, USA

ABSTRACT: Chronic exposure to hypoxia from birth increased the tolerance of the rabbit heart to subsequent ischemia compared with age-matched normoxic controls. The nitric oxide donor GSNO increased recovery of post-ischemic function in normoxic hearts to values not different from hypoxic controls, but had no effect on hypoxic hearts. The nitric oxide synthase inhibitors L-NAME and L-NMA abolished the cardioprotective effect of hypoxia. Message and catalytic activity for constitutive nitric oxide synthase as well as nitrite, nitrate, and cGMP levels were elevated in hypoxic hearts. Inducible nitric oxide synthase was not detected in normoxic or chronically hypoxic hearts. Increased tolerance to ischemia in rabbit hearts adapted to chronic hypoxia is associated with increased expression of constitutive nitric oxide synthase.

Each year, more than 25,000 children undergo corrective surgery for cardiac birth defects. Advances in surgical techniques have made possible the correction of nearly all congenital cardiac defects. Timing of surgery is critical with early surgery desirable to promote more normal development. For example, repair of tetralogy of Fallot is now generally recommended in the first 6 to 12 months of life and routine repair is now being advocated in the first month of life.[1–7] Many children undergoing cardiac surgery in the first year of life exhibit varying degrees of cyanotic heart disease where the myocardium is chronically perfused with hypoxic blood. Understanding the mechanisms by which cyanotic congenital heart disease modifies the myocardium and how that modification affects protective mechanics during ischemia may provide insight into developing treatments for limiting myocardial damage during surgery.

[f]Address correspondence to: John E. Baker, Ph.D., Department of Cardiothoracic Surgery, Medical College of Wisconsin, 8701 Watertown Plank Road, Milwaukee, Wisconsin 53226; Telephone: (414) 456-8706; Fax: (414) 453-9700; E-mail: jbaker@mcw.edu

To investigate the effects of chronic hypoxia on myocardial function and protection, we developed a rabbit model in which rabbit kits were raised in a hypoxic environment from birth. This model of hypoxia simulates the essential characteristics of cyanotic heart disease and has been used to demonstrate that hypoxia from birth increases tolerance to ischemia.[8] The mechanism by which prolonged hypoxia increases tolerance to subsequent ischemia remains unknown. The cardioprotective role of nitric oxide provides some insight into potential mechanisms. The nitric oxide donor S-nitrosoglutathione (GSNO), administered before global ischemia in isolated rat hearts, dramatically improved functional recovery after ischemia.[12] In contrast, the nitric oxide synthase inhibitors N^G-nitro-L-arginine methyl ester (L-NAME)[13] and N^ω-methyl-L-arginine (L-NMA)[14] decreased functional recovery after ischemia. Chronic hypoxia *in vivo* increases expression of nitric oxide synthase in lung.[9–11] However it is not known whether chronic hypoxia *in vivo* increases nitric oxide synthase expression in heart. Based on these findings, we reasoned that increased levels of endogenous nitric oxide may be responsible for protecting the myocardium against ischemia in chronically hypoxic hearts. The objectives of these studies were to determine (1) if chronic hypoxia from birth increases nitric oxide synthase expression and nitric oxide production and (2) if increased tolerance to ischemia in chronically hypoxic hearts is due to adaptive changes in NOS expression.

METHODS

Animals

Animals used in this study received humane care in compliance with the "Guide for the Care and Use of Laboratory Animals" formulated by the National Research Council in 1996.

Creation of Hypoxia from Birth

Pregnant New Zealand White rabbits were obtained from a commercial breeder. Throughout the study, the mother remained in a normoxic environment ($F_IO_2 = 0.21$). For the hypoxic studies, the kits were born in a normoxic environment and then transferred to a hypoxic environmental chamber ($F_IO_2 = 0.12$) immediately after their first feeding. The oxygen level in the chamber was maintained at $F_IO_2 = 0.12$ for 9 days. For the normoxic studies, the kits were raised under identical conditions except that F_IO_2 in the environmental chamber remained at 0.21 for the duration of the study. Previous studies described in detail how hypoxia from birth alters extracellular and intracellular changes as well as gross anatomy of the heart.[15]

Perfusion System

Isolated rabbit hearts were instrumented as previously described.[15] Heparin (150 IU/kg) was administered intraperitoneally before anesthesia. Anesthesia was induced and maintained with halothane (4% and 1–2%, respectively). After 1 min, the heart was rapidly excised and placed in cold (4°C) perfusion medium. Within 30 sec, the aorta was attached to a stainless-steel cannula and the pulmonary artery incised to permit adequate coronary drainage. The heart was then perfused at 39°C in the

Langendorff mode[16] at a perfusion pressure of 42 mm Hg, equivalent to the mean aortic pressure for the age of the animals at the time of study.[17] Saline-filled latex balloons (Biomedix, Elm Grove, WI) were placed in the left and right ventricular cavities and connected through rigid saline-filled catheters to separate pressure transducers. A three-way tap, located immediately above the site of cannulation, allowed the entire perfusate to be diverted away from the heart to produce global, no-flow ischemia. Reperfusion was achieved by repositioning the tap to allow perfusate to be delivered to the heart. The heart and perfusion fluids were immersed in non-gassed physiological saline solution within temperature-controlled chambers to maintain the myocardium at 39°C, normothermia for the rabbit.

Perfusion Media

The standard perfusate was modified Krebs-Henseleit bicarbonate buffer[18] (mmol/l): NaCl, 118.5; $NaHCO_3$, 25.0; KCl, 4.8; $MgSO_4 \cdot 6H_2O$, 1.2; KH_2PO_4, 1.2 (pH 7.4 when gassed with 95% O_2/5% CO_2) in which the calcium content was reduced to 1.8. Glucose (11.1 mmol/l) was added to the perfusate. Before use, all perfusion fluids were filtered through cellulose acetate membranes with pore size 5.0 µm to remove particulate matter. To this perfusate we added nitric oxide donors or nitric oxide synthase inhibitors as needed.

Assessment of Ventricular Function

Left and right ventricular function was monitored continuously throughout each experiment. A latex balloon filled with boiled and degassed saline was inserted into the left ventricle through an incision in the left atrium and secured in place with two 4-0 silk sutures, one in the mitral annulus and the other in the interatrial septum. This reliably held the balloon in place and prevented herniation through the mitral annulus. A second balloon was then inserted across the pulmonic valve into the right ventricle and secured in place with a ligature. Each balloon was slightly larger than the ventricular cavity. The balloons were then connected with rigid fluid-filled catheters to separate pressure transducers (Deseret Medical, Model 8148) for measurement of ventricular pressures and heart rate.

The transducer outputs were amplified with a universal signal conditioner (Model 20-4615-58, Gould, Cleveland, OH) and recorded on an analog chart recorder (Astromed, Providence, RI). End diastolic pressure was initially set to 3 mm Hg for 2 min, and developed pressure (systolic minus diastolic pressure) was measured during steady-state levels of function. The balloons were progressively inflated with a microsyringe to set end-diastolic pressures to 8 mm Hg for the left ventricle and 4 mm Hg for the right ventricle, and developed pressure was recorded during steady-state conditions. Coronary flow rate was measured throughout the experiment by timed collections of the coronary effluent from the right side of the heart into a graduated cylinder. Coronary flow rate was expressed as milliliters per minute.

Ischemia-Reperfusion Studies

Perfusion Sequence

The following experiments were performed in a random order using eight groups of nine hearts each to test the null hypothesis that tolerance to ischemia in rabbit

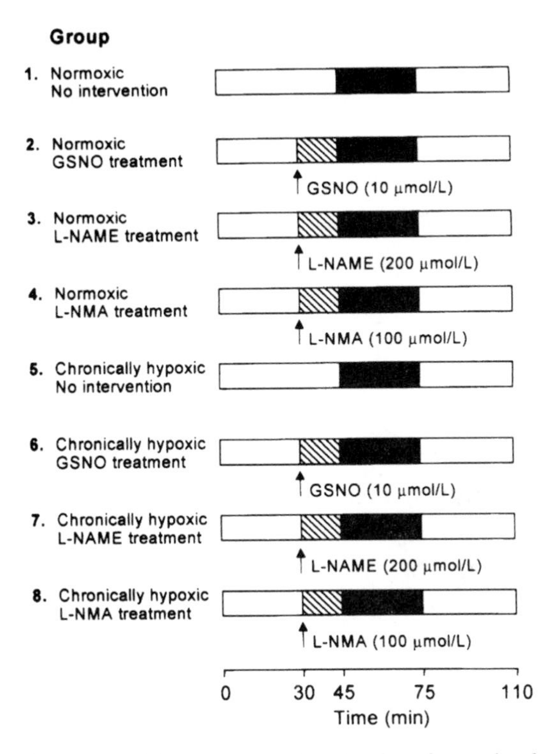

FIGURE 1. Illustration of the experimental protocol used to study adaptation to chronic hypoxia and nitric oxide upon tolerance to myocardial ischemia. Open boxes represent aerobic perfusion, hatched boxes represent aerobic perfusion with drug and closed boxes represent global ischemia.

hearts, either normoxic or hypoxic from birth, is not the result of changes in nitric oxide production. The eight experimental groups were: Group 1, normoxic, no intervention; Group 2, normoxic plus GSNO (10 μmol/l); Group 3, normoxic plus L-NAME (200 μmol/l); Group 4, normoxic plus L-NMA (100 μmol/l); Group 5, hypoxic, no intervention; Group 6, hypoxic plus GSNO (10 μmol/l); Group 7, hypoxic plus L-NAME (200 μmol/l); Group 8, hypoxic plus L-NMA (100 μmol/l). FIGURE 1 illustrates the experimental protocol. Immediately after aortic cannulation, hearts were perfused at constant pressure for 20 min with balloons placed in left and right ventricles. Biventricular function and coronary flow rate were recorded under steady-state conditions. Hearts were perfused with either a nitric oxide donor (GSNO, 10 μmol/l) or nitric oxide synthase inhibitors [L-NAME (200 μmol/l) or L-NMA (100 μmol/l)] for another 15 min before a 30-min period of global, no-flow ischemia. After ischemia, hearts were reperfused for 35 min and indices of cardiac function were measured under steady-state conditions. In this way each heart served as its own control. Dose-response studies (4 hearts/group) performed before these experiments indicated that these doses of GSNO, L-NAME, and L-NMA were optimal for increasing the recovery of left ventricular developed pressure in normoxic

TABLE 1. Hemodynamic values

	Group 1 Normoxic only	Group 2 Normoxic +GSNO	Group 3 Normoxic +L-NAME	Group 4 Normoxic + L-NMA	Group 5 Hypoxic only	Group 6 Hypoxic + GSNO	Group 7 Hypoxic + L-NAME	Group 8 Hypoxic + L-NMA
Pre-Drug								
HR	230±37	231 ±15	249±15	236 ±14	220±34	240±38	234±19	232±18
CRF	5±1[a]	6±2[a]	6±1	6±1	7±1	8±2	7±1	7±1
LVDP	101±9	96±6	97±9	100±8	100±8	91±11	99±7	99±6
RVDP	33±5	34±7	33±7	33±6	46±7[a]	43±6[a]	46±4[a]	46±4[a]
Post-Drug								
HR	—	270±42	236±37	226±32	—	285±41[b]	210±12	220±12
CRF	—	12±2[b]	4±1[b]	5±1	—	14±2[b]	4±1[b]	5±1[b]
LVDP	—	100±7	84±5[b]	80±6[b]	—	94±14	81±4[b]	83±5[b]
RVDP	—	41±8[b]	24±6[b]	27±7[b]	—	54±9[b]	34±3[ab]	36±4[b]
Reperfusion 35 min								
HR	217±44	227±34	210±42	230±16	227±22	195±61	185±52	189±53
CFR	5±1[c]	6±1	4±1[c]	5±1	6±1	8±2[a]	4±1	5±1
LVDP	43±8[ac]	64±9[c]	44±9[c]	46±9[c]	69±9[ac]	62±10[c]	45±10[c]	46±8[c]
RVDP	24±7[c]	29±4[c]	25±5[c]	26±6	39±3[ac]	36±9	34±5[ac]	35±6[c]

NOTATION: HR, heart rate (beats/min); CFR, coronary flow rate (ml/min); LVDP, left ventricular developed pressure (mm Hg); RVDP, right ventricular developed pressure (mm Hg); Group 1, normoxic, no intervention; Group 2, normoxic plus GSNO (10 μmol/l); Group 3, normoxic plus L-NAME (200 μmol/l); Group 4, normoxic plus L-NMA (100 μmol/l); Group 5, hypoxic, no intervention; Group 6, hypoxic plus GSNO (10 μmol/l); Group 7, hypoxic plus L-NAME (200 μmol/l); Group 8, hypoxic plus L-NMA (100 μmol/l). Values are means ± SD, from 9 hearts per group. [a]$p < 0.05$, normoxic versus hypoxic; [b]$p < 0.05$, pre-drug versus post-drug; [c]$p < 0.05$, pre-drug versus reperfusion.

hearts and decreasing the protective effect of chronic hypoxia in hypoxic hearts, respectively. Experiments performed in six hearts with glutathione (10 μmol/l) as the vehicle for nitric oxide demonstrated that this agent did not exert any effect on developed pressure, heart rate, or coronary flow rate (with ANOVA) from the preischemic drug value reported in TABLE 1 or upon recovery of post-ischemic function in both normoxic and chronically hypoxic hearts.

Recovery of developed pressure was expressed as a percentage of its pre-drug value. Results were expressed as the mean ± standard deviation. Statistical analysis was performed by use of repeated measures ANOVA with the Greenhouse-Geisser adjustment used to correct for the inflated risk of a Type I error as a first step, and where this proved significant, the Mann-Whitney test was used as a second step to identify which groups were significantly different.[19] Significance was accepted at a level of $p < 0.05$.

Nitric Oxide Studies

In parallel studies to determine if adaptation to hypoxia in hearts hypoxic from birth was due to alterations in nitric oxide production, coronary effluents were collected and analyzed for nitrite, nitrate, and cGMP release. Ventricular tissue was processed for NOS3 and NOS2 expression, NOS activity, and cGMP content.

Determination of Nitrite and Nitrate

Nitrite (NO_2^-) and nitrate (NO_3^-) are stable degradation products of nitric oxide and are used as indices of nitric oxide production.[20,21] The Quick Chem AE Ion analyzer (Lachat Instruments, Milwaukee, WI) was used to determine changes in nitrite and nitrate levels in coronary effluent from both normoxic and chronically hypoxic hearts.[22] The detection limit for nitrite and nitrate was 25 nmoles/l, representing an increase in sensitivity over the Greiss reaction.[22] Simultaneous measurement of nitrite and nitrate was performed on sample volumes of less than 3 ml.

Exclusion of Endotoxin Levels from Deionized Water

Endotoxin induces NOS2 synthesis in cardiac myocytes.[23] Endotoxin levels in water used for coronary perfusates were determined using the Limulus amebocyte lysate QLL-1000 assay (Whittaker Bioproducts, Walkersville, MD). Standard curves (0.01–0.1 EU/ml) were established with *E. coli* lipopolysaccharide that had been titrated against the federal reference *E. coli* standard. Endotoxin levels in water samples obtained after purification using reverse osmosis, ionic exchange columns, and ultrafiltration using the Milli RO/Milli Q System (Millipore Instruments, Bedford, MA) were below the limits of detection of the assay.

Determination of Cyclic GMP

Coronary effluents (1–2 ml) were lyophilized and then reconstituted in 0.25 ml deionized water. Homogenates of freeze-clamped ventricular tissue were extracted and processed as described previously.[24] cGMP was measured using a commercial enzyme immunoassay kit (Cayman Chemical Co., Ann Arbor, MI).

Myocardial Nitrite, Nitrate, and cGMP Measurements

Basal release of nitrite, nitrate, and cGMP was determined as an index of nitric oxide production from the aerobically perfused heart. Hearts from six 9-day-old rabbits that were normoxic ($F_IO_2 = 0.21$) from birth (Group 9) and six 9-day-old rabbits that were hypoxic ($F_IO_2 = 0.12$) from birth (Group 10) were excised and aerobically perfused with bicarbonate buffer for 30 minutes. The coronary effluent was collected for 1 min in a plastic graduated cylinder and the volume recorded. The air space above the coronary effluent was purged with 100% argon gas for 30 sec and the cylinder top was sealed before analysis. Nitrite and nitrate levels and cGMP levels were determined. The heart was removed from the cannulae and the dry weight determined. Data are shown (mean ± SD) as nmoles of nitrite and nitrate and pmoles of cGMP released/min/g dry weight.

In a separate study, hearts from ten 9-day-old rabbits normoxic from birth (Group 11) and ten 9-day-old rabbits hypoxic from birth (Group 12) were perfused for 30 min with oxygenated Krebs buffer. The hearts were then freeze-clamped between stainless-steel tongs previously cooled to the temperature of liquid nitrogen and analyzed for cGMP content. Data are shown (mean ± SD) as pmoles cGMP/mg dry weight.

Determination of Message Levels for NOS3 and NOS2

To determine if altered nitric oxide synthase (NOS) gene expression correlated with increased tolerance to ischemia, constitutive NOS (NOS3) and inducible NOS (NOS2) transcript levels were determined by Northern analysis. In separate studies, eight rabbits were raised from birth to 9 days of age in a normoxic ($F_IO_2 = 0.21$) environment as in Group 13 and eight rabbits were raised from birth to 9 days of age in a hypoxic environment ($F_IO_2 = 0.12$) as in Group 14. Following anesthesia, hearts from each group were excised and perfused in the Langendorff mode[16] with bicarbonate buffer[18] for 30 min. The free wall of the left ventricle was excised, blotted, and chopped into small pieces (~2 mm^2). Poly$(A)^+$-mRNA was isolated from hearts using the Fast-Track kit (Invitrogen, San Diego, CA). Briefly, tissue was transferred to a dounce-type homogenizer and homogenized in lysis buffer at mid-high speed. The homogenate was incubated at 45°C for 60 min to digest protein and inactivate ribonucleases and then centrifuged to remove debris. The clarified digest was sheared through a 23 gauge needle using a 3 ml syringe, and then oligo (dT) cellulose resin was added to bind the mRNA. The oligo dT cellulose resin was washed and the bound poly$(A)^+$-RNA was eluted with 10 mM Tris, pH 7.5.

Northern analysis for NOS3 and NOS2 message was performed as previously described.[25] Briefly, poly$(A)^+$-mRNA (2–3 μg) was fractionated by agarose electrophoresis and then transferred to Zeta probe nylon membranes. The RNA was linked to the nylon membrane by UV radiation and baking. Hybridization was carried out with cDNA to NOS3 (bovine) that was labeled using a random primer deca labeling kit (Bohering Mannheim, Indianapolis, IN) and ^{32}P-dCTP (Dupont, Boston, MA) to approximately 10^9 cpm/μg protein. The blot was exposed to X-OMAT AR film (Kodak, Rochester, NY) for 6 days at –80°C for permanent record. The blot was then stripped and reprobed sequentially with NOS2 (murine) and exposed for 12 days, and then with α-tubulin and exposed for 2 days. α-Tubulin (rabbit) was used as an internal control to monitor loading and RNA transfer efficiencies. RNA from human umbilical vein endothelial cells subjected to shear stress (15 μg total RNA) was used as a positive control for NOS3 expression. RNA from endotoxin-stimulated U937 cells (15 μg total RNA) was used as positive control for NOS2 expression. Message levels were measured using a Personal Densitometer SI (Molecular Dynamics, Sunnyvale, CA). Relative levels of message were quantified by image analysis using Image Quant.

Determination of NOS Activity

The catalytic activity of the constitutive and inducible isoforms for NOS were determined in hearts chronically hypoxic and normoxic from birth. In separate studies, eight rabbits were raised from birth to 9 days of age in a normoxic environment (Group 15) and eight rabbits were raised from birth to 9 days of age in a hypoxic environment (Group 16). Following anesthesia, hearts from each group were excised and perfused for 30 min with bicarbonate buffer. Approximately 200 mg of the free wall of the left ventricle was removed and chopped into small pieces (~2 mm^2) before being placed into 300 µl homogenization buffer at 4°C. The homogenization buffer was 50 mmol/l Tris, pH 7.5 containing 0.1 mmol/l EDTA and the following protease inhibitors at the final concentrations indicated: pepstatin (10 µg/ml), bestatin (10 µg/ml), chymostatin (10 µg/ml), antipain (10 µg/ml), leupeptin (10 µg/ml), trypsin inhibitor (10 µg/ml), and phenylmethylsulfonylfluoride (100 µg/ml). The tissue was homogenized in a Potter-Elvejehm homogenizer, and the crude homogenate was used for the determination of NOS activity.

NOS activity was determined by measuring the conversion of L-[^{14}C]arginine to L-[^{14}C]citrulline[26] with modifications for heart tissue. For the determination of constitutive NOS activity the reaction mixture was formulated in 50 mmol/l HEPES buffer, pH 7.4, to which the following compounds were added to achieve the concentrations indicated: FAD (2 µmol/l), FMN (2 µmol/l), tetrahydrobiopterin (100 µmol/l), GSH (100 µmol/l), NADPH (200 µmol/l), $CaCl_2$ (200 µmol/l), calmodulin (1 µg/ml), BSA (100 µg/ml), and L-[^{14}C]arginine (0.2 µCi, 2.28 µmol/l). For the determination of inducible NOS activity, calcium and calmodulin were omitted from the reaction mixture and EGTA (1 mmol/l) was added to chelate any remaining free calcium. The reaction was initiated by the addition of 50 µl of the heart homogenate to 200 µl of the reaction mixture at 25°C. At 0, 12, 24, and 37 min, 50-µl portions were removed and quenched by addition of 200 µl stop buffer (100 mmol/l HEPES, pH 5.5, containing 5 mmol/l EDTA). Those samples were then heated in a boiling water bath for 1 min, chilled, and centrifuged. A portion of the supernatant was applied to small Dowex 50 columns (Na^+ form, 1 ml resin) and [^{14}C]citrulline was eluted with 2 ml water. [^{14}C]citrulline levels were measured by liquid scintillation counting. Protein levels in the heart homogenate were determined by the Lowry method using BSA as a standard. NOS activity was expressed as pmoles citrulline formed per 30 min per mg protein.

RESULTS

Pre-Ischemic function

TABLE 1 gives baseline functional data for normoxic and chronically hypoxic rabbit hearts. Coronary flow rate was higher in hypoxic hearts than normoxic controls. Right ventricular developed pressure was higher in hypoxic ventricles than normoxic controls. GSNO (10 µmol/l) increased pre-ischemic coronary flow rate in normoxic and hypoxic hearts. A trend towards increased heart rate was observed with GSNO; but this effect achieved statistical significance only in hypoxic hearts. GSNO increased developed pressure in the right ventricle of normoxic and hypoxic ventricles but had no effect on developed pressure in left ventricles. L-NAME (200 µmol/l) depressed pre-ischemic coronary flow rate and decreased left and right developed pressure in normoxic and hypoxic ventricles. L-NMA (100 µmol/l) also depressed cardiac function in both normoxic and hypoxic hearts but to a lesser degree than observed with L-NAME. Experiments performed in six normoxic and six hypoxic hearts demonstrated that the cardiodepressive effect of L-NAME (200 µmol/l) and L-NMA (100 µmol/l) could be reversed within 15 min from the onset of perfusion by perfusion with L-NAME– and L-NMA–free buffer.

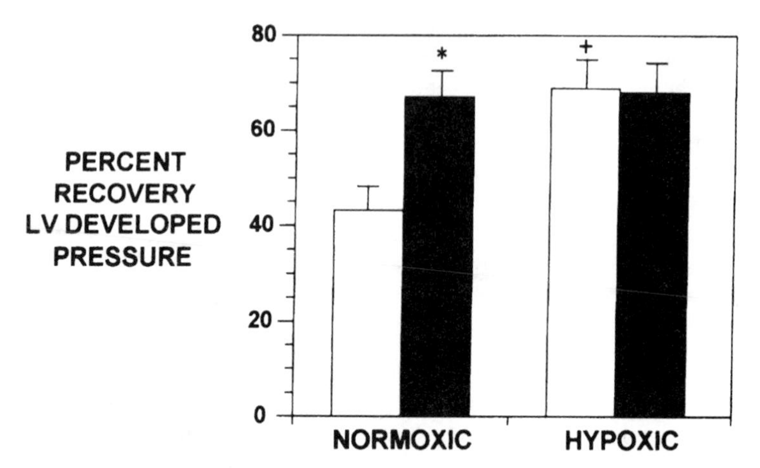

FIGURE 2. Results following a 15-min pretreatment with GSNO before 30-min global ischemia and 35-min reperfusion, groups 2 and 6. Open bars represent data from control hearts. Solid bars represent data from GSNO-treated (10 μmol/l) hearts. Data are means ± SD, $N = 8$ hearts/group. $^{+}p < 0.05$, normoxic versus hypoxic. $^{*}p < 0.05$, control versus GS-NO.

Post-Ischemic Function

TABLE 1 (Group 5 versus Group 1) shows that hearts from hypoxic rabbits were more tolerant to ischemia than normoxic controls. Recovery of post-ischemic left ventricular developed pressure in normoxic (Group 1) and hypoxic (Group 5) hearts was 43 ± 5% and 69 ± 6%, respectively. The right ventricle was more tolerant to ischemia than the left ventricle in both normoxic and hypoxic hearts. TABLE 1 and FIGURE 2 show GSNO (10 μmol/l) increased recovery of developed pressure in normoxic hearts (Group 2) from 43 ± 5% to 67 ± 5%. GSNO did not increase recovery in hypoxic hearts (Group 6, 68 ± 6%) beyond the recovery in Group 5 (69 ± 6%). Thus, GSNO increased recovery in normoxic hearts to the level observed in untreated hypoxic hearts. In contrast, TABLE 1 and FIGURE 3 show that L-NAME (200 μmol/l) did not affect recovery of post-ischemic function in normoxic hearts (Group 3, 45 ± 5%) but actually decreased recovery in hypoxic hearts (Group 7) from 69 ± 6% to 45 ± 3%. Thus, L-NAME decreased recovery in hypoxic hearts to levels observed in untreated normoxic controls. FIGURE 3 also shows that L-NMA (100 μmol/l) did not affect recovery of function in normoxic hearts (Group 4, 43 ± 3%) but decreased recovery in hypoxic hearts (Group 8) to normoxic values (46 ± 4%). Recovery of post-ischemic function in the right ventricle for all drug-treated groups paralleled changes observed in left ventricles.

Message Levels for NOS3 and NOS2

Lanes 2 to 5 of FIGURE 4 show that NOS3 message increased in hearts from rabbits kept chronically hypoxic from birth compared with normoxic age-matched controls. Lanes 1 and 6 show positive controls of total RNA from human umbilical vein

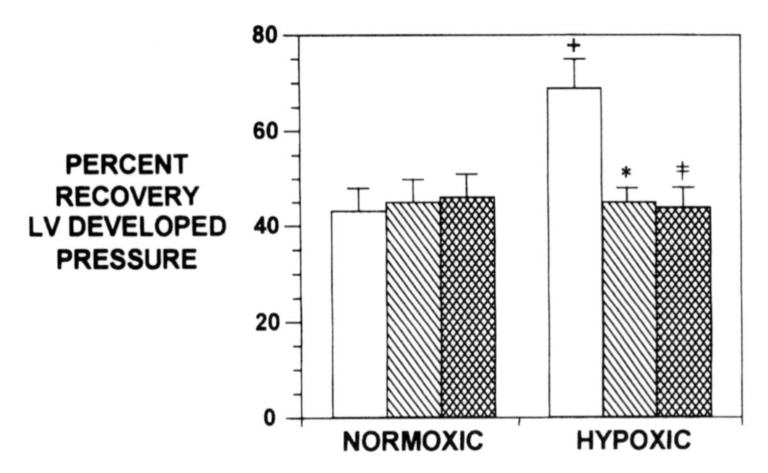

FIGURE 3. Results following a 15-min pretreatment with L-NAME and L-NMA prior to 30-min global ischemia and 35-min reperfusion, groups 3, 4, 7, and 8. Open bars represent data from control hearts. Hatched bars represent data from L-NAME–treated (200 μmol/l) hearts. Cross-hatched bars represent data from L-NMA–treated (100 μmol/l) hearts. Data are means ± SD, $N = 8$ hearts/group. $^{+}p < 0.05$, normoxic versus hypoxic. $^{*}p < 0.05$, control versus L-NAME. $^{‡}p < 0.05$, control versus L-NMA.

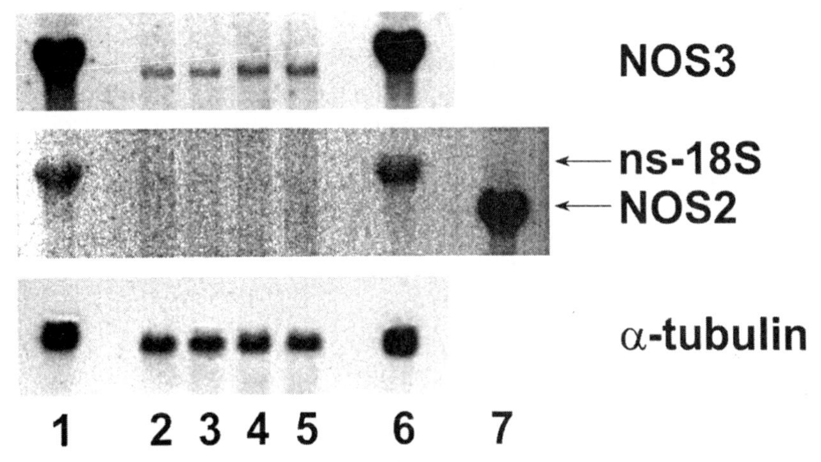

FIGURE 4. Representative Northern analysis for NOS3 and NOS2 in developing hypoxic and normoxic heart.

endothelial cells subjected to shear stress. No transcripts for NOS2 could be detected in normoxic or chronically hypoxic hearts even with the use of poly(A)$^{+}$ RNA. The murine probe for NOS2 was recognized by murine, rat, rabbit and human NOS2 transcripts. Lane 7 of the NOS2 panel shows a positive control for NOS2 expression from human U937 cells stimulated with endotoxin and probed at the same time with the same hybridization buffer and ^{32}P-labeled NOS2 probe. Nonspecific binding to

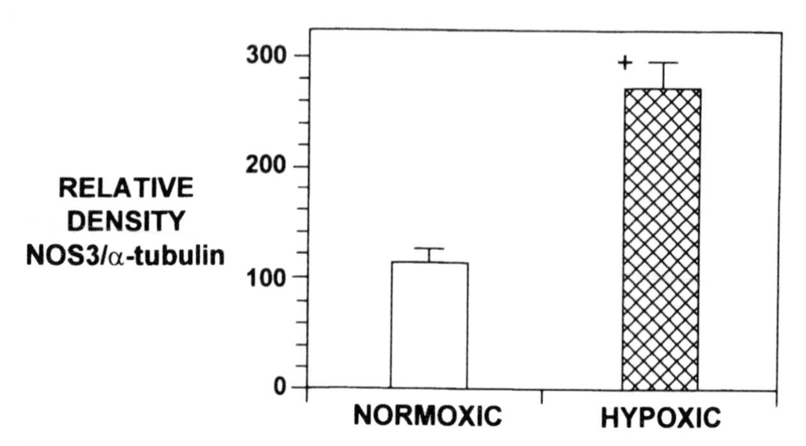

FIGURE 5. Relative expression of NOS3 in chronically hypoxic and normoxic hearts. Image analysis of NOS3/α-tubulin relative density. Open bar represents data from normoxic hearts. Cross-hatched bar represents data from chronically hypoxic hearts. Data are means ± SD from four hearts in each experimental group. $^{+}p < 0.05$, normoxic versus hypoxic.

18S ribosomal RNA in lanes 1 and 6 containing total RNA from human endothelial cells was observed. The affinity of labeled murine NOS2 cDNA for rabbit message is likely greater than for human message based on similarities of other genes between these species. Regardless, no bands corresponding to NOS2 were seen in the poly(A)$^{+}$ RNA from chronically hypoxic or normoxic hearts. α-Tubulin expression remained constant in all groups regardless of experimental treatments. FIGURE 5 shows image analysis of NOS3 and α-tubulin bands and indicates that hypoxia from birth specifically increased NOS3 expression by 238 ± 26%. These data indicate that message levels for NOS3 more than doubled in hypoxic hearts compared to normoxic controls.

NOS Activity

FIGURE 6 shows that constitutive NOS activity in chronically hypoxic hearts (2.1 ± 0.8 pmoles citrulline formed/30 min/mg protein) was 3.3 times higher than in normoxic hearts (0.6 ± 0.5 pmoles citrulline formed/30 min/mg protein). Formation of L-[^{14}C]citrulline was not detected in the absence of calcium and calmodulin indicating that inducible NOS activity in chronically hypoxic and normoxic hearts did not exceed background levels.

Myocardial Nitrite, Nitrate, and cGMP

TABLE 2 shows that myocardial release of nitrite and nitrate was two to three times greater from chronically hypoxic hearts than from normoxic hearts. Nitrate release was greater than nitrite release in both normoxic and chronically hypoxic hearts. Myocardial release of cGMP and myocardial cGMP content in chronically hypoxic rabbits was 1.3 and 2.3 times higher than normoxic control values, respectively. Thus the direction of changes present for myocardial nitrite, nitrate, and

TABLE 2. Nitrite, nitrate, and cGMP in normoxic and chronically hypoxic hearts

	Nitrite release	Nitrate release	Total nitrite and nitrate release	cGMP release	cGMP content
Normoxia	2.1 ± 1.3	8.6 ± 0.6	10.1 ± 1.8	29.5 ± 1.6	1.0 ± 0.7
Hypoxia	4.7 ± 1.0[a]	21.6 ± 2.9[a]	26.2 ± 2.9[a]	38.9 ± 2.6[a]	2.3 ± 1.4[a]

Data shown (mean ± SD) following 30-min aerobic perfusion as nmoles nitrogen oxides and pmoles cGMP released/min/g dry weight and cGMP content as pmoles/mg dry weight. $^{a}p < 0.05$, normoxia versus hypoxia.

cGMP levels in chronically hypoxic hearts confirmed the direction and extent of changes present for message levels and enzyme activity.

DISCUSSION

We have shown that adaptation of rabbits to chronic hypoxia from birth increases the tolerance to myocardial ischemia compared with age-matched normoxic controls. GSNO, a nitric oxide donor, markedly enhanced recovery of left ventricular developed pressure in normoxic hearts compared with the recovery levels observed in hypoxic hearts. GSNO did not, however, affect recovery of function in hypoxic hearts. L-NAME and L-NMA, inhibitors of nitric oxide synthase, completely abolished the cardioprotective effect observed in rabbits chronically exposed to hypoxia from birth. L-NAME and L-NMA did not affect the recovery of function in normoxic hearts. Hypoxia from birth increased mRNA for NOS3 as well as constitutive myocardial NOS activity and cGMP levels in addition to release of nitrite, nitrate, and

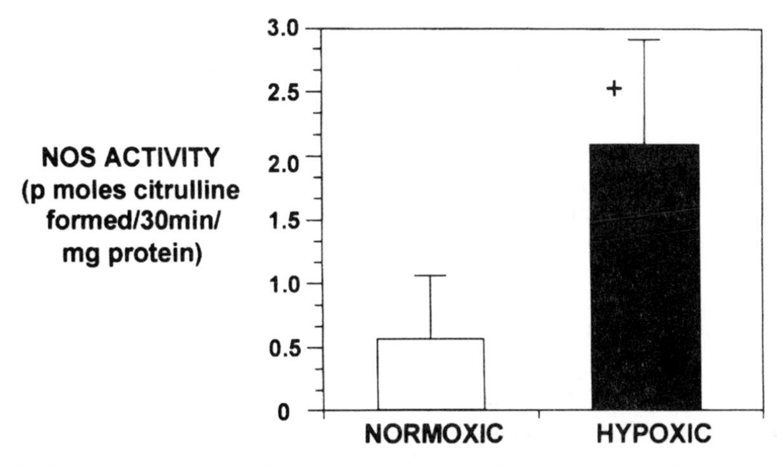

FIGURE 6. NOS activity in normoxic and chronically hypoxic hearts. Open bar represents constitutive NOS activity in normoxic hearts. Closed bar represents constitutive NOS activity in chronically hypoxic hearts. Inducible NOS was not detected in normoxic or chronically hypoxic hearts. Data are means ± SD from eight hearts in each experimental group. $^{+}p < 0.05$, normoxic versus hypoxic.

cGMP from perfused hearts. Increases in NOS3 transcripts and activity suggest that hypoxia increases NOS3 at the level of steady-state expression. These results and the finding that NOS inhibitors decrease tolerance to ischemia only in chronically hypoxic hearts suggest that enhanced expression of NOS3 in hearts adapted to the stress of a hypoxic environment for 7–10 days following birth plays a major role in increasing tolerance to ischemia.

Creation of Hypoxia from Birth

There is no model currently available in rabbits that adequately mimics chronic perfusion of hearts with hypoxic blood caused by a congenital cyanotic defect. Attempts to induce cyanotic defects surgically in newborn animals have not yielded a useful model that survives long enough to allow the myocardium to adapt in ways that mimic changes observed in neonates with cyanotic heart disease. Recently a non-surgical model of chronic hypoxia has been described in the pig where hypoxic conditions ($F_IO_2 = 0.08$) are created 5 days after birth.[27] The piglets are then raised to 28 days of age prior to study. However, the piglet model is relatively expensive and hypoxic conditions are not imposed from birth. For these reasons, we chose to raise rabbits from birth in an hypoxic environment. While true anatomical defects may be lacking in this model, the changes in the myocardium after hypoxia are strikingly similar to those observed in neonates with cyanotic heart disease.[28] With this model we have been able to simulate the essential characteristics of cyanotic congenital heart disease: decreased arterial oxygen levels, polycythemia, decreased weight gain, and overall failure to thrive. The present study shows that adaptation to hypoxia from birth results in increased expression of nitric oxide synthase, which in turn increases the tolerance of isolated hearts to ischemia in comparison with age-matched normoxic controls.

Determinants of Functional Recovery after Ischemia

In preliminary studies, we selected a duration of ischemia of 30 min in normoxic hearts such that upon reperfusion, the left ventricle recovers 40–50% of pre-ischemic function. By determining the period for a 40–50% recovery from an ischemic insult in normoxic hearts, we were better able to detect whether GSNO increased, decreased, or had no effect upon tolerance to ischemia in normoxic and hypoxic hearts. Shorter ischemic durations resulted in 100% recovery in GSNO-treated hearts. Thus, recovery of function after ischemia could be related to the presence of nitric oxide and the duration of ischemia.

Adaptation to Chronic Hypoxia Increases Nitric Oxide Production

In hearts hypoxic from birth, we observed an increase in coronary flow rate, polycythemia, and increased hemoglobin levels compared with age-matched normoxic controls. These adaptive responses to chronic hypoxia increase oxygen delivery to the myocardium in the face of decreased oxygen availability.[15] Adaptation of hearts to chronic hypoxia also increased mRNA levels for NOS3, the activity of constitutive NOS as well as the release of nitrite, nitrate, and cGMP and tissue cGMP content. One of the physiological roles for nitric oxide is control of coronary vasodilation. Nitric oxide activates guanylyl cyclase by binding to the heme site resulting in conversion of GTP to cGMP which relaxes smooth muscle in the coronary vasculature. Smooth muscle cells as well as cardiac cells possess guanylyl cyclase activity. We previously showed that the nitric oxide donor GSNO resulted in an elevated cGMP level in the heart by activation of guanylyl cyclase.[12] Thus, increased nitric oxide production in hypoxic hearts may be an adaptive response that acts synergistically with polycythemia and increased hemoglobin levels to increase oxygen delivery to the heart.

Nitric oxide production, as assessed by constitutive NOS activity and by nitrite and nitrate measurements, was also verified by measuring cGMP as a marker of its biological activity. Observations of unchanged levels of cGMP associated with increased nitrite and nitrate would have suggested that increased nitric oxide production is diverted by superoxide to peroxynitrite. We observed increased levels of cGMP associated with increased nitrite and nitrate, suggesting that nitric oxide synthase generated nitric oxide is vasoactive.

No transcripts for NOS2 were observed in either normoxic or hypoxic hearts. These negative findings are consistent with the moderate increases in nitrite, nitrate, and cGMP. If NOS2 were involved, it is likely that nitric oxide production would increase 10–20-fold. In this study, nitric oxide production in hypoxic hearts was two to three times higher than production for normoxic hearts. In contrast with the present study where message and activity levels for inducible NOS were not detected, Zhao and colleagues[29] reported inducible NOS activity to be present in rabbit hearts. In our studies, hearts were isolated and perfused with a bicarbonate buffer that does not contain neutrophils, platelets, lymphocytes, or macrophages. Zhao studied *in situ* blood-perfused hearts. Thus inducible NOS activity detected in their study may have originated from blood-borne sources and not from myocardium. Recent studies of endothelial cells in culture have shown that 6 h of hypoxia (1% O_2) increases message levels for NOS3 to more than twice basal levels.[30] These *in vitro* findings support our *in vivo* data that chronic hypoxia increases constitutive NOS3 expression in myocardium. Thus a small increase in nitric oxide levels appears to be cardioprotective, whereas a large increase in nitric oxide production may be detrimental, resulting in vasodilation, decreased blood pressure, and, perhaps, vascular leakage.

Increased Nitric Oxide Levels Are Cardioprotective in Chronically Hypoxic Hearts

Availability of nitric oxide was directly related to tolerance to ischemia. GSNO, a nitric oxide donor, given before ischemia in normoxic hearts is cardioprotective.[12] Conversely, L-NAME, a nitric oxide synthase inhibitor, decreases functional recovery[13] and increases the incidence of reperfusion arrhythmias[31] following ischemia in normoxic hearts. Our study is the first to suggest a cardioprotective role for nitric oxide in long-term adaptation to hypoxic stress. The evidence supporting this notion is based on the observation that cardioprotective effects resulting from adaptation to chronic hypoxia are blocked by L-NAME and L-NMA at concentrations that have no effect on the recovery of function in normoxic hearts. Furthermore, GSNO markedly increased cardioprotection in normoxic hearts but not in hearts chronically hypoxic from birth. These results suggest that mechanisms activated by nitric oxide are already maximally activated in hypoxic hearts and that no further protection would be expected in the presence of a nitric oxide donor such as

GSNO. However, increased vasodilation with GSNO is present in chronically hypoxic hearts. This indicates separate signal transduction pathways for vasodilation as an adaptive response to chronic hypoxia and cardioprotection during subsequent ischemia.

Mechanism of Cardioprotection by Nitric Oxide

Nitric oxide interacts with a cellular target in order for its cardioprotective effect to be manifest. The end effector that confers tolerance to ischemia may be the K_{ATP} channel. We recently demonstrated that increased tolerance to ischemia exhibited by chronically hypoxic rabbit hearts is associated with increased activation of K_{ATP} channels,[15] and that chronic myocardial hypoxia results in a shortening of the action potential duration in cardiac Purkinje fibers by increasing current through the K_{ATP} channel.[32] Maximum diastolic potential was also more negative in Purkinje fibers from hypoxic hearts as a result of increased current through K_{ATP} channels.[32] Cyclic GMP release and tissue cGMP were elevated in chronically hypoxic hearts compared with normoxic controls. Thus, increased production of nitric oxide and current through K_{ATP} channels in chronically hypoxic myocardium may be related. We suggest that adaptation to chronic hypoxia results in elevation of nitric oxide, which activates soluble guanylyl cyclase causing cGMP accumulation and possible activation of cGMP-dependent protein kinase. The activated protein kinase then phosphorylates and activates K_{ATP} channels, resulting in potassium efflux and hyperpolarization of the perfused heart, which decreases calcium influx through L-type channels, thereby conferring tolerance to subsequent ischemia. In support of this idea Shinbo and Iijima[33] have shown that nitric oxide facilitates K_{ATP} channel opening in normoxic hearts. Murphy and Brayden[34] have shown that nitric oxide hyperpolarized vascular smooth muscle by activating K_{ATP} channels with the accumulation of cGMP as an intermediate step.

Evidence for Adaptation of Nitric Oxide Synthase to Chronic Stress

Physiological adaptations of normal endothelium occur in response to chronic stress. Chronic exercise increases acetylcholine-stimulated nitrite production in coronary arteries and microvessels as well as NOS3 gene expression in aortic endothelium.[25] This adaptation may contribute to the beneficial effect of exercise in patients with hypertension. Chronic high flow-induced shear stress results in an adaptation of aortic endothelium to increase mRNA for NOS3.[35] In addition to these *in vivo* studies, shear stress increases mRNA for NOS3 in cultured bovine[36,37] and human[38] endothelial cells. Thus, adaptation to exercise and high blood flow also induced NOS3 expression in the myocardium.

CONCLUSION

We conclude that adaptation to hypoxia from birth in immature hearts elevates expression of nitric oxide synthase compared with normoxic controls, which results in increased tolerance to subsequent ischemia. Our study demonstrates a cardioprotective role of nitric oxide in mediating the increased tolerance to ischemia observed in the chronically hypoxic immature heart. The vasodilatory effects of nitric oxide as mediated by the endothelium in response to adaptation to chronic hypoxia appear to be separate from the cardioprotective effects of nitric oxide that may be mediated by increased current through K_{ATP} channels and reduced calcium influx during subsequent ischemia. Further studies are needed to determine age-dependent differences between normoxic and hypoxic heart responses to ischemia during subsequent postnatal maturation, and the role of nitric oxide and K_{ATP} channels in the mechanism of adaptation to hypoxia and tolerance to subsequent ischemia. Nitric oxide formation appears to be an important mechanism in the adaptation of the heart to the stress of chronic hypoxia.

REFERENCES

1. TUCKER, W.Y., K. TURLEY, D.J. ULLYOT *et al.* 1979. Management of symptomatic tetralogy of Fallot in the first year of life. J. Thorac. Cardiovasc. Surg. **78:** 494–501.
2. GUSTAFSON, R.A., G.F. MURRAY, H.E. WARDEN *et al.* 1988. Early primary repair of tetralogy of Fallot. Ann. Thorac. Surg. **45:** 235–241.
3. TOUATI, G.D., P.R. VOUHE, A. AMODEO *et al.* 1990. Primary repair of tetralogy of Fallot in infancy. J. Thorac. Cardiovasc. Surg. **99:** 396–403.
4. GROH, M.A., J.N. MELIONES, E.L. BOVE *et al.* 1991. Repair of tetralogy of Fallot in infancy: effect of pulmonary artery size on outcome. Circulation **84**(Suppl)**:** III206–212.
5. KIRKLIN, J.W., E.H. BLACKSTONE, R.A. JONAS *et al.* 1992. Morphologic and surgical determinants of outcome events after repair of tetralogy of Fallot and pulmonary stenosis: a two-institution study. J. Thorac. Cardiovasc. Surg. **103:** 706–723.
6. DI DONATO, R.M., R.A. JONAS, P. LANG *et al.* 1991. Neonatal repair of tetralogy of Fallot with and without pulmonary atresia. J. Thorac. Cardiovasc. Surg. **101:** 126–137.
7. UVA, M.S., F. LACOUR-GAYET, T. KOMIYA *et al.* 1994. Surgery for tetralogy of Fallot at less than six months of age. J. Thorac. Cardiovasc. Surg. **107:** 1291–1300.
8. BAKER, E.J., L.E. BOERBOOM, G.N. OLINGER *et al.* 1995. Tolerance of the developing heart to ischemia: Impact of hypoxemia from birth. Am. J. Physiol. **268:** H1165–H1173.
9. SHAUL, P.W., A.J. NORTH, T.S. BRANNON *et al.* 1995. Prolonged *in vivo* hypoxia enhances nitric oxide synthase type I and type II gene expression in adult rat lung. Am. J. Respir. Cell Mol. Biol. **13:** 167–174.
10. RESTA, T.C., R.J. GONZALES, W.G. DAIL *et al.* 1997. Selective upregulation of arterial endothelial nitric oxide synthase in pulmonary hypertension. Am. J. Physiol. **272:** H806–H813.
11. LE CRAS, T.D., C. XUE, A. RENGASAMY *et al.* 1996. Chronic hypoxia upregulates endothelial and inducible NO synthase gene and protein expression in rat lung. Am. J. Physiol. **270:** L164–L170.
12. KONOREV, E.A., J. JOSEPH, M.M. TARPEY *et al.* 1995. S-Nitrosoglutathione improves functional recovery in the isolated rat heart following cardioplegic ischemic arrest-evidence for a cardioprotective effect of nitric oxide. J. Pharmacol. Exp. Ther. **274:** 200–206.
13. PABLA, R., A.J. BUDA, D.M. FLYNN *et al.* 1996. Nitric oxide attenuates neutrophil-mediated myocardial contractile dysfunction after ischemia and reperfusion. Circ. Res. **78:** 65–72.
14. ROSSONI, G., Y. BERTI, M. BERNAREGGI *et al.* 1995. Protective effects of ITF296 in the isolated rabbit heart subjected to global ischemia. J. Cardiovasc. Pharmacol. **26:** S44–S52.
15. BAKER, J.E., B.D. CURRY, G.N. OLINGER *et al.* 1997. Increased tolerance of the chronically hypoxic immature heart to ischemia: Contribution of the K_{ATP} channel. Circulation **95:** 1278–1285.

16. LANGENDORFF, O. 1895. Untersuchungen am uberlebenden Saugertierherzen. Pflugers Arch. Gesamte Physiol. **61:** 291–332.
17. BAKER, J.E., L.E. BOERBOOM, G.N. OLINGER *et al.* 1988. Age related changes in the ability of hypothermia and cardioplegia to protect ischemic rabbit myocardium. J. Thorac. Cardiovasc. Surg. **96:** 717–724.
18. KREBS, H.A. & K. HENSELEIT. 1932. Untersuchungen uber die Harnstoffbildung im Tierkorper. Hoppe Seylers Z. Physiol. Chem. **210:** 33–66.
19. LUDBROOK, J. 1994. Repeated measurements and multiple comparisons in cardiovascular research. Cardiovasc. Res. **28:** 303–311.
20. GUTZKI, F.M., D. TSIKAS, U. ALHEID *et al.* 1992. Determination of endothelium-derived nitrite/nitrate by gas chromatography/tandem mass spectrometry using ((^{15}N) $NaNO_2$) as internal standard. Biol. Mass. Spectrom. **21:** 97–102.
21. AKIYAMA, K., H. SUZUKI, P. GRANT *et al.* 1997. Oxidation products of nitric oxide, NO_2 and NO_3 in plasma after experimental myocardial infarction. J. Mol. Cell Cardiol. **29:** 1–9.
22. PRATT, P.F., K. NITHIPATIKOM & W.B. CAMPBELL. 1995. Simultaneous determination of nitrate and nitrite in biological samples by multichannel flow injection analysis. Anal. Biochem. **231:** 383–386.
23. BALLIGAND, J.L., D. UNGUREANU, R.A. KELLY *et al.* 1993. Abnormal contractile function due to induction of nitric oxide synthesis in rat cardiac myocytes follows exposure to activated macrophage-conditioned medium. J. Clin. Invest. **91:** 2314–2319.
24. KONOREV, E.A., J. JOSEPH, M.M. TARPEY *et al.* 1996. The mechanism of cardioprotection by S-nitrosoglutathione monoethyl ester in rat heart during cardioplegic ischemic arrest. Br. J. Pharmacol. **119:** 511–518.
25. SESSA, W.C., K. PRITCHARD, N. SEYEDI, *et al.* 1994. Chronic exercise in dogs increases coronary vascular nitric oxide production and endothelial cell nitric oxide synthase gene expression. Circ. Res. **74:** 349–353.
26. NARAYANAN, K., L. SPACK, K. MCMILLAN *et al.* 1995. S-alkyl-L-thiocitrullines. Potent stereoselective inhibitors of nitric oxide synthase with strong pressor activity *in vivo*. J. Biol. Chem. **270:** 11103–11110.
27. PLUNKETT, M.D., P.J. HENDRY, M.P. ANSTADT *et al.* 1996. Chronic hypoxia induces adaptive metabolic changes in neonatal myocardium. J. Thorac. Cardiovasc. Surg. **712:** 8–13.
28. KIRKLIN, J.W. & B.G. BARRATT-BOYES. 1993. Cardiac Surgery: 609–1596. Churchill Livingston Inc. New York.
29. ZHAO, L., P.A. WEBER, J.R. SMITH *et al.* 1997. Role of inducible nitric oxide synthase in pharmacological "preconditioning" with monophosphoryl lipid A. J. Mol. Cell. Cardiol. **29:** 1567–1576.
30. ARNETT, O., A. MCMILLAN, J.L. DINERMAN *et al.* 1996. Regulation of endothelial nitric-oxide synthase during hypoxia. J. Biol. Chem. **271:** 15069–15073.
31. PABLA, R. & M.J. CURTIS. 1995. Effects of NO modulation on cardiac arrhythmias in the rat isolated heart. Circ. Res. **77:** 984–992.
32. BAKER, J.E., S.J. CONTNEY, G.J. GROSS *et al.* 1997. K_{ATP} channel activation in a rabbit model of chronic myocardial hypoxia. J. Mol. Cell Cardiol. **29:** 845–848.
33. SHINBO, A. & T. IIJIMA. 1997. Potentiation by nitric oxide of the ATP-sensitive K^+ current induced by K^+ channel openers in guinea-pig ventricular cells. Br. J. Pharmacol. **120:** 1568–1574.
34. MURPHY, M.E. & J.E. BRAYDEN. 1995. Nitric oxide hyperpolarizes rabbit mesenteric arteries via ATP-sensitive potassium channels. J. Physiol. **486:** 47–58.
35. NADAUD, S., M. PHILIPPE, J.-F. ARNAL *et al.* 1996. Sustained increase in aortic endothelial nitric oxide synthase expression *in vivo* in a model of chronic high blood flow. Circ. Res. **79:** 857–863.
36. NISHIDA, K., D.G. HARRISON, J.P. NAVAS *et al.* 1992. Molecular cloning and characterization of the consitutive bovine aortic endothelial cell nitric oxide synthase. J. Clin. Invest. **90:** 2092–2096.

37. UEMATSU, M., Y. OHARA, J.P. NAVAS *et al.* 1995. Regulation of endothelial cell nitric oxide synthase mRNA expression by shear stress. Am. J. Physiol. **289:** C1371–C1378.
38. NORIS, M., M. MORIGI, R. DONODELLI *et al.* 1995. Nitric oxide synthesis by cultured endothelial cells is modulated by flow conditions. Circ. Res. **76:** 536–543.

Metabolic Changes in the Normal and Hypoxic Neonatal Myocardium

SALAH ABDEL-ALEEM,[a] JAMES D. ST. LOUIS, G. CHAD HUGHES, AND JAMES E. LOWE

Division of Thoracic Surgery, Duke University Medical Center, Durham, North Carolina 27710, USA

ABSTRACT: Hypoxia is characterized by inadequate oxygen delivery to the myocardium with a resulting imbalance between oxygen demand and energy supply. Several adaptive mechanisms occur to preserve myocardial survival during hypoxia. These include both short- and long-term mechanisms, which serve to achieve a new balance between myocardial oxygen demand and energy production. Short-term adaptation includes downregulation of myocardial function along with upregulation of energy production via anaerobic glycolysis following an increase in glucose uptake and glycogen breakdown. Long-term adaptation includes genetic reprogramming of key glycolytic enzymes. Thus, the initial decline in high-energy phosphates following hypoxia is accompanied by a decrease in myocardial contractility and myocardial energy requirements are subsequently met by ATP supplied from anaerobic glycolysis. Thus, a downregulation in cardiac function and/or enhanced energy production via anaerobic glycolysis are the major mechanisms promoting myocardial survival during hypoxia. In contrast to the aforementioned metabolic changes occurring in adult myocardium, the effects of chronic hypoxia on neonatal myocardial metabolism remain undefined. Studies from our laboratory using a novel neonatal piglet model of chronic hypoxia have shown a shift in cardiac myocyte substrate utilization towards the newborn state with a preference for glucose utilization. We have also shown, using this same model, that chronically hypoxic neonatal hearts were more tolerant to ischemia than non-hypoxic hearts. This ischemic tolerance is likely due to adaptive metabolic changes in the chronically hypoxic hearts, such as increased anaerobic glycolysis and glycogen breakdown.

ENERGY METABOLISM IN MATURE MYOCARDIUM

Free fatty acids (FFA) are the major source of energy in the normal adult myocardium, accounting for 60–70% of ATP generated under aerobic conditions.[1–3] Metabolism of glucose produces most of the remaining ATP, with lactate and ketone body utilization responsible for only small amounts under normal circumstances.

The molecular mechanism of FFA transport into the cardiomyocyte was originally assumed to occur via a simple, non-saturable diffusion process,[4] although evidence is accumulating that this process involves mainly a carrier-mediated, saturable uptake system.[5] After translocation across the sarcolemma, the FFAs are bound to

[a]Address correspondence to: Salah Abdel-aleem, Ph.D., Duke University Medical Center, Box 3954, Durham, NC 27719; Telephone: (919) 684-6742; Fax: (919) 681-7524.

cytosolic fatty acid binding proteins (H-FABP) and delivered to their sites of metabolic conversion in the mitochondria where β-oxidation takes place.

Glucose metabolism in adult cardiac myocytes involves several metabolic steps including glucose uptake, glycolysis, glycogen synthesis, glycogen breakdown, the Krebs cycle, and oxidative phosphorylation. Glucose uptake represents a key metabolic step for glucose utilization in the heart. Glucose is transported across the sarcolemma by specific glucose transporters known as GLUT 1 and 4. Insulin promotes glucose uptake in cardiac myocytes by recruiting pre-existing GLUT 4 transporters, via intracellular vesicles, to the plasma membrane.[6] Once inside the cytosol, glucose is converted to glucose-6-phosphate by hexokinase. This intermediate is then channeled into either glycolysis or glycogen synthesis.

Glycolysis involves several metabolic steps whereby glucose is converted to pyruvate. Pyruvate is then converted to acetyl-CoA in the mitochondria by the pyruvate dehydrogenase complex (PDH). Acetyl-CoA generated from glucose is oxidized through the Krebs cycle. Anaerobic glycolysis implies that pyruvate is converted to lactate. It should be realized that only 2 moles of ATP are generated per mole of glucose by anaerobic glycolysis versus the 38 moles of ATP produced when glucose is completely oxidized through the Krebs cycle.

ENERGY METABOLISM IN IMMATURE MYOCARDIUM

In contrast to adult myocardium where the predominant metabolic substrates are well characterized, the primary energy source utilized by immature myocytes remains controversial. Although it is clear that glucose provides an important source of energy for the immature myocyte (accounting for up to one third of the total energy supply), other substances, including lactate and free fatty acids, are thought to play a significant role. During myocardial development there is a dramatic decrease in the utilization of carbohydrates and a transition to fatty acid metabolism. Studies in 1-day-old rabbits have shown that glucose metabolism via glycolysis provides 48% of total ATP production at this early age, whereas palmitate oxidation provides only 13%. However, by one month of age these percentages have reversed.[7] These findings are consistent with the results of several other studies documenting a change in substrate utilization during postnatal cardiac development.[8] Several authors have suggested that fatty acid metabolism in the neonatal heart is limited because of delayed maturation of the enzymes associated with mitochondrial fatty acid transport.[9] For example, low activities of palmitoyl coenzyme A transferase, acetyl coenzyme A synthetase, and carnitine palmitoyl-transferase (CPT I) have all been reported.[10]

However, recent work has challenged the suggestion that the neonatal heart is unable to utilize fatty acids as an energy source because of enzyme immaturity. Studies conducted in neonatal pigs have shown that while fatty acid metabolism is depressed, the addition of a single substrate (i.e., carnitine) increased the breakdown of free fatty acids threefold.[11] In addition, these studies found that newborn pig myocardium was able to oxidize octanoate (a medium-chain fatty acid entering mitochondria independent of the carnitine transport system) as effectively as mature myocytes. Levels of malonyl-CoA, a potent inhibitor of CPT I, and mitochondrial acetyl-CoA were also found to be significantly higher in the newborn. Taken together, these data suggest that low levels of fatty acid oxidation in newborn myocytes may occur because of decreased L-carnitine and/or CPT I activity; increased malonyl-CoA levels; and/or increased carbohydrate-derived acetyl-CoA in the mitochondria. Earlier studies reporting low levels of L-carnitine in immature myocardium support this hypothesis.[12]

Lactate concentration in the fetal circulation is extremely high, reaching levels as high as 10 mM, while free fatty acid levels are less than 0.025 mM.[8] This may lead to increased lactate oxidation and, secondarily, result in a reciprocal inhibition of fatty acid uptake. In addition, neonatal cardiomyocytes contain a CPT I isoform far less capable of metabolizing long-chain fatty acids than the adult heart isoform.[10,13] In summary, neonatal hearts have limited capacity to utilize long-chain fatty acids and greater ability to utilize glucose as a source of energy.

FUEL UTILIZATION DURING HYPOXIA

Oxidative metabolism of glucose and fatty acids is depressed during hypoxia due to inadequate oxygen delivery. Consequently, anaerobic glycolysis becomes the major pathway for energy production under these circumstances. Initially, glucose uptake is increased due to increased translocation of GLUT 1 and 4 transporters to the plasma membrane.[14] Increased intracellular levels of glucose then lead to increased glycolysis and glycogen synthesis. Glycolysis is also increased due to activation of key glycolytic enzymes, such as PFK, following an increase in AMP and citrate levels. Overall, this leads to an increase in ATP generated by anaerobic glycolysis.

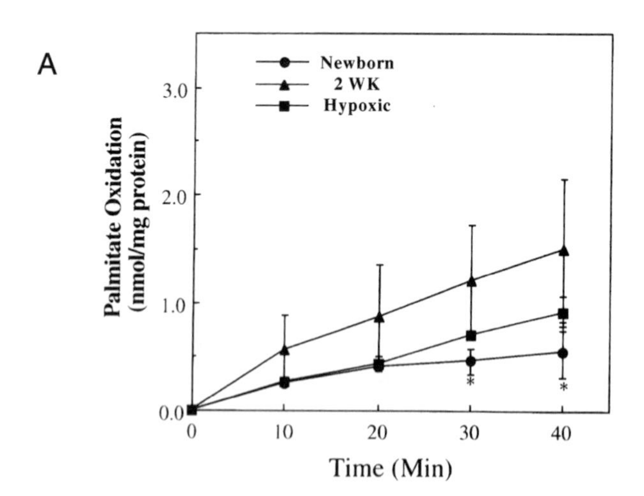

FIGURE 1. The oxidation of (**A**) palmitate, (**B**) glucose, and (**C**) lactate from normal newborn (24-h-old), normal 2-wk-old, and 4-wk-old chronically hypoxic piglets. Data are presented as the mean ± SEM. * and # indicate $p < 0.05$ for newborn versus 2-wk-old and hypoxic 4-wk-old animals, respectively. Double and triple symbols indicate $p < 0.01$ and $p < 0.001$. (Data from Abdel-aleem *et al.*[11] with permission.)

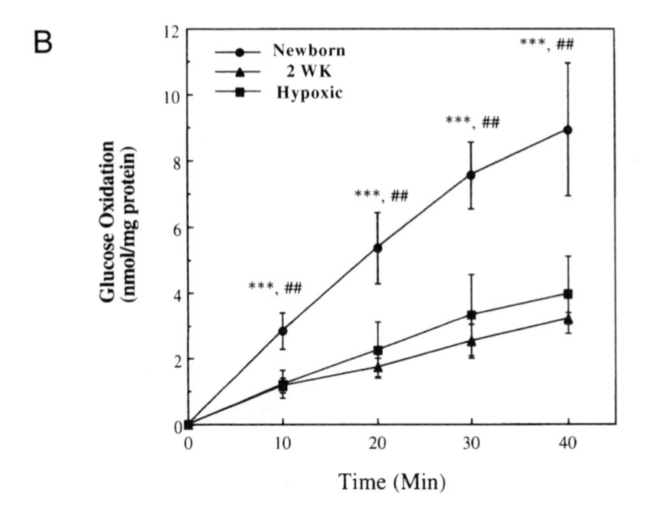

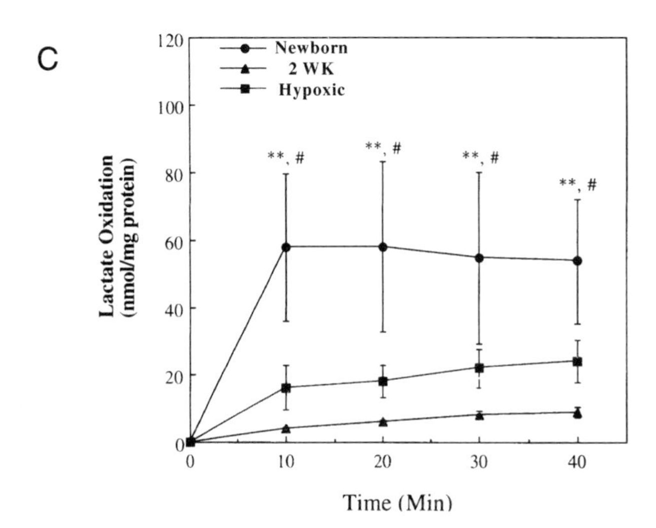

FIGURE 1 (continued).

As ATP is depleted during hypoxia, the activity of PFK is stimulated by allosteric interactions with ADP, AMP, and Pi. Since there is initially little to no accumulation of glycolytic end-products, glycolysis continues at greatly accelerated rates. However, with prolonged hypoxia, accumulation of the end-products of glycolysis, such as lactate, along with intracellular acidosis inhibit PFK and GAPDH. Thus, anaerobic glycolysis stops and the heart loses its only remaining source of energy. If uncorrected, this process eventually results in irreversible cellular injury.

The role of fatty acids and their intermediates in altering cardiac function during hypoxia is less well characterized than following ischemia. Several studies have

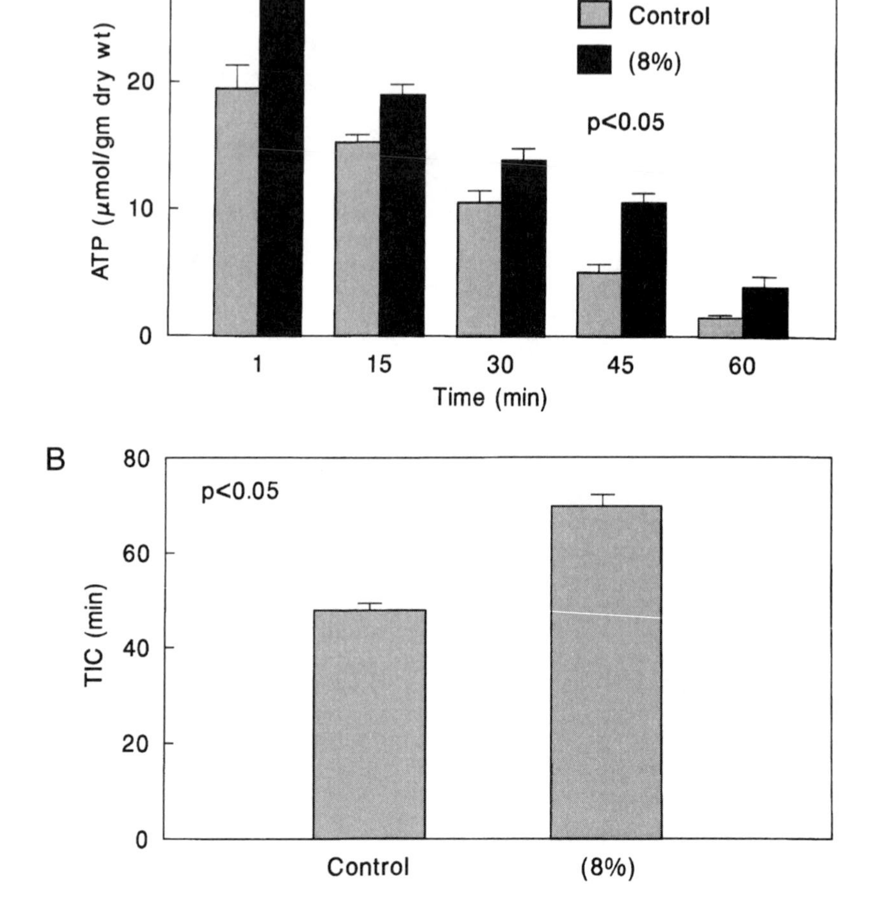

FIGURE 2. (**A**) Myocardial ATP levels and (**B**) time to peak ischemic contracture (TIC) during 60-min global ischemia for control and chronically hypoxic (8%) animals. Data are presented as the mean ± SEM. (Data from Plunkett *et al.*[17] with permission.)

demonstrated the ability of hypoxic myocardium to utilize long-chain fatty acids, although to a lesser extent than under normal conditions.[15] The utilization of fatty acids was shown to be even greater during reoxygenation, despite incomplete recovery of mechanical function. The deterioration in mechanical function following hypoxia may be due in part to the accumulation of metabolic intermediates of fatty acid oxidation. These intermediates, particularly long-chain fatty acyl-CoA and long-chain acylcarnitine, are amphiphilic and have detergent-like effects.[16] Both intermediates have been shown to affect a variety of vital cellular enzymes *in vitro*.

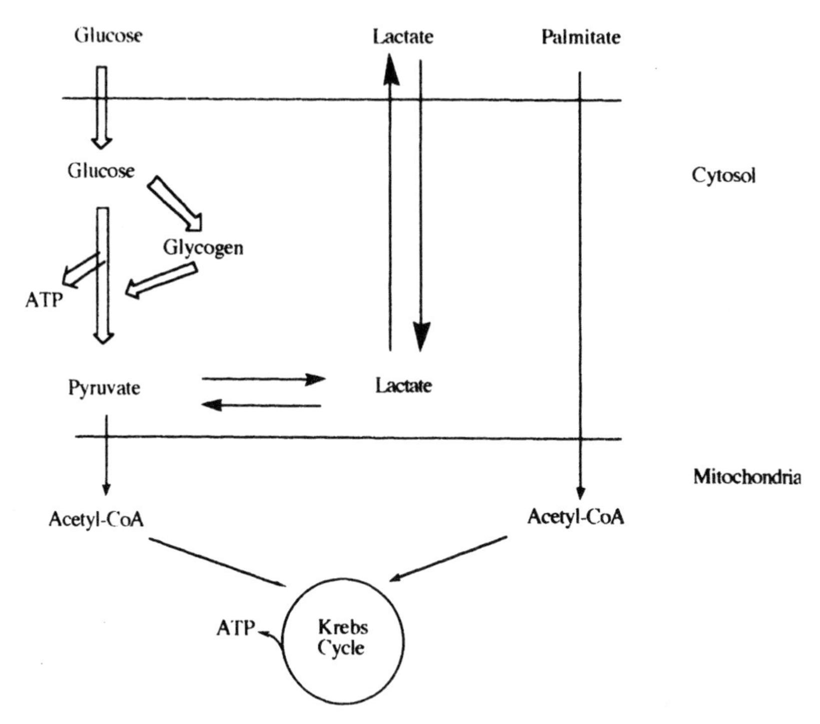

FIGURE 3. Schematic representation of myocardial metabolism following chronic hypoxia. Increased uptake of glucose and utilization via glycolysis, increased glycogen synthesis and breakdown, and increased utilization of lactate represent the major adaptive metabolic changes that occur as a result of hypoxia.

ADAPTIVE METABOLIC CHANGES IN HYPOXIC NEONATAL MYOCARDIUM

A model of chronic hypoxia was developed in our laboratory by placing newborn piglets into custom-built holding tanks in which the oxygen content was maintained at 12%. The animals were exposed to this environment for 4 wk and compared to a control group of piglets receiving the same routine care but exposed to ambient air. At the end of the 4-wk period, the animals were sacrificed and cardiac myocytes isolated.[11] In a second set of experiments during which animals were maintained at 8% oxygen, a transmural biopsy sample was obtained from the left ventricular free wall and rapidly frozen for subsequent determinations of lactate, glycogen, and high-energy phosphate levels. Time to peak ischemic contracture was determined in samples from the left ventricles of these animals as well.[17]

As shown in FIGURE 1, normal newborn pigs (24 h old) had a great capacity to utilize carbohydrate substrates, such as glucose and lactate, whereas palmitate oxidation was severely decreased in these hearts. In contrast, myocytes from normal 2-wk-old pigs utilized palmitate at higher rates than newborn pigs, while glucose and lactate utilization were much less than in newborn hearts. Interestingly, substrate utilization in the 4-wk-old pigs subjected to chronic hypoxia shifted towards carbohydrates despite the fact that these animals were the oldest group. These data suggest that chronic hypoxia is associated with metabolic changes in fuel utilization that favor carbohydrate oxidation.

The correlation between delayed depletion of ATP and time to peak myocardial ischemic contracture is shown in FIGURE 2. The data show a delayed depletion of ATP stores over 60 min of global ischemia in neonatal hearts previously subjected to chronic hypoxia. These hearts were consistently able to better withstand global ischemia than non-hypoxic hearts. These findings suggest that adaptive metabolic changes (FIG. 3) in chronically hypoxic neonatal hearts, such as an increased ability to utilize glucose, may offer protection to the myocardium during an ischemic insult.

REFERENCES

1. NEELY, J.R. & B.E. MORGAN. 1974. Relationship between carbohydrate and lipid metabolism and the energy balance of heart muscle. Annu. Rev. Physiol. **36:** 413–459.
2. SADDIK, M. & G.D. LAPASCHUK. 1991. Myocardial triglyceride turnover and contribution to energy substrate utilization in isolated working rat heart. J. Biol. Chem. **266:** 8162–8170.
3. PAULSON, D.J. & M.F. GRASS. 1982. Endogenous triacylglycerol metabolism in the diabetic heart. Am. J. Physiol. **242:** H1084–1094.
4. NOY, N., T.M. DONELLY & D. ZAKIN. 1986. Physical-chemical model for the entry of water insoluble compounds into cells. Studies of fatty acid uptake by the liver. Biochemistry **25:** 2013–2021.
5. STREMMEL, W. 1988. Fatty acid uptake by isolated myocytes represents a carrier mediated transport process. J. Clin. Invest. **81:** 844–852.
6. JAMES, D.E., M. STRUBE & M. MUECKLER. 1989. Molecular cloning and characterization of an insulin-regulatable glucose transporter. Nature **338:** 83–87.
7. LOPASCHUK, G.D., M.A. SPAFFORD & D.R. MARSH. 1991. Glycolysis is predominant source of myocardial ATP production immediately after birth. Am. J. Physiol. **261:** H1698–H1705.
8. MEDINA, J.M. 1985. The role of lactates as energy substrate for brain during the early neonatal period. Biol. Neonate **48:** 237–244.
9. PHELPS, R.L., B.E. METZGER & N. FREINKEL. 1981. Carbohydrate metabolism in pregnancy. XVII. Diurnal profiles of plasma glucose, insulin, free fatty acids, triglycerides, cholesterol, and individual acids in the late normal pregnancy. Am. J. Obstet. Gynecol. **140:** 730–736.
10. PRIP-BUSS, C., J.P. PEGORIER, P.H. DUEE, C. KOHL & J. GIRARD. 1990. Evidence that the sensitivity of carnitine palmitoyltransferase I to inhibition by malonyl-CoA is an important site of regulation of hepatic fatty acid oxidation in the fetal and newborn heart. Biochem. J. **269:** 409–415.
11. ABDEL-ALEEM, S., J.D. ST. LOUIS, S.C. HENDRICKSON, H.M. EL-SHEWY, K. EL-DAWY D.A. TAYLOR & J.E. LOWE. 1998. Regulation of carbohydrate and fatty acid utilization by L-carnitine during cardiac development and hypoxia. Mol. Cell. Biochem. **180:** 95–103.
12. TOMEC, R.J. & C.L. HOPPEL. 1975. Carnitine palmitoyltransferase in bovine fetal heart mitochondria. Arch. Biochem. Biophys. **170:** 716–723.
13. BROWN, N.F., B.C. WEIS, J.E. HUSTI, D.W. FOSTER & J.D. MCGARRY. 1995. Mitochondrial carnitine palmitoyltransferase I isoform switching in the developing rat heart. J. Biol. Chem. **270:** 8952–8957.
14. WHEELER, T.J., R.D. FELL & M.A. HAUCK. 1994. Translocation of two glucose transporters in heart: effects of rotenone, uncouplers, workload, palmitate, insulin, and anoxia. Biochim. Biophys. Acta **1196:** 191–200.

15. Feldbaum, D., L. Kohman & L. Veit. 1993. Recovery of hypoxic neonatal hearts after cardioplegic arrest. Cardiovasc. Res. **27:** 1123–1126.
16. Katz, A.M. & F.C. Mesino. 1981. Lipid-membrane interactions and the pathogenesis of ischemic damage in the myocardium. Circ. Res. **48:** 1–16.
17. Plunkett, M.D., P.J. Hendry, N.D. Anstadt, E.M. Camporesi, M.T. Amato, J.D. St. Louis & J.E. Lowe. 1996. Chronic hypoxia induces adaptive metabolic changes in neonatal myocardium. J. Thorac. Cardiovasc. Surg. **112:** 8–13.

Regulation of Cardiovascular Development and Physiology by Hypoxia-Inducible Factor 1[a]

GREGG L. SEMENZA,[b] FATON AGANI, NARAYAN IYER, LORI KOTCH, ERIK LAUGHNER, SANDRA LEUNG, AND AIMEE YU

Institute of Genetic Medicine and Departments of Pediatrics and Medicine, The Johns Hopkins University School of Medicine, Baltimore, Maryland 21287, USA

ABSTRACT: Hypoxia is an essential pathophysiologic component of ischemic cardiovascular disease. A better understanding of the molecular mechanisms underlying adaptive responses to hypoxia may lead to novel therapeutic strategies. Hypoxia-inducible factor 1 (HIF-1) is a heterodimeric basic-helix-loop-helix-PAS domain transcription factor that mediates changes in gene expression in response to changes in O_2 concentration. Genes that are transcriptionally activated by HIF-1 in hypoxic cells encode proteins that increase O_2 delivery or allow metabolic adaptation to limited O_2 availability. HIF-1 target genes include those encoding vascular endothelial growth factor (VEGF), erythropoietin, glucose transporters, and glycolytic enzymes. In anemic fetal sheep, increased myocardial vascularization was associated with concomitant increases in the expression of HIF-1 and VEGF. Expression of HIF-1 target genes was not induced by hypoxia in embryonic stem cells lacking expression of the O_2-regulated HIF-1α subunit. Mouse embryos lacking HIF-1α expression arrested in their development by E9.0 and died by E10.5 with cardiovascular malformations and massive cell death throughout the embryo. These studies indicate that HIF-1 functions as a master regulator of O_2 homeostasis that controls the establishment of essential physiologic systems during embryogenesis as well as their subsequent utilization during fetal and postnatal life.

During vertebrate evolution the development of large body size required new strategies to ensure adequate delivery of O_2 and metabolic substrates to all cells. One solution to this problem was the establishment of a circulatory system consisting of three major components: a vehicle for O_2 transport (the erythrocyte); a highway system upon which the vehicle can travel to all possible destinations (the vasculature); and a vehicle propulsion system (the heart). This exquisite physiological system provides a mechanism to assure each cell of the body adequate O_2 and glucose to meet its metabolic demands. Paradoxically, the human organ most susceptible to inadequate perfusion (ischemia) is the heart, infarction of which can interfere with perfusion of the entire organism and lead to its rapid demise. Study of the circulatory

[a]This work was supported by grants from the American Heart Association National Center and the National Institutes of Health (ROI-DK39869 and ROI-HL55338). G.L.S. is an Established Investigator of the American Heart Association.

[b]Address correspondence to: Gregg L. Semenza, M.D., Ph.D., Johns Hopkins Hospital, CMSC-1004, 600 North Wolfe Street, Baltimore, MD 21287-3914; Telephone: 410-955-1619; Fax: 410-955-0484; E-mail: gsemenza@jhmi.edu

TABLE 1. The role of HIF-1–regulated genes in O_2 homeostasis

The role of HIF-1–regulated genes in O_2 homeostasis
1. Increased O_2 delivery
a. Erythropoiesis
Erythropoietin[19,20]
Transferrin[21]
b. Vascularization
Vascular endothelial growth factor[14,18]
Vascular endothelial growth factor receptor-1[22]
c. Vasodilation
Inducible nitric oxide synthase[23,24]
Heme oxygenase 1[25]
2. Metabolic adaptation
a. Glycolysis
Glucose transporters[18,26,27]
Glucose transporter 1
Glucose transporter 3
Glycolytic enzymes[18,27–31]
Aldolase A
Aldolase C
Enolase 1
Glyceraldehyde-3-phosphate dehydrogenase
Hexokinase 1
Hexokinase 2
Lactate dehydrogenase A
Phosphofructokinase L
Phosphoglycerate kinase 1
Pyruvate kinase M
Triosephosphate isomerase
b. Other aspects of energy metabolism
Adenylate kinase 3[27]

system has been subject to a division of labor in which developmental biologists have probed the mechanisms of its ontogeny while physiologists and pathologists have investigated its function and dysfunction. Recent studies of hypoxia-inducible factor 1 (HIF-1) suggest that this transcription factor provides an important link between cardiovascular development and physiology.

HIF-1 is a transcription factor consisting of HIF-1α and HIF-1β subunits, which heterodimerize via basic-helix-loop-helix-PAS (bHLH-PAS) domains.[1,2] The HIF-1β subunit, which was previously identified as the aryl hydrocarbon nuclear translocator protein,[3] can also heterodimerize with several other mammalian bHLH-PAS transcription factors.[4–9] In contrast, the HIF-1α subunit is specific to HIF-1, its expression increases exponentially as O_2 concentration is decreased, and determines the level of HIF-1 DNA-binding activity.[10] In HeLa cells subjected to hypoxia in a tonometer for 4 h, HIF-1α expression was maximal at 0.5% O_2 and half-maximal at 1.5–2% O_2 (FIG. 1). In the heart, epicardial microvascular and myocardial pO_2 measurements of 17 and 12 mm Hg (2.4% and 1.7% O_2, respectively) have been reported.[11,12] Occlusion of a distal branch of the left anterior descending artery for 1 min

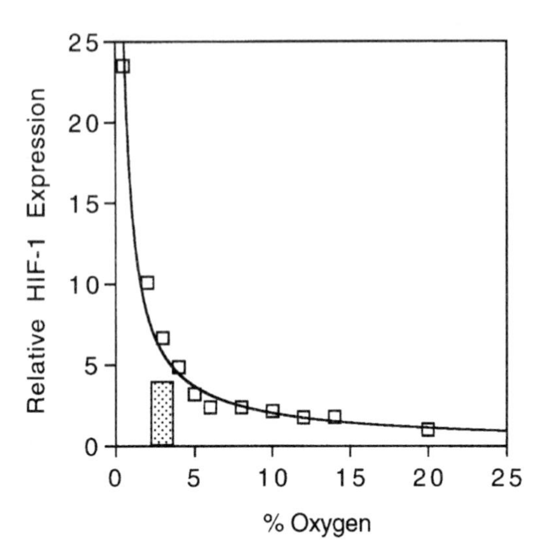

FIGURE 1. Expression of HIF-1 as a function of O_2 concentration. HeLa cells were exposed to various O_2 concentrations for 4 h in a tonometer, nuclear extracts were prepared, and HIF-1α protein expression was analyzed by immunoblot assay using affinity-purified antibodies.[10] Results were normalized relative to expression at 20% O_2. The stippled bar indicates the range of O_2 concentrations that have been measured in the hearts of laboratory animals at rest.[11,12]

resulted in a O_2 concentration of near zero in the ischemic core and an O_2 gradient as distance from the core increased.[12] Assuming that the responses to hypoxia observed in HeLa cells are similar to those that occur *in vivo,* hypoxia associated with ischemic events would occur along the steep portion of the HIF-1α response curve (FIG. 1). Thus, the expression of HIF-1α as a function of O_2 concentration provides a molecular basis for graded transcriptional responses to hypoxia.[10]

A growing number of genes have been identified that (1) play essential roles in O_2 homeostasis; (2) demonstrate increased expression under hypoxic conditions; and (3) contain binding sites for HIF-1 that appear to mediate this response (TABLE 1). The products of these genes function by mediating either increased O_2 delivery or metabolic adaptation to reduced O_2 availability. Because a systemic search for such genes has not been reported, this list is likely to represent only a small fraction of the total number of genes that are transcriptionally activated by HIF-1 in response to hypoxia.

An example of a HIF-1–regulated gene is *VEGF,* which encodes vascular endothelial growth factor, an essential mediator of angiogenesis.[13] HIF-1 mediates transcriptional activation of the *VEGF* gene by binding to a hypoxia response element located approximately 1 kb 5′ to the transcription initiation site.[14,15] The activation of this molecular pathway *in vivo* was investigated in near-term fetal sheep subjected to anemia *in utero.*[16] In these animals, reduction of the hematocrit to 15% over one week resulted in a threefold decrease in arterial O_2 content. To compensate for the decreased blood O_2-carrying capacity, cardiac output increased by 50%, which was associated with striking cardiac hypertrophy manifested by a 30% increase in the

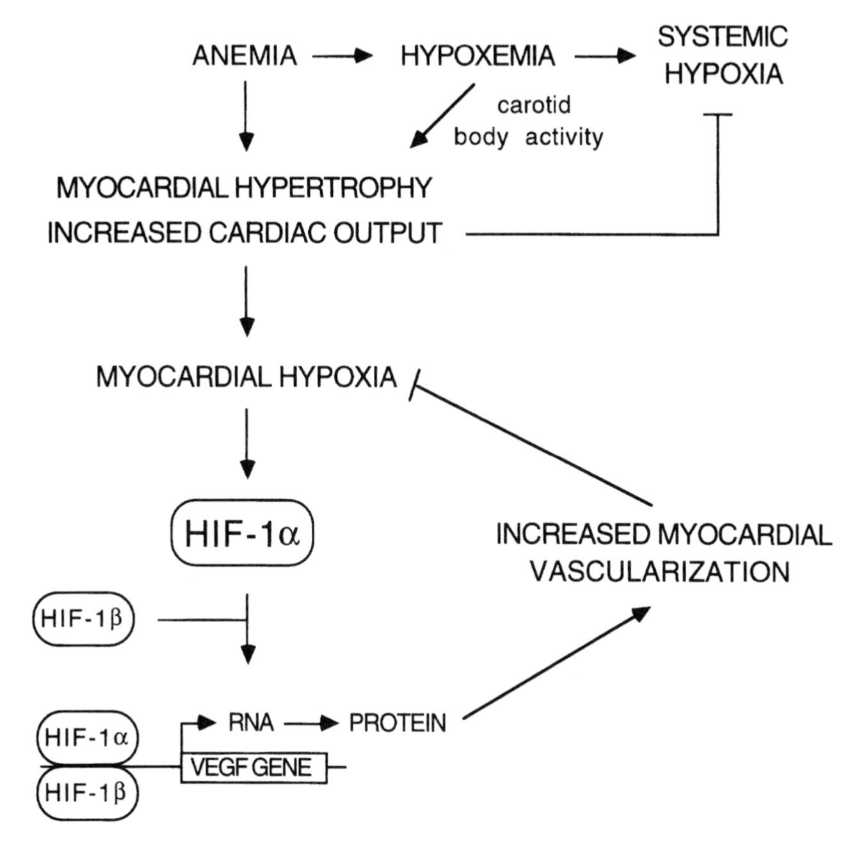

FIGURE 2. Physiological adaptations to chronic anemia in near-term fetal sheep. Anemia results in hypoxemia (decreased arterial O_2 content), which triggers centrally mediated responses that increase cardiac output and systemic O_2 delivery. As a consequence of increased cardiac output and myocardial hypertrophy, increased O_2 consumption occurs. The resulting myocardial hypoxia induces HIF-1α protein expression within affected cells. HIF-1α heterodimerizes with the constitutively expressed HIF-1β subunit to form the biologically active HIF-1 molecule, which binds to DNA and activates *VEGF* gene transcription. VEGF protein stimulates local angiogenesis resulting in increased perfusion of the myocardium. Note that this pathway involves physiological adaptations to both systemic and local hypoxia.

heart body weight ratio. In response to increased myocardial mass and work, myocardial blood flow increased fivefold. Capillary morphometry revealed significantly increased capillary density and minimal capillary diameter and decreased intercapillary distance in the hearts of anemic compared to control animals.[17] Associated with this increased vascularization were three- to fourfold increases in VEGF protein, VEGF mRNA, and HIF-1α protein. The physiologic adaptations of these animals are summarized in FIGURE 2.

To further investigate the role of HIF-1 *in vivo,* a genetic approach was employed in which expression of the mouse *Hif1a* gene, encoding the oxygen-regulated HIF-1α subunit, was inactivated by homologous recombination in embryonic stem (ES) cells.[18] ES cells were generated in which one or both alleles were inactivated (*Hif1a*$^{+/-}$ *and Hif1a*$^{-/-}$ cells, respectively). Compared to *Hif1a*$^{+/+}$ cells, the expression of genes encoding 13 different glucose transporters and glycolytic enzymes was signficantly reduced in *Hif1a*$^{-/-}$ cells, representing the most extensive example of coordinate genetic regulation of a metabolic pathway described in mammals.[18] In *Hif1a*$^{-/-}$ cells, *Vegf* mRNA expression was not induced in response to hypoxia, whereas induction was observed in response to glucose deprivation, indicating that HIF-1 mediates increased *Vegf* expression specifically in response to hypoxia.[18]

To analyze the role of HIF-1 in development, *Hif1a*$^{+/-}$ ES cells were injected into mouse blastocysts and the mutant allele was transmitted through the germline.[18] Matings of *Hif1a*$^{+/-}$ × *Hif1a*$^{+/-}$ F_1 mice revealed a complete absence of *Hif1a*$^{-/-}$ mice in the F_2 generation. Analysis of timed matings revealed that *Hif1a*$^{-/-}$ embryos arrested in development by day E9.0 and died by E10.5. Cardiac malformations included pericardial effusion and increased numbers of presumptive myocardial cells that appeared to obliterate the ventricular lumens. There was also failure of neural tube closure due to extensive cell death within the cephalic mesenchyme. Histologic analysis also revealed massive dilatation of blood vessels in the cephalic region. Analysis of timed matings by whole-mount immunohistochemical staining for PECAM1, an endothelial cell marker, revealed that vascularization of *Hif1a*$^{-/-}$ embryos appeared normal through E8.75. However, by E9.25 the developing vascular network of the cephalic region was replaced by a small number of enormously dilated endothelial-lined vascular structures, consistent with the results obtained by histologic analysis. Whole-mount staining with Nile blue sulfate, which detects dying cells, indicated that cell death was first observed in the region of the neurosomatic junction populated by premigratory cephalic neural crest cells and preceded the vascular defects, suggesting that the loss of mesenchymal supporting cells derived from the neural crest may underlie the observed vascular pathology.[18,32]

The analysis of *Hif1a*$^{-/-}$ embryos described above indicated that HIF-1 is required for the proper development of the cardiovascular system. *Hif1a*$^{+/-}$ mice developed normally but manifested blunted hematopoietic and cardiovascular responses to chronic hypoxia.[33] HIF-1 is thus a master regulator of O_2 homeostasis, as it controls the establishment of essential physiologic systems during embryogenesis as well as their subsequent utilization during fetal and postnatal life. Given the key role of HIF-1 in mediating adaptive responses to hypoxia via the transcriptional activation of genes encoding glucose transporters, glycolytic enzymes, VEGF, and other key proteins (TABLE 1), genetic or pharmacologic manipulations designed to increase HIF1α expression may represent a novel approach to the prevention or treatment of ischemic cardiovascular disease.

REFERENCES

1. WANG, G.L. & G.L. SEMENZA. 1995. Purification and characterization of hypoxia-inducible factor 1. J. Biol. Chem. **270:** 1230–1237.
2. WANG, G.L. *et al.* 1995. Hypoxia-inducible factor 1 is a basic-helix-loop-helix-PAS heterodimer regulated by cellular O_2 tension. Proc. Natl. Acad. Sci. USA **92:** 5510–5514.

3. HOFFMAN, E.C. *et al.* 1991. Cloning of a factor required for activity of the Ah (dioxin) receptor. Science **252:** 954–958.
4. DOLWICK, K.M., H.I. SWANSON & C.A. BRADFIELD. 1993. *In vitro* analysis of Ah receptor domains involved in ligand-activated transcription. Proc. Natl. Acad. Sci. USA **90:** 8566–8570.
5. MOFFETT, P., M. REECE & J. PELLETIER. 1997. The murine Sim-2 gene product inhibits transcription by active repression and functional interference. Mol. Cell. Biol. **17:** 4933–4947.
6. EMA, M. *et al.* 1997. A novel bHLH-PAS factor with close sequence similarity to hypoxia-inducible factor 1α regulates VEGF expression and is potentially involved in lung and vascular development. Proc. Natl. Acad. Sci. USA **94:** 4273–4278.
7. FLAMME, I. *et al.* 1997. HRF, a putative basic helix-loop-helix-PAS-domain transcription factor is closely related to hypoxia-inducible factor 1α and developmentally expressed in blood vessels. Mech. Dev. **63:** 51–60.
8. HOGENESCH, J.B. *et al.* 1997. Characterization of a subset of the basic helix-loop-helix-PAS superfamily that interacts with components of the dioxin signalling pathway. J. Biol. Chem. **272:** 8581–8593.
9. TIAN, H., S.L. MCKNIGHT & D.W. RUSSELL. 1997. Endothelial PAS domain protein 1 (EPAS1), a transcription factor selectively expressed in endothelial cells. Genes Dev. **11:** 72–82.
10. JIANG, B.-H. *et al.* 1996. Hypoxia-inducible factor 1 levels vary exponentially over a physiologically relevant range of O_2 tension. Am. J. Physiol. **271:** C1172–C1180.
11. BENZING, H. *et al.* 1973. Simultaneous measurement of regional blood flow and oxygen pressure in the dog myocardium during coronary occlusion or hypoxic hypoxia. Adv. Exp. Med. Biol. **37:** 541–546.
12. RUMSEY, W.L. *et al.* 1994. Oxygen pressure distribution in the heart *in vivo* and evaluation of the ischemic “border zone.” Am. J. Physiol. **266:** H1676–H1680.
13. FERRARA, N. & T. DAVIS-SMYTH. 1997. The biology of vascular endothelial growth factor. Endocr. Rev. **18:** 4–25.
14. FORSYTHE, J.A. *et al.* 1996. Activation of vascular endothelial growth factor gene transcription by hypoxia-inducible factor 1. Mol. Cell. Biol. **16:** 4604–4613.
15. LIU, Y. *et al.* 1995. Hypoxia regulates vascular endothelial growth factor gene expression in endothelial cells. Circ. Res. **77:** 638–643.
16. DAVIS, L.E. & A.R. HOHIMER. 1991. Hemodynamics and organ blood flow in fetal-sheep subjected to chronic anemia. Am. J. Physiol. **261:** R1542–R1548.
17. MARTIN, C. *et al.* 1998. Cardiac hypertrophy in chronically anemic fetal sheep: increased vascularization is associated with increased myocardial expression of vascular endothelial growth factor and hypoxia-inducible factor 1. Am. J. Obstet. Gynecol. **178:** 527–534.
18. IYER, N.V *et al.* 1998. Cellular and developmental control of O_2 homeostasis by hypoxia-inducible factor 1α. Genes Dev. **12:** 149–162.
19. JIANG, B.-H. *et al.* 1996. Dimerization, DNA binding, and transactivation properties of hypoxia-inducible factor 1. J. Biol. Chem. **271:** 17771–17778.
20. SEMENZA, G.L & G.L. WANG. 1992. A nuclear factor induced by hypoxia via *de novo* protein synthesis binds to the human erythropoietin gene enhancer at a site required for transcriptional activation. Mol. Cell. Biol. **12:** 5447–5454.
21. ROLFS, A. *et al.* 1997. Oxygen-regulated transferrin expression is mediated by hypoxia-inducible factor-1. J. Biol. Chem. **272:** 20055–20062.
22. GERBER, H.-P. *et al.* 1997. Differential transcriptional regulation of the two vascular endothelial growth factor receptor genes: Flt-1 but not Flk-1/KDR is up-regulated by hypoxia. J. Biol. Chem. **272:** 23659–23667.
23. MELILLO, G. *et al.* 1995. A hypoxia-responsive element mediates a novel pathway of activation of the inducible nitric oxide synthase promoter. J. Exp. Med. **182:** 1683–1693.
24. PALMER, L.A. *et al.* 1998. Hypoxia induces type II NOS gene expression in pulmonary artery endothelial cells via HIF-1. Am. J. Physiol. **274:** L212–L219.
25. LEE, P.J. *et al.* 1997. Hypoxia-inducible factor 1 mediates transcriptional activation of heme oxygenase-1 gene in response to hypoxia. J. Biol. Chem. **272:** 5375–5381.

26. EBERT, B.L. *et al.* 1995. Hypoxia and mitochondrial inhibitors regulate expression of glucose transporters via distinct cis-acting sequences. J. Biol. Chem. **270:** 29083–29089.
27. WOOD, S.M. *et al.* 1998. Selection and analysis of a mutant cell line defective in the hypoxia-inducible factor-1α subunit (HIF-1α): characterization of HIF-1α dependent and independent hypoxia-inducible gene expression. J. Biol. Chem. **273:** 8360–8368.
28. FIRTH, J.D. *et al.* 1994. Oxygen-regulated control elements in the phosphoglycerate kinase 1 and lactate dehydrogenase A genes: similarities with the erythropoietin 3′ enhancer. Proc. Natl. Acad. Sci. USA **91:** 6496–6500.
29. FIRTH, J.D. *et al.* 1995. Hypoxic regulation of lactate dehydrogenase A: interaction between hypoxia-inducible factor 1 and cAMP response elements. J. Biol. Chem. **270:** 21021–21027.
30. SEMENZA, G.L. *et al.* 1996. Hypoxia response elements in the aldolase A, enolase 1, and lactate dehydrogenase A gene promoters contain essential binding sites for hypoxia-inducible factor 1. J. Biol. Chem. **271:** 32529–32537.
31. SEMENZA, G.L. *et al.* 1994. Transcriptional regulation of genes encoding glycolytic enzymes by hypoxia-inducible factor 1. J. Biol. Chem. **269:** 23757–23763.
32. KOTCH, L.E. *et al.* 1999. Defective vascularization of HIF-1α-null embryos is not associated with VEGF deficiency but with mesenchymal cell death. Dev. Biol. **209:** In press.
33. YU, A.Y. *et al.* 1999. Impaired physiological responses to chronic hypoxia in mice partially deficient for hypoxia-inducible factor 1α. J. Clin. Invest. **103:** 691–696.

Activity of Cytochrome *c* Oxidase in the Right and Left Ventricular Myocardium of Male and Female Rats Exposed To Intermittent High Altitude Hypoxia[a]

A. STIEGLEROVÁ, Z. DRAHOTA, J. HOUSTEK, M. MILEROVÁ, V. PELOUCH, AND B. OSTADAL[b]

Institute of Physiology, Academy of Sciences of the Czech Republic, Prague, Czech Republic

ABSTRACT: The aim of the present study was to compare the capacity of the oxidative metabolism (total activity of cytochrome *c* oxidase, COX) in the right and left ventricular myocardium of adult rats exposed to intermittent high altitude (IHA) hypoxia simulated in a barochamber (5,000 m, 8 h/day, 5 days/wk, for a total of 32 exposures). In male and female rats, IHA induced significant increases of the right ventricular (RV) weight and protein content, whereas left ventricular (LV) weight and protein content remained unaffected. Consequently, the RV/LV ratio in both sexes markedly increased. Similarly, IHA induced an increase of the total activity of COX in RV in both sexes. The specific activities of COX in homogenate as well as in isolated mitochondria were not changed in IHA-exposed animals, which indicates that the increase of total activity of COX is proportional to the increase of total protein content and RV weight.

INTRODUCTION

Adaptation to chronic hypoxia is characterized by a variety of functional changes that help to maintain homeostasis with minimum energy expenditure.[1] Such adjustment may protect the heart under conditions that require enhanced work and consequently increased metabolism. It was reported in the late 1950s[2] that the incidence of myocardial infarction is lower in people who live at high altitude (Peru, 4,000 m). Epidemiological studies are consistent with experimental studies showing that adaptation protects the heart against acute anoxia *in vitro*,[3,4] myocardial ischemia and ischemia-induced arrhythmias,[5–7] and systemic hypertension.[8] The protective effect can be induced by a relatively short, intermittent exposure of rats to high altitude.[9,10] Moreover, a significant sex difference was demonstrated in the resistance of the cardiac muscle to acute anoxia *in vitro*: the myocardium of control female rats proved to be more resistant to oxygen deficiency. Intermittent high altitude (IHA) hypoxia resulted in markedly enhanced resistance in both sexes, yet the sex difference was

[a]This study is supported by research grants from the Grant Agency of the Czech Republic (306/97/0522).

[b]Address correspondence to: Prof. Dr. B. Ostadal, Institute of Physiology, Academy of Sciences of the Czech Republic, Videnska 1083, 142 20 Prague 4, Czech Republic; Telephone: 420-2-475 2553; Fax: 420-2-475 2125; E-mail: ostadal@biomed.cas.cz

maintained.[11] In addition to protective effects, adaptation to chronic hypoxia may also exert adverse influences on the cardiopulmonary system, including the development of pulmonary hypertension and right ventricular (RV) hypertrophy, which may result in congestive heart failure.[12–14]

Despite the fact that the first experimental study on the cardioprotective effect of adaptation to high altitude was published more than 35 years ago, no satisfactory explanation of this important phenomenon has yet been found. The possible mechanisms involve, for example, an increased capacity for blood and tissue oxygen transport, neurohumoral regulations, and changes in cardiac metabolism.[14,15] According to Moret,[16] the protective effect includes an increased capacity of cardiac anaerobic metabolism, increased energy utilization capacity, and possibly selection of metabolic pathways or substrates with a higher energy efficiency that would decrease the oxygen requirements. This view is supported by our previous findings in chronically hypoxic rats,[17] in which both ventricles had a significantly increased capacity for glucose utilization (hexokinase), as well as for the synthesis and degradation of lactate (lactate dehydrogenase). On the other hand, the ability of the heart to break down fatty acids (3-hydroxyacyl-CoA-dehydrogenase) decreased significantly. Recently, Pissarek and colleagues[18] have found that the long-term exposure to high altitude hypoxia induced overexpression of creatine kinase, suggesting that changes of the creatine kinase isozymic profile could provide a biochemical basis for the cardioprotective effect of adaptation to chronic hypoxia.

In contrast, conflicting results have been reported with regard to cytochrome *c* oxidase (COX), as a specific mitochondrial marker, probably because of the variety of experimental conditions employed or the comparison between populations in which additional factors (e.g., food restriction) may be involved. When comparing high altitude–exposed animals with sea level controls, either no change,[19,20] a decrease,[21,22] or an increase[23,24] in the specific activity of cardiac COX has been reported. The comparison of COX in the right and left ventricular myocardium is, however, almost lacking, male and female hearts having been compared only in the study of Gvozdjakova and colleagues.[22]

The aim of our study was, therefore, to find out whether intermittent exposure of animals to a simulated altitude of 5,000 m influences cardiac oxidative capacity. COX was used as a marker of oxidative metabolism[25] and as an enzyme reacting to oxygen tension.[26] Its activity was evaluated in the hypertrophied RV and non-hypertrophied left ventricular (LV) myocardium. Particular attention was paid to possible differences between the metabolic adaptations of male and female hearts.

MATERIAL AND METHODS

All the investigations conform with the "Guide for the Care and Use of Laboratory Animals," published by the United States National Institutes of Health (NIH publication No 85-23, revised 1985).

Male and female Wistar rats, 90 days old, were exposed to intermittent high altitude (IHA) hypoxia simulated in a hypobaric chamber, 8 h per day, 5 days a week. The acclimatization was stepwise so that the altitude of 5,000 m was reached after five exposures (barometric pressure 53.8 kPa, pO_2 11.2 kPa, pCO_2 0.01 kPa). Total

TABLE 1. Summary of weight parameters

	N	BW (g)	HW (mg)	RV (mg)	LV (mg)	RV/LV
Males						
controls	14	424.2 ±11.3	935.0 ±18	184.0±5.1	557.4±19.5	0.336±0.015
hypoxic	10	441.7 ±11.6	1,032.1±44.9	261.4±25.3	559.4±18.9	0.464±0.033
significance		NS	*a*	*a*	NS	*a*
Females						
controls	14	313.1± 8.3	723.4±18.2	143.7±5	429.4±12.4	0.336±0.012
hypoxic	10	302.1± 6.7	745.1±19.2	174.4±10.2	433.9±14.8	0.412±0.029
significance		NS	NS	*a*	NS	*a*
Sex difference						
controls		*a*	*a*	*a*	*a*	NS
hypoxic		*a*	*a*	*a*	*a*	NS

Body weight (BW), heart weight (HW), left (LV), and right (RV) ventricular weight, and RV/LV ratio in control and hypoxic, male and female rats. Means ± SEM; statistical significance: $^{a}p < 0.05$.

number of exposures was 28–33. The control rats were kept under normoxic conditions for the same period. All of the animals had free access to water and to a standard laboratory diet. Twenty four hours after the last exposure, the animals were weighed and killed by decapitation. Their hearts were separated by the method of Fulton and colleagues[27] into the RV, LV, and the septum and each was weighed.

The samples from the right and left ventricles were quickly cut with scissors into small pieces in cold sucrose medium (STE) containing 250 mM sucrose, 10 mM Tris-HCl, 2 mM EDTA, pH 7.2, and protease inhibitors (1 µl/1 ml; aprotinin 10 mg/ml in 0.01 M HEPES pH 8.0, leupeptin 10 mg/ml in H_2O, pepstatin A 1 mg/ml in 100% ethanol, antipain 1 mg/ml in H_2O, PMSF 50 mg/ml in 100% ethanol–2 µl/ml). A 50-mg sample of the tissue was homogenized for 15 sec in 1 ml of STE buffer by ultrathurax at 0°C and then in a Teflon-glass homogenizer. Aliquots of the homogenate were stored at –70°C for determination of proteins and cytochrome *c* oxidase (complex IV, i.e., COX). The rest of the homogenate was used for isolation of mitochondria. The homogenate was centrifuged for 10 min at 600×*g* and the resulting supernatant for 10 min at 10,000×*g*. Sedimented mitochondria were washed with STE medium and resuspended in the same solution.

The activity of COX in the homogenate and in mitochondria was determined spectrophotometrically by measuring the rate of oxidation of cytochrome *c* at 550 nm.[28] Enzyme activities were expressed as µmol cytochrome *c* oxidized per min per mg of protein (COX activity) and per total weight of the tissue (COX content). The amount of subunits of COX in mitochondria was measured by Western blot analysis[29] using polyclonal antibodies specific for subunit II and IV. Detection of immunocomplexes was performed with EC2 (Amersham) chemiluminescence.

The proteins were determined by the method of Lowry and colleagues,[30] using bovine serum albumin as standard. The data were statistically evaluated by unpaired Student *t* test as indicated in TABLE 1. Where the interactions of factors of altitude and sex were tested, we used the two-way analysis of variance with the Student-Newman-Keuls multiple range test (at 99% and 95% confidence level).

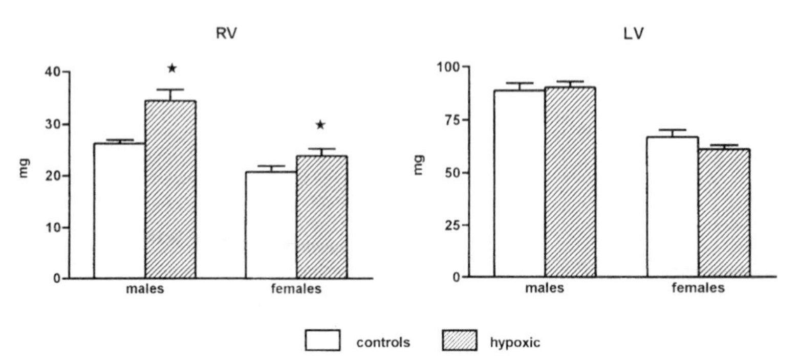

FIGURE 1. Total protein content in the right (RV) and left (LV) ventricular myocardium of control and hypoxic male and female rats. Statistical significance: $*p < 0.05$.

RESULTS

Weight Parameters and Protein Content

Weight parameters are summarized in TABLE 1. Body weight (BW) of control female rats was lower by 26% and total heart weight (HW) by 22% as compared with control males of the same age. The HW/BW ratio was not different.

Exposure to IHA did not influence BW in males or females; the total HW significantly increased in males only. RV weight increased significantly in both sexes, whereas LV weight remained unaffected. RV/LV ratio was, therefore, markedly elevated. The changes in the total protein content in the RV and LV are similar to the changes of their wet weights (FIG. 1); the concentration of ventricular protein was not influenced by IHA hypoxia (TABLE 2).

TABLE 2. Protein concentrations in myocardium[a]

	RV	LV
Males		
controls	143.5 ± 2.8	159.6 ± 4.4
hypoxic	144.0 ± 4.1	163.2 ± 6.0
significance	NS	NS
Females		
controls	148.0 ± 5.3	155.5 ± 4.5
hypoxic	142.7 ± 5.4	151.4 ± 3.9
significance	NS	NS
Sex difference		
controls	NS	NS
hypoxic	NS	NS

[a]Protein concentration (protein/g wet weight) in the right (RV) and left (LV) ventricular myocardium in control and hypoxic male and female rats; means ± SEM, NS = not significant.

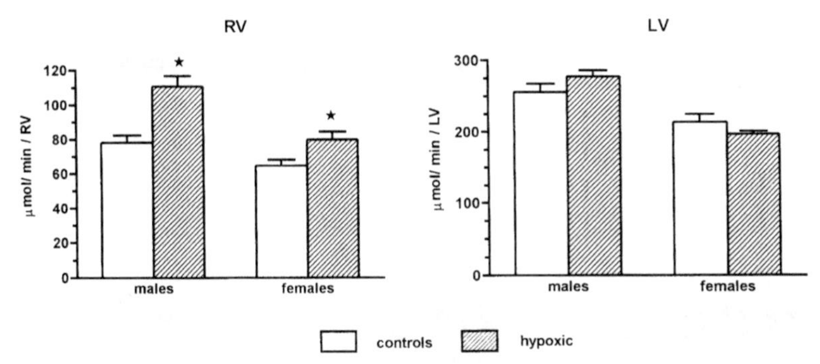

FIGURE 2. Total activity of COX in the right (RV) and left (LV) ventricular myocardium of control and hypoxic male and female rats. Statistical significance: $*p < 0.05$.

COX Activity and Content

The specific activities of COX in homogenates of both RV and LV (expressed per mg of protein) were not changed in IHA hypoxia–exposed males and females as compared with control animals (TABLE 3). When the total activity in the RV and LV was calculated (FIG. 2) a significant increase similar to that found for wet weight and protein content was observed in RV. In males exposed to IHA the total activity of COX comprised 142 ± 7% that of control animals whereas in females it comprised 123 ± 7%; sex difference was not statistically significant. On the other hand, IHA hypoxia did not influence the total activity of COX in LV.

Similarly as in the homogenate, the specific activity of COX in cardiac mitochondria was not influenced by IHA hypoxia (TABLE 3). When the content of COX in iso-

TABLE 3. Specific activity of COX in homogenate and mitochondria

	COX activity (μmol/min/mg protein)			
	Homogenate		Mitochondria	
	RV	LV	RV	LV
Males				
controls	2.9 ± 0.1	2.9 ± 0.1	14.8 ± 0.9	16.0 ± 0.5
hypoxic	3.2 ± 0.1	3.1 ± 0.1	14.2 ± 0.5	14.9 ± 0.7
significance	NS	NS	NS	NS
Females				
controls	3.1 ± 0.1	3.2 ± 0.1	12.0 ± 0.6	15.5 ± 0.9
hypoxic	3.3 ± 0.1	3.2 ± 0.1	10.2 ± 0.7	13.8 ± 0.8
significance	NS	NS	NS	NS
Sex difference				
controls	NS	NS	*a*	NS
hypoxic	NS	NS	*a*	NS

Specific activity of COX in homogenate and mitochondria from the right (RV) and left (LV) ventricular myocardium of control and hypoxic male and female rats. Statistical significance: [a]$p < 0.05$, NS = not significant.

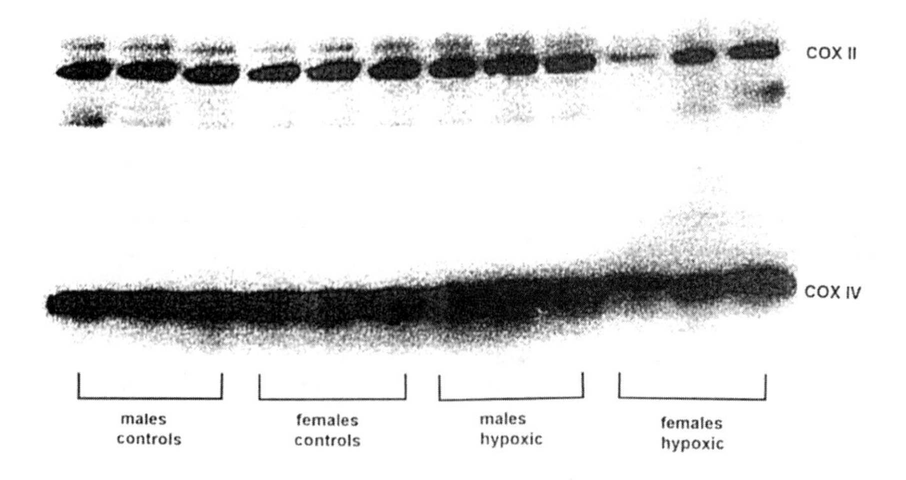

FIGURE 3. Content of COX subunits II and IV in the mitochondria from the right ventricular myocardium; control and hypoxic male and female rats; Western blot analysis.

lated mitochondria was evaluated by specific antibodies against COX subunits II and IV (FIG. 3), densitometric data confirmed the previous findings of enzymatic activities—males and females exposed to IHA had the same quantity of COX in the isolated cardiac mitochondria as control animals.

DISCUSSION

COX is the terminal enzyme of the mitochondrial respiratory chain which reacts directly with molecular oxygen. It is embedded in the lipid bilayer as an asymmetric protein complex. It tranfers the reducing equivalents of the respiratory chain to oxygen and it converts the free energy of electron transport into an electrochemical proton gradient across the inner mitochondrial membrane.[25] The particular role of COX results from its ultimate position in the respiratory chain where a variety of different substrates and enzymes deliver their reducing equivalents. The metabolic activity, and thus the rate of respiration and energy conversion in eukaryotic cells, is therefore, proportional to the activity of COX. Recently it was found that exposure of hepatocytes to low oxygen tension can induce reversible changes in kinetic properties of the enzyme and it was proposed that COX may function also as an oxygen sensor in the intact cell.[26] Since, as mentioned above, there are large discrepancies in evaluation of myocardial COX activity in animals exposed to IHA hypoxia, we concentrated our attention on evaluation of COX activity in our experimental conditions.

Our results have shown that adaptation to chronic hypoxia induces RV hypertrophy in both males and females, but the degree of cardiac enlargement was not significantly different. These data are in good agreement with our previously published observation.[11] In our experimental conditions BW was not affected indicating that food restriction was not involved in the pathogenesis of chronic hypoxia-induced changes.[18,21]

The increase in RV weight was accompanied by an elevation of total protein content and total activity of COX. On the other hand, the specific activities of COX in the homogenate as well as in isolated mitochondria were not changed, which indicates that the biogenesis of mitochondria is activated proportionally to the increase in the total mass of the RV. It is, however, known that the activity of COX may be modified by various factors and assessment of enzyme activity thus does not necessarily correspond with the quantity of the enzyme. We have therefore complemented our data on enzyme activity by measurement of enzyme content in isolated mitochondria by specific antibodies. We have found that the quantity of the enzyme was the same in controls and IHA-exposed animals. Our results therefore confirmed the findings of Costa and colleagues[20] that cardiac mitochondria of rats subjected to moderate hypoxia are unchanged in terms of the mechanisms of electron transfer and energy conservation, since the rate and efficiency of oxidative phosphorylation were not altered. Furthermore, these authors have found an increase in numerical density of mitochondria accompanied by a slight decrease in their mean volume suggesting that the increase in mitochondrial number can be linked to an enlarged surface-to-volume ratio and therefore would be also an effective mechanism of adaptation to chronic hypoxia. Unchanged cardiac COX activity by hypoxic acclimation was found also by Shertzer and Cascarano.[19] Unfortunately, in the above studies no comparison between the hypertrophied RV and non-hypertrophied LV was evaluated so it is difficult to separate hypoxia- or overload-induced changes.

The fact that the total activity of COX was increased exclusively in the RV subjected to hypoxia and pressure overload and not in LV subjected to hypoxia only suggests that cardiac mitochondrial synthesis during the adaptation to chronic hypoxia is related more to the adaptive cellular hypertrophic growth than to chronic hypoxia per se. This hypothesis may be supported by the findings of Nishio and colleagues[31] in rats with aortic constriction. They have observed that mitochondrial content increased in proportion to LV hypertrophy and the levels of mRNAs encoding COX subunit VIc remained constant, again in proportion to cardiac growth. Similarly, Jan-atti-Idrissi and colleagues[32] found changes in mitochondrial function during experimentally induced volume and pressure overload in rats, suggesting that hypertrophy-inducing events exist at the level of the mitochondrion. These data help us resolve the controversy in the literature regarding mitochondrial biogenesis during cardiac hypertrophy and they indirectly indicate that proportional mitochondrial synthesis relative to cellular hypertrophy is regulated at the transcriptional level.

Our results have clearly shown that there is no sex difference in the cardiac mitochondrial function in control animals. Comparable data are unfortunately lacking in the literature. The only information on the sex difference in COX in control rats comes from the study of el Migdadi and colleagues[29] on the adrenal cortex and liver. They have found that adult male rats had higher COX activity in adrenal and liver mitochondria compared to adult female rats. Moreover, there was no significant sex difference in the level of COX II and IV mRNAs. They have suggested a regulatory role of testosterone in the expression of components of the respiratory and steroidogenic electron transport chains. The data on cardiac mitochondria are, however, not available. Under our experimental conditions the degree of IHA-induced changes of COX was comparable in both sexes and proportional to RV hypertrophy. Similarly, Gvozdjakova and colleagues[22] have not observed sex differences in cardiac COX in animals exposed to moderate high altitude. It seems therefore that mitochondrial function is not responsible for any different sensitivity of male and female heart to oxygen deprivation.

It may thus be concluded on the basis of the experimental evidence available that mitochondrial biogenesis in the male and female heart is not significantly different. Adaptation to chronic hypoxia in both sexes results in the development of RV hypertrophy accompanied by proportional increase in protein content and total activity of COX. Nevertheless, the question of the possible role of energetic metabolism in the sexual difference in cardiac resistance to hypoxia requires further investigation.

ACKNOWLEDGMENTS

The authors thank V. Fialová and D. Dufková for their excellent technical assistance.

REFERENCES

1. Durand, J. 1982. Physiologic adaptation to altitude and hyperexis. *In* High Altitude Physiology and Medicine. W. Brendel & R. A. Zink, Eds.: 209–211. Springer-Verlag. New York.
2. Hurtado, A. 1960. Some clinical aspects of life at high altitudes. Ann. Intern. Med. **53:** 247–258.
3. Kopecky, M. & S. Daum. 1958. Tissue adaptation to anoxia in rat myocardium. Cs. Fysiol. **7:** 518–521 (in Czech).
4. Poupa, O., K. Krofta, J. Prochazka & Z. Turek. 1966. Acclimatization to simulated high altitude and acute cardiac necrosis. Fed. Proc. **25:** 1243–1246.
5. Meerson, F.Z., G.A. Gomazkov & M.V. Shimkovich. 1973. Adaptation to high altitude hypoxia as a factor preventing development of myocardial ischemic necrosis. Am. J. Cardiol. **31:** 30–34.
6. Meerson, F.Z., E.E. Ustinova & E.B. Manukhina. 1989. Prevention of cardiac arrhythmias by adaptation: regulatory mechanisms and cardiotropic effect. Biomed. Biochim. Acta **48:** 583–588.
7. Kolar, F., G. Asemu, F. Papousek & B. Ostadal. 1998. Adaptation to chronic hypoxia protects the rat heart against ischemia/induced arrhythmias: involvement of mitochondrial K_{ATP} channel. J. Mol. Cell. Cardiol. **30:** A281.
8. Henley, W.N., L.L. Belush & M.A. Notestine. 1992. Reemergence of spontaneous hypertension in hypoxia-protected rats returned to normoxia as adults. Brain Res. **579:** 211–218.
9. Widimsky, J., D. Urbanova, J. Ressl, B. Ostadal, V. Pelouch & J. Prochazka. 1973. Effect of intermittent altitude hypoxia on the myocardium and lesser circulation in the rat. Cardiovasc. Res. **7:** 798–808.
10. McGrath, J.J., J. Prochazka, V. Pelouch & B. Ostadal. 1973. Physiological response of rats to intermittent high altitude stress: effect of age. J. Appl. Physiol. **34:** 289–293.
11. Ostadal, B., J. Prochazka, V. Pelouch, D. Urbanova & J. Widimsky. 1984. Comparison of cardiopulmonary responses of male and female rats to intermittent high altitude hypoxia. Physiol. bohemoslov. **33:** 129–138.
12. Ostadal, B. & J. Widimsky. 1990. Chronic intermittent hypoxia and cardiopulmonary system. Prog. Resp. Res. **26:** 1–8.

13. OSTADAL, B., F. KOLAR, V. PELOUCH, J. PROCHAZKA & J. WIDIMSKY. 1994. Intermittent high altitude and the cardiopulmonary system. *In* The Adapted Heart. M. Nagano, N. Takeda & N. S. Dhalla, Eds.: 173–182. Raven Press. New York.
14. KOLAR, F. 1996. Cardioprotective effects of chronic hypoxia: relation to preconditioning. *In* Myocardial Preconditioning. C. L. Wainwright & J. R. Parratt, Eds.: 261–275. Springer Verlag. Berlin.
15. OSTADAL, B., I. OSTADALOVA, F. KOLAR, V. PELOUCH & N.S. DHALLA. 1998. Cardiac adaptation to chronic hypoxia. Adv. Organ Biol.**6:** 43–60.
16. MORET, P.R. 1980. Hypoxia and the heart. Heart and Heart-like Organs **2:** 339–387.
17. BASS, A., B. OSTADAL, J. PROCHAZKA, V. PELOUCH, M. SAMANEK & M. STEJSKALOVA. 1989. Intermittent high altitude induced changes in energy metabolism in the rat myocardium and their reversibility. Physiol. bohemoslov. **38:** 155–161.
18. PISSAREK, M., X. BIGARD, P. MATEO, C.-T. GUEZENNEC & J.A. HOERTER. 1997. Adaptation of cardiac myosin and creatin kinase to chronic hypoxia: role of anorexia and hypertension. Am. J. Physiol. **272:** H1690–H1695.
19. SHERTZER, H.G. & J. CASCARANO. 1972. Mitochondrial alterations in heart, liver, and kidney of altitude-acclimated rats. Am. J. Physiol. **223:** 632–636.
20. COSTA, L.E., A. BOVERIS, O.R. KOCH & A.C. TAQUINI. 1988. Liver and heart mitochondria in rats submitted to chronic hypobaric hypoxia. Am. J. Physiol. **255:** 123–129.
21. GOLD, A.J. & L.C. COSTELLO. 1974. Effects of altitude and semistarvation on heart mitochondrial function. Am. J. Physiol. **227:** 1336–1339.
22. GVOZDJAKOVA, A. J. KUCHARSKA, O. RAJECOVA, E. MIKLOVICOVA, I. HERICHOVA, P. BODEK & J. GVOZDJAK. 1992. Metabolic adaptation of myocardial mitochondria to mild altitude hypoxia. Int. J. Cardiol. **36:** 103–106.
23. OU, L.C. & S.M. TENNEY. 1970. Properties of mitochondria from hearts of cattle acclimatized to high altitude. Respir. Physiol. **8:** 151–159.
24. WILBERT, D., J.R. BOWERS, R.F. BURLINGTON, B.K. WHITTEN, R.C. DAUM & M.A. POSIVIATA. 1971. Ultrastructural and metabolic alterations in myocardium from altitude-acclimated rats. Am. J. Physiol. **220:** 1885–1889.
25. KADENBACH, B., V. FRANK, T. RIEGER & J. NAPIWOTZKI. 1997. Regulation of respiration and energy transduction in cytochrome *c* oxidase isozymes by allosteric effectors. Mol. Cell. Biochem. **174:** 131–135.
26. CHANDEL, N.S., G.R. BUDINGER, S.M. CHOE & P.T. SCHUMACHER. 1997. Cellular respiration during hypoxia. Role of cytochrome oxidase as the oxygen sensor in hepatocytes. J. Biol. Chem. **272:** 18808–18816.
27. FULTON, R.M.M, E.C. HUTCHINSON & A.M. JONES. 1952. Ventricular weight in cardiac hypertrophy. Brit. Heart. J. **14:** 413.
28. WHARTON, D.C. & A. TLAGOLOFF. 1967. Cytochrome oxidase from beef heart mitochondria. Methods Enzymol. **10:** 245–253.
29. SCHAGGER, H. & G. VON JAGOW. 1987. Trinine-sodium-dodecyl sulfate-polyacrylamide gel electrophoresis for the separation of proteins in the range from 1 to 100 kDa. Anal. Biochem. **166:** 368–379.
30. LOWRY, O.H., H.J. ROSEBROUGH, A.L. FARR & R.J. RANDALL. 1951. Protein measurement with the folin phenol reagent. J. Biol. Chem. **193:** 265–275.
31. NISHIO, M.L., O.I. ORNATSKY, E.E. CRAIG & D.A. HOOD. 1995. Mitochondrial biogenesis during pressure overload induced cardiac hypertrophy in adult rats. Can. J. Physiol. Pharmacol. **73:** 630–637.
32. JANNATI-IDRISSI, R., B. BESSON, M. LAPLACE & M.H. BUI. 1995. *In situ* mitochondrial function in volume overload and pressure overload-induced cardiac hypertrophy in rats. Basic Res. Cardiol. **90:** 305–313.
33. EL-MIGDADI, F., S. GALLANT & A.C. BROWNIE. 1995. Sex differences in cytochromes oxidase and P-45011 beta in the rat adrenal cortex. Mol. Cell. Endocrinol. **112:** 185–94.

Quantitative Analysis of Collagens and Fibronectin Expression in Human Right Ventricular Hypertrophy[a]

T.H.F. PETERS,[b,c] H.S. SHARMA,[b,d] E. YILMAZ,[b] AND A.J.J.C. BOGERS[c]

[b]*Pharmacology,* [c]*Cardiothoracic Surgery, Erasmus University Medical Center, Rotterdam, The Netherlands*

ABSTRACT: One of the main features in human tetralogy of Fallot (TF) is right ventricular hypertrophy (RVH) due to pressure (sub-pulmonary stenosis) and volume overload (ventricular septal defect). Currently, primary correction at a young age is the treatment of choice. To unravel the role of extracellular matrix in RVH, we examined myocardial expression of collagens and fibronectin in TF patients with primary correction (TF1, age 0.7 ± 0.2 yr.), secondary surgery (TF2, age 36.9 ± 4.6 yr), and in age-matched control patients. Sirius red staining quantified by video imaging showed significantly increased interstitial staining for collagens in both TF1 and TF2 groups as compared to respective controls. Fibronectin was expressed in extracellular spaces, perivascular regions, and in some cardiomyocytes. Quantitative analysis of fibronectin revealed increased expression in only TF1 group as compared to respective control. Our results indicate an increased amount of myocardial extracellular matrix deposition as a sign of fibrosis during RVH in patients with TF.

INTRODUCTION

Tetralogy of Fallot (TF) is a common form of cyanotic congenital heart disease, with an incidence rate of 1 out of 2,000 newborns. TF is characterized by overriding of the aorta, a ventricular septal defect, (sub)valvular pulmonary stenosis, and right ventricular hypertrophy (RVH), resulting in hypoxemia due to diminished pulmonary flow.[1] The RVH in human TF is an adaptive response of cardiomyocytes to increased pressure as well as volume overload caused by (sub)pulmonary stenosis and by ventricular septal defect, respectively. The adaptive response requires proportionate increase of coronary flow or growth of the coronary vasculature, leading to myocardial remodeling as well as development of fibrosis and, without treatment, ultimately results in cardiac failure.[2–5]

In myocardial fibrosis, collagens and fibronectin play a prominent role. Damage of the collagen structure compromises the myocyte support, decreases myocardial strength and stiffness, and allows expansion of the tissue.[6] Collagen fibers are organized in the collagen network, which is found in the extracellular space of the myo-

[a]This work is supported by the Netherlands Heart Foundation (NHS 96.082).

[d]Address correspondence to: Hari S. Sharma, Ph.D., Institute of Pharmacology, Erasmus University, P.O. Box 1738, 3000 DR Rotterdam, The Netherlands; Telephone: 31 10 4087963; Fax: 31 10 4089458; E-mail: SHARMA@FARMA.FGG.EUR.NL

cardium.[7–10] In myocardial fibrosis a disproportionate accumulation, either reactive or reparative, of collagen has been observed. Experimental[11] and clinical data[12,13] show that a rise in collagen content increases myocardial stiffness and promotes abnormalities of cardiac function during hypertrophy. In a morphometrical study, an increase in fibrosis in TF was associated with an increased diameter of myocytes and an increase of myocardial disarray.[14] In addition, the perivascular accumulation of collagen fibers may impair the vasodilator capacity of intramyocardial coronary arteries and may contribute to the decrease in coronary reserve.[15]

Fibronectin is found in the extracellular matrix of most tissue, serving as a bridge between cells and interstitial collagen mesh network and influencing diverse processes, including cell growth, adhesion, migration, and wound repair.[16] In rats, fetal fibronectin was shown to have accumulated during development of cardiac hypertrophy by pressure overload.[17] The hypertrophied heart exhibits significant qualitative as well as quantitative changes in gene expression. The altered expression patterns in hypertrophy include transient expression of proto-oncogenes.[18] It is thought that those changes in cardiac hypertrophy reflect a change toward an embryonic program of gene expression.[19] However, it is still not clear whether those altered expression patterns are general markers of cardiac hypertrophy or markers of a specific parallel pathogenic process, such as TF. Animal studies have shown that the levels of mRNA for fibronectin and collagens were elevated in cardiac hypertrophy.[17]

Most attention in research on human TF has so far focused on clinical treatment and surgical methods to limit the myocardial injury. TF patients are usually operated on during their first year of life. The aim of early primary repair is to close the ventricular septal defect and to remove the right ventricular outflow tract obstruction, thus relieving the hypoxemia and eliminating the stimulus for the adaptive RVH as well as preserving right ventricular function.[1,20] However, after corrective surgery some patients develop right ventricular failure due to volume-overload caused by pulmonary regurgitation and may for this reason require further secondary corrective surgery later in life.[21,22] Histopathological studies on TF myocardial tissue reported that the myocardial cell diameter was reduced in patients after corrective surgery, indicating regression of RVH. Nevertheless, it is not yet known to what extent the RVH in TF patients regresses. Little attention has been paid to the molecular component of this disease. In this study, we examined the degree of fibrosis in human TF by measuring the expression of myocardial fibrosis markers, such as fibronectin and collagen, in right ventricular biopsies obtained during corrective surgery for TF and comparing the data with that of age-matched patients with normal right ventricle.

MATERIALS AND METHODS

Biopsies

The present study was approved by the Medical Ethical Committee of the University Hospital, Erasmus University, Rotterdam. Myocardial tissue biopsies were obtained from patients who underwent primary corrective surgery (TF1, mean age 0.7 ± 0.2 yr, $N = 11$), secondary surgery (TF2, mean age 36.9 ± 4.6 yr, $N = 6$), and age-matched control patients. All control patients had clinically normal right ventricle and underwent autograft aortic root replacement (C1, mean age 1.5 ± 0.2 yr, $N =$

6 and C2, mean age 31.7 ± 4.2 yr, $N = 12$). Myocardial tissue was fixed in 4% paraformaldehyde in PBS for minimal 24 h and further processed for dehydration and embedding in paraffin for histological and immunohistochemical studies.[23]

Sirius Red Staining

The total collagen in myocardial tissue specimens was stained with Sirius red F3BA.[24] Tissue sections of 6 μm thickness, were treated with 0.2% aqueous phosphomolybdic acid and incubated in 0.1% Sirius red. Before dehydration, the slides were treated with 0.01N HCl and mounted. The Sirius red–stained area was determined as percentage of total tissue area using a Kontron-KS 400 (Kontron Electronik/Zeiss, Eching, Germany) computerized image analysis system. Distribution of collagen fibers in the interstitial space as well as in the perivascular region was measured as Sirius red–positive area. Twelve different images from each section were analyzed to calculate the mean percentage of stained tissue area and statistically significant values were accepted at $p \leq 0.05$.

Immunohistochemistry

After fixation and dehydration, the cardiac tissue was embedded in paraffin. Sections of 6 μm thickness were cut and mounted on poly-L-lysine–coated microscope slides, followed by immunohistochemistry using the avidin-biotin complex (ABC) method (BioGenex, San Ramon, CA). The sections were deparaffinized and quenched for endogenous peroxidase by 2% hydrogen peroxide in methanol. Nonspecific binding sites were blocked by 10% normal goat serum. Human serum preabsorbed polyclonal antibodies, against human fibronectin in 1:1,000 dilution (Life Technologies, Breda, The Netherlands), were applied as primary antiserum and the sections were incubated at room temperature for 30 min. Negative controls were performed by omission of the primary antibody. After washing in 0.5% Tween-20 in PBS solution, the sections were incubated with mouse biotinylated anti-rabbit IgG (BioGenex, San Ramon, CA) for 30 min and subsequently, with peroxidase conjugated streptavidin. Color was developed using 3,3′-diaminobenzidine tetrahydrochloride dehydrate (DAB) and then sections were counter-stained with hematoxylin. Sections were mounted and visualized under the light microscope and photographed. A semiquantitative analysis of the sections was done by two independent observers using a staining score ranging from 0 (no staining) to 4 (very strong, dark brown, staining) to assess the level of fibronectin expression in the myocardial tissue obtained from TF patients and age-matched controls.

FIGURE 1. Right ventricular total collagen content in patients with tetralogy of Fallot. Micrographs of right ventricular tissue obtained from patients undergoing surgery (**A**) for autograft aortic root replacement (Control), (**B**) for primary repair due to tetralogy of Fallot (TF1), and (**C**) for secondary surgery (TF2). Tissue sections were prepared and stained with collagen-specific stain, Sirius red. Collagen fibers appear red and are localized in interstitial and perivascular areas. Note the interstitial fibrosis in the case of TF patients. Bar = 250 μm. (**D**) Significantly enhanced interstitial collagen content in TF1 group as compared to the control. Distribution of collagen fibers in tissue was visualized under normal and polarized light and quantified using video imaging software. Values are fold induction and shown as mean ± SEM of sirius red–positive interstitial/total tissue area (*arrows*).

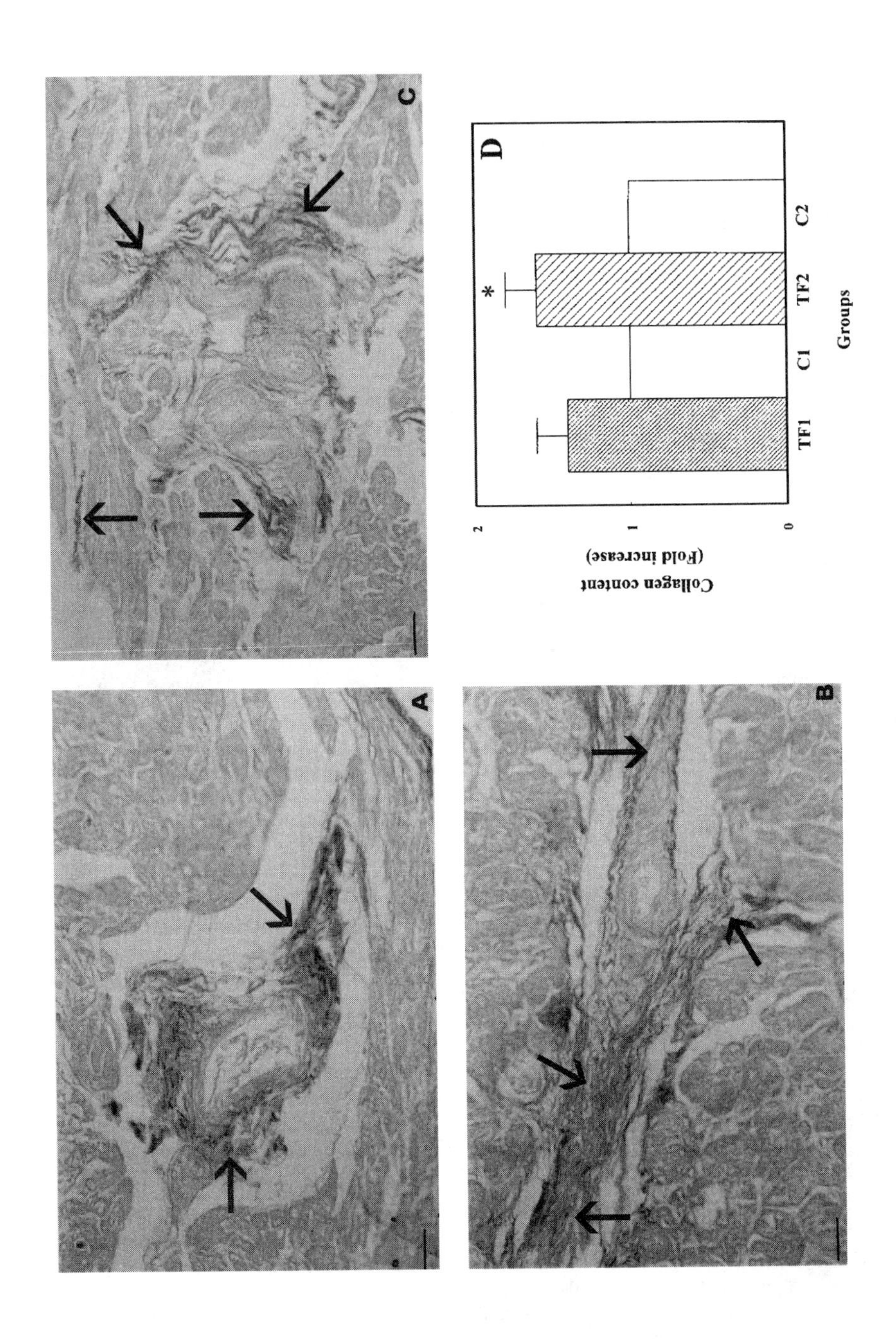
A
B
C
D
Collagen content
(Fold increase)
0
1
2
*
TF1
C1
TF2
C2
Groups

RESULTS AND DISCUSSION

Sirius red staining was performed for the total collagens in order to assess the degree of myocardial fibrosis. The red staining was quantified by video imaging and showed a significantly increased interstitial and perivascular staining for total collagens in TF1 (1.4 ± 0.2 fold) (FIG. 1A and D) and TF2 (1.6 ± 0.2 fold) (FIG. 1B and 1D) as compared to their respective controls (FIG. 1C and 1D). The immunolocalization of fibronectin showed that fibronectin was expressed in the interstitium, in the perivascular area, as well as in some cardiomyocytes. Semiquantitative analysis using a staining score ranging from 0–4, revealed that the fibronectin expression was significantly increased in TF1 (FIG. 2A and 2D) as compared to control (3.0 ± 0.2 versus 2.6 ± 0.2). There were no differences in fibronectin expression in patients from TF2 (FIG. 2B and 2D) as compared with age-matched controls (FIG. 2C and 2D). Our results indicate an increased amount of myocardial extracellular matrix deposition in RVH in patients with TF, with an apparent increase of total collagen and a slight increase in fibronectin at young age.

The apparent development of cardiac hypertrophy is induced by changes in cardiac gene expression that provide the heart a means of compensation for increased hemodynamic load.[25] In this regard, our data are in agreement with the histopathologic findings from the RV myocardium in preoperative TF, which show interstitial fibrosis, myofibrillar disorganization, disarray, and degenerative changes, in addition to myocardial cell hypertrophy.[18,26,27] The changes found in our study of expression of collagens and fibronectin could be attributed to altered structure or function of the myocardium. It is believed that changes in gene expression accompanying cardiac hypertrophy are the result of a multifactorial process and the observed changes may therefore be concomitant phenomena. The alteration in ventricular gene expression might be an indicator of cardiac hypertrophy and may result from a number of different stimuli. We assume that the changes in the right ventricular fibronectin and collagen expression in TF patients could be as a result of increased hemodynamic load as it has been often found to be parallel with the increase in ventricular mass.[19]

In the case of TF patients, the early increase of collagen and fibronectin deposition in the right ventricle may occur because the original myocardial extracellular matrix has been expanded and weakened due to the hemodynamic overload. The myocardium will compensate until enough new collagen has been produced to restore tensile strength and to resist the distending forces. Our findings in the TF1 and TF2 groups fit into this concept as the TF2 shows a more prominent increase in the

---

FIGURE 2. Immunohistochemical localization of fibronectin in right ventricular tissue of patients with tetralogy of Fallot. Micrographs showing human right ventricular tissue stained with rabbit–anti-human fibronectin polyclonal antibodies (as described in *Materials and Methods*) from patients undergoing surgery (**A**) for autograft aortic root replacement (Control), (**B**) for primary repair for tetralogy of Fallot (TF1), and (**C**) for secondary surgery (TF2). Bar = 500 μm. (**D**) Significantly enhanced interstitial fibronectin staining in the TF1 group as compared to the respective controls. A semiquantitative analysis of the section was done by two independent observers using a staining score ranging from 0 (no staining) to 4 (very strong, dark brown, staining) to assess the levels of fibronectin staining (*arrows*). Values are shown as mean ± SEM.

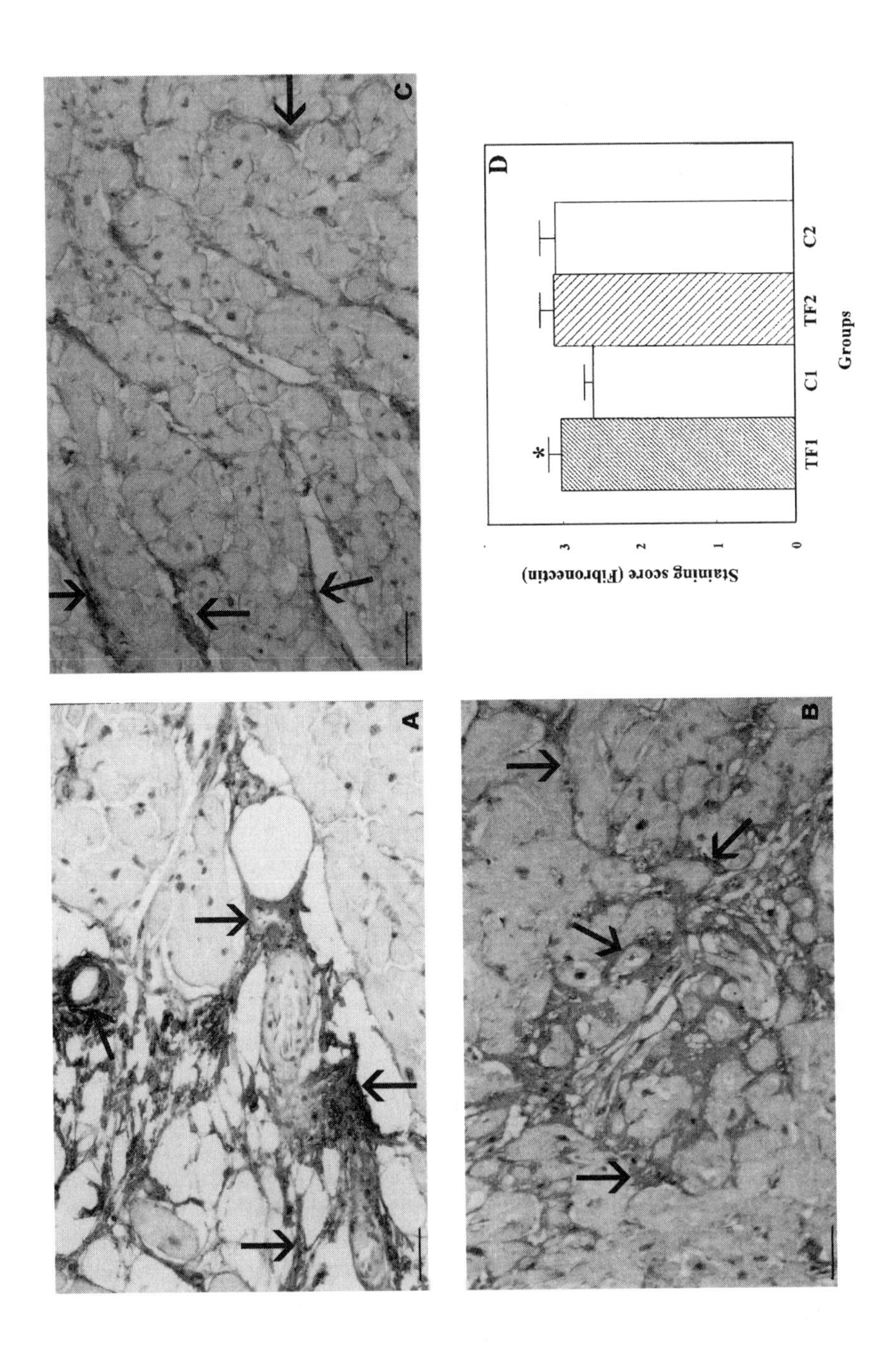
A
B
C
D
Staining score (Fibronectin)
0
1
2
3
*
TF1
C1
TF2
C2
Groups

amount of collagen as compared to TF1. Corrective surgery limits the myocardial overload and may therefore limit the amount of damage to the myocardial collagen matrix.[6] Our study provides further evidence that myocardial architecture in patients with TF is altered towards fibrotic state as the expression levels of extracellular matrix components like collagens and fibronectin were elevated. However, further research at the mRNA level would add to the notion that the gene expression of a number of proteins involved in fibrosis was transcriptionally altered.

SUMMARY AND CONCLUSION

In the present study the degree of myocardial fibrosis at protein level in patients with tetralogy of Fallot (TF) was examined by assessing quantitatively the expression of total collagens and fibronectin. We found a significant increase in staining for interstitial and total collagens at primary and secondary corrective surgery as compared to the age-matched control patients. However, immunohistochemical localization of fibronectin revealed significant increase in this protein levels at primary correction only. Our results clearly demonstrate an increased amount of myocardial extracellular matrix deposition resulting in tissue fibrosis in TF patients with right ventricular hypertrophy. This vital information could be of great help in assessing the timing of surgery as well as post-operative prognosis.

REFERENCES

1. CASTANEDA, A.R. *et al.* 1994. Cardiac Surgery of Neonate and Infant: 215–234. Saunders. Philadelphia.
2. ARAI, M. *et al.* 1994. Sarcoplasmic reticulum gene expression in cardiac hypertrophy and heart failure. Circ. Res. **74:** 555–564.
3. VAN BILSEN, M. & K.R. CHIEN. 1993. Growth and hypertrophy of the heart: towards an understanding of cardiac specific and inducible gene expression. Cardiovasc. Res. **27:** 1140–1149.
4. BOLUYT, M.O. *et al.* 1994. Alterations in cardiac gene expression during the transition from stable hypertrophy to heart failure. Marked upregulation of genes encoding extracellular matrix components. Circ. Res. **75:** 23–32.
5. SCHWARTZ, K. *et al.* 1993. Molecular phenotype of hypertrophied and failing myocardium. Circulation **87:** VII-5–VII-10.
6. WHITTAKER, P. 1997. Collagen and ventricular remodeling after acute myocardial infarcion: concepts and hypotheses. Basic Res. Cardiol. **92:** 79–81.
7. WEBER, K.T. *et al.* 1994. Collagen network of the myocardium: function, structural remodeling and regulatory mechanisms. J. Mol. Cell Cardiol. **26:** 279–292.
8. BISHOP, J.E. *et al.* 1994. Increased collagen synthesis and decreased collagen degradation in right ventricular hypertrophy induced by pressure overload. Cardiovasc. Res. **28:** 1581–1585.
9. BRILLA, C.G. *et al.* 1991. Impaired diastolic function and coronary reserve in genetic hypertension. Role of interstitial fibrosis and medial thickening of intramyocardial coronary arteries. Circ. Res. **69:** 107–115.
10. CHAPMAN, D. *et al.* 1990. Regulation of fibrillar collagen types I and III and basement membrane type IV collagen gene expression in pressure overloaded rat myocardium. Circ. Res. **67:** 787–794.
11. JALIL, J.E. *et al.* 1989. Fibrillar collagen and myocardial stiffness in the intact hypertrophied rat left ventricle. Circ. Res. **64:** 1041–1050.

12. Hess, O.M. *et al.* 1981. Diastolic function and myocardial structure in patients with myocardial hypertrophy. Special reference to normalized viscoelastic data. Circulation **63:** 360–371.
13. McLenachan, J.M. & H.J. Dargie. 1990. Ventricular arrhythmias in hypertensive left ventricular hypertrophy. Relationship to coronary artery disease, left ventricular dysfunction, and myocardial fibrosis. Am. J. Hypertens. **3:** 735–740.
14. Kawai, S. *et al.* 1984. A morphometrical study of myocardial disarray associated with right ventricular outflow tract obstruction. Jpn. Circ. J. **48:** 445–456.
15. Strauer, B.E. 1990. The significance of coronary reserve in clinical heart disease. J. Am. Coll. Cardiol. **15:** 775–783.
16. Farhadian, F. *et al.* 1995. Fibronectin expression during physiological and pathological cardiac growth. J. Mol. Cell. Cardiol. **27:** 981–990.
17. Samuel, J.L. *et al.* 1991. Accumulation of fetal fibronectin mRNAs during the development of rat cardiac hypertrophy induced by pressure overload. J. Clin. Invest. **88:** 1737–1746.
18. Brand, T. *et al.* 1992. Proto-oncogene expression in porcine myocardium subjected to ischemia and reperfusion. Circ. Res. **71:** 1351–1360.
19. Vikstrom, K.L. *et al.* 1998. Hypertrophy, pathology, and molecular markers of cardiac pathogenesis. Circ. Res. **82:** 773–778.
20. Starnes, V.A. *et al.* 1994. Current surgical management of tetralogy of Fallot. Ann. Thorac. Surg. **58:** 211–215.
21. Murphy, J.G. *et al.* 1993. Long-term outcome in patients undergoing surgical repair of tetralogy of Fallot. N. Engl. J. Med. **329:** 593–599.
22. Warner, K.G. *et al.* 1993. Restoration of the pulmonary valve reduces right ventricular volume overload after previous repair of tetralogy of Fallot. Circulation **88:** II189–197.
23. Sharma, H.S. *et al.* 1994. Expression and immunohistochemical localization of vascular endothelial growth factor during ischemia induced ventricular dysfunction in pigs. Circulation **90:** I-522.
24. Takahashi, T. *et al.* 1992. Age-related differences in the expression of proto-oncogene and contractile protein genes in response to pressure overload in the rat myocardium. J. Clin. Invest. **89:** 939–946.
25. Katz, A.M. 1990. Cardiomyopathy of overload. A major determinant of prognosis in congestive heart failure. N. Engl. J. Med. **322:** 100–110.
26. Mitsuno, M. *et al.* 1993. Fate of right ventricular hypertrophy in tetralogy of Fallot after corrective surgery. Am. J. Cardiol. **72:** 694–698.
27. Brand, T. *et al.* 1993. Expression of nuclear proto-oncogenes in isoproterenol-induced cardiac hypertrophy. J. Mol. Cell. Cardiol. **25:** 1325–1337.

Interaction of Bradykinin with Angiotensin, Prostacyclin, and Nitric Oxide in Myocardial Preservation[a]

MOTOAKI SATO,[b] DIPAK K. DAS,[b,d] AND RICHARD M. ENGELMAN[c]

[b]*Department of Surgery, University of Connecticut School of Medicine, Farmington, Connecticut 06030, USA*

[c]*Department of Cardiac Surgery, Baystate Medical Center, Springfield, Massachusetts 01199, USA*

ABSTRACT: This review focuses on the importance of bradykinin in myocardial preservation during ischemic arrest. Bradykinin is released from the heart spontaneously in response to ischemic stress, which may be viewed as a survival signal of the heart against ischemia. Bradykinin appears to function as a signaling molecule by controlling the release of other intracellular modulators, such as prostacyclins and nitric oxide, which also exert beneficial effects on the ischemic myocardium.

INTRODUCTION

Mammalian heart appears to be equipped with its own defense mechanism. In response to an acute injury, such as ischemia, a number of endogenous substances are released. These intracellular mediators include adenosine, prostacyclin, bradykinin, and nitric oxide, which are all cardioprotective. Ischemic stress also induces the release of detrimental mediators, e.g., thromboxane and endothelin. The released mediators appear to modulate each other's function. For example, the cardioprotective effects of angiotensin-converting enzyme (ACE) inhibitors against ischemia-reperfusion injury are mainly attributed to their ability to block the enzymatic breakdown of endogenous bradykinin. Indeed, preservation of bradykinin is primarily responsible for the cardioprotective actions of many ACE inhibitors, including ramiprilat.[1,2] Bradykinin is equally effective when applied exogenously.[3] Bradykinin, in turn, functions by stimulating endothelial B_2 receptors, which results in the release of prostacyclin and NO.[4] This review will focus on the interaction of bradykinin with angiotensin, prostacyclin, and nitric oxide, the other mediators released from the heart in response to an acute ischemic insult.

[a]This study was supported by National Institutes of Health grants HL 22559, HL 33889, and HL 56803.

[d]Address correspondence to: Dipak K. Das, Ph.D., University of Connecticut, School of Medicine, Farmington, CT 06030-1110 USA; Telephone: (860) 679-3687; Fax: (860) 679-4606; E-mail: DDAS@NEURON.UCHC.EDU

EFFECTS OF BRADYKININ IN ISCHEMIC MYOCARDIUM

Endogenously produced bradykinin plays a significant role in preserving vascular tone and myocardial protection. Infusion of bradykinin has been shown to reduce arrhythmias associated with ischemia-reperfusion in canine,[3] and to protect isolated hearts subjected to local ischemia and subsequent reperfusion.[5] The beneficial effects of bradykinin in heart are further supported by the observations that both intracoronary administration of bradykinin and treatment with drugs that induce the release of intracellular bradykinin are equally cardioprotective.[6,7] Conversely, any drug that antagonizes bradykinin release, by blocking bradykinin receptors, aggravates cellular injury associated with ischemia and reperfusion.[8]

Bradykinin can directly cause vasorelaxation via B_1 receptor activation.[9] In a recent study, a bradykinin B_2 receptor antagonist HOE 140 was shown to abolish the beneficial effects of ischemic preconditioning.[10,11] In this study, HOE 140 inhibited the bradykinin-mediated postischemic ventricular recovery. In another study, bradykinin caused translocation of protein kinase C isoforms α, ε, and ξ, a mechanism shared by ischemic preconditioning.[12]

MODULATION OF THE RELEASE AND SYNTHESIS OF ANGIOTENSIN, PROSTACYCLIN, NITRIC OXIDE, AND ENDOTHELIN BY BRADYKININ

Angiotensin II has been shown to be an important mediator, because blockade of renin, ACE, or AT_1 receptors produces similar reductions in the ventricular fibrillation that occurs following reperfusion after global ischemia in the isolated rat heart.[13] Angiotensin II can facilitate the release of noradrenaline from prejunctional sympathetic terminals.[14] When catecholamines are oxidized during reperfusion, free radicals are formed, which have been shown to contribute to reperfusion injury. ACE inhibitors, by blocking the formation of angiotensin II, prevent the facilitation of noradrenaline release from sympathetic nerve endings and thereby protect ischemic hearts from reperfusion injury.

ACE inhibitors appear to have beneficial effects in protecting the hearts against ischemia. For example, ACE inhibitors are able to limit infarct size and in hearts with post-ischemic insults ACE inhibitors attenuate the incidence and duration of reperfusion arrhythmias.[15] Long-term treatment with ACE inhibitors prolongs survival in rats after myocardial infarction with chronic congestive heart failure.[16] In human patients, severity of ischemia was related to neuroendocrine activation and ACE inhibition was found to be effective in moderating the severity of ischemia.[17] In another study, angiotensin II type 1 receptor antagonist was effective protection against myocardial ischemia-reperfusion injury, whereas exogenous angiotensin II accelerated this injury through angiotensin II type 1 receptor.[18]

Cardioprotective effects of ACE inhibitors are mediated, at least partially, through bradykinin.[19,20] Activation of ACE not only generates angiotensin II, it also causes degradation of bradykinin.[8] ACE inhibition increases coronary blood flow and ameliorates myocardial ischemia, primarily due to accumulation of bradykinin and production of nitric oxide from the ischemic myocardium.[21] The beneficial effects of bradykinin and ACE inhibition are realized via the formation of prostaglandins.[22] A recent study demonstrated that the beneficial action of bradykinin was dependent on an unrestrained action of prostacyclin and NO, because when bradykinin was given in conjunction with a NO blocker or a cyclooxygenase inhibitor, the beneficial effects of bradykinin were completely abolished.[23,24] Animal studies suggest that bradykinin could be involved in the protective action of ACE inhibitors in myocardial ischemia.[25] The anti-ischemic effect of ACE inhibitor ramiprilat was abolished by antagonizing bradykinin receptors or inhibiting nitric oxide synthase.[26]

In endothelial cells and isolated ischemic rat hearts, angiotensin II can stimulate cGMP production via the enhancement of NO.[27] ACE inhibition was found to induce NO and prostacyclin (PGI) formation in cultured bovine endothelial cells and to protect isolated ischemic rat hearts.[28] This study suggests that ACE inhibition results in the accumulation of endogenous bradykinin, which increases the synthesis of NO and PGI and protects the heart from ischemia-reperfusion injury. In human ophthalmic artery, bradykinin markedly stimulated the production of NO and this, along with endothelin, was found to play an important role in the regulation of local blood flow.[29] A recent investigation has shown that pretreatment with the nitric oxide synthase (NOS)–inhibitor L-NAME blocked the antiarrhythmic effects of preconditioning in the dog, suggesting that an effect to increase NO production may be a part of the protective mechanism.[30] This indirectly suggests a role for bradykinin in the preconditioning process as this peptide stimulates NO production.[31] Bradykinin given through columns of venous or arterial endothelial cells induced a dose-dependent release of NO and PGI_2.[32] Another study indicated that an imbalance between the endothelial production of endothelin and NO affects post-ischemic coronary blood flow and recovery of ventricular function.[33]

Bradykinin was found to induce changes in ET-1 mRNA in a biphasic manner in capillary endothelial cells, where the early induction was not dependent upon new protein synthesis, but the late induction was dependent on new protein synthesis.[34] This study also showed that the calcium ionophore ionomycin raised ET-1 mRNA levels in a manner similar to bradykinin. ET-1 steady-state levels were increased by angiotensin II.[35] Intracoronary infusion of bradykinin reduced the release of noradrenaline and endothelin, augmented post-ischemic ventricular recovery, and decreased reperfusion arrhythmias.[36] Endothelin accelerated, dose dependently, the formation of angiotensin II in cultured porcine endothelial cells via ACE activation.[37] In a recent study, ischemia was found to decrease ET-1 secretion rate by 55–65%, which was increased three- to fourfold upon reperfusion.[38] Perfusion of these hearts with angiotensin II increased ET-1 secretion. This study also measured the endogenous cardiac ET-1 level and the results did not support a vasoconstrictor action for endogenous ET-1 in rat hearts following ischemia-reperfusion, but rather pointed to a possible vasodilator role of the peptide under these conditions. Incubation with the ACE inhibitor captopril inhibited ET-1 secretion by endothelial cells and this inhibition was reversed by coincubation with an inhibitor for NO synthesis, suggesting that NO participates in captopril-induced inhibition of ET-1 secretion.[39] Interestingly, in the presence of a bradykinin B_2 receptor antagonist, captopril did not inhibit but rather stimulated ET-1 secretion, whereas bradykinin inhibited this ET-1 secretion and this inhibition by bradykinin was reversed by coincubation with the NO blocker suggesting that captopril inhibited ET-1 secretion from endothelial cells through bradykinin.

BRADYKININ AS A SIGNALING MOLECULE

Bradykinin acts via G protein–coupled receptor and bradykinin B_2 receptor.[40,41] Binding of this hormone to these receptors induces signal transduction including activation of PLC, production of inositol triphosphate, and release of Ca^{2+} from intracellular stores.[42] This signal transduction pathway leads to the formation of another second messenger, diacylglycerol, which in turn activates PKC.[43] Both bradykinin and endothelin can perturb the membrane by Ca^{2+} homeostasis of mammaliam cells.[44] Such signal transduction mechanism of bradykinin is further supported by a study that demonstrated that bradykinin at physiological concentrations robustly stimulated phosphoinositide turnover and this effect was susceptible to sensitization by receptor agonists of bradykinin or ET-1.[45] The authors' observations further suggested that bradykinin receptors are coupled to phospholipase C, and PKC plays a prominent role in the negative-feedback regulation of bradykinin-evoked phosphoinositide response. A study has demonstrated that the three neuropeptides, endothelin, bradykinin, and angiotensin II, are linked to stimulation of phosphoinositide turnover and potentiate signal transduction that generates second messenger Ca^{2+}.[46]

In a recent study investigating the effects of the calcium channel blockers on the response of endothelin, bradykinin, and NO in isolated porcine ciliary arteries, lacidipine and nifedipine significantly decreased the sensitivity to ET-1 as compared to control.[47] On the other hand, endothelium-dependent relaxations to bradykinin remained unaffected by the calcium channel blockers, suggesting that calcium channel blockers selectively inhibit ET-1–induced contractions. In human endothelial cells, staurosporine inhibition of PKC reduced basal ET-1 release by 50%, while cAMP increased its release by 68%.[48] The results of this study suggested that inhibition of endothelin secretion could result from cross-talk between the adenylate cyclase and PLC pathways. Angiotensin II pretreatment was found to activate PKC in isolated rabbit hearts.[49] NO stimulates the soluble cGMP, a second messenger, which has been found to modulate phosphoinositide turnover and formation of diacylglycerol, which in turn activates PKC.[50,51] In endothelial cells, angiotensin II stimulates the production of cGMP, which is also augmented by NO synthesis.[52] It has been found that angiotensin II enhances NO production due to the AT_2 receptor stimulation.[53] In cardiac muscle, AT_1 receptor has been shown to couple to second-messenger systems that activate PKC.[54]

A recent study revealed that pretreatment with angiotensin II activated PKC and limited myocardial infarction in isolated rabbit hearts.[55] In cardiac tissue, α_1 adrenoceptor stimulation is coupled with phosphoinositide (PI) response.[38] Thus, prazosin, an α_1 adrenoceptor antagonist, and neomycin, which binds to PI-4,5 P_2, were found to inhibit PI-4,5 P_2 hydrolysis, simultaneously blocking all the components of inotropic responses of the left ventricular muscle.[56] Hydrolysis of PI-4,5 P_2 (via stimulation of phospholipase C)[57] generates two second messengers, diacylglycerol and IP_3, which may lead to a number of intracellular events. In addition, hydrolysis of phosphatidyl choline via stimulation of phospholipase D can generate phosphatidic acid, which is dephosphorylated by phosphatidate phosphatase into diacylglycerol and makes a major contribution to the enhanced diacylglycerol level during ischemia.[58] During ischemia and reperfusion diacylglycerol is generated in the presence of increased cytosolic Ca^{2+}, and Ca^{2+}-activated phospholipid-dependent PKC

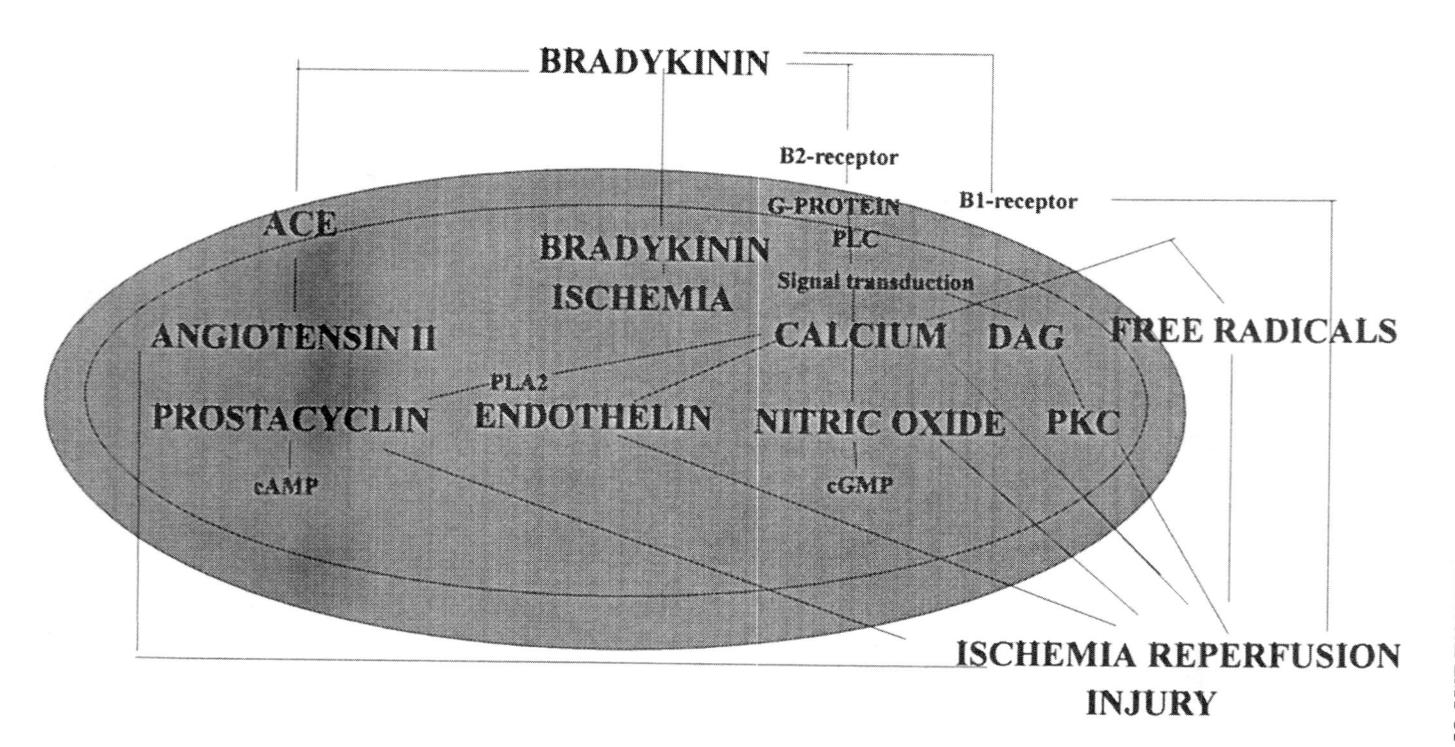

FIGURE 1. Interaction of bradykinin, angiotensin, prostacyclin, and nitric oxide in myocardial preservation. ACE, Angiotensin converting enzyme; cAMP, Cyclic adenosine monophosphate; cGMP, Cyclic guanosine monophosphate; DAG, Diacylglycerol; PKC, Protein kinase C; PLC, Phospholipase C; PLA_2, Phospholipase A_2.

is likely to be translocated to the plasmalemmal membrane from the cytosol and then becomes activated.[59] Our laboratory demonstrated ischemia-reperfusion induced PI turnover and generation of second messengers through the activation of phospholipase C.[60]

SUMMARY AND CONCLUSION

In normal heart, coronary vasomotor tone is regulated by various circulating hormones including bradykinin, endothelin, nitric oxide (NO), and prostacyclins. Ischemia-reperfusion triggers the release of these vasoactive hormones thereby upsetting the intrinsic regulatory mechanisms.[61] This review should make clear that the release of these endogenous mediators plays a significant role in myocardial ischemia-reperfusion injury. The initial signaling event appears to be triggered by the activation of endogenous bradykinin which acts directly via the B_1 receptor and indirectly by simultaneously activating ACE and B_2 receptor on the endothelial cell surface (FIG. 1). Activation of ACE stimulates detrimental angiotensin II production, while B_2 receptor coupled with G protein potentiates the signal transduction, generating a series of second messengers by activating PLC. Activation of PLC mobilizes cellular Ca^{2+}, which acts as the second messenger to stimulate the formation of endothelin, nitric oxide, and prostacyclin (PGI). The production of PGI is probably mediated through the activation of Ca^{2+}-dependent PLA_2. Additionally, intracellular Ca^{2+} overloading causes the production of oxygen free radicals. Activation of PLC also leads to the generation of another second messenger, diacylglycerol, which translocates and activates PKC.

In conclusion, this review focuses on the importance of bradykinin in myocardial preservation during ischemic arrest. Bradykinin is released from the heart spontaneously in response to ischemic stress which may be viewed as a survival signal of the heart against ischemia. Bradykinin appears to function as a signaling molecule by controlling the release of other intracellular modulators such as prostacyclins and nitric oxide, which also exert beneficial effects on the ischemic myocardium.

REFERENCES

1. MASSOUDY, P., B.F. BECKER & E. GERLACH. Bradykinin accounts for improved postischemic function and lowered glutathione release of guinea pig hearts, treated with the ACE inhibitor ramiprilat. J. Cardiovasc. Pharmacol. **23:** 632–639.
2. BAUMGARTEN, C.R., W. LINZ, G. KUNKEL, B.A. SCHOLKENS & G. WEIMER. 1993. Ramiprilat increases bradykinin outflow from isolated hearts of rat. Br. J. Pharmacol. **108:** 293–295.
3. VEGH, A., L. SZEKERES & J.R. PARRATT. 1991. Local intracoronary infusions of bradykinin profoundly reduce the severity of ischemia-induced arrhythmias in anesthetized dogs. Br. J. Pharmacol. **104:** 294–295.
4. CHAHINE, R., A. ADAM, N. YAMAGUCHI, R. GASPO, D. REGOLI & R. NADEAU. 1993. Protective effects of bradykinin on the ischemic heart: implications of the B_1 receptor. Br. J. Pharmacol. **108:** 318–322.
5. SCHOLKENS, B.A., W. LINZ & W. KONIG. 1988. Effects of the angiotensin converting enzyme inhibitor, ramipril, in isolated ischemic rat heart are abolished by a bradykinin antagonist. J. Hypertension (Suppl 4): S25–S28.

6. Baumgarten, C.R., W. Linz, G. Kunkel, B.A. Scholkens & G. Wiemer. 1993. Ramiprilat increases bradykinin outflow from isolated hearts of rat. Br. J. Pharmacol. **108:** 293–295.
7. Martorana, P.A., B. Kettenbach, G. Breipohl, W. Linz & B.A. Scholkens. 1990. Reduction of infarct size by local angiotensin-converting enzyme inhibition is abolished by a bradykinin antagonist. Eur. J. Pharmacol. **182:** 395–396.
8. Yang, H., E.G. Erdos & Y. Levin. 1970. A dipeptidyl carboxypeptidase that converts angiotensin and inactivates bradykinin. Biochim. Biophys. Acta **214:** 374–376.
9. Regoli, D. & J. Barabe. 1980. Pharmacology of bradykinin and related kinins. Pharmacol. Rev. **32:** 1–46.
10. Wall, T.M., R. Sheehy & J.C. Hartman. 1994. Role of bradykinin in myocardial preconditioning. J. Pharmacol. Exp. Ther. **270:** 681–689.
11. Goto, M. Y. Liu, X.-M. Yang, J.L. Ardell, M.V. Cohen & J.M. Downey. 1995. Role of bradykinin in the protection of ischemic preconditioning in rabbit hearts. Circ. Res. **77:** 611–621.
12. Brew, E.C., M.B. Rehring, T.F. Gamboni-Robertson, F. McIntyre, R. Harken & A.H. Banerjee. 1995. Role of bradykinin in cardiac functional protection after global ischemia-reperfusion in rat heart. Am. J. Physiol. **269:** H1370–H1378.
13. Fleetwood, G., S. Boutinet, M. Meier & J.M. Wood. 1991. Involvement of the renin-angiotensin system in ischemic damage and reperfusion arrhythmias in the isolated rat heart. J. Cardiovasc. Pharmacol. **17:** 351–357.
14. Peach, M.J. & D.E. Dostal. 1990. The angiotensin II receptor and the actions of angiotensin II. J. Cardiovasc. Pharmacol. **16**(suppl IV)**:** S25–S30.
15. Ertl, G., R.A. Kloner, R.W. Alexander & E. Braunwald. 1982. Limitation of experimental infarct size by an angiotensin-converting enzyme inhibitor. Circulation **65:** 40–48.
16. Sweet, C.S., S.E. Emmert, I.I. Stabilito & G.T. Ribeiro. 1987. Increased survival in rats with congestive heart failure treated with enalapril. J. Cardiovasc. Pharmacol. **10:** 636–642.
17. Remme, W.J., D.A.C. Kruyssen, M.P. Look, M. Bootsma & P.W. De Leeuw. 1994. Systemic and cardiac neuroendocrine activation and severity of myocardial ischemia in humans. J. Am. Coll. Cardiol. **23:** 82–91.
18. Yoshiyama, M., S. Kim, H. Yamagishi, T. Omura, T. Tani, S. Yanagi, I. Toda, M. M. Teragaki, K. Akioka, K. Takeuchi & T. Takeda. 1994. Cardioprotective effect of the angiotensin II type 1 receptor antagonist TC116 on ischemia reperfusion injury. Am. Heart J. **128:** 1–6.
19. Linz, W. & B.A. Scholkens. 1992. Role of bradykinin in the cardiac effects of angiotensin-converting enzyme inhibitors. J. Cardiovasc. Pharmacol. **20**(Suppl 9)**:** S83–S90.
20. Wiemer, G., B.A. Scholkens, R.H.A. Becker & R. Busse. 1991. Ramiprilat enhances endothelial autacoid formation by inhibiting breakdown of endothelium-derived bradykinin. Hypertension **18:** 558–563.
21. Kitakaze, M., T. Minamino, K. Node, K. Komamura, Y. Shinozaki, H. Mori, H. Kosaka, M. Inoue, M. Hori & T. Kamada. 1995. Beneficial effects of inhibition of angiotensin-converting enzyme on ischemic myocardium during coronary hypoperfusion in dogs. Circulation **92:** 950–961.
22. Schror, K. 1992. Role of prostaglandins in the cardiovascular effects of bradykinin and angiotensin-converting enzyme inhibitors. J. Cardiovasc. Pharmacol. **20** (Suppl 9)**:** S68–S73.
23. Zhu, P., C.E. Zaugg, D. Simper, P. Hornstein, P.R. Allegrini & P.T. Buser. 1995. Bradykinin improves postischemic recovery in the rat heart: role of high energy phosphates, nitric oxide, and prostacyclin. Cardiovasc. Res. **29:** 658–663.
24. Hartman, J.C. 1995. The role of bradykinin and nitric oxide in the cardioprotective action of ACE inhibitors. Ann. Thorac. Surg. **60:** 789–792.
25. Linz, L., P.A. Martorana & B. Scholkens. 1990. Local inhibition of bradykinin degradation in ischemic hearts. J. Cardiovasc. Pharmacol. **15:** S99–S109.
26. Hartman, J.C. 1995. The role of bradykinin and nitric oxide in the cardioprotective action of ACE inhibitors. Ann. Thorac. Surg. **60:** 789–792.

27. Wiemer, G., B.A. Scholkens, A. Wagner, H. Heitsch & W. Linz. 1993. The possible role of angiotensin II subtype AT_2 receptors in endothelial cells and isolated ischemic rat hearts. J. Hypertension **11**(Suppl 5): S234–S235.
28. Linz, W., G. Wiemer & B.A. Scholkens. 1992. ACE-inhibition induces NO-formation in cultured bovine endothelial cells and protects isolated ischemic rat hearts. J. Mol. Cell Cardiol. **24:** 909–919.
29. Haefliger, I.O., J. Flammer & T.F. Luscher. 1992. Nitric oxide and endothelin-1 are important regulators of human ophthalmic artery. Invest. Ophthalmol. Vis. Sci. **33:** 2340–2343.
30. Vegh, A., L. Szekeres & J. Parratt. 1992. Preconditioning of the ischemic myocardium: Involvement of the L-arginine nitric oxide pathway. Br. J. Pharmacol. **107:** 648–652.
31. Wiemer, G., B.A. Scholkens, R.H. Becker & R. Busse. 1991. Ramiprilat enhances endothelial autocoid formation by inhibiting breakdown of endothelium-derived bradykinin. Hypertension **18:** 558–563.
32. D'Orleans-Juste, P., J.A. Mitchell, E.G. Wood, M. Hecker & J.R. Vane. 1992. Comparison of the release of vasoactive factors from venous and arterial bovine cultured endothelial cells. Can. J. Physiol. Pharmacol. **70:** 687–694.
33. Hiramatsu, T., J.M. Forbess, T. Miura, S.J. Roth, M.A. Cioffi & J.E. Mayer. 1996. Effects of endothelin-1 and L-arginine after cold ischemia in lamb hearts. Ann. Thorac. Surg. **61:** 36–41.
34. Marsden, P.A., D.M. Dorfman, T. Collins, B.B. Brenner, S.T. Orkin & B.J. Ballerman. 1991. Am. J. Physiol. **261:** F117–F125.
35. Imai, T., Y. Hirata, T. Emori, M. Yanagisawa, T. Masaki & F. Marumo. 1992. Hypertension **19:** 753–757.
36. Ribuot, C., N. Yamaguchi, D. Godin, L. Jette, A. Adam & R. Nadeau. 1994. Intracoronary infusion of bradykinin: effects on noradrenaline overflow following reperfusion of ischemic myocardium in the anesthetized dog. Fundam. & Clin. Pharmacol. **8:** 532–538.
37. Kawaguchi, H., H. Sawa & H. Yasuda. 1991. Effect of endothelin on angiotensin converting enzyme activity in cultured pulmonary artery endothelial cells. J. Hypertension **9:** 171–174.
38. Brunner, F. 1995. Tissue endothelin-1 levels in perfused rat heart following stimulation with agonists and in ischemia and reperfusion. J. Mol. Cell Cardiol. **27:** 1953–1963.
39. Momose, N., K. Fukuo, S. Morimoto & T. Ogihara. 1993. Captopril inhibits endothelin-1 secretion from endothelial cells through bradykinin. Hypertension **21:** 921–924.
40. McEachern, A.E., E.R. Shelton, R. Obernolte, P. Zuppan, J. Fujisaki, R.W. Aldrich & K. Jarnagin. 1991. Proc. Natl. Acad. Sci. USA **88:** 7724–7728.
41. Abd Alla, S., J. Buschko, U. Quitterer, A. Maidhof, M. Haasemann, G. Breipohl, J. Knolle & W. Muller-Esterl. 1993. J. Biol. Chem. **268:** 17277–17285.
42. Farmer, S.G. & R.M. Burch. 1992. Annu. Rev. Pharmacol. Toxicol. **32:** 511–536.
43. Burch, R., S. Farmer & L. Steranka. 1990. Bradykinin receptor antagonists. Med. Res. Rev. **10:** 237–269.
44. Quitterer, U., C. Schroder, W.M. Ester & H. Rehm. 1995. Effects of bradykinin and endothelin-1 on the calcium homeostasis of mammalian cells. J. Biol. Chem. **270:** 1992–1995.
45. Lin, W.W. & D.M. Chuang. 1992. Regulation of bradykinin-induced phosphoinositide turnover in cultured cerebellar astrocytes: possible role of protein kinase C. Neurochem. Int. **21:** 573–579.
46. Ogino, Y. & T. Costa. 1992. The epithelial phenotype of human neuroblastoma cells expresses bradykinin, endothelin, and angiotensin II receptors that stimulate phosphoinositide hydrolysis, J. Neurochem. **58:** 46–56.
47. Meyer, P., M.G. Lang, J. Flammer & T. Luscher. 1995. Effects of calcium channel blockers on the response to endothelin-1, bradykinin and sodium nitroprusside in porcine ciliary arteries. Eye Res. **60:** 505–510.

48. Stewart, D.J., P. Cernacek, F. Mohamed, D. Blais, K. Cianflone & J.C. Monge. 1994. Role of cyclin nucleotides in the regulation of endothelin-1 production by human endothelial cells. Am. J. Physiol. **266:** H944–H951.
49. Liu, Y., A. Tsuchida, M.V. Cohen & J.M. Downey. 1995. Pretreatment with angiotensin II activates protein kinase C and limits myocardial infarction in isolated rabbit hearts. J. Mol. Cell Cardiol. **27:** 883–892.
50. Maulik, N., D.T. Engelman, M. Watanabe, R.M. Engelman, G. Maulik, G.A. Cordis & D.K. Das. 1995. Nitric oxide signaling in ischemic heart. Cardiovasc. Res. **30:** 593–601.
51. Maulik, N., D.T. Engelman, M. Watanabe, R.M. Engelman, J.A. Rousou, J.E. Flack, D.W. Deaton, N.V. Gorbunov, N.M. Elsayed, V.E. Kagan & D.K. Das. 1996. Nitric oxide/carbon monoxide. A molecular switch for myocardial preservation during ischemia. Circulation **94**(Suppl II)**:** 398–406.
52. Buonassisi, V. & J.C. Venter. 1976. Hormone and neurotransmitter receptors in an established vascular endothelial cell line. Proc. Natl. Acad. Sci. USA **73:** 1612–1616.
53. Wiemer, G., B.A. Scholkens, A. Wagner, H. Heitsch & W. Linz. 1993. The possible role of angiotensin II subtype AT_2 receptors in endothelial cells and isolated ischemic rat hearts. J. Hypertension **11**(Suppl 5)**:** S234–S235.
54. Sadoshima, J.-I. & S. Izumo. 1993. Signal transduction pathways of angiotensin II-induced *c-fos* gene expression in cardiac myocytes *in vitro*: role of phospholipid-derived second messengers. Circ. Res. **73:** 424–438.
55. Liu, Y., A. Tsuchida, M.V. Cohen & J.M. Downey. 1995. Pretreatment with angiotensin II activates protein kinase C and limits myocardial infarction in isolated rabbit hearts. J. Mol. Cell Cardiol. **27:** 883–892.
56. Otani, H., H. Otani & D.K. Das. 1986. Evidence that phosphoinositide response is mediated by α_1-adrenoceptor stimulation but not linked with excitation-contraction coupling in cardiac muscle. Biochem. Biophys. Res. Commun. **136:** 863–869.
57. Otani, H., H. Otani & D.K. Das. 1988. α_1-adrenoceptor-mediated phosphoinositide breakdown and inotropic response in rat left ventricular papillary muscles. Circ. Res. **62:** 8–17.
58. Otani, H., M.R. Prasad, R. Engelman, H. Otani, G. Cordis & D.K. Das. 1988. Enhanced phosphodiesteratic breakdown and turnover of phosphoinositides during reperfusion of ischemic heart. Circ. Res. **63:** 930–936.
59. Moraru, I.I., L.M. Popescu, N. Maulik, X. Liu & D.K. Das. 1992. Phospholipase D signaling in ischemic heart. Biochim. Biophys. Acta **1139:** 148–154.
60. Prasad, R., L. Popescu, I. Moraru, X. Liu, R.M. Engelman & D.K. Das. 1991. Role of phospholipase A_2 and phospholipase C in myocardial ischemic reperfusion injury. Am. J. Physiol. **260:** H877–H883.
61. Parratt, J.R., A. Vegh & J.G. Papp. 1995. Bradykinin as an endogenous myocardial protective substance with particular reference to ischemic preconditioning—a brief review of the evidence. Can. J. Physiol. Pharmacol. **73:** 837–842.

Alternatives for Myocardial Protection:

Adenosine-Enhanced Ischemic Preconditioning[a]

JAMES D. MCCULLY[b] AND SIDNEY LEVITSKY

Division of Cardiothoracic Surgery, Beth Israel Deaconess Medical Center and Harvard Medical School, Boston, Massachusetts 02115, USA

ABSTRACT: Intrinsic to the development of new myoprotective protocols for use in cardiac surgery are the requirements of new protocols to be equal to or better than conventional cardioplegia in providing for enhanced post-ischemic functional recovery and decreased myocardial infarct size. Our data suggest that adenosine-enhanced ischemic preconditioning, in which a bolus injection of adenosine to the myocardium is used coincident with ischemic preconditioning, meets these requirements, providing equal cardioprotection as that of cold blood cardioplegia, significantly decreasing myocardial infarct size and significantly enhancing post-ischemic myocardial functional recovery in both the isolated perfused rabbit heart and in the *in situ* blood-perfused sheep heart. These results further suggest that adenosine-enhanced ischemic preconditioning may provide an effective, alternative myocardial protective protocol to reduce the morbidity and mortality in cardiac surgery.

Myocardial ischemia occurs as the result of attenuation or cessation of coronary blood flow such that oxygen delivery to the myocardium is insufficient to meet oxygen requirements.[1] In global myocardial ischemia, coronary blood flow is completely obstructed resulting in the termination of substrate delivery and the discontinuance of catabolite removal. While it is generally accepted that the cessation of coronary blood flow, and thus oxygen delivery, is the initial step in the process leading to myocardial ischemic injury, the sequence of events following the initial insult remains controversial.[2,3]

Cardioplegia is used as a myoprotective agent for the alleviation of surgically induced ischemic injury incurred during cardiac operations to allow for the functional preservation of the myocardium. These solutions allow for the rapid electromechanical arrest of the myocardium through alteration of cellular electrochemical gradients.[4] Most cardioplegia solutions use high potassium concentrations to arrest the heart. The use of hypothermic potassium cardioplegia in adult open heart surgery increases the available intraoperative time and has been correlated with improved post-ischemic myocardial functional recovery and reduced postoperative mortality.[4] Po-

[a]This study was supported by the National Institutes of Health (HL 29077) and the American Heart Association.

[b]Address correspondence to: James D. McCully, Ph.D., Division of Cardiothoracic Surgery, Beth Israel Deaconess Medical Center, 110 Francis Street, Suite 2C, Boston, MA 02215; Telephone: 617-667-0725; Fax: 617-975-5245.

tassium-induced arrest maintains the heart in a depolarized state, significantly decreasing the energy demand of the myocardium. However, basal metabolic energy requirements are sustained under potassium-induced arrest and thus still constitute a significant energy expenditure.[5] In addition, depolarization leads to the alteration of the ion flux across the sarcolemmal membrane and is associated with both increased $[Ca^{2+}]_i$ accumulation and the significant depletion of cellular ATP reserves.[6]

ALTERNATIVES TO CARDIOPLEGIA: ISCHEMIC PRECONDITIONING

Murry and colleagues[7] were the first to describe ischemic preconditioning (IPC), an endogenous myocardial protection in which the imposition of one or more brief periods of ischemia (3–5 min) followed by reperfusion "preconditions" the heart such that infarct size and myocardial necrosis is significantly reduced during the subsequent induction of sublethal ischemia. Although the mechanism(s) by which preconditioning affords myocardial protection has yet to be elucidated, numerous investigations by several groups have indicated that IPC is associated with decreased ventricular arrthymia; preservation of creatine phosphate, ATP, and intracellular pH; decreased ultrastructural abnormalities; induction of heat shock proteins; increased release of adenosine; activation of A_1 and A_3 receptors; activation of G proteins; and activation of protein kinase C.[7–12] The effects of IPC, while potent, appear to be transitory in that the effects of IPC are lost if the sublethal ischemic insult occurs 60–90 min after IPC is performed.[13]

The induction of endogenous myocardial protection via preconditioning appears reduce myocardial infarct volume in all species studied. However, the effects of preconditioning on post-ischemic myocardial functional recovery have been shown to vary among species—in contrast to the protective effects of cardioplegia.[1,10,11,14,15] In the rat heart, preconditioning has been shown to reduce myocardial infarction and enhance post-ischemic myocardial functional recovery.[10,12,14,16] In contrast, in the rabbit heart, while preconditioning has been shown to reduce myocardial infarction, no enhancement of postischemic myocardial functional recovery occurs.[11,17–19] Kolocassides and colleagues[16] have previously demonstrated that in the rat heart preconditioning and cardioplegia each provide similar levels of myocardial protection by reducing myocardial infarction and enhancing post-ischemic myocardial functional recovery. The use of preconditioning in combination with cardioplegia failed to provide any additive protection.

POTENTIAL ROLE OF ISCHEMIC PRECONDITIONING IN HUMANS

At present the applicability of IPC as an adjunct to conventional cardioplegia in humans remains to be determined. Direct clinical evidence for IPC in humans with infarct size as an endpoint cannot be obtained. Collateral evidence exists to suggest that IPC may occur in patients undergoing balloon angioplasty or may be a byproduct of cardiopulmonary bypass.[20–22] Circumstantial evidence from percutaneous transluminal coronary angioplasty has shown that more severe ischemia, as characterized by pain, ST segment changes, and lactate production, occurs following the first balloon inflation and that subsequent inflations are less injurious.[20,21] Confounding the interpretation of parallel human examples simulating IPC are the effects of therapeutic interventions, the contribution of collateral vessels, and the use of vastly differing preconditioning periods. In percutaneous transluminal coronary angioplasty, balloon inflation is only 90 sec, a time shown to be too short to induce preconditioning in animal studies.[20] Similar doubts have arisen regarding experiments using *in vitro* monolayer cultures of quiescent human ventricular cardiomyocytes in which it has been shown that cellular injury is significantly decreased in preconditioned cells.[23] Preconditioning in these *in vitro* experiments was performed using either 10, 20, or 30 min of ischemia and 10, 20, or 30 min of reperfusion before induction of global ischemia. Results from this study indicated that 20-min ischemia and 20-min reperfusion provided the best protection from the effects of 90-min ischemia based on enzyme leakage, hydrogen ion release, and cellular viability.[23]

Yellon and colleagues[24] have shown that in patients on cardiopulmonary bypass the use of IPC (two 3-min periods of ischemia and 2-min reperfusion) before 10-min ischemia significantly preserved ATP measured during the initial reperfusion period. While scant, these data suggest that IPC may be a valuable adjunct to conventional cardioplegia and may allow for enhanced post-ischemic myocardial protection in the human myocardium.

ADENOSINE AND ADENOSINE RECEPTORS

Downey and colleagues have proposed that adenosine, a ubiquitous biological compound formed as a consequence of the breakdown of high energy phosphate (ATP) during preconditioning plays a central role in the cardioprotection afforded by IPC.[25] Extracellular adenosine acts on specific receptors on the cell surface, the adenosine receptors, which have their active sites exposed to the extracellular space. Three types of adenosine receptors have been identified as the A_1, A_2, and A_3 receptors. The A_1 receptor is located on cardiomyocytes and is coupled to its effectors (ionic channels and adenylate cyclase) via a pertussis toxin–sensitive G protein.[26] Activation of A_1 receptors has been shown to delay ischemic contracture and to improve glucose utilization by stimulation of anaerobic glycolysis.[27–29] The A_2 receptor is present in adult cardiac tissue, on coronary vascular smooth muscle, and endothelial cells.[26] Activation of the A_2 receptor is believed to elicit cAMP-dependent vasodilation, is thought to be involved in the stimulation of gluconeogenesis and the release of EDRF (nitric oxide), and may be involved in the inhibition of neutrophil adherence and aggregation.[26] The A_3 receptor is present in cardiac tissue and has been shown to be similar to the A_1 receptor, in that it too is coupled to a pertussis toxin–sensitive G protein.[30] It has been proposed that endogenous adenosine, acting via the A_1 in pig and dog and perhaps the A_3 receptor in the rabbit heart, mediates preconditioning.[7,10,13,27]

Several potential beneficial effects of IPC have been ascribed to adenosine. These include coronary and collateral artery vasodilation, allowing for increased oxygen supply, and related effects that act to decrease myocardial oxygen demand, such as negative inotropism, chronotropism, and dromotropism.[27,31] Adenosine, by its property to antagonize calcium channels, has been shown to inhibit the sinoatrial and the atrioventricular nodes and myocardial contraction, thereby inducing cardiac arrest.[32] In comparison to potassium-induced arrest, it has been shown that adenosine cardioplegia provides for shorter cardiac arrest time and improved mechanical recovery.[32] Mentzer and Lasley[33] have shown that the use of adenosine as a cardioplegic agent allows for enhanced preservation of myocardial function and energetics. Adenosine has also been implicated in the protection afforded against myocardial infarction ("second window of protection") observed 24 h after the imposition of IPC.[34] In rabbit hearts it has been shown that a 5-min infusion with adenosine (140 mg/kg/min) followed by a 10-min washout before ischemia reduced infarct size from 41 to 25% as compared to 10% in IPC-treated hearts.[35] Toombs and colleagues[36] have shown that pretreatment with exogenous adenosine (140 μg/kg/min, for 5 min with a 10-min washout) was effective in reducing infarct size but did not reduce stunning. This agrees with the reports of others who have shown that transient infusion of adenosine followed by washout is ineffectual in attenuating myocardial stunning.[14,18]

Lawson and Downey[13] suggest that adenosine is both a mediator and a trigger for preconditioning and that continued occupancy of adenosine receptors during ischemia is required before preconditioning can be achieved. Adenosine receptor blockade, using non-selective antagonists, either before or after IPC, has been shown to suppress the effects of IPC.[10,13] Investigations comparing the cardioprotective effects of IPC with adenosine receptor blockade administered either at the time of both ischemia and reperfusion or of reperfusion only indicate that endogenous adenosine protects the heart from injury during both ischemia and reperfusion.[37,38] However, it is important to note that when the adenosine receptor antagonist was administered after a 30-min reperfusion, no cardioprotection was observed.[38]

Investigation as to the contribution of the specific adenosine receptors suggests that the cardioprotection afforded by IPC during ischemia is primarily regulated by the A_1 receptor and possibly the A_3 receptor, whereas protection from reperfusion-induced injury appears to be by a non A_1 receptor type and possibly A_2.[37,39] Downey and colleagues[40] have shown that the use of the selective and potent A_1 receptor agonist 8-cyclopentyl-1,3-dipropyl xanthine (220 μM, DPCPX) failed to block the protection afforded by ischemic preconditioning in the rabbit heart. Further investigation indicated that blockade of the A_3 receptor was poorly blocked by DPCPX,[39] suggesting that the cardioprotective effects afforded by ischemic preconditioning may be mediated by the A_3 and not the A_1 receptor. This hypothesis has been confirmed by Liu and colleagues,[39] who showed that use of a specific A_3 receptor antagonist blocked the protection afforded by ischemic preconditioning.

ADENOSINE SUPPLEMENTATION

It has been previously noted that while sufficient evidence exists to indicate that endogenous adenosine plays a central role in the cardioprotection afforded by ischemic preconditioning, it is not optimal since the administration of exogenous adenosine or its analogs increases the degree of cardioprotection.[41] The use of adenosine deaminase inhibitors, adenosine transport inhibitors, or a combination of both has been previously shown to be effective in increasing the local production of adenosine.[42–47] However, limitations for the use of these pharmacological agents include possible compromise of immune function and systemic hemodynamic effects.[42–47]

Acadesine is an adenosine-regulating agent that has been shown in clinical trials to elevate endogenous adenosine levels and to reduce perioperative myocardial infarction.[48] While acadesine appears to act in all species and provides cardioprotection similar to that afforded by adenosine, it does not act directly on the adenosine receptors nor is it an adenosine percursor.[49] Blockade of adenosine receptors or the removal of endogenous adenosine by adenosine deaminase abolishes the cardioprotective effects of acadesine.[50] Acadesine is a purine nucleoside analog, metabolized via inosine monophosphate to uric acid. Conversion from inosine monophosphate to AMP is blocked by the phosphorylated metabolite of acadesine (ZMP), which prevents conversion to adenosine or adenine nucleotides.[51] These results support the contention that endogenous adenosine plays an important role in cardioprotection. The action of acadesine in providing for cardioprotection appears to involve amplification of the endogenous purine pathway, but, the mechanism leading to enhanced endogenous adenosine levels remains to be resolved.

ADENOSINE-ENHANCED ISCHEMIC PRECONDITIONING: AN ALTERNATIVE TO CARDIOPLEGIA

Previous reports have indicated that there are differential responses to steady-state, as compared to bolus, adenosine injections.[52,53] In human patients, adenosine has been shown to cause pain and discomfort. Langervist and colleagues[52] have shown that when delivered by steady-state infusion adenosine was associated with myocardial ischemia as determined by lactate production, ST segment depression, and chest pain. Adenosine delivery by intracoronary bolus injection was found to obviate these effects.[52]

Using the hypothesis that adenosine plays a central role in the protection afforded by IPC and that increased interstitial fluid levels of adenosine are associated with this response, we speculated that the use of an intracoronary bolus injection of adenosine when used coincident with IPC, a myocardial protective protocol we have termed "adenosine-enhanced ischemic preconditioning," may allow for enhanced myocardial protection. To test this hypothesis a series of experiments using the isolated perfused rabbit heart was designed to investigate and compare the cardioprotective effects of IPC, magnesium-supplemented potassium cardioplegia (K/Mg), and adenosine-enhanced ischemic preconditioning.[54] In these experiments IPC was performed using a single cycle, 5-min zero-flow global ischemia and 5-min reperfusion before onset of a subsequent 30-min ischemia and 120-min reperfusion. Global ischemia (GI) was achieved by cross-clamping of the aorta. Adenosine-enhanced ischemic preconditioning (APC) was achieved by the administration of a single bolus injection of adenosine (1 mmol in 10 ml) via the aortic root coincident with IPC. K/Mg cardioplegia hearts were infused with magnesium-supplemented potassium cardioplegia (20 mmol/l, KCl and $MgSO_4$) then subjected to 30-min ischemia and 120-min reperfusion. To separate the effects of adenosine from that of adenosine-enhanced ischemic preconditioning, a control group (ADO) received a 10-ml bolus injection of 1 mM adenosine.

Infarct volume in GI hearts was $32.9 \pm 5.1\%$ and $1.03 \pm 0.3\%$ in control hearts (FIG. 1). IPC and ADO decreased infarct volume to $10.23 \pm 2.6\%$ and $7.0 \pm 1.6\%$, respectively ($p < 0.001$ versus GI) but did not enhance post-ischemic functional recovery. K/Mg and APC each significantly decreased infarct volume to $2.9 \pm 0.8\%$

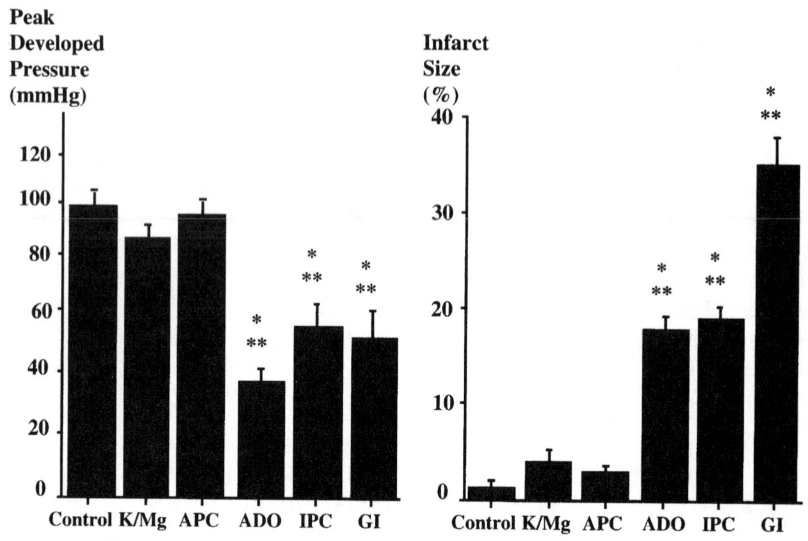

FIGURE 1. Left ventricular peak developed pressure (LVPDP) and infarct size in Langendorff-perfused rabbit hearts after 30-min global ischemia and 120-min reperfusion. Results are shown for control, global ischemia (GI), K/Mg cardioplegia (K/Mg), ischemic preconditioning (IPC), adenosine-enhanced ischemic preconditioning hearts (APC), and adenosine-only hearts (ADO). All results are shown as the mean and standard error of the mean for $N = 6$ for each group. *Significant differences at $p < 0.05$ versus control hearts. **Significant differences at $p < 0.05$ versus APC and K/Mg hearts. There was no significant difference between control, K/Mg, and APC hearts.

and 2.8 ± 0.55% respectively; ($p < 0.001$ versus GI, $p = 0.02$ versus IPC, and $p = 0.05$ versus ADO). In addition both K/Mg and APC were found to significantly enhance post-ischemic functional recovery ($p < 0.001$ versus GI, IPC, and ADO). Importantly, there was no significant difference in post-ischemic functional recovery between control, K/Mg, and APC groups.

These results indicated that the use of a bolus injection of adenosine when used coincident with ischemic preconditioning (APC) significantly extended and amended the protection afforded by ischemic preconditioning (IPC) by both significantly decreasing myocardial infarct size and significantly enhancing post-ischemic functional recovery in the crystalloid perfused heart model, in contrast to IPC, which decreased infarct size but failed to enhance post-ischemic functional recovery. Significantly our findings indicated that APC was as effective as K/Mg cardioplegia, providing both significantly decreased myocardial infarct size and enhanced post-ischemic functional recovery.

The significance of APC as a cardioprotective protocol could not be claimed without further investigation in the blood-perfused heart model. An earlier investigation comparing crystalloid- and blood-perfused hearts showed that blood-perfused hearts exhibit a greater resistance to ischemia and a superior response to cardioplegia as compared to crystalloid-perfused hearts.[55] Sandhu and colleagues[56] have shown that IPC was effective in reducing infarct size in both buffer-perfused and blood-perfused hearts but that infarct size in buffer-perfused hearts was much greater than in crystalloid-perfused hearts. It should be noted, however, that no significant improvement in post-ischemic function was observed with IPC in either buffer-perfused or blood-perfused hearts.

In order to determine the efficacy of APC cardioprotection in the blood-perfused heart, the *in situ* sheep heart model of global ischemia was used with myocardial function assessed by the preload recruitable stroke–work (PRSW) relationship, the linearized Frank-Starling correlation, and tau (the time constant of isovolumic pressure decay).[57] In these experiments sheep were used for cardiopulmonary bypass. APC hearts received a bolus injection of adenosine via the aortic root at the immediate start of ischemic preconditioning (5-min zero-flow global ischemia, 5-min reperfusion) before global ischemia. To test the effectiveness of APC, comparisons were made to hearts receiving hypothermic blood cardioplegia arrest (CBC). A control group received IPC only. Our results (FIG. 2) indicated that infarct size was significantly decreased ($p < 0.01$) in APC ($3.0 \pm 0.8\%$) and CBC ($2.6 \pm 0.2\%$) hearts compared to IPC ($16.3 \pm 1.6\%$). In addition our results indicated that PRSW, mean arterial pressure, and tau were significantly preserved ($p < 0.05$) in APC and CBC hearts compared to IPC hearts. Of clinical import, it was found that APC was as effective as hypothermic blood cardioplegia arrest (CBC) in significantly decreasing infarct size and enhancing post-ischemic functional recovery. There were no significant differences between APC and CBC hearts.

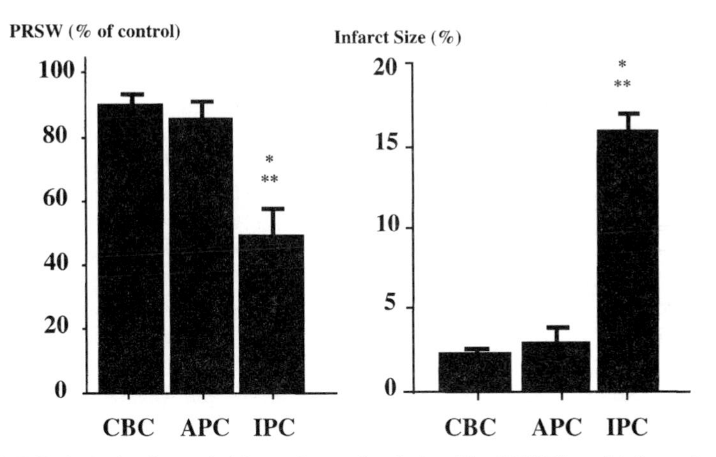

FIGURE 2. Preload recruitable stroke work relationship (PRSW) and infarct size after 30-min global ischemia and 120-min reperfusion in the *in situ* blood-perfused sheep heart. Results are shown for K/Mg cardioplegia (K/Mg), ischemic preconditioning (IPC), and adenosine-enhanced ischemic preconditioning hearts (APC). All results are shown as the mean and standard error of the mean for $N = 6–8$ for each group. *Significant differences at $p < 0.05$ versus K/Mg hearts. There was no significant difference between K/Mg and APC hearts.

MECHANISM OF ADENOSINE-ENHANCED ISCHEMIC PRECONDITIONING

At present the mechanism by which a bolus injection of adenosine to the myocardium coincident with IPC (APC) confers superior cardioprotection remains to be fully elucidated. Previous investigators have suggested that adenosine plays a central role both as mediator and trigger in the cardioprotection afforded by IPC and that continued occupancy of adenosine receptors during ischemia is required before preconditioning can be achieved.[25] Our results indicate that the use of an intracoronary bolus adenosine (1 mmol/100 g) by itself significantly decreases myocardial infarct volume in the rabbit heart, but does not enhance post-ischemic myocardial functional recovery. This would agree with previous reports showing that no direct inotropic effects are associated with adenosine.[58] While we have not determined the effect of APC on interstitial adenosine levels, we speculate that APC rapidly increases interstitial adenosine to levels greater than those achieved by steady-state infusion, thereby accounting for the rapid saturation of myocardial adenosine receptors. We also speculate that the level of adenosine receptor saturation may be directly correlated with both the reduction of myocardial infarct size and the degree of post-ischemic functional recovery attained. Our results further suggest that the effects of APC are cumulative in that myocardial infarct size reduction is enhanced as compared to either IPC or ADO alone.

The mode of adenosine augmentation and the method of administration of adenosine would appear to be of primary importance to allow for enhanced infarct size limitation and enhanced post-ischemic functional recovery. Previous reports have utilized either adenosine or adenosine-regulating agents to enhance the infarct-size limiting effects of IPC, but the effects of such protocols have been varied.[46,47] Recently, Cohen and colleagues[59] have reported that the use of an intravenous bolus injection of adenosine via jugular vein (0.2 mg/kg) resulted in minimal but significant reduction in infarct size, but that higher adenosine concentrations (0.4 mg/kg) provided no protection and were associated with cardiac slowing and marked hypotension. In our investigations, the 10 mmol concentration of adenosine was injected directly into the myocardium via the aortic root.[60] With this technique for adenosine administration we have shown that the systemic effects associated with infusion via the jugular vein are obviated; only transient, non-significant decreases in LV systolic pressure, LV developed pressure, and mean arterial pressure occur; and that these hemodynamic alterations are eliminated 2.4 ± 0.3 min after the bolus injection.[60]

Intrinsic to the development of new myoprotective protocols for use in cardiac surgery are the requirements of new protocols to be equal to or better than conventional cardioplegia in providing for enhanced post-ischemic functional recovery and decreased myocardial infarct size.[16] Our data suggest that adenosine-enhanced ischemic preconditioning, in which a bolus injection of adenosine to the myocardium is used coincident with ischemic preconditioning, meets these requirements, providing equal cardioprotection as that of cold-blood cardioplegia, significantly decreasing myocardial infarct size and significantly enhancing post-ischemic myocardial functional recovery. These results further suggest that APC may provide an effective, alternative myocardial protective protocol to reduce the morbidity and mortality in cardiac surgery.

REFERENCES

1. KATZ, A.M. 1972. Effects of ischemia on contractile processes of heart muscle. Am. J. Cardiol. **32:** 456–460.
2. JENNINGS, R.B. & K.A. REIMER. 1981. Lethal myocardial ischemic injury. Am. J. Pathol. **102:** 241–255.
3. JENNINGS, R.B. & C. STEENBERGEN. 1985. Nucleotide metabolism and cellular damage in myocardial ischemia. Am. Rev. Physiol. **47:** 727–749.
4. WRIGHT, R., S. LEVITSKY, K. RAO, C. HOLLAND & H. FEINBERG. 1978. Potassium cardioplegia. Arch. Surg. **113:** 976–980.
5. STERNBERGH, W.C., L.A. BRUNSTING, A. S. ABD-ELFATTAH & A.S. WECHSLER. 1989. Basal metabolic energy requirements of polarized and depolarized arrest in rat heart. Am. J. Physiol. **256:** H846–H851.
6. STEENBERGEN, C., E. MURPHY, J. WATTS & R. LONDON. 1990. Correlation between cytosolic free calcium, contracture, ATP, and irreversible ischemic injury in perfused rat heart. Circ. Res. **66:** 135–146.
7. MURRY, C.E, R.B. JENNINGS & K.A. REIMER. 1986 Preconditioning with ischemia: A delay of lethal cell injury in ischemic myocardium. Circulation **74:** 1124–1136.
8. LI, G.C., J.A. VASQUEZ, K.P. GALLAGHER & B.R. LUCCHESI. 1990. Myocardial protection with preconditioning. Circulation **82:** 609–619.
9. KIDA, M., H. FUJIWARA, M. ISHIDA *et al.* 1990. Ischemic preconditioning preserves creatine phosphate and intracellular pH. Circulation **84:** 2495–2503.
10. LASLEY, R.D., G.M. ANDERSON & R.M. MENTZER. 1993. Ischemic preconditioning enhance postischemic recovery of function in the rat heart. Cardiovasc. Res. **27:** 565–570.
11. COHEN, M.V., G.S. LIU & J.M. DOWNY. 1991. Preconditioning causes improved wall motion as well as smaller infarcts after transient coronary occlusion in rabbits. Circulation **84:** 341–349.
12. STEENBERGEN, C., M.E. PERLMAN, R.E., LONDON & E. MURPHY. 1993. Mechanism of preconditioning: Ionic alterations. Circ. Res. **72:** 112–125.
13. LAWSON, C.S. & J.M. DOWNY. 1993. Preconditioning: state of the art myocardial protection. Cardiovasc. Res. **27:** 542–550.
14. CAVE, A.C., C.S. COLLIS, J.M. DOWNEY & D.J. HEARSE. 1993. Improved functional recovery by ischemic preconditioning is not mediated by adenosine in the globally ischemic isolated rat heart. Cardiovasc. Res. **27:** 663–668.
15. JENKINS, D.P., W.B. PUGSLEY & D.M. YELLON. 1995. Ischemic preconditioning in a model of global ischemia: Infarct size limitation, but no reduction of stunning. J. Mol. Cell Cardiol. **27:** 1623–1632.
16. KOLOCASSIDES, K.G., M. GALINANES & D.J. HEARSE. 1996. Ischemic preconditioning, cardioplegia or both? Differing approaches to myocardial and vascular protection. J. Mol. Cell Cardiol. **28:** 623–634.
17. BOILING, S.F., D.A. OLSZANSKI, K.F. CHILDS, K.P. GALLAGHER & X-H. NING. 1994. Stunning, preconditioning, and functional recovery after global myocardial ischemia. Ann. Thorac. Surg. **58:** 822–827.
18. ASIMAKIS, G.K., S.D. LICK & V.R. CONTI. 1996. Transient ischemia cannot precondition the rabbit heart against postischemic contractile dysfunction. Ann. Thorac. Surg. **62:** 543–549.
19. LASLEY, R.D., M.A. NOBLE, P.J. KOYN & R.M. MENTZER, JR. 1995. Different effects of an adenosine A_1 analogue and ischemic preconditioning in isolated rabbit hearts. Ann. Thorac. Surg. **60:** 1698–1703.
20. DEUTSCH, E., M. BERGER, W.G. KUSSMAUT, J.W. HIRSFIELD, H.C. HERRMANN & M.D. LASKEY. 1990. Adaptation to ischemia during percutaneous transiuminal coronary angioplasty. Clinical hemodynamic and metabolic features. Circulation **82:** 2044–2051.
21. OLDROYD, K.G., J.G. PATERSON, A.G. RUMLEY *et al.* 1992. Coronary venous lipid peroxide concentrations after coronary angioplasty: correlation with biochemical and electrocardiographic evidence of myocardial ischemia. Br. Heart J. **68:** 43–47.
22. BURNS, P.G., I.B. KRUKENKAMP, C.A. CALDERONE, G.R. GAUDETTE, E.A. BUKARI & S. LEVITSKY. 1995. Does cardiopulmonary bypass alone elicit myoprotective conditioning? Circulation **92:** II447–451.

23. IKONOMIDIS, J.S., L.C. TUMIATI, R.D. WEISEL, D.A.G. MICKLE & R.K. LI. 1994. Preconditioning of human ventricular cardiomyocytes with brief periods of simulated ischemia. Cardiovasc. Res. **28:** 1285–1291.
24. YELLON, D.M., A.M. ALKULAIFI & W.B. PUGSLEY. 1993. Preconditioning the human myocardium. Lancet **342:** 276–277.
25. DOWNEY, J.M. 1992. Ischemic preconditioning: Nature's own cardioprotective intervention. Trends Cardiovasc. Med. **2:** 170–176.
26. MUBAGWA, K., K. MULLANE & W. FLAMENG. 1996. Role of adenosine in the heart and circulation. Cardiovasc. Res. **32:** 797–813.
27. ELY, S.W. & R.M. BERNE. 1992. Protective effects of adenosine in myocardial ischemia. Circulation **85:** 893–904.
28. BELLARDINELL, L. 1993. Adenosine system in the heart. Drug. Dev. Res. **28:** 263–267.
29. WYATT, D.A., M.C. EDMUNDS, R. RUBIO, R.M. BERNE, R.D. LASLEY & R.M. MENTZER, JR. 1989. Adenosine stimulates glycolytic flux in isolated perfused rat hearts by A_1 adenosine receptors. Am. J. Physiol. (Heart Circ. Physiol.) **257:** H952–H957.
30. ZHOU, Q.Y., C. LI, M.E. OLAH, R.A. JOHNSON, G.L. STILES & O. CIVELLI. 1992. Molecular cloning and characterization of and adenosine receptor: the A_3 adenosine receptor. Proc. Natl. Acad. Sci. USA **89:** 7432–7436.
31. MELDRUM, D.R., M.B. MITCHELL, A. BANERJEE & A.H. HARKEN. 1993. Cardiac preconditioning. Arch. Surg. **128:** 1208–1211.
32. SCHUBERT, T., H. VETTER, P. OWEN, B. REICHART & L.H. OPIE. 1989. Adenosine cardioplegia. J. Thorac. Cardiovasc. Surg. **98:** 1057–1065.
33. MENTZER, R.M. JR., R. BUNGER & R.D. LASLEY. 1993. Adenosine enhanced preservation of myocardial function and energetics. Possible involvement of the adenosine A_1 receptor system. Cardiovasc. Res. **27:** 28–35.
34. BAXTER, G.F., M.S. MARBER, V.C. PATEL & D.M. YELLON. 1994. Adenosine receptor involvement in a delayed phase of myocardial protection 24 hours after ischemic preconditioning. Circulation **90:** 2993–3000.
35. LASLEY, R.D, P.J.KOYN, J.O. HEGGE & R.M. MENTZER, JR. 1995. Effects of ischemic and adenosine preconditioning on interstitial fluid adenosine and myocardial infarct size. Am. J. Physiol. (Heart Circ. Physiol.) **269:** HI460–1466.
36. TOOMBS, C.F., D.S. MCGEE, W.E. JOHNSTON & J. VINTEN-JOHANSEN. 1992. Myocardial protective effects of adenosine. Circulation **86:** 986–994.
37. ZHAO, Z-Q., K. NAKANISHI, D.S. MCGEE, P. TAN & J. VINTEN-JOHANSEN. 1994. A_1 receptor mediated myocardial infarct size reduction by endogenous adenosine is exerted primarily during ischemia. Cardiovasc. Res. **28:** 270–279.
38. ZHAO, Z-Q., D.S. MCGEE, K. NAKANISHI, C.F. TOOMB, W.E. JOHNSTON, M.S. ASHAR & J. VINTEN-JOHANSEN. 1993. Receptor mediated cardioprotective effects of endogenous adenosine are exerted primarily during reperfusion after coronary occlusion in the rabbit. Circulation **88:** 709–719.
39. LIU, G.S., S.C. RICHARDS, R.A. OLSSON, K. MULLANE, R.S. WALSH & J.M. DOWNEY. 1994. Evidence that the A_3 receptor may mediate the protection afforded by preconditioning in the isolated rabbit heart. Cardiovasc. Res. **28:** 1057–1061.
40. DOWNEY, J.M., G.S. LIU & J.D. THORNTON. 1993. Adenosine and the anti-infarct effects of preconditioning. Cardiovasc. Res. **27:** 3–8.
41. MULLANE, K., M. GALIFIANES & D.J. HEARSE. 1996. Amplification of endogenous adenosine by adenosine regulating agents: A therapeutic approach to the treatment of cardiac ischemic syndromes. *In* Purines and Myocardial Protection. A.S. Abd-Elfattah & A.S. Wechsler, Eds.: 231–258. Kluwer Publishers. New York.
42. DORHEIM, T.A., A. HOFFMAN, D.G.L. VAN WYLEN & R.M. MENTZER, JR. 1991. Enhanced interstitial fluid adenosine attenuates myocardial stunning. Surgery **110:** 136–145.
43. SANDHU, G.S., A.C. BURRIER & D.R. JANERO. 1993. Adenosine deaminase inhibitors attenuate ischemic injury and preserve energy balance in guinea pig heart. Am. J. Physiol. (Heart Circ. Physiol.) **265:** HI249–HI256.
44. MCCLANAHAN, T.B., B.J. MARTIN, L.J. WOLKE, T.E. MERTZ, W.D. KLOHS & K.P. GALLAGHER. 1992. Inhibition of adenosine deaminase with pentostatin reduces infarct size in rabbits. Circulation **86:** 1–23.

45. Van Belle, H. 1993. Nucleoside transport inhibition: a therapeutic approach to cardioprotection via adenosine? Cardiovasc. Res. 27: 68–76.
46. Mizumura, T., J.A. Auchampach, J. Linden *et al.* 1996. PD 81,723, an allosteric enhancer of the A_1 adenosine receptor, lowers the threshold for ischemic preconditioning in dogs. Circ. Res. **79:** 415–423.
47. Abd-Elfattah, A.S., M.E. Jessen, J. Lekven & A.S. Wechsler. 1998. Differential cardioprotection with selective inhibitors of adenosine metabolism and transport: Role of purine release in ischemic and reperfusion injury. Mol. Cell. Biochem. **180:** 179–191.
48. Mangano, D.T. 1994. Multicenter study of acadesine for the prevention of myocardial infarction and other adverse cardiovascular outcomes associated with coronary artery bypass graft surgery. Eur. Heart J. **15:** 66.
49. Boiling, S.F., M.A. Groh, A.M. Mattison, R.A. Grinage & K.A. Gallagher. 1992. Acadesine (AICA-riboside) improves post-ischemic cardiac recovery. Ann. Thorac. Surg. **54:** 93–98.
50. Cronstein, B.N., M.A. Eberle, H.E. Gruber & R.E. Levin. 1991. Methotrexate inhibits neutrophil function by stimulating adenosine release from connective tissue cells. Proc. Natl. Acad. Sci. USA **88:** 2441–2445.
51. Sabina, R.L, D. Patterson & D. W. Holmes. 1985. 5-amino-4-imidazolecarboxamide riboside (Z-riboside) metabolism in eukaryotic cells. J. Biol. Chem. **260:** 6107–6114.
52. Langervist, B., C. Sylven, E. Theodorsen, L. Kaijser, G. Helmius & A. Waldenstrom. 1992. Adenosine induced chest pain: a comparison between intracoronary bolus injection and steady state infusion. Cardiovasc. Res. **26:** 810–814.
53. Utterback, D.B., E.D. Staples, S.E. White, J.A. Hill & L.M. Belardinelli. 1954. Basis for the selective reduction of pulmonary vascular resistance in humans during infusion in humans. J. Appl. Physiol. **76:** 724–730.
54. McCully, J.D., M. Uematsu, R.A. Parker & S. Levitsky. 1998. Adenosine enhanced ischemic preconditioning provides enhanced post-ischemic recovery and limitation of infarct size in the rabbit heart. J. Thorac. Cardiovasc. Surg. **116:** 154–162.
55. Qiu, Y. & D.J. Hearse. 1992. Comparison of ischemic vulnerability and responsiveness to cardioplegic protection in crystalloid perfused versus blood perfused hearts. J. Thorac. Cardiovasc. Surg. **103:** 960–968.
56. Sandhu, R., R.J. Diaz & G.J. Wilson. 1993. Comparison of ischaemic preconditioning in blood perfused and buffer perfused isolated heart models. Cardiovasc. Res. **27:** 602–607.
57. McCully, J.D., M. Uematsu & S. Levitsky. 1999. Adenosine enhanced ischemic preconditioning provides equal cardioprotection as cold blood cardioplegia. Ann. Thorac. Surg. **67:** 699–704.
58. Yao, Z. & G.J. Gross. 1994. A comparison of adenosine induced cardioprotection and ischemic preconditioning in dogs: efficacy, time course and the role of K_{ATP} channels. Circulation **89:** 1229–1236.
59. Cohen, M.V., J.D. Thornton, C.S. Thornton *et al.* 1997. Intravenous co-infusion of adenosine and norepinephrine preconditions the heart without adverse effects. J. Thorac. Cardiovasc. Surg. **114:** 236–242.
60. Uematsu, M., G.R. Gaudette, J.O. Laurikka, S. Levitsky & J.D. McCully. 1999. Adenosine enhanced preconditioning decreases myocardial infarction following regional ischemia in the blood perfused sheep heart. Ann. Thorac. Surg. **66:** 382–387.

Optimal Myocardial Preconditioning in Humans[a]

GIDEON COHEN, TOSHIZUMI SHIRAI, RICHARD D. WEISEL,[b] VIVEK RAO, FRANK MERANTE, LAURA C. TUMIATI, MOLLY K. MOHABEER, MICHAEL A. BORGER, REN-KE LI, AND DONALD A.G. MICKLE

Division of Cardiovascular Surgery, The Toronto Hospital, and the Centre for Cardiovascular Research, University of Toronto, Toronto, Ontario, Canada

ABSTRACT: We developed a model of ischemia and reperfusion (I and R) in human ventricular myocytes (CM). CM injury and metabolics were studied after various interventions: endogenous preconditioning (PC) with anoxia, hypoxia, and anoxic or hypoxic supernatants; endogenous PC with or without SPT or adenosine deaminase; and exogenous adenosine PC before, during, or after I or continuously, with or without SPT. To assess the clinical implications of PC and the possible mediating effects of adenosine, patients undergoing elective coronary bypass surgery (CABG) received either a high or low dose of adenosine. Patients not receiving adenosine served as controls. Adenosine levels, high-energy phosphate levels, and metabolic parameters were evaluated from blood samples and left ventricular biopsy samples. Our cellular model studies indicated that preconditioning conferred protection to human CM via an adenosine-mediated pathway. Adenosine simulated PC without a fall in ATP. Adenosine administered to patients during CABG stimulated myocardial metabolism while preventing the degradation of high energy phosphates. A prospective randomized trial of adenosine administered to high-risk patients for myocardial protection is required.

INTRODUCTION

Recent advances in cardiac surgery have emphasized improved methods of intraoperative myocardial protection to prevent postoperative ventricular dysfunction. Ischemic preconditioning, first described by Murry and colleagues[1] is the most powerful endogenously mediated form of myocardial protection known. Unfortunately, attempts to reproduce this phenomenon clinically have been largely unsuccessful.[2–4] Such shortcomings have prompted the search for a pharmacologic substitute which could safely and effectively duplicate the beneficial effects of ischemic preconditioning in humans.

Adenosine, an endogenous nucleoside, is believed to play a role in the protection afforded by ischemic preconditioning either directly, by acting as a substrate for nu-

[a]Supported by the Heart and Stroke Foundation of Canada (Grant T2683). G.C., V.R., F.M., and M.A.B. are Research Fellows of the Heart and Stroke Foundation of Ontario. R.D.W. is a Career Investigator of the Heart and Stroke Foundation of Ontario. R.K.L. is a Research Scholar of the Heart and Stroke Foundation of Ontario.

[b]Address correspondence to: Richard D. Weisel, M.D., EN 14-215, The Toronto Hospital, 200 Elizabeth Street, Toronto, Ontario, M5G 2C4, Canada.

cleotide resynthesis, or indirectly, by stimulating adenosine receptors and facilitating a second messenger pathway.[2–5] Recently, however, the protective role of adenosine has been disputed.[6–8] Moreover, although animal data has been widely described, limited human data exist with which to support or refute the adenosine-mediated hypothesis of preconditioning, and knowledge regarding the optimal method of adenosine administration remains limited.

We have developed a unique model of ischemia and reperfusion in human ventricular cardiomyocytes. The quiescent nature of these myocytes upon exposure to low volume ischemia simulates the low flow and non-contractile conditions encountered during cardioplegic arrest. Using this model, we attempted to define the role and mechanism of myocardial preconditioning in humans. In addition, to determine the clinical applicability of our *in vitro* studies, we undertook a clinical evaluation of adenosine administered to patients undergoing coronary bypass surgery.

MATERIALS AND METHODS

Cell Studies

Experimental Design

Cultures of human ventricular myocytes obtained from biopsies of the right ventricular outflow tract of patients undergoing corrective surgery for tetralogy of Fallot were established as previously described.[9–11] Our *in vitro* technique of simulating "ischemia" and "reperfusion" in cultured cardiomyocytes[10] was applied as follows: After 30 min of stabilization in 15 ml of normoxic phosphate-buffered saline (PBS), ischemia was simulated by placing the cells in a sealed Plexiglas chamber flushed with 100% nitrogen to maintain anoxic conditions, while exposing the cells to a low volume (1.5 ml) of deoxygenated PBS ($pO_2 = 0$ mm Hg) for a period of 90 minutes. A small sample of deoxygenated PBS (2 ml) was placed in a center dish within the sealed chamber to monitor temperature, pH, and osmolality, and to confirm anoxic conditions at the end of each ischemic period. Reperfusion was accomplished by exposure to 15 ml normoxic PBS for 30 minutes. "Preconditioning" was simulated by exposing the cells to 20 min of ischemia and 20 min of reperfusion before prolonged (90 min) ischemia.

Assessment of Cellular Injury and Metabolism

After each intervention, cell plates were incubated with 0.4% Trypan Blue dye (TB; Sigma Chemical Co., St. Louis, MO) and assessed for injury under an inverted light microscope at 200× magnification. Injured cells unable to exclude the large molecular weight dye stained blue. The number of blue-stained cells was counted from five standard locations on each plate and expressed as a percentage of the total number of cells. All counts were performed by a single observer who was blinded to the intervention.

Selected experiments involved biochemical assays for extracellular lactate concentrations and cellular adenosine triphosphate (ATP) content. After removal from the culture dish, the recovered extracellular fluid was analyzed for lactate using an enzymatic method (Stat-Pack; La Jolla, CA). The remaining cardiomyocytes were

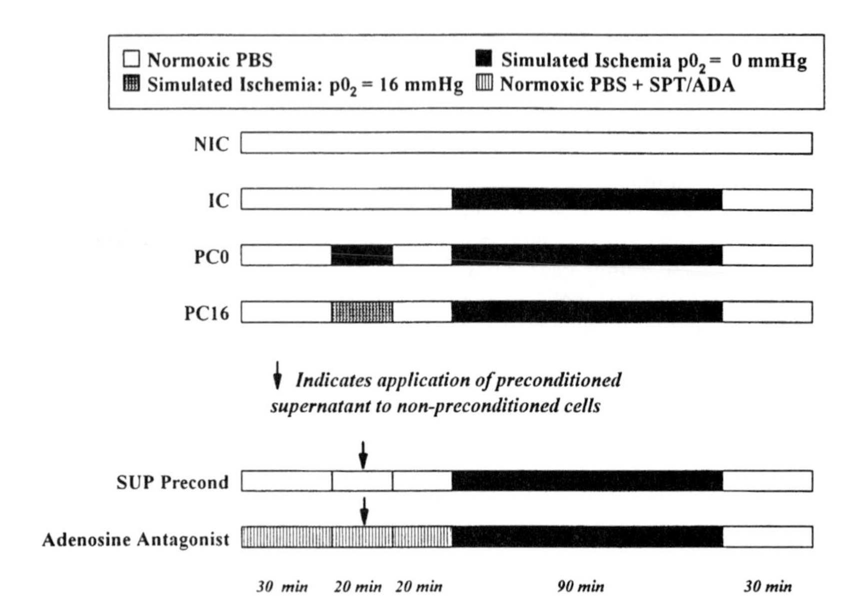

FIGURE 1. Endogenous preconditioning studies. (Study 1) Cells underwent either anoxic (PC0) or hypoxic (PC16) preconditioning for 20 min before prolonged ischemia and reperfusion. (Study 2) Non-preconditioned cells were preconditioned for 20 min using the supernatant of anoxic-preconditioned cells (SUP0) or of hypoxic-preconditioned cells (SUP16). (Study 4) Supernatant from anoxic-preconditioned cells was treated with SPT or ADA and then applied to non-preconditioned cells that had been pretreated with SPT or ADA. All groups were compared to non-ischemic controls (NIC), which underwent 190-min stabilization, and to ischemic controls (IC), which underwent 70-min stabilization followed by prolonged ischemia (90 min) and reperfusion (30 min).

flash-frozen and used to determine intracellular ATP concentrations using high performance liquid chromatography.[12–14]

Endogenous Preconditioning Studies

Study 1: Graded Preconditioning

We compared the protective effects of two grades of ischemic preconditioning on cellular injury following prolonged ischemia and reperfusion. The following groups were studied: (1) incubation in PBS for 190 min (Non-ischemic Control; NIC); (2) stabilization, followed by prolonged ischemia and reperfusion (Ischemic Control; IC); (3) stabilization followed by preconditioning with anoxic PBS ($pO_2 = 0$ mm Hg) for 20 min, reperfusion for 20 min, and prolonged ischemia and reperfusion (Anoxic Preconditioning; PC0); (4) stabilization followed by 20-min preconditioning with hypoxic PBS ($pO_2 = 16$ mm Hg), 20-min reperfusion, and prolonged ischemia and reperfusion (Hypoxic Preconditioning, PC16) (FIG. 1).

Study 2: Supernatant Preconditioning Studies

Preconditioned supernatant collected from cells that underwent either anoxic (SUP0) or hypoxic (SUP16) preconditioning was applied to non-preconditioned cells for 20 min, after which the cells were exposed to 20 min of reperfusion followed by prolonged ischemia and reperfusion (FIG. 1).

Study 3: Measurement of Endogenous Adenosine Concentrations

Using step-gradient high-performance liquid chromatography, adenosine levels were measured in the supernatants of cells that underwent either anoxic (PC0) or hypoxic (PC16) preconditioning. The resultant values were quantified after evaluating a known adenosine standard.

Study 4: Adenosine Receptor Antagonist and Adenosine Deaminase Studies

To determine the role of adenosine in human preconditioning, supernatant from anoxically preconditioned cells (SUP0) was applied to non-preconditioned cells along with either 100 μmol/l of the selective adenosine receptor antagonist 8-(*p*-sulfophenyl)theophylline (SPT; Sigma) or 6.7 U/l of adenosine deaminase (ADA; Sigma) before prolonged ischemia and reperfusion. Both additives, in addition to being applied along with the supernatant, were applied to the non-preconditioned cells for 30 min before and 20 min after exposure to the preconditioned supernatant (FIG. 1).

Exogenous Preconditioning Studies

Study 5: Optimal Dose and Timing of Adenosine

A dose-response analysis was undertaken using varying doses (0–200 μmol/l) of exogenous adenosine (ADE; Sigma) dissolved in normoxic or anoxic PBS. ADE was

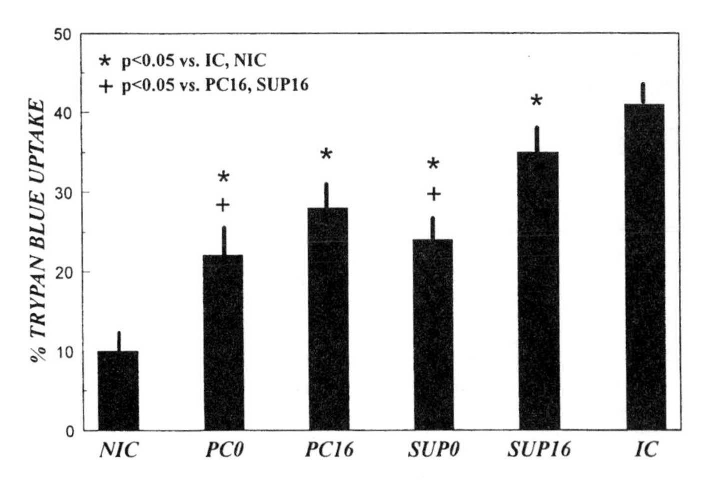

FIGURE 2. Anoxic preconditioning (PC0) and preconditioning with the supernatant of anoxically preconditioned cells (SUP0) reduced cellular injury to a greater extent than did hypoxic preconditioning (PC16) or preconditioning with the supernatant of hypoxically preconditioned cells (SUP16) ($^{+}p < 0.05$). All forms of preconditioning reduced cellular injury compared to ischemic controls (IC) ($^{*}p < 0.05$ versus IC). (NIC, Non-ischemic Controls.)

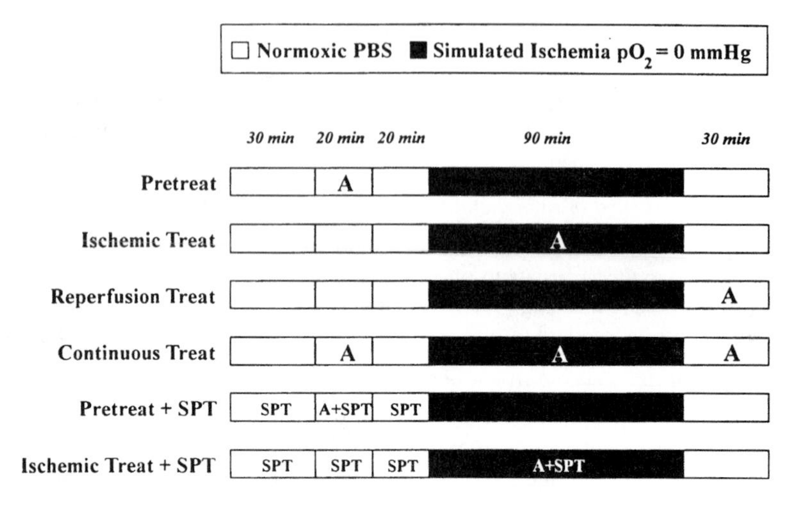

FIGURE 3. Exogenous preconditioning studies. Exogenous adenosine (A) was applied to cells either before (Pretreat), during (Ischemic Treat), or after (Reperfusion Treat) prolonged ischemia and reperfusion, or during all three phases (Continuous Treat). Cells treated with adenosine before or during ischemia were simultaneously treated with SPT (Pretreat + SPT and Ischemic Treat + SPT, respectively).

applied to the cells for 20 min after 30-min stabilization, after which the cells were exposed to 20 min of reperfusion followed by prolonged ischemia and reperfusion. Once the optimal (most protective) dose of adenosine was determined (according to TB exclusion tests), the optimal timing was determined by incubating the cells with ADE either before ischemia (Pretreatment), during ischemia (Ischemic treatment), during reperfusion (Reperfusion treatment), or during all three phases (Continuous treatment) (FIG. 3).

Study 6: Selective Adenosine Receptor Antagonist Studies

To determine whether ADE preconditioning is dependent on a receptor-mediated effect or a substrate effect, cells undergoing ADE pretreatment or ischemic treatment were simultaneously exposed to SPT (FIG. 3).

Human Studies

We endeavored to further define the beneficial effects of ADE and to determine the optimal mode of administration of exogenous ADE by initiating a Phase II prospective evaluation in patients undergoing elective coronary bypass surgery (CABG). Since ADE's protective effects are hypothesized to be both receptor- and substrate-mediated, and since late benefits may be related to a free radical–scavenging pathway, the effects of exogenous ADE were evaluated both before and during the ischemic crossclamp period, as well as during reperfusion. Thirty-three patients undergoing elective CABG using tepid (29°C) 4:1 blood cardioplegia were assigned to receive ADE, while 40 patients received no ADE (control group). Among the patients given ADE, 21 received a 10-min pre-crossclamp intravenous infusion at 100 μmol/kg/min via the venous reservoir of the cardiopulmonary bypass circuit, followed by a 500 μmol infusion via the first 500 ml of high potassium cardioplegia (Low Dose). The remaining 12 patients received a 200 μmol/kg/min pre-crossclamp and reperfusion ADE infusion, in addition to a 2 mM cardioplegic infusion throughout the crossclamp period (High Dose). Arterial and coronary sinus blood samples along with left ventricular biopsies were obtained before (pre-crossclamp), during (crossclamp), and after (post-crossclamp) crossclamp to evaluate ADE levels, high-energy phosphate levels, and metabolic parameters. Postoperative hemodynamic parameters (pulse rate/rhythm, systolic/diastolic blood pressure, mean arterial pressure, pulmonary arterial pressure, cardiac output, cardiac index, and systemic vascular resistance) were monitored to evaluate the clinical benefit, if any, of ADE administration.

Statistical Analysis

The SAS Statistical Package (SAS Institute, Cary, NC) was employed for analysis of all data. Data are expressed as the mean ± standard deviation in the text and mean ± standard error in the figures, with eight plates per group unless otherwise specified. Analysis of variance (ANOVA) was used to simultaneously compare continuous variables at different time periods. When statistically significant differences were found, they were specified by Duncan's multiple range test (DMR). Clinical data were analyzed via two-way repeated measures ANOVA for the interactive effect of group versus time. Non-significant variables were analyzed without the interactive component. Statistical significance was assumed for $p < 0.05$.

RESULTS

Cellular Studies

Endogenous Preconditioning

FIGURE 2 shows the results of TB assessments for cellular injury. The most severe injury was seen in cells that underwent prolonged ischemia and reperfusion only (IC). Anoxic preconditioning with a $pO_2 = 0$ mm Hg (PC0) reduced cellular injury to a greater extent than did hypoxic preconditioning (PC16). Extracellular lactate concentrations in cells that underwent anoxic preconditioning (PC0) were elevated immediately following preconditioning, although no significant differences were found in comparison to ischemic controls during the same time periods. Intracellular ATP levels decreased significantly in the PC0 group immediately following preconditioning (PC0, 1.21 ± 0.35; IC, 2.2 ± 0.43 mmol/g DNA; $p < 0.05$). Although during ischemia, the reduction in ATP was less profound in the preconditioned group, no differences were found in ATP levels after prolonged ischemia or reperfusion in comparison to ischemic controls.

Preincubation with the supernatant of cells preconditioned using anoxic PBS (SUP0) was more protective than preincubation with the supernatant of cells preconditioned using hypoxic PBS (SUP16) (FIG. 2).

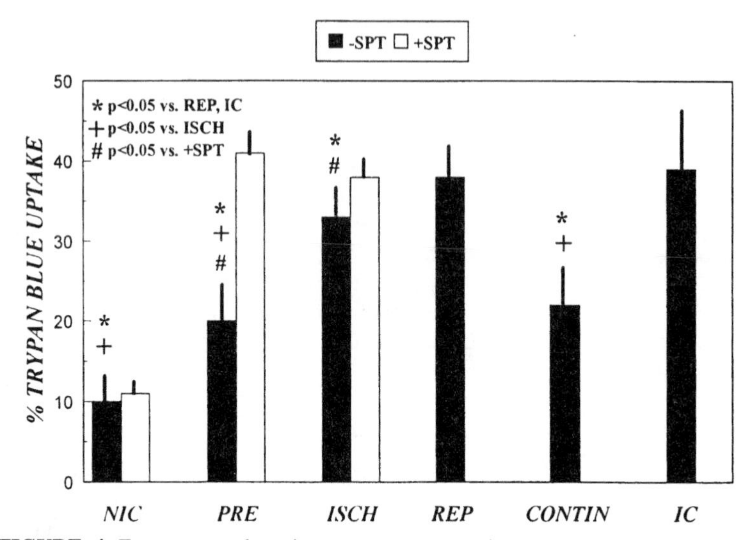

FIGURE 4. Exogenous adenosine was most protective when administered before ischemia (PRE). Application of adenosine during ischemia (ISCH) was protective to a significantly lesser degree. The two protective effects were not found to be additive when adenosine was administered continuously (CONTIN). Adenosine administered during reperfusion (REP) was not protective. All groups were compared to both ischemic controls (IC) and non-ischemic controls (NIC). All protective effects were abolished when SPT was applied to adenosine-treated cells, regardless of timing. Adenosine and SPT had no effect on non-ischemic controls (NIC).

HPLC analysis revealed a greater concentration of endogenous ADE in the supernatant of anoxically preconditioned cells (SUP0) in comparison to hypoxically preconditioned cells (SUP16) (ADE concentrations: SUP0, 12.5 nmol/l; SUP16, 7.0 nmol/l; Non-ischemic Controls, 2 nmol/l; $p = 0.018$, SUP0 versus SUP16).

The protective effects of SUP0 were abolished when the supernatant and the non-preconditioned cells were first treated with SPT. Similarly, the protective effects of the preconditioned supernatant were abolished and no ADE was measurable when the supernatant and cells were first treated with ADA.

Exogenous Preconditioning

Exogenous ADE was found to be most protective when applied before ischemia (Pretreatment) at a dose of 50 μmol. Application of ADE during ischemia (Ischemic treatment) was protective to a lesser degree than was ADE pretreatment. The two protective effects were not found to be additive when ADE was administered continuously (Continuous treatment). ADE applied during reperfusion (Reperfusion treatment) was not protective (FIG. 4).

ADE treatment resulted in a significant preservation of ATP after prolonged ischemia and reperfusion. Comparison between groups revealed that cells pretreated with ADE or continuously treated with ADE demonstrated the greatest degree of ATP preservation in comparison to ischemic controls (IC). Application of ADE during ischemia (Ischemic treatment) resulted in only partial preservation of ATP. These

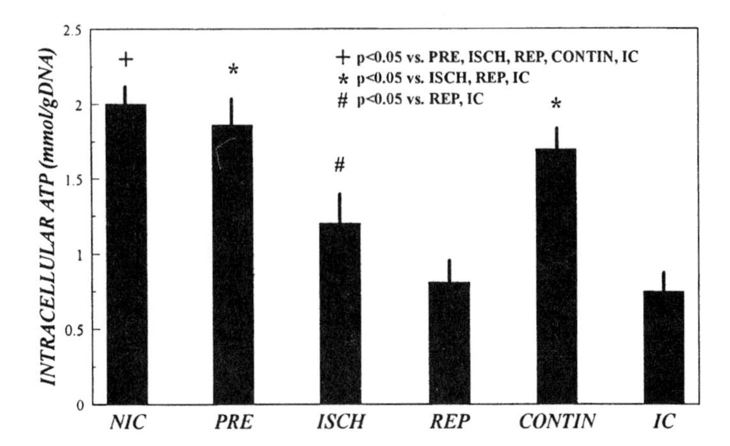

FIGURE 5. Administration of adenosine before (PRE) or continuously (CONTIN) resulted in a preservation of ATP following ischemia and reperfusion in comparison to ischemic controls (IC). Administration of adenosine during ischemia (ISCH) revealed preservation of ATP to a lesser degree. Adenosine applied during reperfusion did not afford any ATP-preservative properties.

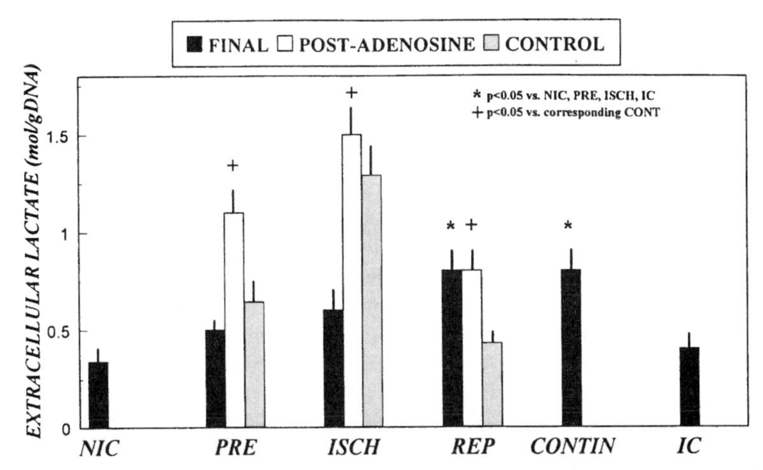

FIGURE 6. Extracellular lactate concentrations following ischemia and reperfusion (FINAL) were elevated in cells that received adenosine continuously (CONTIN) or during reperfusion (REP). In evaluating the direct effects of adenosine (POST-ADENOSINE), lactate levels were elevated immediately after adenosine administration in all groups compared to untreated controls (CONTROL). (NIC, Non-ischemic controls; PRE, Pretreatment; ISC, Ischemic treatment; IC Ischemic controls)

preservative effects were non-additive when ADE was applied continuously (Continuous treatment). ADE applied during reperfusion (Reperfusion treatment) did not prevent the degradation of ATP (FIG. 5).

To determine the direct effects of ADE on lactate production, supernatant lactate concentrations were measured either before ischemia, at the end of ischemia, or at the

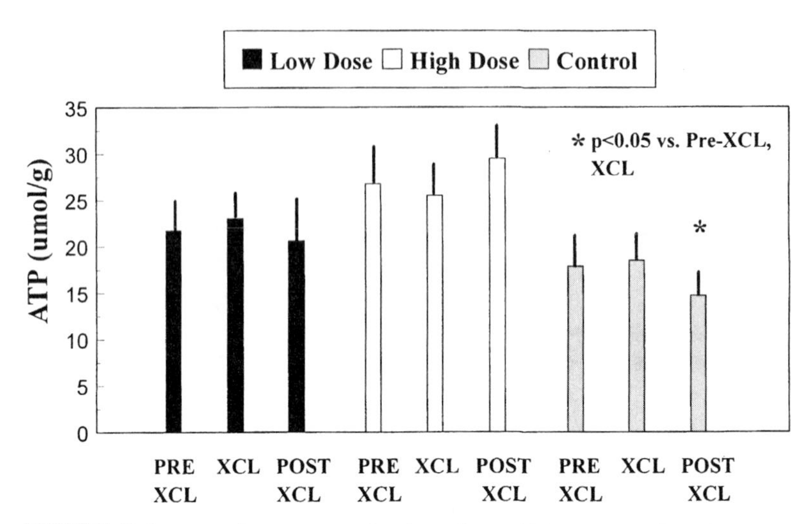

FIGURE 7. In comparison to controls where tissue ATP concentrations decreased by 15% during the crossclamp (XCL) period, tissue ATP levels were preserved in both the Low Dose and High Dose adenosine groups ($p < 0.05$).

end of reperfusion, with and without ADE treatment. Under such circumstances, supernatant lactate levels were found to be elevated in all groups immediately after ADE treatment ("Post-ADE" lactate) in comparison to non-treatment controls (FIG. 6). SPT abolished the protective and lactate elevating effects of ADE as assessed by TB exclusion, intracellular ATP concentrations, and supernatant lactate concentrations.

Human Studies

The pre-crossclamp intravenous ADE infusion induced controllable hypotension in the High Dose but not the Low Dose patients, although elevated serum ADE levels were not measurable in either group. During the cardioplegic ADE infusions, serum ADE levels increased dramatically in both groups (High Dose: pre-crossclamp = 1.49 ± 0.14 nmol/g serum and crossclamp = 1,182.59 ± 9.6 nmol/g serum. Low Dose: pre-crossclamp = 1.5 ± 0.36 nmol/g serum and crossclamp = 466.03 ± 64.7 nmol/g serum; $p < 0.01$). Similarly, markedly elevated tissue levels of ADE were found in myocardial biopsy samples during the cardioplegic infusion only (Low Dose: pre-crossclamp = 0.19 ± 0.11 μmol/g and crossclamp = 1.38 ± 0.24 μmol/g; $p < 0.01$). Arterial-coronary sinus differences suggested myocardial metabolism of ADE during the cardioplegic infusion. In comparison to controls where tissue ATP levels decreased by 15% during crossclamp, tissue ATP levels were preserved in both the Low Dose and High Dose ADE groups with crossclamping (Low Dose: pre-crossclamp = 21.7 ± 3.5 μmol/g and post-crossclamp = 20.6 ± 5.1 μmol/g. High Dose: pre-crossclamp = 26.8 ± 4.2 μmol/g and post-crossclamp = 29.5 ± 4.7. Controls: pre-crossclamp = 17.9 ± 3.2 μmol/g and post-crossclamp = 14.7 ± 2.5 μmol/g; $p < 0.05$) (FIG. 7). Patients receiving ADE tended to produce more lactate during the pre-crossclamp and early crossclamp periods in comparison to controls (Pre-crossclamp: Low Dose = –0.09 ± 0.08 mmol/l, High Dose

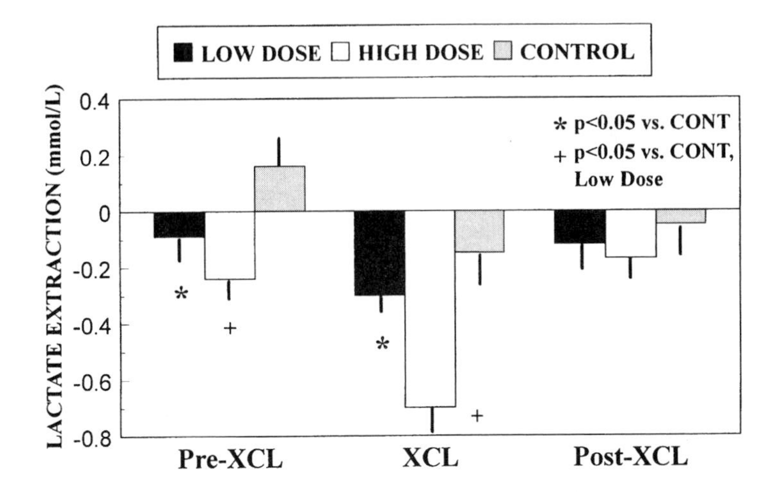

FIGURE 8. Patients receiving adenosine as part of the High Dose or Low Dose groups revealed increased myocardial lactate production in comparison to controls both before (Pre-XCL) and during (XCL) the crossclamp period ($p < 0.05$).

= –0.24 ± 0.06 mmol/l, Control = 0.16 ± 0.1 mmol/l. Crossclamp: Low Dose = –0.3 ± 0.06 mmol/l, High Dose = –0.7 ± 0.12 mmol/l, Control = 0.15 ± 0.1 mmol/l; $p < 0.05$) (FIG. 8). No metabolic or hemodynamic differences were noted between groups after crossclamp removal.

DISCUSSION

Despite recent advances in myocardial protection, the prevalence of low cardiac output syndrome (the requirement for inotropic or intra-aortic balloon pump support to maintain adequate systolic blood pressures and cardiac index) after CABG remains relatively high (approximately 9%).[15] In the absence of intraoperative myocardial infarction, the development of low output syndrome after CABG represents inadequate intraoperative myocardial protection.

Ischemic preconditioning is by far the most potent form of myocardial protection known. The cardioprotective effects of ischemic preconditioning have been shown in various species, including humans.[16–18] However, the protective effects of clinical ischemic preconditioning have recently been called into question.[19] Such uncertainty emphasizes the need for identification of a pharmacologic mediator that safely and effectively reproduces the beneficial effects of ischemic preconditioning in humans. Ideally, this mediator would be applied in the form of a simple additive to be administered in conjunction with cardioplegia during cardiac surgery.

ADE may represent such a mediator. Evidence to support the presence of a humoral mediator was first introduced by Przyklenk and colleagues who reported that protection was afforded to non-ischemic myocardial regions adjacent to those that underwent ischemic preconditioning.[16] The authors suspected that preconditioning induced ADE release, which in turn initiated a sequence of cellular signalling events, resulting in protection from a subsequent prolonged ischemic episode. Using a microdialysis technique, van Wylen and colleagues found increases in ADE and other soluble purines in canine myocardial interstitial fluid during the ischemic and reperfusion phases of preconditioning.[17] Since data regarding the role of ADE in human preconditioning remain limited, we endeavored to study both endogenously released ADE and exogenously administered ADE in our human cellular model of simulated cardioplegic arrest. Such a model permits an evaluation of preconditioning in human cardiomyocytes in the absence of alternate cell types (i.e., endothelial cells) and independent of the hemodynamic effects associated with the clinical infusion of pharmacologic preconditioning agonists.

Endogenous Preconditioning

The ability to precondition our cells against prolonged ischemia and reperfusion is similar to the effect seen *in vivo*.[1,9] The degree of ischemia was crucial in regulating the protective effects of ischemic preconditioning. Anoxic preconditioning (pO_2 = 0 mm Hg) conferred greater protection than did hypoxic preconditioning (pO_2 = 16 mm Hg) as assessed by TB exclusion. Thus, the ischemic stimulus of ischemic preconditioning cannot be minimized (in an effort to limit the detrimental effects of ischemia) without reducing the degree of protection afforded. Although lactate levels were elevated immediately after the ischemic preconditioning stimulus, lactate levels were similar in both preconditioned and ischemic control groups after both ischemia and reperfusion. Similarly, although intracellular ATP levels decreased significantly immediately after ischemic preconditioning, both groups demonstrated similar degrees of ATP degradation after both ischemia and reperfusion. This finding implies some recovery of ATP levels in the preconditioned group and emphasizes the possible benefits of a pharmacologic substitute that could presumably precondition without creating an initial ATP "debt." This hypothesis was substantiated when exogenous ADE administration was found to preserve ATP levels compared to ischemic controls.

We demonstrated that the protective effects of ischemic preconditioning could be transferred to non-preconditioned cells via the supernatant of preconditioned cells. Once again, the degree of ischemia was crucial in determining the protective effects of the supernatant, with anoxia being more protective than hypoxia. To support our hypothesis that the crucial mediator was indeed ADE, we demonstrated that the supernatants of anoxically (pO_2 = 0 mm Hg) preconditioned cells had the greatest concentrations of ADE and conferred the most protection. Conversely, the supernatants of non-preconditioned cells had the lowest amounts of ADE and conferred no protection. These findings demonstrate once again that maximal ischemia is necessary for the greatest protection and that the degree of ischemia and the degree of protection are both appropriately reflected by the amount of ADE generated and released with preconditioning.

To determine whether endogenous (ischemic) preconditioning functions via an ADE-mediated receptor pathway, cells undergoing supernatant preconditioning were simultaneously incubated with either the non-selective ADE receptor blocker SPT or with ADA. In both cases, the protective effects of ischemic preconditioning were abolished, implying an ADE-mediated receptor phenomenon.

Exogenous Preconditioning

The application of exogenous ADE was an attempt to facilitate the clinical applicability of ischemic preconditioning. To assess the possible benefits of exogenous ADE, we treated our cells with varying doses of ADE either before (Pretreatment), during (Ischemic treatment), or after (Reperfusion treatment) ischemia, or during all three phases (Continuous treatment). We determined that ADE was most protective when applied before ischemia (Pretreatment) and followed by pre-ischemic reperfusion. Administration of ADE during ischemia (Ischemic treatment) had a slight protective effect that was not as great as that seen with ADE pretreatment. This discrepancy was likely due to the absence of a normoxic reperfusion period (before ischemia) in the ischemic treatment group, a condition that seems to be necessary for the maximal effect of ADE. Unlike previous reports in the literature, ADE applied during reperfusion (reperfusion treatment) had no effect. We suspect that ADE pretreatment provided the maximum attainable protective effect since continuous treatment did not provide any additional benefits.

The effects of ADE pretreatment were receptor-mediated since protection was afforded despite a period of pre-ischemic reperfusion (at which time no ADE was present) and since the protective effects were abolished by simultaneous incubation with receptor antagonists. Using the same principle, we confirmed that the mild protective effects conferred by ischemic ADE treatment were also secondary to receptor activation and not secondary to a direct substrate-mediated effect, as has been previously hypothesized.

Unlike the case with ischemic preconditioning, ADE pretreatment resulted in a significant preservation of intracellular ATP levels after prolonged ischemia and reperfusion. This finding may be due to the fact that no ATP debt was incurred during the exogenous ADE preconditioning process. Although ADE pretreatment did not affect final lactate concentrations (after prolonged ischemia and reperfusion) compared to controls, ADE did increase extracellular lactate concentrations immediately after its application. This phenomenon is likely due to a previously reported stimulatory effect of ADE on glycolysis, along with an increase in glucose uptake and utilization.[20] Such an effect may further facilitate ATP production.

Clinical Preconditioning

The results of our preliminary trial suggest that ADE can be administered safely to CABG patients at low doses. Although measurable tissue or serum levels of ADE were not detectable during intravenous administration, ADE significantly increased lactate production during the pre-crossclamp and early crossclamp periods. This effect is believed to be secondary to an ADE-mediated increase in intracellular fructose-6 phosphate concentrations.[20] Fructose-6 phosphate acts as a substrate for the rate-limiting glycolytic enzyme phosphofructokinase. Stimulating the forward flow of glycolysis via this method likely facilitates lactate production under normoxic conditions. Low Dose ADE either prevented the degradation or stimulated production of high energy phosphates during the crossclamp period. Although the two mechanisms are likely independent, the "preconditioning" source of ATP may be augmented by ATP produced with the ADE-mediated increase in glycolytic flux. The absence of any hemodynamic benefit was likely due to the elective (low risk) nature of the patients enrolled in this study. Since the incidence of low output syndrome (LOS) in such patients is exceedingly low, a significant reduction in the rate of LOS with ADE treatment would be difficult to demonstrate due to a relatively small number of events. As such, future studies should involve higher risk patients susceptible to higher rates of postoperative complications.

Although ADE demonstrated protective effects, our *in vitro* studies seemed to suggest an effect that falls short of that observed with ischemic preconditioning. This feature has prompted ongoing attempts to elucidate a possible "final effector" of preconditioning, which could more effectively harness the beneficial effects of brief ischemia. ATP-mediated potassium channel opening may represent such a final effector pathway. Unfortunately, early attempts to apply non-specific channel openers clinically have been unsuccessful due to a marked arrhythmogenic effect. Future development of clinically available mitochondrial-specific K_{ATP} channel openers may preclude such a limitation.

SUMMARY

The aforementioned series of experiments have attempted to define the mechanisms and benefits of myocardial preconditioning in a human model of simulated "ischemia" and "reperfusion." In doing so, we have emphasized the importance of exogenous adenosine as a possible pharmacologic substitute for use in clinical preconditioning. We have shown:

(1) Ischemic (anoxic) preconditioning protects human cardiomyocytes from prolonged ischemia and reperfusion through an adenosine-receptor, protein kinase C–mediated pathway.
(2) A maximal ischemic stimulus is necessary for the maximal protective effects of ischemic preconditioning to be realized, resulting in the degradation of ATP before prolonged ischemia and reperfusion (ATP debt).
(3) Exogenous adenosine applied before ischemia effectively mimics the protective effects of ischemic preconditioning.
(4) Exogenous adenosine preserves intracellular ATP levels during prolonged ischemia without first incurring an ATP debt.
(5) Exogenous adenosine facilitates lactate production likely by stimulating glycolysis, which in turn, may contribute further ATP.
(6) Adenosine was safe for use as an intravenous and cardioplegic additive in patients undergoing elective CABG and revealed lactate-stimulatory and ATP-preservative effects.

CONCLUSIONS

Adenosine pretreatment effectively protects human ventricular myocytes from the injurious effects of ischemia and reperfusion. Clinical trials in high-risk surgical patients are necessary to further define the beneficial effects of adenosine in humans.

REFERENCES

1. MURRY, C.E., R.B. JENNINGS & K.A. REIMER. 1986. Preconditioning with ischemia: a delay of lethal cell injury in ischemic myocardium. Circulation **74:** 1124–1136.
2. BOLLING, S.F., K.F. CHILDS & X.H. NING. 1994. Adenosine's effect on myocardial functional recovery: substrate or signal? J. Surg. Res. **57**(5): 591–595.
3. ARMSTRONG, S. & C.E. GANOTE. 1994. Adenosine receptor specificity in preconditioning of isolated rabbit cardiomyocytes: evidence of A_3 receptor involvement. Cardiovasc. Res. **28:** 1049–1056.
4. LIU, G.S., J. THORNTON, D.M. VAN WINKLE, A.W.H. STANLEY, R.A. OLSSON & J.M. DOWNEY. 1991. Protection against infarction afforded by preconditioning is mediated by A_1 adenosine receptors in rabbit heart. Circulation **84:** 350–356.
5. LIU, G.S., C.S. RICHARDS, R.A. OLSSON, K. MULLANE, R.S. WALSH & J.M. DOWNEY. 1994. Evidence that the adenosine A_3 receptor may mediate the protection afforded by preconditioning in the isolated rabbit heart. Cardiovasc. Res. **28:** 1057–1061.
6. LI, Y. & R.A. KLONER. 1993. The cardioprotective effects of ischemic preconditioning are not mediated by adenosine receptors in rat hearts. Circulation **87**(5): 1642–1648.
7. CAVE, A.C., C.S. COLLIS, J.M. DOWNEY & J.M. HEARSE. 1993. Improved functional recovery by ischemic preconditioning is not mediated by adenosine in the globally ischemic rat heart. Cardiovasc. Res. **27:** 663–668.
8. YAO, Z. & G. GROSS. 1994. A comparison of adenosine induced cardioprotection and ischemic preconditioning in dogs. Circulation **89:** 1229–1236.
9. IKONOMIDIS, J.S., L.C. TUMIATI, R.D. WEISEL, D.A.G. MICKLE & R.K. LI. 1994. Preconditioning human ventricular myocytes with brief periods of simulated ischemia. Cardiovasc. Res. **28:** 1285–1291.
10. TUMIATI, L.C., D.A.G. MICKLE, R.D. WEISEL, W.G. WILLIAMS & R.K. LI. 1994. An *in vitro* model to study myocardial ischemic injury. J. Tissue Cult. Methods **16:** 1–9.
11. LI, R.-K., R.D. WEISEL, W.G. WILLIAMS & D.A.G. MICKLE. 1992. Methods of culturing cardiomyocytes from human pediatric ventricular myocardium. J. Tiss. Cult. Meth. **14:** 93–100.
12. WEISEL, R.D., D.A.G. MICKLE, C.D. FINKLE, L.C. TUMIATI, M.M. MADONIK & J. IVANOV. 1989. Delayed myocardial metabolic recovery after blood cardioplegia. Ann. Thorac. Surg. **48:** 503–507.
13. HULL-RYDE, E.A., W.R. LEWIS, C.D. VERONEE & J.E. LOWE. 1986. Simple step gradient elution of the major high-energy compounds and their metabolites in cardiac muscle using high performance liquid chromatography. J. Chromatogr. **377:** 165–174.
14. BURTON, K. 1956. A study of the conditions and mechanisms of the diphenylamine reaction for the colorimetric estimation of deoxyribonucleic acid. Biochem. J. **62:** 315–323.
15. PERRAULT, L.P., A. MENASCHE, A. BEL, T. DE CHAUMARAY, J. PEYNET, A. MONDRY, P. OLIVERO, R. EMANOIL-RAVIER & J.-M. MOALIC. 1996. Ischemic preconditioning in cardiac surgery: a word of caution. J. Thorac. Cardiovasc. Surg. **112:** 1378–1386.
16. PRZYKLENK, K., B. BAUER, M. OVIZE, R.A. KLONER & P. WHITTAKER. 1993. Regional ischemic preconditioning protects remote virgin myocardium from subsequent sustained coronary occlusion. Circulation **87:** 893–899.
17. VAN WYLEN, D.G.L. 1994. Effect of ischemic preconditioning on interstitial purine metabolite and lactate accumulation during myocardial ischemia. Circulation **89:** 2283–2289.
18. CARR, C.S., R.J. HILL, H. MASAMUNE *et al.* 1997. Evidence for a role for both the adenosine A_1 and A_3 receptors in protection of isolated human atrial muscle against simulated ischemia. Cardiovasc. Res. **36**(1): 52–59.
19. WALKER, D.M., J.M. WALKER, W.B. PUGSLEY, C.W. PATTISON & D.M. YELLON. 1995. Preconditioning in isolated superfused human muscle. J. Molec. Cell Cardiol. **27**(6): 1349–1357.
20. MENTZER, R.M., JR., R. BUNGER & R.D. LASLEY. 1993. Adenosine enhanced preservation of myocardial function and energetics. Possible involvement of the adenosine A_1 receptor system. Cardiovasc. Res. **27:** 28–35.

Surgical Stress and the Heat Shock Response: *In Vivo* Models of Stress Conditioning

G.A. PERDRIZET,[a] D.S. SHAPIRO, AND M.J. REWINSKI

Surgical Research, Hartford Hospital, Hartford, Connecticut and University of Connecticut Health Center, Farmington, Connecticut USA

> *"Cum melius et utilius sit in tempore occurrere quam post causam vulneratam quaerrere remedium." (Prevention is better than cure.)*
>
> — *Bracton, circa 1240*

ABSTRACT: All forms of surgical therapy are stressful and injurious. The majority of surgical procedures are performed electively and provide an opportunity to condition the patient before surgery to maximize outcome. We have successfully protected the spinal cord and kidneys from warm ischemia-reperfusion injury with whole-body heat shock (42.5°C, 15 min, HS) and recovery (37°C, 6−8 h) before acute aortic occlusion. Control rabbits experienced an 88% incidence of paralysis (7/8) after acute spinal cord ischemia, while HS-pretreated animals never became paralyzed (0/9, $p < 0.001$). Control pig kidneys showed partial function (4/8 survival) after 90-min warm ischemia, while HS-pretreated kidneys always functioned (8/8 survival, $p < 0.04$). A positive temporal association was made between the HS-associated functional protection and the enhanced expression of inducible HSP70. The induction of the heat-shock response (cellular stress response) to protect tissues from lethal acute ischemia-reperfusion injury could be employed in a wide range of medical and surgical settings.

INTRODUCTION

Complex surgical procedures involving the aorta consistently produce varying degrees of ischemia-reperfusion injury (IRI) in a wide variety of organs. Complications such as stroke, renal failure, and paralysis are considered a direct result of the obligatory IRI sustained during operative repair of aortic aneurysms. These IRI-related complications contribute a major portion of the morbidity and mortality associated with these surgical interventions. The incidence of acute spinal cord paralysis is reported in the clinical literature to range between 4–40% for the repair of some forms of thoracoabdominal aneurysms.[2] Furthermore, visceral ischemia syndromes are also observed and directly contribute to overall mortality.[3]

[a]Address correspondence to: Dr. G.A. Perdrizet, Hartford Hospital, Trauma Program, 80 Seymour Street, Hartford, CT 06102.

Presently, most efforts to reduce IRI-related complications have focused on techniques applied during the operative procedure. These preventative approaches fall into two broad categories: (1) ensure adequate blood flow to vulnerable tissues during the operative procedure and (2) protect vulnerable tissues by a variety of techniques, such as limiting the duration of ischemia, the application of some form of hypothermia, and/or administration of pharmacologic agents (such as mannitol, calcium channel blockers, or corticosteroids). For the individual patient, these approaches frequently fall short of the desired goal.

Little attention has been directed to the potential for preoperatively conditioning the at-risk tissues to increase ischemic tolerance and assist in recovery from acute IRI. The feasibility of this approach was originally demonstrated in an animal model of organ preservation, wherein ischemic tolerance of the rat kidney was dramatically enhanced by preoperative "stress conditioning" with whole-body hyperthermia.[4] Whole-body hyperthermia administered preoperatively resulted in enhanced expression of the inducible isoform of the 70 kD heat-shock protein (HSP70), which persists during the time period in which tissues are exposed to acute IRI. The stress-conditioning approach has subsequently been extended to several other animal models of clinically relevant IRI.[5,6]

Information about the pathophysiology of acute IRI has classically focused on the consequences of the loss of cellular energy charge and these have been extensively reviewed.[7] Currently it is unclear which of these changes is pathologic versus physiologic. Modern molecular genetic techniques are generating new knowledge regarding the changes in gene expression that occur in association with acute IRI. Changes in kinase and phosphatase activities, signal transduction pathways, and programmed cell death pathways are but a few examples currently under intense investigation. We have chosen to focus our studies on the recently described family of genes regulating HSP synthesis.[8]

HSP70 gene expression is one of the dominant products of protein synthesis within the cell stressed by acute IRI, as well as by any one of a myriad of noxious agents and conditions. This is important from the perspective of tissue responses to acute IRI. HSPs are involved in an array of essential biochemical functions within the cell. These functions include cell cycling, protein synthesis and degradation, and protein transport between subcellular compartments. An important function of the HSPs is to assist other complex cellular proteins to fold properly into functional proteins. Proteins that assist other proteins in the process of folding have recently been classified into a group of biomolecules designated "molecular chaperones."[9] The family of HSPs has been assigned membership to this class of molecular chaperones. Folding and unfolding of complex proteins occur continually within the cell, permitting transmembrane transportation and subcellular compartmentalization of macromolecules. Molecular chaperones prevent misfolding and subsequent denaturation and loss of protein function. Conceivably, the ability to prevent protein denaturation during IRI would help the cell preserve its enzymatic functions and assist in post-ischemic functional recovery. We tested the hypothesis that stress conditioning by whole-body hyperthermia and recovery before surgically induced ischemia will protect spinal cord and renal tissues from acute IRI in animal models. The increased ischemic tolerance observed in these tissues is associated with the increased synthesis of inducible HSP70.

MATERIALS AND METHODS

Rabbit Spinal Cord Ischemia

Three groups of anesthetized New Zealand White rabbits were subjected to spinal cord ischemia by a 20-min infra-renal aortic occlusion, defined by a drop in femoral mean arterial pressure (MAP) to 0–8 mm Hg. Carotid MAP was maintained at 50–80 mm Hg during aortic occlusion. Femoral and carotid MAP were maintained at 45–60 mm Hg during reperfusion for all animals. Control animals (Group 1, unstressed) received no treatment before aortic occlusion. Heat shock animals (Group 2, HS) were pretreated with whole-body hyperthermia (core temperature 42.5°C ± 0.3 for 15 min) followed by 6–8 h of normothermic recovery (37°C) before aortic occlusion. Sham animals (Group 3, sham HS) were subjected to the same anesthesia, hydration, and restraint as the HS group but did not receive the hyperthermic pretreatment. Arterial blood gas determinations were made immediately before and after aortic occlusion to maintain consistent acid-base balance and ventilation.

Animals undergoing aortic occlusion were allowed to awaken from anesthesia and neurologic evaluations were performed at 24 and 48 h postoperatively, using a six-point scale described elsewhere.[10] Animals found to be paraplegic at any stage were euthanized and autopsied. Animals that showed normal or partial function were followed for 48 h, euthanized, and autopsied. Tissue samples were snap-frozen in liquid nitrogen at the time of surgery immediately before aortic occlusion (skeletal muscle) and at the time of autopsy (spinal cord, skeletal muscle, kidney, liver, and heart). Tissue samples were processed for light microscopy and HSP70 analysis by Western blot techniques. Protein lysates were separated by protein gel electrophoresis and developed using a monoclonal antibody (SPA-810, StressGen, Victoria, BC) specific for the inducible isoform of mammalian HSP70.

Porcine Renal Ischemia

Yorkshire pigs, weighing 15 to 20 kg, received halothane anesthesia. The carotid artery was cannulated for blood pressure monitoring and a pulmonary artery catheter placed via the iliac vein to monitor core body temperature. After 10 min of hypotension (systolic BP < 50 mm Hg), the endotracheal tube was clamped and the animal was exsanguinated. Warm ischemia was measured from the time when blood pressure fell below 50 mm Hg. Heparin (250 U/kg) and mannitol (12.5 g) were given intravenously to all donors at the onset of hypotension.

We followed three experimental groups. Control animals (Group 1, $N = 8$, unstressed) received a 90-min warm ischemia as described above. Heat-shock animals (Group 2, $N = 6$, HS) were placed on arteriovenous shunt (iliac artery to external jugular vein) with a heat exchanger and pump in the circuit. Group 2 animals were heat-pretreated by raising their core-body temperature to 42.5°C for 15 min followed by a period of recovery (4–6 h at 37–38°C) before exposure to the 90-min warm ischemia. Group 3 animals ($N = 6$, sham HS) were identical to Group 2 animals except they were not heated, but they were placed on the arteriovenous bypass circuit and the core-body temperature was maintained at 37–38°C followed by the same period of recovery (4–6 h at 37–38°C) before exposure to the 90-min warm ischemia. Group 3 animals were included to control for any nonthermal stresses that may have been introduced during the use of general anesthesia and placement of the arterio-venous shunt. Group 1 animals represent animals that were completely unstressed before ischemia and reflect the baseline ischemic tolerance in this model.

After a 90-min warm ischemia, the kidneys in all groups were flushed *in situ* with Euro-Collins solution and stored at 4°C for 20 h, followed by transplantation into littermate recipients. The transplants were placed in the right iliac fossa using end-to-end anastomosis of the renal artery to common iliac artery and end-to-side anastomosis of the renal vein to common iliac vein. The ureter was anastomosed to the bladder using a submucosal tunnel. A bilateral native nephrectomy was then performed. All animals were given water and standard pig chow and received daily oral cyclosporine (10 mg/kg), azathioprine (2.5 mg/kg), and prednisone 1 mg/kg) beginning on the first postoperative day.

Baseline and daily postoperative serum creatinine levels were determined for 10 days, at which time all animals were euthanized and autopsied. HSP70 expression by renal tissues was determined. Kidney biopsies were taken at the time of transplantation and snap-frozen in liquid nitrogen and subsequently placed in lysis buffer (4°C) for extraction of proteins. Protein extracts of similar concentration were loaded and separated on one-dimensionsal polyacrylamide gel electrophoresis (7.5%). Western blots were developed using monoclonal antibody (SPA-810, StressGen, Victoria, BC) specific for the inducible isoform of mammalian HSP70. Graft loss secondary to technical failure or rejection was excluded from the tabulation of results (seven in Group 1 and five in Group 3). The Fisher Exact Test was used for statistical analysis of recipient survival and Student's t test was used for analysis of serum creatinines.

RESULTS

Rabbit Spinal Cord Ischemia

There are no statistically significant differences in carotid or femoral mean arterial pressures between experimental groups during any stage of the aortic occlusion (data not shown). Unstressed control animals in Group 1 exhibited an 88% incidence of hindlimb paralysis ($N = 8$, TABLE 1). Group 2 animals preconditioned with heat shock and recovery were never paraplegic ($N = 9$, $p < 0.001$). Animals in Group 3 exhibited an intermediate degree of protection, as five animals regained only partial function, one was paralyzed, and one demonstrated normal function. Tissue samples taken at the time of aortic occlusion showed high levels HSP70, while sham-stressed

TABLE 1. Stress conditioning prevents paralysis after 20-min acute spinal cord ischemia in the rabbit[a]

	Pretreatment	Normal	Paretic	Paralyzed (%)
Group 1 ($N = 8$)	None	0	1	7 (88[b])
Group 2 ($N = 9$)	Heat shock	8	1	0 (0[b])
Group 3 ($N = 7$)	Sham	1	5	1 (14)

[a]Neurologic function at 24 h after aortic occlusion.
[b]Group 1 versus Group 2 or Group 3, $p \leq 0.001$.

TABLE 2. Stress conditioning protects pig kidneys after 90-min warm ischemia

	Pretreatment	Serum creatinine[a]	Survival[b]
Group 1	None	11.2 ± 4.3	4/8
Group 2	Heat shock	3.5 ± 2.4	8/8
Group 3	Sham	9.3 ± 5.7	4/6

[a]Day 7 after reperfusion, Student's t test: $p < 0.01$, Group 1 versus Group 2.
[b]Day 10 after reperfusion, Fisher Exact Test: $p < 0.04$, Group 1 versus Group 2.

and unstressed control animals exhibited little or no HSP70 expression (data not shown).

Porcine Renal Ischemia

Survival of recipients was 100% in Group 2 (HS) as compared to 50% in Group 1 (controls) and 66% in Group 3 (sham control) as shown in TABLE 2. Comparison of groups 1 and 2 is marginally statistically significant at $p < 0.04$, probably reflecting the small number of animals in each group. At the time of organ revascularization, kidneys from groups 1 and 3 appeared cyanotic and oliguric, in contrast to the Group 2 kidneys which were pink and diuresing. Average baseline serum creatinine levels (mg/dl) were the same in all groups at the initiation of ischemia (Group 1 = 1.4, Group 2 = 1.4, and Group 3 = 1.2), indicating similar renal function before transplantation. After transplantation, all recipients had a similar rise in serum creatinine until postoperative Day 4 when the Group 2 kidneys, which had been pretreated with heat shock, began to improve. Mean creatinine levels on Day 7 were: Group 1, 11.2 ± 4.3 mg/dl, Group 2, 3.5 ± 2.4 mg/dl, and Group 3, 9.3 ± 5.7 mg/dl. The difference between the serum creatinines from groups 1 and 2 is statistically significant ($p <$ 0.01). Associated with the improved functional recovery of the Group 2 kidneys is the enhanced production of HSP70 (data not shown). The same level of HSP70 production was not seen in tissues not subjected to HS treatment nor was it seen in the HS-treated tissues before the critical 6-h period of normothermic recovery (data not shown). Kidneys from donors that had been HS-treated and allowed to recover clearly show improved functional recovery after warm ischemic injury and cold storage.

DISCUSSION

Preoperative stress conditioning by whole-body hyperthermia and recovery can protect spinal cord and renal tissues from severe, acute IRI *in vivo*. These findings confirm and extend our previous experience in a rodent model of organ preservation. The potent state of cytoprotection observed *in vivo* is associated with molecular changes at the cellular level, most notably the enhanced expression of the inducible isoform of HSP70. The precise mechanisms by which HSP70 is involved in the development of this protected phenotype are currently being investigated. Acute IRI continues to detract from clinical outcomes after complex surgical therapies. Thoughtful integration of the cellular stress response through implementation of stress-conditioning protocols can convert a lethal ischemic insult into a sublethal, survivable event. Stress conditioning offers the physician the opportunity to practice preventative medicine at the molecular level.

CONCLUSIONS

(1) Many surgical stresses are characterized by acute IRI.
(2) Heat-shock gene expression is a dominant metabolic response to acute IRI.
(3) Stress conditioning by induction of heat-shock gene expression increases ischemic tolerance in mammalian tissues and organs.
(4) Cytoprotection induced by stress conditioning is associated with enhanced expression of the inducible isoform of mammalian SP70.
(5) Stress conditioning applied to the preoperative setting will improve clinical outcomes. Clinically convenient methods will need to be developed to reach this goal.

REFERENCES

1. Bracton. 1240. Oxford Dictionary of English Proverbs (*De Legibus*). 1966. 2nd edit. p. 517. Clarendon Press.
2. Crawford, E., J. Crawford, H. Safi *et al.* 1986. Thoracoabdominal aortic aneurysms: preoperative and intraoperative factors determining immediate and long-term results of operations in 605 patients. J. Vasc. Surg. **3:** 389–409.
3. Svensson, L.G., S. Crawford, K. Hess *et al.* 1993. Experience with 1509 patients undergoing thoracoabdominal aortic operations. J. Vasc. Surgery. **17:** 357–370.
4. Perdrizet, G.A., T.G. Heffron, F.C. Buckingham *et al.* 1989. Stress conditioning: a novel approach to organ preservation. Curr. Surg. **46:** 23–25.
5. Perdrizet, G.A. 1995. Heat shock and tissue protection. New Horizons **3:** 312–320.
6. Perdrizet, G.A. 1996. The heat shock response and organ transplantation. Transplantation Rev. **10:** 78–98.
7. Granger, D.N. & R.J. Korthuis. 1995. Physiologic mechanisms of postischemic tissue injury. Ann. Rev. Physiol. **57:** 311–331.
8. Morimoto, R.I., A. Tissieres, G. Georgopoulos. 1994. The Biology of Heat Shock Proteins and Molecular Chaperones. Cold Spring Harbor Laboratory Press. Cold Spring Harbor, NY.
9. Ellis, R., S.M. van der Vies. 1991. Molecular chaperones. Ann. Rev. Biochem. **60:** 321–347.
10. Ushio, Y. *et al.* 1977. Treatment of experimental spinal cord compression caused by extradural neoplasms. J. Neurosurg. **47:** 380.

The Role of the Myocardial Sodium-Hydrogen Exchanger in Mediating Ischemic and Reperfusion Injury

From Amiloride to Cariporide[a]

MORRIS KARMAZYN[b]

Department of Pharmacology and Toxicology, University of Western Ontario, Medical Sciences Building, London, Ontario, Canada N6A 5C1

ABSTRACT: There is convincing evidence that the Na-H exchanger (NHE) plays a pivotal role in mediating tissue injury during ischemia and reperfusion. Extensive studies with NHE inhibitors have consistently shown protective effects against ischemic and reperfusion injury in a large variety of experimental models and animal species, particularly in terms of attenuating contractile dysfunction. These protective effects of NHE inhibition appear to be superior to other strategies, including ischemic preconditioning. Such studies have contributed greatly to the overwhelming evidence that NHE activation mediates ischemic and reperfusion injury. The NHE inhibitor HOE 642 (cariporide) is currently undergoing clinical evaluation in high-risk cardiac patients. Moreover, there is now emerging evidence that NHE may be involved in mediating cardiotoxicity directly produced by various ischemic metabolites such as lipid amphiphiles or reactive oxygen species. NHE inhibition also attenuates apoptosis in the ischemic myocardium, a process that may be of importance in the subsequent development of postinfarction heart failure. In conclusion, NHE represents an important adaptive process in response to intracellular acidosis that results in a paradoxical contribution to cardiac tissue injury.

NHE AND THE ISCHEMIC MYOCARDIUM: A BRIEF HISTORICAL PERSPECTIVE

NHE represents one of the major pH regulatory systems in the cardiac cell. The concept that this system may be involved in cardiac pathology was first proposed by Lazdunski and coworkers in 1984[1] based on the observation that sodium influx concomitant with proton efflux may produce undesirable effects through disordered calcium homeostasis. The first experimental evidence came from the author's laboratory in 1988,[2] where it was reported that amiloride, a relatively non-specific NHE inhibitor, protected the ischemic and reperfused myocardium. Since that initial observation dozens of studies have reported on the protective effects of NHE inhib-

[a]Studies from author's laboratory are supported by the Medical Research Council of Canada. The author is a Career Investigator of the Heart and Stroke Foundation of Ontario.

[b]Address correspondence to: Dr. Morris Karmazyn, Department of Pharmacology and Toxicology, University of Western Ontario, Medical Sciences Building, London, Ontario, Canada N6A 5C1; Telephone: (519) 661-3872; Fax: (519) 661-4051; E-mail: mkarm@julian.uwo.ca

itors including more selective amiloride analogues and the more recently developed compounds HOE 694 and HOE 642 (cariporide). It has been particularly impressive that virtually all reports from a variety of laboratories have demonstrated protective effects. These impressive findings formed the basis for the rapid approval and establishment of a multicentered international clinical trial, the GUARDIAN study, to assess the effects of cariporide in high-risk patients with acute coronary syndromes. The four major group of patients recruited into this study include (1) patients with unstable angina, (2) patients with non–q wave myocardial infarction, (3) unstable patients requiring percutaneous transluminal coronary angioplasty, and (4) unstable or high-risk patients requiring coronary artery bypass surgery. The two primary endpoints are myocardial infarction and mortality. The results of the trial are expected in 1999. Taken together, these developments represent rapid progress in the development of novel strategies in cardiovascular therapeutics that will hopefully result in a reduction in morbidity and mortality in patients with heart disease.

INTRODUCTION: pH_i REGULATION AND NHE

Changes in intracellular pH (pH_i) can produce marked effects on cardiac contractility, particularly acidosis-induced negative inotropic effects. Although the mechanisms involved in pH-regulated contractility are very complex, they reflect the direct interfering effects of protons on various cellular processes involved with excitation-contraction coupling.[3] It is therefore critical that the cell possesses mechanisms by which pH_i is regulated especially after intracellular acidosis as a consequence of myocardial ischemia. Two major alkalinizing exchangers exist in the cardiac cell, the NHE and a Na-HCO_3^- symport. The NHE represents one of the key mechanisms for restoring pH_i following ischemia-induced acidosis by extruding protons concomitantly with sodium influx. The simultaneous entry of sodium during NHE activation indicates that this process is also an important route for increasing intracellular sodium concentrations during various conditions and represents the major mechanism postulated to mediated NHE-dependent cardiac injury through modulation of intracellular calcium levels, as discussed further below. To date, at least five (a mitochondrial NHE-6 isoform has been identified although its function is unknown) distinct isoforms of the exchanger have thus far been identified that possess structural differences as well as varying sensitivities to inhibition by pharmacological agents. It appears that the ubiquitous subtype 1 (NHE-1), a glycoprotein with a molecular weight of approximately 110 kD, is the predominant isoform in the mammalian myocardium. NHE-1 comprises two major functional domains: a hydrophobic region that spans the membrane 12 times and that is critical for exchange activity, and a hydrophilic moiety that is likely of importance for hormonal modulation of the exchanger. Further details concerning the molecular structure and regulation of the NHE can be found in a number of recent review articles and monographs.[4–6] The activity of NHE-1 can be modulated by a number of growth factors, hormones, and neurotransmitters (via various kinases, including tyrosine kinases, Ca-calmodulin kinase, MAP kinases, and PKC coupled to G proteins), as well as by hypertonic shrinking and mechanical stimuli. Most of these signals stimulate NHE by shifting the pH_i-activity curve towards the alkaline range, thus stimulating the enzymatic activity of the transporter at constant pH_i and moving

TABLE 1. Beneficial effects of Na-H exchange inhibitors on the ischemic and reperfused heart

Enhanced/accelerated systolic recovery after reperfusion
Diminished ischemic and reperfusion-induced contracture
Reduced arrhythmias including supression of postinfarction ventricular fibrillation
Prevention of postinfarction mortality
Reduced calcium and sodium overload
Preservation of energy metabolites
Reduced necrosis
Reduced apoptosis
Reduced toxicity of various ischemic metabolites and paracrine/autocrine factors

it closer to its maximal rate.[7] Conversely, inhibition of the exchanger can be accomplished by a variety of drugs, the prototypical being amiloride and its *N*-5 disubstituted derivatives.[8] Recently, the benzoyl guanidinium compounds 3-methylsulfonyl-4-piperidinobenzoyl-guanidine methanesulfonate (HOE 694) and 4-isopropyl-3-methylsulfonylbenzoyl-guanidine methanesulfonate (HOE 642) have been shown to be effective NHE inhibitors. HOE 642 (cariporide) is of particular interest as it appears to be a selective inhibitor of the NHE-1 isoform, the primary if not sole subtype found in heart, rendering it particularly attractive for therapeutic intervention in cardiac disorders while minimizing the potential for side effects.[9]

EFFECTS OF NHE INHIBITORS ON THE ISCHEMIC AND REPERFUSED MYOCARDIUM

Evidence in the literature strongly supports the concept that NHE inhibition bestows excellent myocardial protection against ischemic and reperfusion injury. As discussed in a number of recent reviews[6,10–12] and as summarized in TABLE 1, these salutary effects have been demonstrated on numerous parameters of cardiac function, including enhanced contractility, reduced contracture, and a decrease in the incidence of arrhythmias. In addition, improvements in biochemical and ultrastructural indices have been extensively demonstrated with NHE inhibition. Such protection has been demonstrated with the amiloride series of agents and with both HOE 694 and HOE 642. This protection is associated with diminished tissue sodium and calcium content, in support of a close association between NHE and Na-Ca exchange activity.[13,14] Indeed, reduction in calcium overload appears to represent a major mechanism of action of NHE inhibition (see below).

INTERACTION BETWEEN NHE INHIBITORS AND OTHER CARDIOPROTECTIVE STRATEGIES

Studies have been done to ascertain potential interactions between NHE inhibitors and other pharmacological agents or approaches used to protect the myocardium. Such interactions are of potential importance as they may be relevant when utilizing multifaceted approaches towards myocardial protection. For example, it has been shown that amiloride enhanced the protection afforded by reduction of extracellular sodium and calcium concentrations in isolated working rat hearts subjected to 30 min of cardioplegic arrest.[15] Moreover, in isolated working rat hearts subjected to ischemia, administration of amiloride in combination with the hydroxyl radical scavenger desferrioxamine produced superior cardioprotective effects compared to each drug alone.[16] These results are therefore suggestive of a specific and distinct target for the beneficial effects of NHE inhibition rendering this approach attractive for potential superior cardioprotective strategies using drug combination protocols. Moreover, we have recently demonstrated additive protective effects of HOE 642 when the drug is administered in combination with either of the volatile anesthetics sevoflurane or isoflurane in isolated ischemic and reperfused rat hearts.[17] Although indicative of distinct mechanisms of action, these findings also suggest that the combination of HOE 642 and these volatile agents produces superior cardioprotection, which may be of importance under clinical conditions where effective cardioprotection is desired during surgical procedures.

IS NHE INHIBITION A SUPERIOR CARDIOPROTECTIVE STRATEGY? COMPARISON WITH ISCHEMIC PRECONDITIONING

Detailed comparisons between NHE inhibition and other modes of cardioprotection have not been extensively studied yet these types of studies are important in order to design the most effective therapeutic approaches. Work in our laboratory has compared ischemic preconditioning with NHE inhibition with cariporide in hearts subjected to increasing periods of zero-flow ischemia followed by 30-min reperfusion. Ischemic preconditioning was carried out with two 5-min cycles of ischemia separated by a 10-min reperfusion before initiating prolonged ischemia. Alternatively, experiments were also done in the presence of 5 μM cariporide. The essence of our findings is that improved recovery of function is similar with the shorter ischemia durations although cariporide-treated hearts recovered significantly faster. The most marked observation was that cardioprotective effects of cariporide were still evident when ischemia was extended to 90 min, whereas no salutary effects were seen with ischemic preconditioning. Accordingly, it appears that NHE inhibition is advantageous and superior to ischemic preconditioning, particularly under conditions of prolonged ischemia when the effects of the latter are no longer evident.

MECHANISMS OF NHE INVOLVEMENT IN ACUTE ISCHEMIC AND REPERFUSION INJURY

A number of concepts are emerging regarding the mechanisms underlying NHE involvement in the ischemic myocardium and it appears that NHE may be involved in multiple mechanisms. FIGURE 1 outlines these concepts and shows that these mechanisms are interrelated, suggesting that although calcium is the final mechanism, the activation of NHE and the role of the antiporter in mediating injury likely involve multifaceted aspects.

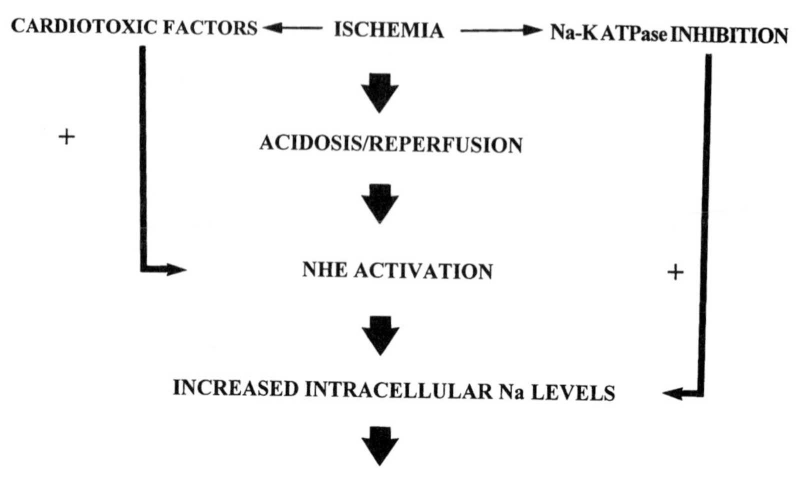

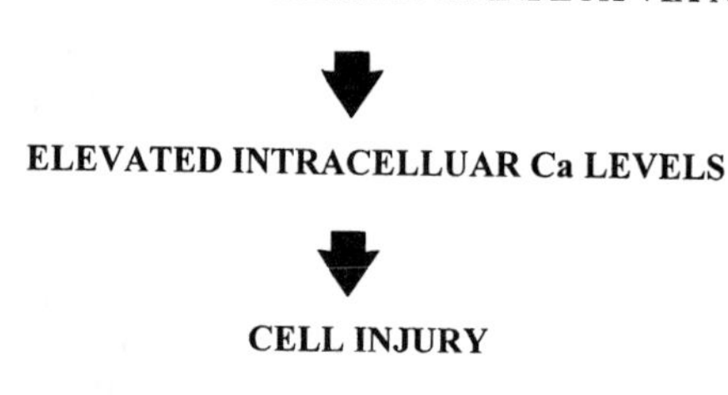

FIGURE 1. Pathways of NHE activation and its involvement in acute responses to myocardial ischemia and reperfusion. See text for details.

Modulation of Intracellular Calcium Levels

The role of calcium is based on the proposal that reintroduction of flow to the previously ischemic, and thereby acidotic, cardiac cell establishes a rapid transsarcolemmal proton gradient resulting in activation of NHE. This has been reviewed in several publications.[1,6,10–12,14] While this would contribute to restoration of pH_i, the concomitant sodium influx could result in increased intracellular calcium concentration via the Na-Ca exchanger due to reduced calcium efflux resulting from the reduction of the sodium gradient driving the Na-Ca exchanger. Moreover, it should be emphasized that in the ischemic cardiac cell Na-K ATPase is inhibited resulting in an elevation in intracellular sodium concentration due to reduced ability to extrude sodium. Activation of NHE, particularly upon reperfusion, which in itself is greater due to the prior ischemia-induced accumulation of protons, provokes a greater elevation in intracellular sodium and calcium concentrations particularly under conditions of defective ion regulatory mechanisms. The net result of large elevations in intracellular calcium levels coupled with intracellular alkalosis due to NHE-mediated proton extrusion is tissue damage manifested by intracellular calcium overload, contracture, and depressed systolic function. Moreover, there is also evidence, particularly that based on NMR studies, to suggest that NHE activation during ischemia per se, that is prior to reperfusion, also contributes to both calcium and sodium overloading, providing yet another contributing factor to cell injury.[18]

Attenuation of Cardiotoxic Effects of Ischemic Metabolites

The above hypothesis suggests that the primary mechanism for NHE activation is intracellular acidosis. However, further NHE activation occurs because of direct stimulation by metabolites produced by the ischemic myocardium. For example, levels of endothelin-1 (ET-1), a potent NHE activator, are elevated in myocardial ischemia and may produce deleterious effects on the reperfused myocardium, inducing both diastolic and systolic abnormalities.[19] We have shown that the toxicity produced by ET-1 can be attenuated by NHE inhibition, suggesting an important role of the antiporter in mediating the detrimental effect of the peptide on the ischemic and reperfused myocardium.[20] NHE activation may also represent an important mechanism for arrhythmogenesis in the reperfused myocardium particularly under conditions of elevated catecholamine levels. For example, although α_1 adrenergic agonists enhance ventricular arrhythmias in the reperfused myocardium this effect can be markedly decreased by NHE inhibition.[21]

We have recently shown that lysophosphatidylcholine, one of the predominant tissue metabolites that accumulates rapidly in the ischemic myocardium, is a potent NHE activator in the cardiac cell and that the cardiotoxic effects of this amphiphile, at least at low concentrations, can be markedly attenuated by NHE inhibitors.[22] In addition, it appears that at least some of the direct toxic effects of hydrogen peroxide can be attenuated by NHE inhibition.[23] Moreover, we have recently demonstrated that the ability of very low, sub-toxic concentrations of hydrogen peroxide to compromise postischemic ventricular recovery can be attenuated by NHE inhibition.[24] Taken together, these observations open up the possibility that a variety of intracellular factors produced during ischemia may contribute to tissue dysfunction through NHE-dependent processes.

Apoptosis

There is now increasing evidence that apoptosis or "programmed cell death" is an important response of the myocardium to ischemia. Apoptosis is rapid, precedes cell necrosis, and appears to contribute the overall sequelae of cardiac injury.[25–27] We recently demonstrated that HOE 642 significantly attenuated the development of early apoptosis in hearts subjected to 30-min global ischemia with or without reperfusion.[28] Moreover, dietary cariporide inhibits reperfusion-associated apoptosis in the acutely infarcted myocardium (unpublished data). This is clearly an important area for further study, particularly, as discussed below, since apoptosis is emerging as an important contributor to the postinfarction remodeling process leading to heart failure.

EVIDENCE FOR A ROLE OF NHE IN POSTINFARCTION RESPONSES

As evidenced from the preceding discussion, most studies on NHE involvement in heart disease have centered on acute responses. One study has shown that adding

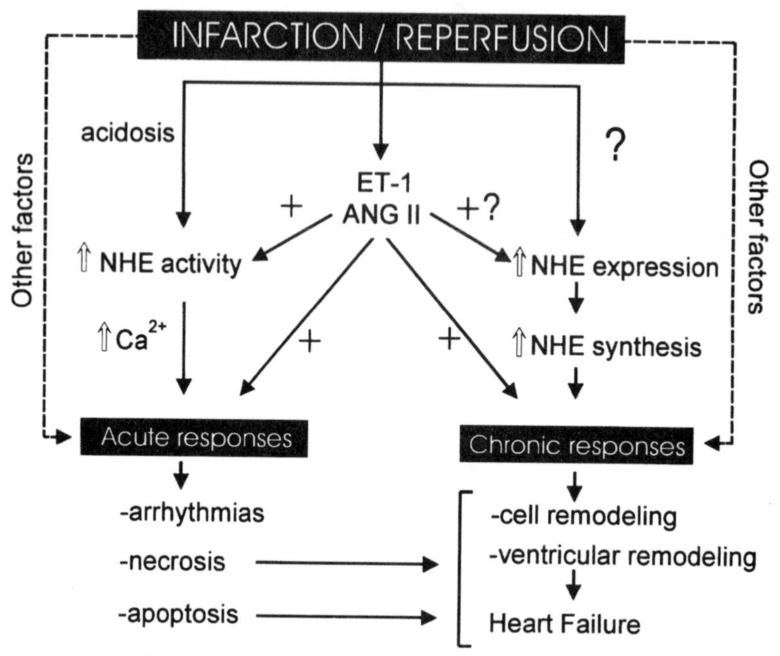

FIGURE 2. Role of NHE in the acute responses to myocardial ischemia and reperfusion and potential consequences in terms of chronic postinfarction responses. See text for details.

amiloride to the drinking water of rats with infarcted myocardium resulted in a significant attenuation of ventricular remodeling.[29] Preliminary data from our laboratory demonstrate that dietary cariporide completely prevents ventricular fibrillation and mortality in these animals and reduces other forms of arrhythmias. Moreover, the degree of apoptosis was decreased as was the ability of infarction to upregulate NHE-1 expression. The potential benefits of the antiarrhythmic effects of cariporide are obvious in terms of early management following myocardial infarction. Apoptosis has emerged as a potentially critical factor in the response to infarction[30] and evolution to heart failure.[31–33] Thus, the fact that cariporide can inhibit this phenomenon[28] further reinforces its potential usefulness in postinfarction responses. Although the relevance is unclear at present, increased NHE-1 expression postinfarction is intriguing and suggests that NHE influences not only acute, but also chronic postinfarction responses, the latter occurring through an as-yet undefined mechanism of upregulated NHE-1 expression. Paracrine/autocrine regulation by ET-1 or angiotensin II may contribute to this process. These concepts are summarized in FIGURE 2.

SUMMARY

There is now strong evidence that NHE activation in the ischemic and reperfused heart plays a major role in restoring pH_i, which at the same time contributes to tissue damage most likely via a number of complex mechanisms. This concept is supported by the fact that virtually all studies thus far reported have demonstrated cardioprotective effects of NHE inhibitors. In addition to its role in acute ischemia and reperfusion, it is likely that the antiporter will also be found to be of importance in other scenarios of ischemic injury, such as that involving long-term cardiac preservation. The beneficial effects of NHE inhibitors coupled with the likely low toxicity of these agents, particularly with respect to the novel isoform-specific inhibitors, provide promise for the development of new strategies for the protection of the ischemic myocardium as well for the heart subjected to reperfusion procedures.

REFERENCES

1. LAZDUNSKI, M., C. FRELIN & P. VIGNE. 1985. The sodium/hydrogen exchange system in cardiac cells: its biochemical and pharmacological properties and its role in regulating internal concentrations of sodium and internal pH. J. Mol. Cell. Cardiol. **17:** 1029–1042.
2. KARMAZYN, M. 1988. Amiloride enchances postischemic ventricular recovery: possible role of Na^+/H^+ exchange. Am. J. Physiol. **255:** H608–H615.
3. ORCHARD, C.H. & J.C. KENTISH. 1990. Effects of changes of pH on the contractile function of cardiac muscle. Am. J. Physiol. **258:** C967–C981.
4. WAKABAYASHI, S., M. SHIGEKAWA & J. POUYSSÉGUR. 1997. Molecular physiology of vertebrate Na^+/H^+ exchangers. Physiol. Rev. **77:** 51–74.
5. FLIEGEL, L., ED. 1996. The Na^+/H^+ Exchanger. R.G. Landes Company. Austin, TX.
6. FRÖHLICH, O. & M. KARMAZYN. 1997. The Na-H exchanger revisited. An update on Na-H exchange regulation and the role of the exchanger in hypertension and cardiac function in health and disease. Cardiovasc. Res. **36:** 138–148.
7. BIANCHINI, L. & J. POUYSSÉGUR. 1996. Regulation of the Na^+/H^+ exchanger isoform NHE1: role of phosphorylation. Kidney Int. **49:** 1038–1041.
8. KLEYMAN, T.R. & E.J. CRAGOE. 1988. Amiloride and its analogs as tools in the study of ion transport. J. Membr. Biol. **105:** 1–21.
9. SCHOLZ, W., U. ALBUS, L. COUNILLON, H. GÖGELEIN, H-J. LANG, W. LINZ, A. WEICHER & B.A. SCHÖLKENS. 1995. Protective effects of HOE642, a selective sodium-hydrogen exchange subtype 1 inhibitor, on cardiac ischaemia and reperfusion. Cardiovasc. Res. **29:** 260–268.
10. KARMAZYN, M. 1996. Sodium-hydrogen exchange in myocardial ischemic and reperfusion injury. Mechanisms and therapeutic implications. *In* The Na^+/H^+ Exchanger. L. Fliegl, Ed.: 189–215. R.G. Landes Company. Austin, TX.
11. AVKIRAN, M. 1996. Sodium-hydrogen exchange in myocardial ischemia and reperfusion: A critical determinant of injury? *In* Myocardial Ischemia: Mechanisms, Reperfusion, Protection. M. Karmazyn, Ed.: 299–311. Birkhäuser Verlag. Basel.
12. KARMAZYN, M. 1996. The sodium-hydrogen exchange system in the heart. Its role in ischemic and reperfusion injury and thereapeutic implications. Can. J. Cardiol. **12:** 1074–1082.
13. TANI, M. & J.R. NEELY. 1989. Role of intracellular Na^+ in Ca^{2+} overload and depressed recovery of ventricular function of reperfused ischemic rat hearts. Possible involvement of H^+-Na^+ and Na^+- Ca^{2+} exchange. Circ. Res. **65:** 1045–1056.
14. PIERCE, G.N. & M.P. CZUBRYT. 1995. The contribution of ionic imbalance to ischemia/reperfusion-induced injury. J. Mol. Cell. Cardiol. **27:** 53–63.
15. YAMADA, T., M. TAKAGI, T. KUGIMIYA, N. MIYAGAWA, R. SHIBATA, H. HASHIYADA & H. YAMAGUCHI. 1995. Myocardial recovery during post-ischemic reperfusion: optimal concentrations of Na^+ and Ca^{2+} in the reperfusate and protective effects of amiloride added to the cardioplegic solution. Heart & Vessels **10:** 310–317.
16. KARWATOWSKA-PROKOPCZUK, E., E. CZARNOWSKA & A. PROKOPCZUK. 1995. Combined therapy with dimethylthiourea, diltiazem and amiloride/dimethylamiloride in the ischemic/reperfused heart. Cardiovasc. Res. **30:** 70–78.

17. Mathur, S. & M. Karmazyn. 1997. Interaction between anesthetics and the sodium-hydrogen exchange inhibitor HOE 642 (Cariporide) in ischemic and reperfused rat hearts. Anesthesiology **87:** 1460–1469.
18. Murphy, E., M. Perlman, R.E. London & C. Steenbergen. 1991. Amiloride delays the ischemia-induced rise in cytosolic calcium. Circ. Res. **68:** 1250–1258.
19. Karmazyn, M. 1996. The role of endothelins in cardiac function in health and disease. *In* Myocardial Ischemia: Mechanisms, Reperfusion, Protection. M. Karmazyn, Ed.: 209–230. Birkhäuser Verlag. Basel.
20. Khandoudi, N., J. Ho & M. Karmazyn. 1994. Role of Na^+-H^+ exchange in mediating effects of endothelin-1 on normal and ischemic/reperfused hearts. Circ. Res. **75:** 369–378.
21. Yasutake, M. & M. Avkiran. 1995. Exacerbation of reperfusion arrhythmias by α_1 adrenergic stimulation: a potential role for receptor mediated activation of sarcolemmal sodium-hydrogen exchange. Cardiovasc. Res. **29:** 222–230.
22. Hoque, A.N.E., J.V. Haist & M. Karmazyn. 1997. Sodium-hydrogen exchange inhibition protects against mechanical, ultrastructural and biochemical impairment induced by low concentrations of lysophosphatidylcholine in isolated rat hearts. Circ. Res. **80:** 95–102.
23. Hoque, A.N.E. & M. Karmazyn. 1997. Effect of sodium-hydrogen exchange inhibitionon functional and metabolic impairment produced by oxidative stress in the isolated rat heart. Can. J. Physiol. Pharmacol. **75:** 326–334.
24. Myers, M.L., P. Farhangkhoee & M. Karmazyn. 1998. Hydrogen peroxide induced impairment of post-ischemic recovery of rat ventricular function is prevented by the sodium-hydrogen exchange inhibitor HOE 642 (cariporide). Cardiovasc. Res. **40:** 290–296.
25. Karmazyn, M. & J.R. Bend. 1997. Biochemical and molecular and biochemical mechanisms of myocardial injury. *In* Comprehensive Toxicology (Cardiovascular Toxicology). S.P. Bishop, Ed. **6:** 255–278. Elsevier Science. Amsterdam.
26. Umansky, S.R. & L.D. Tomei. 1997. Apoptosis in the heart. Adv. Pharmacol. **41:** 383–407.
27. MacLellan, W.R. & M.D. Schneider. 1997. Death by design. Programmed cell death in cardiovascular biology and disease. Circ. Res. **81:** 137–144.
28. Chakrabarti, S., A.N.E Hoque & M. Karmazyn. 1997. A rapid ischemia-induced apoptosis in isolated rat hearts and its attenuation by the Na-H exchange inhibitor HOE 642 (cariporide). J. Mol. Cell. Cardiol. **29:** 3169–3174.
29. Hasegawa, S., N. Nakano, Y. Taniguchi, S. Imai, K. Murata & T. Suzuki. 1995. Effects of Na^+-H^+ exchange blocker amiloride on left ventricular remodeling after anterior myocardial infarction in rats. Cardiovasc. Drugs Ther. **9:** 823–826.
30. Colucci, W.S. 1996. Apoptosis in the heart. N. Engl. J. Med. **335:** 1224–1226.
31. Olivetti, G., R. Abbi, F. Quaini, J. Kajstura, W. Cheng, J.A Nitahara, E. Quaini, C. Di Loretto, C.A. Beltrami, S. Krajewski, J.C. Reed & P. Anversa. 1997. Apoptosis in the failing human heart. N. Engl. J. Med. **336:** 1131–1141.
32. Leri, A., Y. Liu, A. Malhotra, Q. Li, P. Stiegler, P.P. Claudio, A. Giordano, J. Kajstura, T.H. Hintze & P. Anversa. 1998. Pacing-induced heart failure in dogs enhances the expression of p53 and p53-dependent genes in ventricular myocytes. Circulation **97:** 194–203.
33. Olivetti, G., F. Quaini, R. Sala, C. Lagrasta, D. Corradi, E. Bonacina, S.R. Gambert, E. Cigola & P. Anversa. 1996. Acute myocardial infarction in humans is associated with activation of programmed myocyte cell death in the surviving portion of the heart. J. Mol. Cell. Cardiol. **28:** 2005–2016.

Regulation of Cardiac Sarcolemmal Na^+/H^+ Exchanger Activity by Endogenous Ligands

Relevance to Ischemia[a]

METIN AVKIRAN[b] AND ROBERT S. HAWORTH

Cardiovascular Research, The Rayne Institute, St Thomas' Hospital, London SE1 7EH, United Kingdom

ABSTRACT: The cardiac sarcolemmal Na^+/H^+ exchanger (NHE) extrudes one H^+ in exchange for one Na^+ entering the myocyte, utilizing for its driving force the inwardly directed Na^+ gradient that is maintained by the Na^+/K^+ ATPase. The exchanger is quiescent at physiological values of intracellular pH but becomes activated in response to intracellular acidosis. Recent evidence suggests that a variety of extracellular signals (e.g., adrenergic agonists, thrombin, and endothelin) also modulate sarcolemmal NHE activity by altering its sensitivity to intracellular H^+. Since sarcolemmal NHE activity is believed to be an important determinant of the extent of myocardial injury during ischemia and reperfusion, regulation of exchanger activity by endogenous ligands associated with ischemia is likely to be of pathophysiological importance.

The plasma membrane Na^+/H^+ exchanger (NHE) is a ubiquitous electroneutral exchanger that extrudes one H^+ in exchange for one Na^+, utilizing as its driving force the inwardly directed Na^+ gradient maintained by Na^+/K^+ ATPase.[1,2] The exchanger is thought to mediate a number of physiological functions in various cell types, including the regulation of intracellular pH and cell volume (by virtue of the ability of the exchanger to transport H^+ and Na^+, respectively) and the control of cell growth and proliferation (by mediating the actions of a number of mitogens and growth factors).[3] Abnormalities in NHE activity have also been implicated in pathophysiological processes, such as renal acid-base disorders.[3]

With respect to the cardiovascular system, increased NHE activity has been linked with hypertension,[4] platelet activation,[5] and the proliferative response of arterial smooth muscle cells to injury.[6] Additionally, recent evidence suggests that upregulation of NHE expression and/or activity may be associated with cardiac hypertrophy in both *in vivo*[7] and *in vitro*[8,9] models. However, as discussed in depth elsewhere in this volume, the strongest evidence for an important role for NHE in

[a]Dr. Avkiran is the holder of a British Heart Foundation Senior Lectureship Award (BS/93002) and Dr. Haworth is supported through a British Heart Foundation Project Grant (PG/95159).

[b]Address correspondence to: Dr. Metin Avkiran, Cardiovascular Research, The Rayne Institute, St Thomas' Hospital, Lambeth Palace Road, London SE1 7EH, United Kingdom; Telephone: 44-171-928 9292 ext. 3375; Fax: 44-171-928 0658; E-mail: m.avkiran@umds.ac.uk

cardiac pathophysiology is that implicating the sarcolemmal exchanger in the unfavorable sequelae of ischemia and reperfusion, such as arrhythmias, contractile dysfunction, and infarction (for reviews see Avkiran[10] and Fröhlich and Karmazyn[11]). Indeed, novel pharmacological inhibitors of the exchanger, such as HOE694[12] and cariporide (HOE642),[13] have been developed for potential use in the therapy of ischemic heart disease.[14] Notably, the clinical efficacy of cariporide is currently being evaluated in a multi-national study (the "Guard in Ischemia Against Necrosis [GUARDIAN]" study) involving 12,000 patients with acute coronary syndromes. Despite these exciting advances, however, much remains unknown regarding the molecular mechanisms that regulate cardiac sarcolemmal NHE activity, particularly in the setting of ischemia and reperfusion.

CARDIAC SARCOLEMMAL NHE ACTIVITY DURING ISCHEMIA AND REPERFUSION

The sarcolemmal NHE of cardiac myocytes comprises the ubiquitous NHE1 isoform of this multi-gene family[15]; the exchanger is quiescent at physiological values of intracellular pH but becomes activated in response to intracellular acidosis,[16,17] which is known to develop rapidly during myocardial ischemia.[18] Lazdunski and colleagues[16] were the first to propose a role for the sarcolemmal NHE in the pathogenesis of ischemia and reperfusion-induced injury in myocardium. According to the "Lazdunski Hypothesis," the sarcolemmal NHE is inactive during ischemia, despite the presence of intracellular acidosis, due to inhibition by extracellular acidosis. However, according to this hypothesis, the rapid normalization of extracellular pH upon reperfusion results in the generation of an outwardly directed H^+ gradient, leading to increased sarcolemmal NHE activity and thereby predisposing the myocardium to intracellular Na^+ and Ca^{2+} overload, with detrimental consequences. Consistent with this, several studies have shown that pharmacological inhibitors of NHE, given only at the time of reperfusion, can afford substantial cardioprotection.[19–22] Nevertheless, in other studies, such treatment protocols have been found to be ineffective[23–27] or to provide only partial protection,[28–32] relative to treatment before the onset of ischemia. In contrast, as reviewed previously,[10] there is widespread consensus among published studies regarding the significant cardioprotective benefit afforded by NHE inhibitors when given before the onset of ischemia (which in many cases[23–32] has been shown to be superior to that afforded by these drugs when given only during reperfusion), regardless of inter-study variations in models, severity of ischemia, and functional endpoints. On the basis of the available data, therefore, it is likely that the sarcolemmal NHE retains significant activity during ischemia as well as during subsequent reperfusion, and that exchanger activity during both periods is important in determining the ultimate extent of injury. Thus, the superior protection afforded by pre-ischemic treatment with NHE inhibitors in many studies probably arises from inhibition of exchanger activity during ischemia and early reperfusion. In this regard, the hypothesis that significant sarcolemmal NHE activity is retained during ischemia is supported by studies that have shown that intracellular Na^+ accumulation during ischemia is attenuated in the presence of NHE inhibitors.[33,34]

How does the sarcolemmal NHE retain its activity during ischemia in the face of the significant extracellular acidosis known to accompany intracellular acidosis? Firstly, it is important to note that, although the sarcolemmal NHE is undoubtedly inhibited by extracellular acidosis,[17,35] such inhibition is not absolute. Contrary to a common misconception, the primary regulator of NHE activity is not the trans-membrane H^+ gradient, but the intracellular pH, through the interaction of intracellular H^+ with the "H^+ sensor" site of the exchanger protein.[1] Indeed, work from the Vaughan-Jones laboratory has shown that the sarcolemmal NHE can remain active and extrude H^+ against an inwardly directed H^+ gradient, provided the intracellular pH is sufficiently low.[35] Secondly, certain processes associated with ischemia, such as the accumulation of lipid metabolites and the imposition of oxidant stress, may upregulate NHE activity, since exogenous lysophosphatidylcholine[36] and hydrogen peroxide[37,38] have both been shown recently to stimulate the sarcolemmal exchanger in cultured neonatal[37] and freshly isolated adult[36,38] rat ventricular myocytes. Finally, as discussed in some detail below, various endogenous, receptor-mediated pathways with relevance to ischemia have been shown to stimulate sarcolemmal NHE activity, apparently by increasing the sensitivity of the exchanger to intracellular H^+.

REGULATION OF CARDIAC SARCOLEMMAL NHE ACTIVITY BY ENDOGENOUS LIGANDS

Effects of Catecholamines

It is well established that myocardial ischemia results in the activation of the sympathetic nervous system, as well as the local release of norepinephrine within the ischemic zone.[39] Furthermore, there is evidence that α_1-adrenergic signaling is upregulated in ischemic myocardium.[40] In this regard, it is interesting to note that the majority of the published work on catecholamine-induced changes in sarcolemmal NHE activity has concentrated on the role of α_1-adrenoceptors (α_1-ARs). Thus, in isolated ventricular myocytes from the rat and guinea pig, it has been shown that α_1-AR agonists (such as phenylephrine[41,42] and 6-fluoronorepinephrine,[43] usually in the presence of a β_1-AR antagonist) increase sarcolemmal NHE activity, while α_1-AR antagonists (such as prazosin[42,43]) inhibit such NHE-stimulatory effects. Notably, α_1-adrenergic stimulation appears to retain its ability to increase sarcolemmal NHE activity in the presence of extracellular acidosis,[41] which has important implications for NHE regulation under ischemic conditions.

Due to the lack of selectivity of the pharmacological agents used in previous studies, it has not been possible until recently to draw any conclusions regarding the identity of the α_1-AR subtype(s) involved in α_1-adrenergic stimulation of sarcolemmal NHE activity. α_1-AR subtypes are classified by the International Union of Pharmacology[44] as α_{1A}-, α_{1B}-, and α_{1D}-ARs, which correspond respectively to the recombinant subtypes previously referred to as α_{1c}, α_{1b}, and α_{1d}-ARs (the last of which has also been referred to as the α_{1a}- or $\alpha_{1a/d}$-AR). Prompted by (1) the substantial evidence supporting a key role for sarcolemmal NHE activity in the pathogenesis of ischemia-reperfusion–induced injury (see above), (2) the reported ability of non-selective α_1-adrenergic agonists to increase sarcolemmal NHE activity[41–43] and (3) our earlier observation[45] that the pro-arrhythmic effect of the non-selective

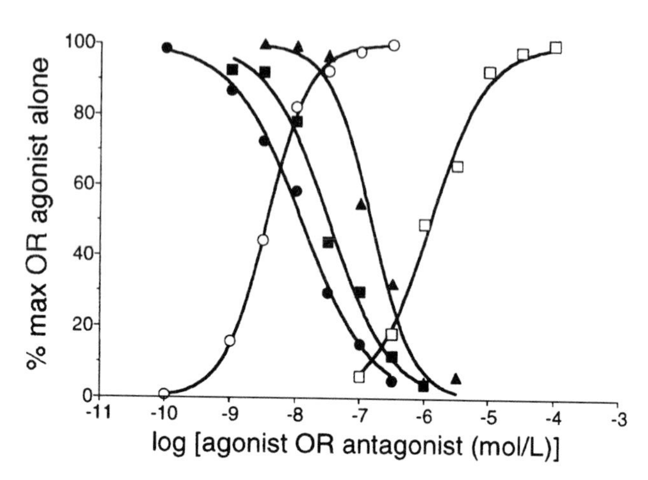

FIGURE 1. α_1-Adrenergic stimulation of sarcolemmal NHE activity in adult rat ventricular myocytes. Figure shows agonist dose-response curves for A616103 (○) and phenylephrine (□), as well as antagonist inhibition curves for prazosin (●), WB4101 (■), and 5-methylurapidil (▲) (all antagonists tested against 10 μmol/l phenylephrine). EC_{50} = 3.6 nmol/l for A61603 and 1.24 μmol/l for phenylephrine. IC_{50} = 12 nmol/l for prazosin, 32 nmol/l for WB4101, and 149 nmol/l for 5-methylurapidil. (Data from Yokoyama *et al.*[46])

α_1-adrenergic agonist phenylephrine could be reversed not only by NHE inhibition but also by an α_{1A}-AR–selective antagonist, we have recently attempted to delineate the roles of α_1-AR subtypes in regulating sarcolemmal NHE activity in adult rat ventricular myocytes.

FIGURE 1, adapted from our earlier study,[46] shows the stimulatory effects of phenylephrine and the α_{1A}-AR–selective agonist A61603 on sarcolemmal NHE activity and the inhibitory effects of the competitive antagonists prazosin, WB4101, and 5-methylurapidil on the response to 10 μM phenylephrine. Comparison of the relative potencies of these agents, as depicted in FIGURE 1, with their reported relative potencies and affinities at native[47] and recombinant[48] α_1-AR subtypes of rat origin provides evidence, for the first time, that α_1-adrenergic stimulation of sarcolemmal NHE activity is likely to be mediated selectively via the α_{1A}-AR subtype.[46] Since the α_{1A}-AR is the dominant α_1-AR subtype expressed in human myocardium[49] and myocardial hypertrophy appears to be accompanied by its transcriptional induction,[50] confirmation of α_{1A}-AR–mediated regulation of sarcolemmal NHE activity may not only provide a potential target for therapeutic intervention but may also reveal a mechanism for the increased susceptibility of hypertrophied myocardium to the consequences of ischemia and reperfusion (such as arrhythmias and contractile dysfunction).

In considering adrenergic regulation of the sarcolemmal NHE, it is important to note that β-adrenergic stimulation also affects exchanger activity. There is agreement among published studies that, in contrast to the effect of α_1-adrenergic stimulation, β_1-adrenergic stimulation inhibits sarcolemmal NHE activity in a variety of species,[42,51,52] probably through a cAMP-mediated pathway.[51–53] Therefore, the effects of the endogenous catecholamines norepinephrine and epinephrine on sarcolemmal NHE activity may depend on the relative density or availability of α_1-versus β_1-ARs, which can be modulated by genetic factors (which may account for species-specific responses); accompanying disease (such as heart failure, which is associated with β_1-AR downregulation, or ischemia, which enhances α_1-AR signaling); or pharmacological therapy (in particular, the use of adrenergic antagonists).

Effects of Thrombin

The most common cause of acute myocardial ischemia in man is intracoronary thrombosis,[54] and thrombosis is associated with elevated levels of thrombin in the vicinity of the evolving thrombus.[55] Therefore, the biological actions of thrombin may be of pathophysiological significance during myocardial ischemia in the clinical setting. In this regard, it is now well-established that, in addition to its role in blood coagulation and thrombus formation, thrombin induces a variety of cellular responses through receptor-mediated pathways (for review see Coughlin[56]). Recently, we have published the first evidence that both thrombin and the synthetic thrombin receptor activating hexapeptide SFLLRN increase sarcolemmal NHE activity in adult rat ventricular myocytes.[57] The common ability of thrombin and SFLLRN to stimulate sarcolemmal NHE activity is consistent with this action being mediated by the thrombin receptor first cloned by Vu and colleagues[58] and is now known as protease-activated receptor 1 (PAR1), the mRNA for which we have shown to be expressed by adult rat ventricular myocytes.[57] However, recent findings suggest that other protease-activated receptors may also be involved. In this regard, Connolly and colleagues[59] have recently shown that in mice with targeted disruption of the PAR1 gene, responsiveness to thrombin is lost in some cell types (e.g., fibroblasts) but retained in others (e.g., platelets). This indicates the existence of additional thrombin receptor(s) and has led to the suggestion that different thrombin receptors may have tissue-specific roles.[59] Indeed, a second thrombin receptor (PAR3) has now been cloned and appears to be expressed in human myocardium.[60] Furthermore, there is preliminary evidence[61] for the expression of functional PAR2, a trypsin-activated receptor that is responsive also to the PAR1-activating peptide SFLLRN,[62] in neonatal rat ventricular myocytes. These developments necessitate verification of the hypothesis that cardiac sarcolemmal NHE is regulated by PAR1 and require determination of the roles, if any, of PAR2 and PAR3. Defining which of these receptors regulate sarcolemmal NHE activity clearly is critical to the potential therapeutic manipulation of this signaling pathway.

Effects of Endothelin

There is evidence that endothelin is released during myocardial ischemia and reperfusion[63] and that this release is accompanied by upregulation of endothelin receptors.[64] Therefore, the cellular actions of endothelin may also assume pathophysiological importance during myocardial ischemia and reperfusion. Within the context of the present article, it is notable that endothelin has been shown to stimulate sarcolemmal NHE activity, in isolated rat ventricular myocytes[65,66] as well as in canine cardiac Purkinje fibers.[52]

FUNCTIONAL IMPACT OF NHE-STIMULATORY LIGANDS IN ISCHEMIA AND REPERFUSION

What is the functional impact of receptor-mediated stimulation of sarcolemmal NHE activity in the setting of myocardial ischemia and reperfusion? Much of the evidence in this area has been obtained through the application of exogenous agonists in *in vitro* models of ischemia and reperfusion. Thus, work in Karmazyn's laboratory has shown that, in isolated rat hearts, both α_1-AR stimulation (in the presence of an adenosine antagonist)[67] and endothelin[68] exacerbate post-ischemic contractile dysfunction. Of particular relevance to the present article, the deleterious effects of both stimuli could be reversed by NHE inhibition,[67,68] thus implying a key role for the exchanger in the injurious mechanisms downstream of receptor activation. Consistent with this, Brunner and Opie[69] have shown recently that the deleterious effects of endothelin during ischemia and reperfusion could be attenuated not only by ET_A receptor antagonism but also by NHE inhibition. Furthermore, α_1-AR stimulation selectively within the ischemic zone has been shown by the authors' group[45] to exacerbate reperfusion-induced arrhythmias, with this proarrhythmic effect abolished by α_{1A}-AR antagonism or NHE inhibition, implicating the exchanger in the downstream mechanisms.

Within the context of ischemia and reperfusion, α_1-AR stimulation has also been implicated in the induction of ischemic preconditioning in rat myocardium.[70] Since ischemic preconditioning is associated with reduced intracellular acidosis during the prolonged ischemia,[71] it is possible that α_1-adrenergic stimulation of sarcolemmal NHE activity may contribute to this phenomenon. However, Gabel and colleagues[72] have shown recently that H^+ efflux during the prolonged ischemic period is not increased in preconditioned hearts. Furthermore, any stimulation of sarcolemmal NHE activity is unlikely to contribute to the cardioprotective mechanism(s) of ischemic preconditioning, since we have shown such protection to be retained (and indeed enhanced) in the presence of NHE inhibition.[73]

With regard to thrombin-induced effects during ischemia and reperfusion, Goldstein and colleagues[74] have shown that, in the canine heart *in vivo*, the incidence of malignant ventricular arrhythmias during acute ischemia is greater following thrombotic coronary occlusion than non-thrombotic balloon occlusion, implicating an arrhythmogenic role for factors (such as thrombin) associated with thrombus formation. Indeed, thrombin has now been shown to induce a potent arrhythmogenic effect during ischemia and reperfusion in isolated rat hearts,[75,76] in a manner that appears to be reversible by NHE inhibition.[76] A role for the sarcolemmal NHE in mediating the arrhythmogenic action of thrombin is supported by evidence that activation of the thrombin receptor exacerbates the intracellular accumulation of Na^+ during ischemia,[77] an observation that is consistent with stimulation of exchanger activity.

CONCLUSION

It is clear from the evidence discussed above that sarcolemmal NHE activity is modulated by a number of endogenous stimuli (e.g., catecholamines, thrombin, and endothelin), through receptor-mediated mechanisms, and that stimulation of the exchanger through these receptors may be of pathophysiological significance during ischemia and reperfusion. Undoubtedly, there are other, currently unidentified, receptors that also regulate sarcolemmal NHE activity in a positive or negative manner. The identification of such receptors and delineation of the intracellular signaling mechanisms that facilitate receptor-mediated regulation of sarcolemmal NHE activity may identify common pathways, which might represent fertile targets for the development of novel therapies for ischemic heart disease.

REFERENCES

1. Wakabayashi, S., M. Shigekawa & J. Pouysségur. 1997. Molecular physiology of vertebrate Na^+/H^+ exchangers. Physiol. Rev. **77:** 51–74.
2. Orlowski, J. & S. Grinstein. 1997. Na^+/H^+ exchangers of mammalian cells. J. Biol. Chem. **272:** 22373–22376.
3. Mahnensmith, R.L. & P.S. Aronson. 1985. The plasma membrane sodium-hydrogen exchanger and its role in physiological and pathophysiological processes. Circ. Res. **57:** 773–788.
4. Rosskopf, D., R. Dusing & W. Siffert. 1993. Membrane sodium-proton exchange and primary hypertension. Hypertension **21:** 607–617.
5. Siffert, W. 1995. Regulation of platelet function by sodium-hydrogen exchange. Cardiovasc. Res. **29:** 160–166.
6. Lucchesi, P.A. & B.C. Berk. 1995. Regulation of sodium-hydrogen exchange in vascular smooth muscle. Cardiovasc. Res. **29:** 172–177.
7. Takewaki, S., M. Kuro-o, Y. Hiroi, T. Yamazaki, T. Noguchi, A. Miyagishi, K. Nakahara, M. Aikawa, I. Manabe, Y. Yazaki & R. Nagai. 1995. Activation of Na^+-H^+ antiporter (NHE-1) gene expression during growth, hypertrophy and proliferation of the rabbit cardiovascular system. J. Mol. Cell. Cardiol. **27:** 729–742.
8. Schlüter, K-D., M. Schäfer, C. Balser, G. Taimor & H.M. Piper. 1998. Influence of pH_i and creatine phosphate on α-adrenoceptor-mediated cardiac hypertrophy. J. Mol. Cell. Cardiol. **30:** 763–771.
9. Yamazaki, T., I. Komuro, S. Kudoh, Y. Zou, R. Nagai, R. Aikawa, H. Uozumi & Y. Yazaki. 1998. Role of ion channels and exchangers in mechanical stretch-induced cardiomyocyte hypertrophy. Circ. Res. **82:** 430–437.
10. Avkiran, M. 1996. Sodium-hydrogen exchange in myocardial ischemia and reperfusion: a critical determinant of injury? *In* Myocardial Ischemia: Mechanisms, Reperfusion, Protection. M. Karmazyn, Ed.: 299–311. Birkhauser Verlag. Basel.
11. Fröhlich, O. & M. Karmazyn. 1997. The Na-H exchanger revisited: an update on Na-H exchange regulation and the role of the exchanger in hypertension and cardiac function in health and disease. Cardiovasc. Res. **36:** 138–148.
12. Scholz, W., U. Albus, H.J. Lang, W. Linz, P.A. Martorana, H.C. Englert & B.A. Schölkens. 1993. HOE 694, a new Na^+/H^+ exchange inhibitor and its effects in cardiac ischaemia. Br. J. Pharmacol. **109:** 562–568.
13. Scholz, W., U. Albus, L. Counillon, H. Gögelein, H.J. Lang, W. Linz, A. Weichert & B.A. Schölkens. 1995. Protective effects of HOE642, a selective sodium-hydrogen exchange subtype 1 inhibitor, on cardiac ischaemia and reperfusion. Cardiovasc. Res. **29:** 260–268.
14. Scholz, W. & U. Albus. 1995. Potential of selective sodium-hydrogen exchange inhibitors in cardiovascular therapy. Cardiovasc. Res. **29:** 184–188.
15. Fliegel, L. & J.R.B. Dyck. 1995. Molecular biology of the cardiac sodium/hydrogen exchanger. Cardiovasc. Res. **29:** 155–159.
16. Lazdunski, M., C. Frelin & P. Vigne. 1985. The sodium/hydrogen exchange system in cardiac cells: its biochemical and pharmacological properties and its role in regulating internal concentrations of sodium and internal pH. J. Mol. Cell. Cardiol. **17:** 1029–1042.

17. WALLERT, M.A. & O. FRÖHLICH. 1989. Na^+-H^+ exchange in isolated myocytes from adult rat heart. Am. J. Physiol. **257:** C207–C213.
18. DENNIS, S.C., W. GEVERS & L.H. OPIE. 1991. Protons in ischemia: where do they come from; where do they go to? J. Mol. Cell. Cardiol. **23:** 1077–1086.
19. MENG, H.P. & G.N. PIERCE. 1990. Protective effects of 5-(N,N-dimethyl)amiloride on ischemia-reperfusion injury in hearts. Am. J. Physiol. **258:** H1615–H1619.
20. DU TOIT, E.F. & L.H. OPIE. 1993. Role for the Na^+/H^+ exchanger in reperfusion stunning in isolated perfused rat heart. J. Cardiovasc. Pharmacol. **22:** 877–883.
21. MENG, H.P., T.G. MADDAFORD & G.N. PIERCE. 1993. Effect of amiloride and selected analogues on postischemic recovery of cardiac contractile function. Am. J. Physiol. **264:** H1831–H1835.
22. MADDAFORD, T.G. & G.N. PIERCE. 1997. Myocardial dysfunction is associated with activation of Na^+/H^+ exchange immediately during reperfusion. Am. J. Physiol. **273:** H2232–H2239.
23. KARMAZYN, M. 1988. Amiloride enhances postischemic ventricular recovery: possible role of Na^+-H^+ exchange. Am. J. Physiol. **255:** H608–H615.
24. MOFFAT, M.P. & M. KARMAZYN. 1993. Protective effects of the potent Na/H exchange inhibitor methylisobutyl amiloride against post-ischemic contractile dysfunction in rat and guinea-pig hearts. J. Mol. Cell. Cardiol. **25:** 959–971.
25. MYERS, M.L., S. MATHUR, G-H. LI & M. KARMAZYN. 1995. Sodium-hydrogen exchange inhibitors improve postischaemic recovery of function in the perfused rabbit heart. Cardiovasc. Res. **29:** 209–214.
26. KLEIN, H.H., S. PICH, R.M. BOHLE, J. WOLLENWEBER & K. NEBENDAHL. 1995. Myocardial protection by Na^+-H^+ exchange inhibition in ischemic, reperfused porcine hearts. Circulation **92:** 912–917.
27. SHIMADA, Y., D.J. HEARSE & M. AVKIRAN. 1996. Impact of extracellular buffer composition on cardioprotective efficacy of Na^+/H^+ exchanger inhibitors. Am. J. Physiol. **270:** H692–H700.
28. HENDRIKX, M., K. MUBAGWA, F. VERDONCK, K. OVERLOOP, P. VAN HECKE, F. VANSTAPEL, A. VAN LOMMEL, E. VERBEKEN, J. LAUWERYNS & W. FLAMENG. 1994. New Na^+/H^+ exchange inhibitor HOE 694 improves postischemic function and high-energy phosphate resynthesis and reduces Ca^{2+} overload in isolated perfused rabbit heart. Circulation **89:** 2787–2798.
29. ROHMANN, S., H. WEYGANDT & K.O. MINCK. 1995. Preischaemic as well as postischaemic application of a Na^+/H^+ exchange inhibitor reduces infarct size in pigs. Cardiovasc. Res. **30:** 945–951.
30. GARCIA-DORADO, D., M.A. GONZALEZ, J.A. BARRABES, M. RUIZ-MEANA, J. SOLARES, R. M. LIDON, J. BLANCO, Y. PUIGFEL, H.M. PIPER & J. SOLER-SOLER. 1997. Prevention of ischemic rigor contracture during coronary occlusion by inhibition of Na^+-H^+ exchange. Cardiovasc. Res. **35:** 80–89.
31. SHIPOLINI, A.R., M. GALIÑANES, S.J. EDMONDSON, D.J. HEARSE & M. AVKIRAN. 1997. Na^+/H^+ exchanger inhibitor HOE-642 improves cardioplegic myocardial preservation under both normothermic and hypothermic conditions. Circulation **96:** II266–II273.
32. LINZ, W., U. ALBUS, P. CRAUSE, W. JUNG, A. WEICHERT, B. A. SCHÖLKENS & W. SCHOLZ. 1998. Dose-dependent reduction of myocardial infarct mass in rabbits by the NHE-1 inhibitor cariporide (HOE 642). Clin. Exp. Hypertens. **20:** 733–749.
33. MURPHY, E., M. PERLMAN, R.E. LONDON & C. STEENBERGEN. 1991. Amiloride delays the ischemia-induced rise in cytosolic free calcium. Circ. Res. **68:** 1250–1258.
34. PIKE, M.M., C.S. LUO, D. CLARK, K.A. KIRK, M. KITAKAZE, M.C. MADDEN, E.J. CRAGOE, JR. & G.M. POHOST. 1993. NMR measurements of Na^+ and cellular energy in ischemic rat heart: role of Na^+/H^+ exchange. Am. J. Physiol. **265:** H2017–H2026.
35. VAUGHAN-JONES, R.D. & M.L. WU. 1990. Extracellular H^+ inactivation of Na^+-H^+ exchange in the sheep cardiac Purkinje fibre. J. Physiol. **428:** 441–466.
36. HOQUE, A.N.H., J.V. HAIST & M. KARMAZYN. 1997. Na^+-H^+ exchange inhibition protects against mechanical, ultrastructural, and biochemical impairment induced by low concentrations of lysophosphatidylcholine in isolated rat hearts. Circ. Res. **80:** 95–102.

37. SABRI, A., K.L. BYRON, A.M. SAMAREL, J. BELL & P.A. LUCCHESI. 1998. Hydrogen peroxide activates mitogen-activated protein kinases and Na^+-H^+ exchange in neonatal rat cardiac myocytes. Circ. Res. **82:** 1053–1062.
38. SNABAITIS, A.K., D.J. HEARSE & M. AVKIRAN. 1998. Activation of the Na^+/H^+ exchanger by hydrogen peroxide [abstract]. J. Mol. Cell. Cardiol. **30:** A339.
39. SCHÖMIG, A. & G. RICHARDT. 1990. Cardiac sympathetic activity in myocardial ischemia: release and effects of noradrenaline. Basic Res. Cardiol. **85**(Suppl 1): 9–30.
40. CORR, P.B., K.A. YAMADA & S.D. DATORRE. 1990. Modulation of α-adrenergic receptors and their intracellular coupling in the ischemic heart. Basic Res. Cardiol. **85**(Suppl 1): 31–45.
41. PUCÉAT, M., O. CLÉMENT-CHOMIENNE, A. TERZIC & G. VASSORT. 1993. α_1-adrenoceptor and purinoceptor agonists modulate Na-H antiport in single cardiac cells. Am. J. Physiol. **264:** H310-H319.
42. LAGADIC-GOSSMANN, D. & R.D. VAUGHAN-JONES. 1993. Coupling of dual acid extrusion in the guinea-pig isolated ventricular myocyte to α_1- and β-adrenoceptors. J. Physiol. **464:** 49–73.
43. WALLERT, M.A. & O. FRÖHLICH. 1992. α_1-adrenergic stimulation of Na-H exchange in cardiac myocytes. Am. J. Physiol. **263:** C1096–C1102.
44. HIEBLE, J.P., D.B. BYLUND, D.E. CLARKE, D.C. EIKENBURG, S.Z. LANGER, R.J. LEFKOWITZ, K.P. MINNEMAN & R.R. RUFFOLO, JR. 1995. International Union of Pharmacology X. Recommendation for nomenclature of α_1-adrenoceptors: consensus update. Pharmacol. Rev. **47:** 267–270.
45. YASUTAKE, M. & M. AVKIRAN. 1995. Exacerbation of reperfusion arrhythmias by α_1-adrenergic stimulation: a potential role for receptor-mediated activation of sarcolemmal sodium-hydrogen exchange. Cardiovasc. Res. **29:** 222–230.
46. YOKOYAMA, H., M. YASUTAKE & M. AVKIRAN. 1998. α_1-Adrenergic stimulation of sarcolemmal Na^+/H^+ exchanger activity in rat ventricular myocytes: evidence for selective mediation by the α_{1A}-adrenoceptor subtype. Circ. Res. **82:** 1078–1085.
47. KNEPPER, S.M., S.A. BUCKNER, M.E. BRUNE, J.F. DEBERNARDIS, M.D. MEYER & A. A. HANCOCK. 1995. A-61603, a potent α_1-adrenergic receptor agonist, selective for the α_{1A} receptor subtype. J. Pharmacol. Exp. Ther. **274:** 97–103.
48. LAZ, T.M., C. FORRAY, K.E. SMITH, J.A. BARD, P.J. VAYSSE, T.A. BRANCHEK & R.L. WEINSHANK. 1994. The rat homologue of the bovine α_{1c}-adrenergic receptor shows the pharmacological properties of the classical α_{1A} subtype. Mol. Pharmacol. **46:** 414–422.
49. PRICE, D.T., R.J. LEFKOWITZ, M.G. CARON, D. BERKOWITZ & D.A. SCHWINN. 1994. Localization of mRNA for three distinct α_1-adrenergic receptor subtypes in human tissues: implications for human α-adrenergic physiology. Mol. Pharmacol. **45:** 171–175.
50. ROKOSH, D.G., A.F.R. STEWART, K.C. CHANG, B.A. BAILEY, J.S. KARLINER, S.A. CAMACHO, C.S. LONG & P.C. SIMPSON. 1996. α_1-adrenergic receptor subtype mRNAs are differentially regulated by α_1-adrenergic and other hypertrophic stimuli in cardiac myocytes in culture and *in vivo*: repression of α_{1B} and α_{1D} but induction of α_{1C}. J. Biol. Chem. **271:** 5839–5843.
51. GUO, H., J.A. WASSERSTROM & J.E. ROSENTHAL. 1992. Effect of catecholamines on intracellular pH in sheep Purkinje fibres. J. Physiol. **458:** 289–306.
52. WU, M.L. & Y.Z. TSENG. 1993. The modulatory effects of endothelin-1, carbachol and isoprenaline upon Na^+-H^+ exchange in dog cardiac Purkinje fibres. J. Physiol. **471:** 583–597.
53. WU, M.L. & R.D. VAUGHAN-JONES. 1994. Effect of metabolic inhibitors and second messengers upon Na^+-H^+ exchange in the sheep cardiac Purkinje fibre. J. Physiol. **478:** 301–313.
54. DAVIES, M.J., N. WOOLF & W.B. ROBERTSON. 1976. Pathology of acute myocardial infarction with particular reference to occlusive coronary thrombi. Br. Heart J. **38:** 659–664.
55. WAGNER, W.R. & J.A. HUBBELL. 1990. Local thrombin synthesis and fibrin formation in an in vitro thrombosis model result in platelet recruitment and thrombin stabilization on collagen in heparinized blood. J. Lab. Clin. Med. **116:** 636–650.
56. COUGHLIN, S.R. 1994. Thrombin receptor function and cardiovascular disease. Trends Cardiovasc. Med. **4:** 77–83.
57. YASUTAKE, M., R.S. HAWORTH, A. KING & M. AVKIRAN. 1996. Thrombin activates

the sarcolemmal Na^+/H^+ exchanger: evidence for a receptor-mediated mechanism involving protein kinase C. Circ. Res. **79:** 705–715.
58. Vu, T.K., D.T. Hung, V.I. Wheaton & S.R. Coughlin. 1991. Molecular cloning of a functional thrombin receptor reveals a novel proteolytic mechanism of receptor activation. Cell **64:** 1057–1068.
59. Connolly, A.J., H. Ishihara, M.L. Kahn, R.V. Farese & S.R. Coughlin. 1996. Role of the thrombin receptor in development and evidence for a second receptor. Nature **381:** 516–519.
60. Ishihara, H., A.J. Connolly, D. Zeng, M.L. Kahn, Y.W. Zheng, C. Timmons, T. Tram & S.R. Coughlin. 1997. Protease-activated receptor 3 is a second thrombin receptor in humans. Nature **386:** 502–506.
61. Steinberg, S.F., G.A. Muske, A. Pak & H. Zhang. 1997. Cardiomyocytes express the proteinase-activated receptor-2 (PAR-2) which activates phosphoinositide hydrolysis, stimulates mitogen-activated protein kinase, enhances automaticity, and elevates intracellular calcium [abstract]. Circulation **96:** I-613.
62. Lerner, D.J., M. Chen, T. Tram & S.R. Coughlin. 1996. Agonist recognition by proteinase-activated receptor 2 and thrombin receptor: importance of extracellular loop interactions for receptor function. J. Biol. Chem. **271:** 13943–13947.
63. Tonnessen, T., P.A. Naess, K.A. Kirkeboen, J. Offstad, A. Ilebekk & G. Christensen. 1993. Endothelin is released from the porcine coronary circulation after short-term ischemia. J. Cardiovasc. Pharmacol. **22**(Suppl 8)**:** S313–S316.
64. Liu, J., R. Chen, D.J. Casley & W.G. Nayler. 1990. Ischemia and reperfusion increase ^{125}I-labeled endothelin-1 binding in rat cardiac membranes. Am. J. Physiol. **258:** H829–H835.
65. Kramer, B.K., T.W. Smith & R.A. Kelly. 1991. Endothelin and increased contractility in adult rat ventricular myocytes. Role of intracellular alkalosis induced by activation of the protein kinase C-dependent Na^+-H^+ exchanger. Circ. Res. **68:** 269–279.
66. Ito, N., Y. Kagaya, E.O. Weinberg, W.H. Barry & B.H. Lorell. 1997. Endothelin and angiotensin II stimulation of Na^+-H^+ exchange is impaired in cardiac hypertrophy. J. Clin. Invest. **99:** 125–135.
67. Khandoudi, N., M.P. Moffat & M. Karmazyn. 1994. Adenosine-sensitive α_1-adrenoceptor effects on reperfused ischaemic hearts: comparison with phorbol ester. Br. J. Pharmacol. **112:** 1007–1016.
68. Khandoudi, N., J. Ho & M. Karmazyn. 1994. Role of Na^+-H^+ exchange in mediating effects of endothelin-1 on normal and ischemic/reperfused hearts. Circ. Res. **75:** 369–378.
69. Brunner, F. & L.H. Opie. 1998. Role of endothelin A receptors in ischemic contracture and reperfusion injury. Circulation **97:** 391–398.
70. Banerjee, A., C. Locke Winter, K.B. Rogers, M.B. Mitchell, E.C. Brew, C.B. Cairns, D.D. Bensard & A.H. Harken. 1993. Preconditioning against myocardial dysfunction after ischemia and reperfusion by an α_1-adrenergic mechanism. Circ. Res. **73:** 656–670.
71. Asimakis, G.K., K. Inners-McBride, G. Medellin & V.R. Conti. 1992. Ischemic preconditioning attenuates acidosis and postischemic dysfunction in isolated rat heart. Am. J. Physiol. **263:** H887–H894.
72. Gabel, S.A., H.R. Cross, R.E. London, C. Steenbergen & E. Murphy. 1997. Decreased intracellular pH is not due to increased H^+ extrusion in preconditioned rat hearts. Am. J. Physiol. **273:** H2257–H2262.
73. Shipolini, A.R., H. Yokoyama, M. Galiñanes, S.J. Edmondson, D.J. Hearse & M. Avkiran. 1997. Na^+/H^+ exchanger activity does not contribute to protection by ischemic preconditioning in the isolated rat heart. Circulation **96:** 3617–3625.
74. Goldstein, J.A., M.C. Butterfield, Y. Ohnishi, T.J. Shelton & P.B. Corr. 1994. Arrhythmogenic influence of intracoronary thrombosis during acute myocardial ischemia. Circulation **90:** 139–147.
75. Jacobsen, A.N., X-J. Du, K.A. Lambert, A.M. Dart & E.A. Woodcock. 1996. Arrhythmogenic action of thrombin during myocardial reperfusion via release of inositol 1,4,5-triphosphate. Circulation **93:** 23–26.

76. YOKOYAMA, H. & M. AVKIRAN. 1997. Protein kinase C-mediated stimulation of the sarcolemmal Na^+/H^+ exchanger contributes to the arrhythmogenic action of thrombin [abstract]. Circulation **96:** I-58.
77. YAN, G.X., T.H. PARK & P.B. CORR. 1995. Activation of thrombin receptor increases intracellular Na^+ during myocardial ischemia. Am. J. Physiol. **268:** H1740–H1748.

Na^+/H^+ Exchangers

Molecular Diversity and Relevance to Heart

JOHN ORLOWSKI[a]

Department of Physiology, McGill University, Montreal, H3G 1Y6, Canada

ABSTRACT: During the last several years, significant advances have been made in our understanding of the molecular, cellular, and physiological diversity of mammalian Na^+/H^+ exchangers. This transporter forms a multigene family of at least six members (NHE1–NHE6) that share ~20–60% amino acid identity. NHE1 is the most predominant isoform expressed in heart and it contributes significantly to myocardial pH_i homeostasis, which is important for maintaining contractility. However, hyperactivation of NHE1 during episodes of cardiac ischemia and reperfusion disrupts the intracellular ion balance, leading to cardiac dysfunction and damage in several animal models, but which can be prevented by pharmacological antagonists of NHE1. Molecular studies have indicated that the predicted transmembrane segments M4 and M9 contain several residues involved in drug sensitivity. Molecular dissection of the drug binding region should facilitate the rational design of more potent and isoform-specific drugs that may provide therapeutic benefit in the prevention of cardiac ischemia and reperfusion injuries.

ROLES OF THE Na^+/H^+ EXCHANGER IN CARDIAC PHYSIOLOGY AND PATHOPHYSIOLOGY

Myocardial function is greatly influenced by changes in intracellular pH (pH_i). For example, myocardial acidosis results in marked decreases in contractility,[1] which is associated with reduced myosin-ATPase activity,[2] diminished binding of Ca^{2+} to troponin C of the contractile apparatus,[3] decreased ion currents through voltage-activated Na^+ and Ca^{2+} channels,[4–6] and reductions in gap junction conductance.[7] Hence, regulation of pH_i is of critical importance for maintaining cardiac function.

At least three different ion transporters contribute to myocardial pH_i regulation; the Cl^-/HCO_3^- exchanger,[8,9] the Na^+-HCO_3^- cotransporter,[10,11] and the Na^+/H^+ exchanger.[12–14] An increase in pH_i activates the Cl^-/HCO_3^- exchanger, which extrudes intracellular HCO_3^- for extracellular Cl^-. By contrast, intracellular acidification activates both the Na^+-HCO_3^- cotransporter and the Na^+/H^+ exchanger, with the latter being the predominant mechanism for restoring myocardial pH_i to the neutral range (pH_i 7.1 to 7.3).[10,11,13]

Aside from its role in normal myocardial pH_i homeostasis, accumulating evidence points to the Na^+/H^+ exchanger as a contributing factor in the pathophysiology of cardiac ischemia and reperfusion injuries. During cardiac ischemia, ATP stores

[a]Address correspondence to: Dr. John Orlowski, Department of Physiology, McGill University, McIntyre Medical Science Bldg., 3655 Drummond St., Montreal, Quebec H3G 1Y6 Canada; Telephone: (514) 398-8335; Fax: (514) 398-7452; E-mail: orlowski@physio.mcgill.ca

are depleted as a consequence of depressed mitochondrial activity and lactic acid levels are increased due to anaerobic metabolism of glucose. This results in a rapid decrease in both intracellular and extracellular pH, which precipitates a series of other changes in myocardial ion homeostasis, primarily Na^+_i and Ca^{2+}_i overloads, which then lead to cardiac dysfunction and tissue damage (for further details[15–19]). Ischemia elevates Na^+_i by two mechanisms: the acidosis that occurs during the first few minutes of ischemia leads to an influx of Na^+ by activation of the Na^+/H^+ exchanger, and the diminished ATP levels cause depression of Na^+,K^+-ATPase activity, which normally extrudes Na^+_i. Indeed, the Na^+/H^+ exchanger accounts for as much as 50% of the cardiac membrane's basal permeability to Na^+ following intracellular acidification.[20–22] Furthermore, the reduction in ATP levels also causes a decrease in the pH_i sensitivity (or threshold for activation) of the Na^+/H^+ exchanger, thereby impairing its ability to fully restore pH_i to neutral.[23] The net result is a chronic state of cellular acidosis.

The elevation of Na^+_i reduces the transmembrane Na^+ gradient, thereby inhibiting Na^+/Ca^{2+} exchangers that, under normal conditions, extrude Ca^{2+}_i in exchange for Na^+_o. Moreover, if Na^+_i increases sufficiently the Na^+/Ca^{2+} exchanger could reverse and mediate Ca^{2+} influx. This Ca^{2+}_i overload is associated with cardiac arrhythmias and, if untreated, contributes to contractile failure. Reperfusion of the failing heart with physiological fluids to restore pH_i is the standard approach to rescuing the tissue, but may lead to further tissue damage. This has been referred to as the "pH paradox." Rapid removal of the acidic extracellular fluid generates a large transmembrane pH gradient that drives Na^+/H^+ exchange. This further augments Na^+_i and markedly elevates Ca^{2+}_i, causing reperfusion arrhythmias, contractile failure, and cellular necrosis. Thus, the Na^+/H^+ exchanger appears to play a central role in injuries caused by ischemia and reperfusion.

The involvement of Na^+/H^+ exchangers in ischemia- and reperfusion-induced injuries, however, is most convincingly demonstrated by animal studies showing that treatment with amiloride, a relatively weak inhibitor of the Na^+/H^+ exchanger, significantly reduces Na^+ and Ca^{2+} overload and is cardioprotective.[24] Similar protective effects are obtained with amiloride analogues,[25–33] and benzoyl guanidinium compounds such as HOE694,[34–38] HOE642 (cariporide),[39–43] and compound 246,[44] which are more potent and selective antagonists of the Na^+/H^+ exchanger. The beneficial effects of these compounds are obtained only during the early stages (within several minutes) of ischemia and reperfusion when the Na^+/H^+ exchanger is most active. The antiarrhythmic action of amiloride has also been demonstrated in human clinical studies, where it suppressed inducible ventricular tachycardia[45] and spontaneous ventricular premature beats.[46] Thus, these observations strongly implicate overactivation of the Na^+/H^+ exchanger as a central factor in ischemia- and reperfusion-induced injuries.

EXPRESSION AND LOCALIZATION OF Na^+/H^+ EXCHANGER ISOFORMS IN HEART

In mammals, at least six Na^+/H^+ exchanger isoforms (NHE1 to NHE6) are known to exist and they exhibit distinct differences in their primary structures (~20–60%

amino acid identity), patterns of tissue expression, membrane localization, functional properties, and physiological roles.[47,48]

Mammalian cardiac tissue expresses predominantly the NHE1 mRNA,[49–52] albeit minor amounts of NHE2 mRNA are also detected in some species.[50] Indeed, NHE1 is present in virtually all tissues and most cell types examined, consistent with its proposed "housekeeping" role to maintain intracellular pH and cell volume.[49,53,54] Thus, the functional characteristics of the cardiac sarcolemmal Na^+/H^+ exchanger described in numerous studies are most likely those of NHE1.

Recent immunological studies have demonstrated that NHE1 is localized predominantly at the intercalated disc regions and to a lesser extent along the transverse tubular systems of both atrial and ventricular muscle cells.[81] Unexpectedly, NHE1 was not detected along the lateral sarcolemmal membranes. This distribution differs somewhat from the Cl^-/HCO_3^- exchangers which accumulate mainly at the lateral sarcolemma and transverse tubules of isolated adult rat ventricular myocytes.[55] The location of the other major cardiac pH regulatory protein, the Na^+-HCO_3^- cotransporter, is currently unknown. The physiological relevance of the high density of NHE1 at the intercalated discs is unclear. While speculative, in this region it may serve to regulate the opening of gap junction channels, which are highly sensitive to minor fluctuations in pH_i within the physiological range,[7,56] and thereby to influence impulse conduction between myocytes.

The heart also expresses NHE6, but it is localized to the mitochondria inner membrane[57] where it is responsible for extruding Na^+ from the alkaline matrix of respiring mitochondria[58] and, as such, may contribute to organellar volume homeostasis.[59] This process may also be functionally coupled to the efflux of Ca^{2+} from the mitochondria by the recycling of Na^+ between the mitochondrial Na^+/H^+ and Na^+/Ca^{2+} exchangers.[59,60] There are indications that the mitochondrial NHE is also responsible for mediating transport of NH_4^+ from the mitochondrial matrix.[61]

STRUCTURAL AND FUNCTIONAL FEATURES OF THE Na^+/H^+ EXCHANGER

The NHE isoforms exhibit similar membrane topologies, with 12 predicted membrane-spanning (M) regions at the N-terminus and a large cytoplasmic region at the C-terminus. The most highly conserved regions of the NHE isoforms are the membrane-spanning segments, which probably mediate cation transport and drug binding. The C-terminal regions are highly hydrophilic and exhibit a lower degree of similarity among isoforms. Structural studies indicate that this latter region is involved in regulation by growth factors and other mitogens, consistent with it being oriented towards the cytoplasmic side of the membrane.[47,48]

Even less is known about the tertiary or quaternary structure of Na^+/H^+ exchangers, although recent evidence suggests that they exist in the membrane as homodimers.[62,63] The site of interaction between the monomers resides in the putative transmembranous region,[63] possibly linked by disulfide bonding,[62] although the precise location(s) of contact have yet to be defined.

As mentioned above, the NHE is a known target for inhibition by the diuretic compound amiloride and its analogues.[64] Amiloride analogues containing hydrophobic substituents on the 5-amino group of the pyrazine ring have higher affinity and specificity for the NHE relative to other ion transporters. Using a heterologous expression system, NHE isoforms exhibit a wide range of affinities for amiloride and its analogues, which span over two orders of magnitude and show the following order of sensitivity: NHE1 $\geq$ NHE2 $\gg$ NHE3.[65,66] Recently, HOE694[67,68] and its related compound HOE642[39] have also been found to inhibit the isoforms with a similar rank order as the amiloride compounds, but over a larger concentration range (three to four orders of magnitude). Other pharmacological agents, such as cimetidine, clonidine, and harmaline, also exhibit differential affinities for the NHE isoforms.[65,66] While these compounds are chemically unrelated to amiloride or HOE694, they possess either an imidazoline or guanidinium moiety and hence bear some structural similarity to these compounds.

Biochemical analyses indicate that inhibition by amiloride compounds, cimetidine,[73] and HOE694[67] is reduced by high external Na^+. This competitive inhibition suggests they bind near the external Na^+ transport site and may also share a common site. However, under different anionic buffer conditions, amiloride and its derivatives also inhibit transport noncompetitively, suggesting that the external Na^+- and amiloride-binding sites may not be identical.[74,75] Furthermore, the extracellular Na^+- and amiloride-binding sites can be altered independently of each other using genetic selection techniques.[76] Taken together, these data indicate that amiloride and other antagonists probably interact with multiple sites on the exchanger.

Consistent with this idea, recent molecular studies of human NHE1 have shown that two predicted membrane-associated domains are targets for interaction with amiloride and its analogues. Residues in the fourth (Phe^{161}, Leu^{163}, Gly^{174})[77,78] and the ninth (His^{349})[79] transmembrane segments appear to contribute to amiloride sensitivity without affecting Na^+ affinity. Likewise, mutagenesis of a homologous residue in the fourth transmembrane domain of rabbit NHE2 ($Leu^{143} \rightarrow Phe^{143}$) also reduced its sensitivity to amiloride compounds.[80] However, mutations at each of these sites produced only modest changes in drug sensitivity and did not confer the degree of drug resistance observed for the NHE3 isoform.[65,67,77] Thus, other residues of the exchanger are presumably involved in determining drug sensitivity.

A recent analysis of chimeric NHE1 and NHE3 proteins identified a 66 amino acid segment containing the putative ninth transmembrane (M9) domain and its adjacent loops that significantly influences drug sensitivity.[68] Homologous substitution of this region between isoforms caused a reciprocal change in the drug sensitivities of NHE1 and NHE3 by one to three orders of magnitude, depending on the drug. The greatest changes in affinity were for ethylisopropylamiloride and HOE694. These alterations differ from those caused by mutations at His^{349} in the putative M9 domain of human NHE1, where either a modest twofold increase ($His^{349} \rightarrow$ Tyr or Phe) or twofold decrease ($His^{349} \rightarrow$ Gly or Leu) in amiloride sensitivity was observed, whereas other amino acid substitutions at this position had no effect.[79] This suggests that other residues within this region serve as major determinants in conferring drug sensitivity. Further molecular dissection of the drug binding region could be helpful in developing more potent and isoform-specific drugs that may be of therapeutic benefit in the prevention of cardiac ischemia and reperfusion injuries.

REFERENCES

1. ORCHARD, C.H. & J.C. KENTISH. 1990. Effects of changes of pH on the contractile function of cardiac muscle. Am. J. Physiol. **258:** C967–C981.
2. KENTISH, J.C. & W.G. NAYLER. 1979. The influence of pH on the Ca^{2+}-regulated ATPase of cardiac and white skeletal myofibrils. J. Mol. Cell. Cardiol. **11:** 611–617.
3. BLANCHARD, E.M. & R.J. SOLARO. 1984. Inhibition of the activation and troponin calcium binding of dog cardiac myofibrils by acidic pH. Circ. Res. **55:** 382–391.
4. ZHANG, J.F. & S.A. SIEGELBAUM. 1991. Effects of external protons on single cardiac sodium channels from guinea pig ventricular myocytes. J. Gen. Physiol. **98:** 1065–1083.
5. IRISAWA, H. & R. SATO. 1986. Intra- and extracellular actions of proton on the calcium current of isolated guinea pig ventricular cells. Circ. Res. **59:** 348–355.
6. SATO, R., A. NOMA, Y. KURACHI & H. IRISAWA. 1985. Effects of intracellular acidification on membrane currents in ventricular cells of the guinea pig. Circ. Res. **57:** 553–561.
7. SPRAY, D.C., R.L. WHITE, F. MAZET & M.V. BENNETT. 1985. Regulation of gap junctional conductance. [Review]. Am. J. Physiol. **248:** H753–H764.
8. VAUGHAN-JONES, R.D. 1979. Regulation of chloride in quiescent sheep-heart Purkinje fibres studied using intracellular chloride and pH-sensitive micro-electrodes. J. Physiol. (Lond.) **295:** 111-137.
9. LIU, S., D. PIWNICA-WORMS & M. LIEBERMAN. 1990. Intracellular pH regulation in cultured embryonic chick heart cells. Na^+-dependent Cl^-/HCO_3^- exchange. J. Gen. Physiol. **96:** 1247–1269.
10. LAGADIC-GOSSMANN, D., K.J. BUCKLER & R.D. VAUGHAN-JONES. 1992. Role of bicarbonate in pH recovery from intracellular acidosis in the guinea-pig ventricular myocyte. J. Physiol. (Lond.) **458:** 361–384.
11. DART, C. & R.D. VAUGHAN-JONES. 1992. $Na(^+)$-HCO_3^- symport in the sheep cardiac Purkinje fibre. J. Physiol. (Lond.) **451:** 365-385.
12. PIWNICA-WORMS, D. & M. LIEBERMAN. 1983. Microfluorometric monitoring of pH_i in cultured heart cells: Na^+-H^+ exchange. Am. J. Physiol. **244:** C422–C428.
13. LAZDUNSKI, M., C. FRELIN & P. VIGNE. 1985. The sodium/hydrogen exchange system in cardiac cells: its biochemical and pharmacological properties and its role in regulating internal concentrations of sodium and internal pH. J. Mol. Cell. Cardiol. **17:** 1029–1042.
14. WALLERT, M.A. & O. FRÖHLICH. 1989. Na^+-H^+ exchange in isolated myocytes from adult rat heart. Am. J. Physiol. **257:** C207–C213.
15. KARMAZYN, M. & M.P. MOFFAT. 1993. Role of Na^+/H^+ exchange in cardiac physiology and pathophysiology: Mediation of myocardial reperfusion injury by the pH paradox. Cardiovasc. Res. **27:** 915–924.
16. SCHOLZ, W. & U. ALBUS. 1993. Na^+/H^+ exchange and its inhibition in cardiac ischemia and reperfusion. Basic Res. Cardiol. **88:** 443–455.
17. PIERCE, G.N. & H. MENG. 1992. The role of sodium-proton exchange in ischemic/reperfusion injury in the heart. Am. J. Cardiovasc. Pathol. **4:** 91–102.
18. FLIEGEL, L. & J.R.B. DYCK. 1995. Molecular biology of the cardiac sodium/hydrogen exchanger. Cardiovasc. Res. **29:** 155–159.
19. DUFF, H.J. 1995. Clinical and *in vivo* antiarrhythmic potential of sodium-hydrogen exchange inhibitors. Cardiovasc. Res. **29:** 189–193.
20. FRELIN, C., P. VIGNE & M. LAZDUNSKI. 1984. The role of the Na^+/H^+ exchange system in cardiac cells in relation to the control of the internal Na^+ concentration. A molecular basis for the antagonistic effect of ouabain and amiloride on the heart. J. Biol. Chem. **259:** 8880–8885.
21. KIM, D. & T.W. SMITH. 1986. Effects of amiloride and ouabain on contractile state, Ca and Na fluxes, and Na content in cultured chick heart cells. Mol. Pharmacol. **29:** 363–371.
22. TANI, M. & J.R. NEELY. 1991. Deleterious effects of digitalis on reperfusion-induced arrhythmias and myocardial injury in ischemic rat hearts: possible involvements of myocardial Na^+ and Ca^{2+} imbalance. Basic Res. Cardiol. **86:** 340–354.

23. WEISSBERG, P.L., P.J. LITTLE, E.J. CRAGOE, JR. & A. BOBIK. 1989. The pH of spontaneously beating cultured rat heart cells is regulated by an ATP-calmodulin-dependent Na^+/H^+ antiport. Circ. Res. **64:** 676–685.
24. KARMAZYN, M. 1988. Amiloride enhances postischemic ventricular recovery: possible role of Na^+/H^+ exchange. Am. J. Physiol. **255:** H608–H615.
25. KARMAZYN, M., M. RAY & J.V. HAIST. 1993. Comparative effects of Na^+/H^+ exchange inhibitors against cardiac injury produced by ischemia/reperfusion, hypoxia/reoxygenation, and the calcium paradox. J. Cardiovasc. Pharmacol. **21:** 172–178.
26. MOFFAT, M.P. & M. KARMAZYN. 1993. Protective effects of the potent Na/H exchange inhibitor methylisobutyl amiloride against post-ischemic contractile dysfunction in rat and guinea-pig hearts. J. Mol. Cell. Cardiol. **25:** 959–971.
27. MENG, H.P. & G.N. PIERCE. 1990. Protective effects of 5-(*N*,*N*-dimethyl)amiloride on ischemia-reperfusion injury in hearts. Am. J. Physiol. **258:** H1615–H1619.
28. MENG, H.-P., T.G. MADDAFORD & G.N. PIERCE. 1993. Effect of amiloride and selected analogues on postischemic recovery of cardiac contractile function. Am. J. Physiol. **264:** H1831–H1835.
29. DUFF, H.J., C.E. BROWN, E.J. CRAGOE, JR. & M. RAHMBERG. 1991. Antiarrhythmic activity of amiloride: mechanisms. J. Cardiovasc. Pharmacol. **17:** 879–888.
30. MYERS, M.L., S. MATHUR, G.-H. LI & M. KARMAZYN. 1995. Sodium-hydrogen exchange inhibitors improve postischaemic recovery of function in the perfused rabbit heart. Cardiovasc. Res. **29:** 209–214.
31. KAPLAN, S.H., H. YANG, D.E. GILLIAM, J. SHEN, J.J. LEMASTERS & W.E. CASCIO. 1995. Hypercapnic acidosis and dimethyl amiloride reduce reperfusion induced cell death in ischaemic ventricular myocardium. Cardiovasc. Res. **29:** 231–238.
32. TANI, M., K. SHINMURA, H. HASEGAWA & Y. NAKAMURA. 1996. Effect of methylisobutyl amiloride on $[Na^+]_i$, reperfusion arrhythmias, and function in ischemic rat hearts. J. Cardiovasc. Pharmacol. **27:** 794–801.
33. PIERCE, G.N., W.C. COLE, K. LIU, H. MASSAELI, T.G. MADDAFORD, Y.J. CHEN, C.D. MCPHERSON, S. JAIN & D. SONTAG. 1993. Modulation of cardiac performance by amiloride and several selected derivatives of amiloride. J. Pharmacol. Exp. Ther. **265:** 1280–1291.
34. SCHOLZ, W., U. ALBUS, H.J. LANG, W. LINZ, P.A. MARTORANA, H.C. ENGLERT & B.A. SCHÖLKENS. 1993. HOE 694, a new Na^+/H^+ exchange inhibitor and its effects in cardiac ischaemia. Br. J. Pharmacol. **109:** 562–568.
35. HENDRIKX, M., K. MUBAGWA, F. VERDONCK, K. OVERLOOP, P. VAN HECKE, F. VANSTAPEL, A. VAN LOMMEL, E. VERBEKEN, J. LAUWERYNS & W. FLAMENG. 1994. New Na^+-H^+ exchange inhibitor HOE 694 improves postischemic function and high-energy phosphate resynthesis and reduces Ca^{2+} overload in isolated perfused rabbit heart. Circulation **89:** 2787–2798.
36. HARPER, I.S., J.M. BOND, E. CHACON, J.M. REECE, B. HERMAN & J.J. LEMASTERS. 1993. Inhibition of Na^+/H^+ exchange preserves viability, restores mechanical function, and prevents the pH paradox in reperfusion injury to rat neonatal myocytes. Basic Res. Cardiol. **88:** 430–442.
37. YASUTAKE, M., C. IBUKI, D.J. HEARSE & M. AVKIRAN. 1994. Na^+/H^+ exchange and reperfusion arrhythmias: Protection by intracoronary infusion of a novel inhibitor. Am. J. Physiol. **267:** H2430–H2440.
38. MYERS, M.L. & M. KARMAZYN. 1996. Improved cardiac function after prolonged hypothermic ischemia with the Na^+/H^+ exchange inhibitor HOE 694. Ann. Thorac. Surg. **61:** 1400–1406.
39. SCHOLZ, W., U. ALBUS, L. COUNILLON, H. GÖGELEIN, H.-J. LANG, W. LINZ, A. WEICHERT & B.A. SCHÖLKENS. 1995. Protective effects of HOE642, a selective sodium-hydrogen exchange subtype 1 inhibitor, on cardiac ischaemia and reperfusion. Cardiovasc. Res. **29:** 260–268.
40. XUE, Y.X., N.N. AYE & K. HASHIMOTO. 1996. Antiarrhythmic effects of HOE642, a novel Na^+-H^+ exchange inhibitor, on ventricular arrhythmias in animal hearts. Eur. J. Pharmacol. **317:** 309–316.

41. AYE, N.N., Y.X. XUE & K. HASHIMOTO. 1997. Antiarrhythmic effects of cariporide, a novel Na^+-H^+ exchange inhibitor, on reperfusion ventricular arrhythmias in rat hearts. Eur. J. Pharmacol. **339:** 121–127.
42. SHIPOLINI, A.R., M. GALIÑANES, S.J. EDMONDSON, D.J. HEARSE & M. AVKIRAN. 1997. Na^+/H^+ exchanger inhibitor HOE-642 improves cardioplegic myocardial preservation under both normothermic and hypothermic conditions. Circulation **96:** 266–273.
43. CHAKRABARTI, S., A.N. HOQUE & M. KARMAZYN. 1997. A rapid ischemia-induced apoptosis in isolated rat hearts and its attenuation by the sodium-hydrogen exchange inhibitor HOE 642 (Cariporide). J. Mol. Cell. Cardiol. **29:** 3169–3174.
44. BAUMGARTH, M., N. BEIER & R. GERICKE. 1997. (2-methyl-5-(methylsulfonyl)benzoyl) guanidine Na^+/H^+ antiporter inhibitors. J. Med. Chem. **40:** 2017–2034.
45. DUFF, H.J., L.B. MITCHELL, K.M. KAVANAGH, D.E. MANYARI, A.M. GILLIS & D.G. WYSE. 1989. Amiloride: antiarrhythmic and electrophysiological actions in patients with sustained ventricular tachycardia. Circulation **79:** 1257–1263.
46. MYERS, M. 1990. Diuretic therapy and ventricular arrhythmias in persons 65 years of age and older. Am. J. Cardiol. **65:** 599–603.
47. ORLOWSKI, J. & S. GRINSTEIN. 1997. Na^+/H^+ exchangers in mammalian cells. J. Biol. Chem. **272:** 22373–22376.
48. WAKABAYASHI, S., M. SHIGEKAWA & J. POUYSSÉGUR. 1997. Molecular physiology of vertebrate Na^+/H^+ exchangers. Physiol. Rev. **77:** 51–74.
49. ORLOWSKI, J., R.A. KANDASAMY & G.E. SHULL. 1992. Molecular cloning of putative members of the Na/H exchanger gene family. cDNA cloning, deduced amino acid sequence, and mRNA tissue expression of the rat Na/H exchanger NHE-1 and two structurally related proteins. J. Biol. Chem. **267:** 9331–9339.
50. WANG, Z., J. ORLOWSKI & G.E. SHULL. 1993. Primary structure and functional expression of a novel gastrointestinal isoform of the rat Na/H exchanger. J. Biol. Chem. **268:** 11925–11928.
51. TSE, C.-M., S. LEVINE, C. YUN, S. BRANT, L.T. COUNILLON, J. POUYSSÉGUR & M. DONOWITZ. 1993. Structure/function studies of the epithelial isoforms of the mammalian Na^+/H^+ exchanger gene family. J. Membr. Biol. **135:** 93–108.
52. FLIEGEL, L., J.R.B. DYCK, H. WANG, C. FONG & R.S. HAWORTH. 1993. Cloning and analysis of the human myocardial Na^+/H^+ exchanger. Mol. Cell. Biochem. **125:** 137–143.
53. TSE, C.-M., A.I. MA, V.W. YANG, A.J.M. WATSON, S. LEVINE, M.H. MONTROSE, J. POTTER, C. SARDET, J. POUYSSÉGUR & M. DONOWITZ. 1991. Molecular cloning and expression of a cDNA encoding the rabbit ileal villus cell basolateral membrane Na^+/H^+ exchanger. EMBO J. **10:** 1957–1967.
54. HILDEBRANDT, F., J.H. PIZZONIA, R.F. REILLY, N.A. REBOUÇAS, C. SARDET, J. POUYSSÉGUR, C.W. SLAYMAN, P.S. ARONSON & P. IGARASHI. 1991. Cloning, sequence, and tissue distribution of a rabbit renal Na^+/H^+ exchanger transcript. Biochim. Biophys. Acta Gene Struct. Expression **1129:** 105–108.
55. PUCÉAT, M., I. KORICHNEVA, R. CASSOLY & G. VASSORT. 1995. Identification of band 3-like proteins and Cl^-/HCO_3^- exchange in isolated cardiomyocytes. J. Biol. Chem. **270:** 1315–1322.
56. WHITE, R.L., J.E. DOELLER, V.K. VERSELIS & B.A. WITTENBERG. 1990. Gap junctional conductance between pairs of ventricular myocytes is modulated synergistically by H^+ and Ca^{++}. J. Gen. Physiol. **95:** 1061–1075.
57. NUMATA, M., K. PETRECCA, N. LAKE & J. ORLOWSKI. 1998. Identification of a mitochondrial Na^+/H^+ exchanger. J. Biol. Chem. **273:** 6951–6959.
58. BRIERLEY, G.P., M.H. DAVIS, E.J. CRAGOE, JR. & D.W. JUNG. 1989. Kinetic properties of the Na^+/H^+ antiport of heart mitochondria. Biochemistry **28:** 4337–4354.
59. CROMPTON, M. & I. HEID. 1978. The cycling of calcium, sodium, and protons across the inner membrane of cardiac mitochondria. Eur. J. Biochem. **91:** 599–608.
60. CROMPTON, M., R. MOSER, H. LUNDI & E. CARAFOLI. 1978. The interrelations between the transport of sodium and calcium in mitochondria of various mammalian tissues. Eur. J. Biochem. **82:** 25–31.
61. SASTRASINH, M., P. YOUNG, E.J. CRAGOE, JR. & S. SASTRASINH. 1995. The Na^+/H^+ antiport in renal mitochondria. Am. J. Physiol. **268:** C1227–C1234.
62. FLIEGEL, L., R.S. HAWORTH & J.R.B. DYCK. 1993. Characterization of the placental

brush border membrane Na^+/H^+ exchanger: Identification of thiol-dependent transitions in apparent molecular size. Biochem. J. **289:** 101–107.
63. Fafournoux, P., J. Noël & J. Pouysségur. 1994. Evidence that Na^+/H^+ exchanger isoforms NHE1 and NHE3 exist as stable dimers in membranes with a high degree of specificity for homodimers. J. Biol. Chem. **269:** 2589–2596.
64. Kleyman, T.R. & E.J. Cragoe, Jr. 1988. Amiloride and its analogs as tools in the study of ion transport. J. Membr. Biol. **105:** 1–21.
65. Orlowski, J. 1993. Heterologous expression and functional properties of the amiloride high affinity (NHE-1) and low affinity (NHE-3) isoforms of the rat Na/H exchanger. J. Biol. Chem. **268:** 16369–16377.
66. Yu, F.H., G.E. Shull & J. Orlowski. 1993. Functional properties of the rat Na/H exchanger NHE-2 isoform expressed in Na/H exchanger-deficient Chinese hamster ovary cells. J. Biol. Chem. **268:** 25536–25541.
67. Counillon, L., W. Scholz, H.J. Lang & J. Pouysségur. 1993. Pharmacological characterization of stably transfected Na^+/H^+ antiporter isoforms using amiloride analogs and a new inhibitor exhibiting anti-ischemic properties. Mol. Pharmacol. **44:** 1041–1045.
68. Orlowski, J. & R.A. Kandasamy. 1996. Delineation of transmembrane domains of the Na^+/H^+ exchanger that confer sensitivity to pharmacological antagonists. J. Biol. Chem. **271:** 19922–19927.
69. Kinsella, J.L. & P.S. Aronson. 1981. Amiloride inhibition of the Na^+-H^+ exchanger in renal microvillus membrane vesicles. Am. J. Physiol. **241:** F374–F379
70. Mahnensmith, R.L. & P.S. Aronson. 1985. Interrelationships among quinidine, amiloride, and lithium as inhibitors of the renal Na^+-H^+ exchanger. J. Biol. Chem. **260:** 12586–12592.
71. Paris, S. & J. Pouysségur. 1983. Biochemical characterization of the amiloride-sensitive Na^+/H^+ antiport in Chinese hamster lung fibroblasts. J. Biol. Chem. **258:** 3503–3508.
72. L'Allemain, G., A. Franchi, E.J. Cragoe, Jr. & J. Pouysségur. 1984. Blockade of the Na^+/H^+ antiport abolishes growth factor-induced DNA synthesis in fibroblasts. Structure-activity relationships in the amiloride series. J. Biol. Chem. **259:** 4313–4319.
73. Ganapathy, V., D.F. Balkovetz, Y. Miyamoto, M.E. Ganapathy, V.B. Mahesh, L.D. Devoe & F.H. Leibach. 1986. Inhibition of human placental Na^+-H^+ exchanger by cimetidine. J. Pharmacol. Exp. Ther. **239:** 192–197.
74. Ives, H.E., V.J. Yee & D.G. Warnock. 1983. Mixed type inhibition of the renal Na^+/H^+ antiporter by Li^+ and amiloride. Evidence for a modifier site. J. Biol. Chem. **258:** 9710–9716.
75. Warnock, D.G., W.-C. Yang, Z.-Q. Huang & E.J. Cragoe, Jr. 1988. Interactions of chloride and amiloride with the renal Na^+/H^+ antiporter. J. Biol. Chem. **263:** 7216–7221.
76. Franchi, A., E.J. Cragoe, Jr. & J. Pouysségur. 1986. Isolation and properties of fibroblast mutants overexpressing an altered Na^+/H^+ antiporter. J. Biol. Chem. **261:** 14614–14620.
77. Counillon, L., A. Franchi & J. Pouysségur. 1993. A point mutation of the Na^+/H^+ exchanger gene (NHE1) and amplification of the mutated allele confer amiloride resistance upon chronic acidosis. Proc. Natl. Acad. Sci. USA **90:** 4508–4512.
78. Counillon, L., J. Noël, R.A. Reithmeier & J. Pouysségur. 1997. Random mutagenesis reveals a novel site involved in inhibitor interaction within the fourth transmembrane segment of the Na^+/H^+ exchanger-1. Biochemistry **36:** 2951–2959.
79. Wang, D., D.F. Balkovetz & D.G. Warnock. 1995. Mutational analysis of transmembrane histidines in the amiloride-sensitive Na^+/H^+ exchanger. Am. J. Physiol. **269:** C392–C402.
80. Yun, C.H.C., P.J. Little, S.K. Nath, S.A. Levine, J. Pouysségur, C.M. Tse & M. Donowitz. 1993. Leu^{143} in the putative fourth membrane spanning domain is critical for amiloride inhibition of an epithelial Na^+/H^+ exchanger isoform (NHE-2). Biochem. Biophys. Res. Commun. **193:** 532–539.
81. Petrecca, K., R. Atanasiu, S. Girinstein, J. Orlowski & A. Shrier. 1999. Subcellular localization of the Na^+/H^+ exchanger NHE1 in rat myocardium. Am. J. Physiol. **276:** H709–H717.

Nitric Oxide and the Vascular Endothelium in Myocardial Ischemia-Reperfusion Injury[a]

JAKOB VINTEN-JOHANSEN,[b] ZHI-QING ZHAO, MASANORI NAKAMURA, JAMES E. JORDAN, RUSSELL S. RONSON, VINOD H. THOURANI, AND ROBERT A. GUYTON

Department of Surgery, Division of Cardiothoracic Surgery, The Cardiothoracic Research Laboratory, The Carlyle Fraser Heart Center, Crawford Long Hospital, Emory University School of Medicine, Atlanta, Georgia 30365, USA

ABSTRACT: The normal coronary vascular endothelium (VE) tonically releases nitric oxide (NO) by converting L-arginine to citrulline by a constitutive NO synthase. Reperfusion after myocardial ischemia reduces basal and stimulated release of NO. This "vascular reperfusion injury" is mediated largely by neutrophils (PMN) through specific interactions between adhesion molecules on the endothelium and the PMN, an interaction that precedes myocyte injury. NO inhibits the PMN-mediated reperfusion injury by direct effects on both the PMN and the vascular endothelium. Cardioprotective strategies include augmentation of endogenous NO by the precursor L-arginine and the administration of exogenous NO donors at the time of perfusion, which (1) attenuates PMN adherence to the coronary artery and venous endothelium, (2) reduces PMN-mediated endothelial dysfunction, (3) reduces PMN accumulation in the area at risk, and (4) reduces infarct size. Hence, NO represents a powerful therapeutic tool with which to attenuate the consequences of ischemia-reperfusion injury on vascular injury and infarction.

INTRODUCTION

Nitric oxide is a naturally occurring autacoid, released by the endothelium and other tissues, that has numerous physiologic actions ranging from inducing vasodilation to modulating cell proliferation (FIG. 1). NO is a radical species that has an extremely short half-life and hence can only diffuse short distances before being inactivated. Nevertheless, NO exerts potent paracrine and autocrine physiologic actions during its short lifetime. The pioneering studies of Kubes and colleagues[1,2] and McCall and colleagues[3] demonstrated another important physiologic effect of NO— the inhibition of neutrophil-mediated inflammatory processes. Recognizing that neutrophils played a central role in ischemic-reperfusion injury,[4–8] the potent anti-

[a]Supported in part by grant HL-46179 from the National Institutes of Health (National Heart, Lung, and Blood Institute), grant 97-30209N from the American Heart Association, by the Thoracic Surgery Foundation for Research and Education (V.H.T), and by the Carlyle Fraser Heart Center.

[b]Address correspondence to: J. Vinten-Johansen, Ph.D., The Cardiothoracic Research Laboratory, Carlyle Fraser Heart Center of Crawford Long Hospital, Emory University School of Medicine, 550 Peachtree Street N.E., Atlanta, Georgia 30365; Telephone: 404-686-2511; Fax: 404-686-4888; E-mail: jvinten@emory.edu

neutrophil effects of NO launched a new direction in research on myocardial protection in both the nonsurgical and the cardiac surgery arena, in which protection of the myocardium also involved protection of the coronary vascular endothelium. Subsequent research has shown that the anti-inflammatory effects of NO are both complex and broad spectrum, involving the attenuation of endothelial cell activation and expression of adhesion molecules[9,10] both acutely (<3 h) and in the longer term (>3 h) through the regulation of transcription, modulation of cytokine production or release, and direct inhibition of neutrophil functions (FIG. 1). Numerous studies have shown that protection of the coronary vascular endothelium is associated with reduction of infarct size and to a large extent reduction of postischemic contractile dysfunction. However, the causal link, i.e., that protection of the endothelium directly affects infarct size or contractile dysfunction, remains to be drawn. Furthermore, the realization that postischemic injury may be largely initiated and promulgated during reperfusion strengthened the concept of reperfusion injury, and identified the endothelium as an active participant in (as well as target of) the pathogenesis of this "reperfusion injury." The potent actions of NO therapy during reperfusion indicated a therapeutic "window" for the effective delivery of pharmacologic agents directed toward ameliorating postischemic endothelial injury and, hence, attenuating myocardial infarction and contractile dysfunction. This article summarizes the effects of NO

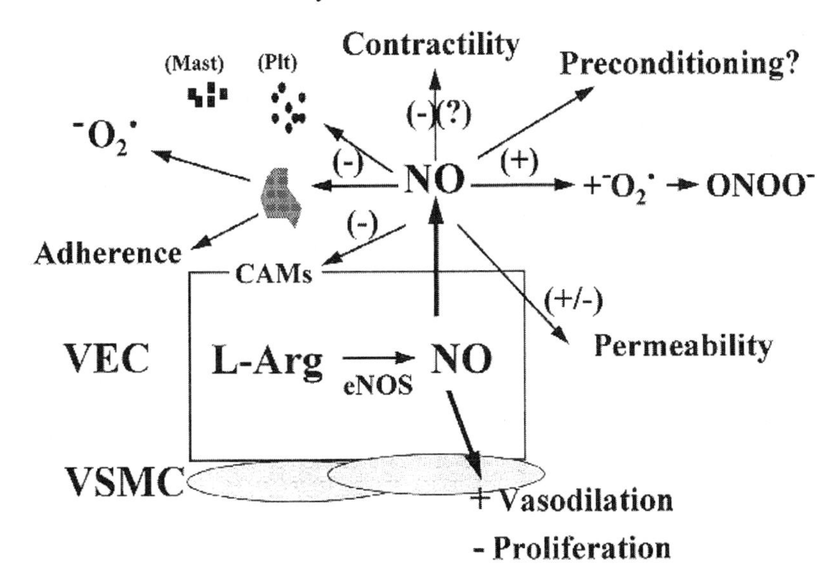

FIGURE 1. Nitric oxide (NO) derived from the vascular endothelium (VEC) has many physiological effects related to the protection of the ischemic-reperfused heart. NO attenuates (–) activation of neutrophils and thereby inhibits superoxide anion production ($^-O_2^\bullet$) and adherence to the VEC, as well as attenuates mast cell and platelet (Plt) function. NO has variable effects on contractility and myocardial metabolism and may promote (+) or trigger the second window of preconditioning. On the other hand, NO forms peroxynitrite ($ONOO^-$), which may be deleterious to myocardial viability if not detoxified or otherwise neutralized, perhaps in the form of a nitrosothiol or other nitroso adduct. L-Arg = L-arginine; eNOS = endothelial nitric oxide synthase. Mean ± SEM.

on protection of the coronary vascular endothelium and the myocyte (contractile function and infarction) from ischemic-reperfusion injury.

In contrast to these cardioprotective actions, NO has also been implicated in promulgating injury from its actions as a radical species or from the generation of potentially deleterious metabolites, such as peroxynitrite ($ONOO^-$). Therefore, a duality of opposing physiological actions is associated with endogenous and exogenous NO, the mechanisms of which are not fully known.

REPERFUSION INJURY IMPAIRS RELEASE OF NITRIC OXIDE BY THE CORONARY VASCULAR ENDOTHELIUM

Ischemia and reperfusion cause injury to the vascular endothelium, expressed as a reduction in both basal and stimulated NO release[11–14] and a reduction in the physiological functions of the endothelium. Nitric oxide release measured directly *in vitro* after ischemia-reperfusion has been shown to be reduced in agreement with the obtunded responses to nitric oxide synthase (NOS) inhibitors.[15,16] The impaired basal release of NO results in a decrease in the *in vitro* vasoconstrictor response normally observed with addition of inhibitors of NOS due to loss of tonic NO-dependent vasorelaxation,[17,18] while coronary artery segments in organ chambers demonstrate attenuated vasorelaxation responses to agonist stimulators of endothelial nitric oxide synthase (eNOS), such as acetylcholine or bradykinin, implying impaired agonist-stimulated release of nitric oxide.[12,19,20] Similar events also occur in coronary veins from ischemic-reperfused myocardium.[21] Decreased *in vivo* endothelial vasodilator responses to intracoronary acetylcholine infusions have also been reported[19,22] after coronary artery occlusion and reperfusion, in agreement with the *in vitro* findings. In the absence of reperfusion, postischemic endothelial dysfunction is minimally expressed after short-term regional ischemia (60–90 min),[12,17] but may be expressed after more prolonged ischemia (>90 min).[13] However, in the presence of reperfusion, endothelial dysfunction is expressed as early as 2.5 min after the start of reflow, and persists for hours[10,11] to days[23] (FIG. 2) after the initiation of reperfusion. FIGURE 3 shows coronary artery endothelial function (assayed as vasodilator responses to agonist stimulators of NOS) after 45 min of global normothermic ischemia with or without blood reperfusion using extracorporeal support.[14] Maximal vasorelaxation responses to the endothelium-dependent, receptor-dependent agonist without reperfusion acetylcholine were not significantly reduced in hearts subjected to ischemia only compared to controls, but vasorelaxation responses in ischemic-reperfused hearts were significantly reduced by approximately 40% compared to controls. Impaired responses to acetylcholine and other agonist stimulators similar to those observed after global ischemia are also observed after regional ischemia-reperfusion.[17,20,24] A modest rightward shift in the entire concentration-relaxation response curve to acetylcholine occurred in coronary arteries exposed to ischemia only (Mean $\pm$ SEM, EC_{50} of $4.0 \pm 0.5 \times 10^{-8}$ M versus control $2.2 \pm 0.3 \times 10^{-8}$ M, $p < 0.05$), while a greater shift (in addition to a reduced maximal response) was seen in ischemic-reperfused vessels ($6.0 \pm 0.2 \times 10^{-8}$ M, $p < 0.001$ versus Control vessel). Impairment in maximal and concentration-dependent responses similar to those seen in FIGURE 3 was also observed for the Ca^{2+} ionophore A23187, an endothelium-depen-

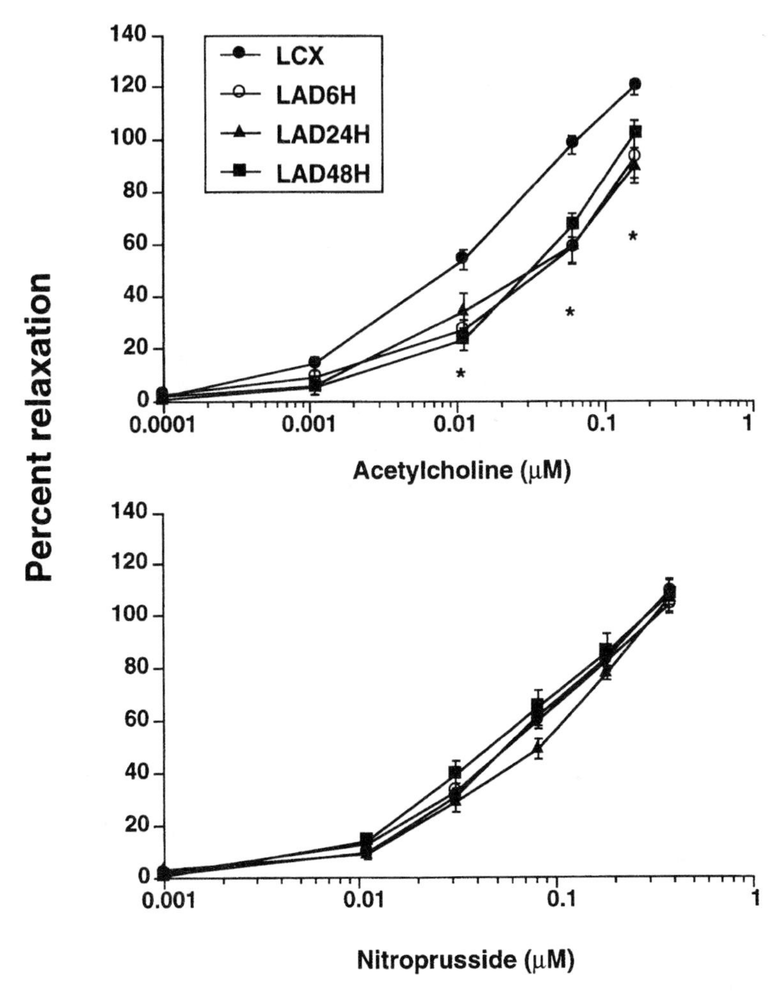

FIGURE 2. Vasorelaxation responses of ischemic-reperfused left anterior descending (LAD) coronary arteries to incremental concentrations of acetylcholine (endothelium-dependent, receptor-dependent agonist) and nitriprusside (endothelium-independent smooth muscle relaxant). Reperfusion was allowed to continue for 6 h (6H), 24 h (24H), or 48 h (48H) after 60-min LAD occlusion. The left circumflex coronary artery (LCX) was used as a control (non-ischemic) artery. *$p < 0.05$ versus LCX. Mean ± SEM.

dent receptor-independent vasodilator. Smooth muscle relaxation responses to the NO donor acidified (pH 2.0) $NaNO_2$ were complete, indicating normal function of the vascular smooth muscle. These data suggest that endothelial dysfunction involved not only damage to the receptor-transduction complex (attenuated ACh responses), but also to the more distal processes regulating eNOS activity or damage to the enzyme itself, based on responses to A23187.[14]

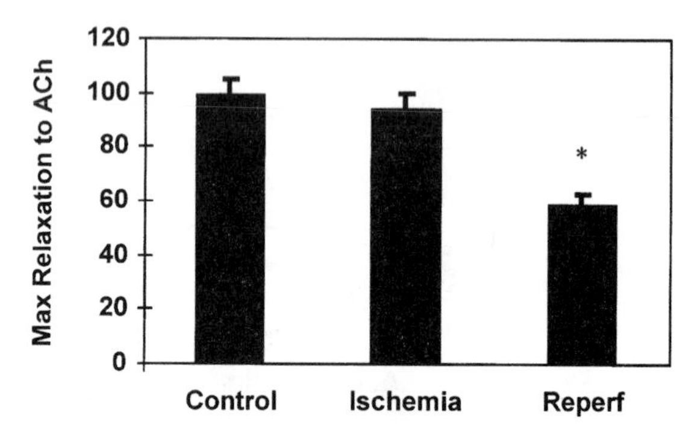

FIGURE 3. Coronary artery endothelial relaxation responses to incremental concentrations of acetylcholine (ACh) in vessels taken from hearts exposed to no ischemia (Control), 45-min global normothermic ischemia alone (Ischemia), or 45-min global ischemia followed by 1 h reperfusion (Reperf). There was a significant reduction in endothelium-dependent relaxation in the arteries taken only from ischemic-reperfused hearts. $^*p < 0.05$ versus Control and Ischemia. Mean ± SEM.

Endothelial dysfunction after ischemia-reperfusion was also associated with morphological abnormalities in endothelial structure, including partial or complete detachment of endothelial cells from the basement membrane, hypervesiculation of endothelial cells present, and neutrophil attachments. Impaired endothelial nitric oxide synthase (eNOS) activity after ischemia has recently been reported by Giraldez and colleagues[25] in which loss of eNOS activity in isolated perfused hearts paralleled the time course in the loss of functional reactivity to NOS stimulators. In addition to impaired basal and agonist-stimulated vasodilator responses of the coronary artery endothelium, endothelial dysfunction after ischemia-reperfusion is also characterized by an increased adherence of unstimulated neutrophils.[17] The adherence of unstimulated neutrophils, which is normally prevented by the tonic release of NO, is increased after reperfusion. Both adherence of unstimulated neutrophils to coronary artery endothelium and the loss of basally released NO (indirectly measured by vasocontraction responses to inhibitors of NOS) progress during reperfusion.[17,18]

ADHESION MOLECULES IN MYOCARDIAL ISCHEMIC-REPERFUSION INJURY

Three families of adhesion molecules are involved in neutrophil interactions with the endothelium during ischemia-reperfusion: selectins, β_2-integrins, and the immunoglobulin superfamily. The selectins (P-selectin, L-selectin, E-selectin) are glycoproteins involved in the early interactions between neutrophils and the coronary vascular endothelium during reperfusion. P-selectin is not constitutively expressed but is found stored preformed in α-granules of platelets and in Weibel-Palade bodies of endothelial cells. P-selectin expression on the surface of endothelial cells can be induced by humoral mediators (such as thrombin, complement fragments, and histamine) and oxidants (such as hydrogen peroxide). After ischemia, P-selectin surface expression is maximally upregulated after 10–20 min of reperfusion and is subsequently shed.[26–28] P-selectin is involved in one of the earliest interactions—the loose tethering or "rolling" of neutrophils over endothelium[29–31]—necessary for further interactions to establish firm adherence of PMN to endothelium. This and subsequent interaction culminates in myocardial injury[32] and microvascular injury, such as neutrophil embolization (no-reflow phenomenon) and possibly myocardial infarction.[33] Accordingly, neutralization of P-selectin reduces neutrophil adherence, neutrophil-mediated injury to endothelium, and myocardial infarction.[32,34] E-selectin is expressed on the surface of endothelial cells and because of its slower time course of upregulated surface expression (4–6 h) by cytokines (rather than fast-response mediators), this adhesion molecule may be involved in later reperfusion events.

L-selectin is constitutively expressed on the surface of neutrophils and may be the counterligand for P-selectin on the endothelium.[35] L-selectin may therefore also be involved in the very early interaction between neutrophils and endothelium. A high affinity glycoprotein ligand for P-selectin, located on leukocyte microvillae, has recently been identified (P-selectin glycoprotein ligand-1, PSGL-1)[36] that might mediate, in part, neutrophil rolling on purified P-selectin[36] and on intact endothelium. Cell-cell interaction with this adhesion molecule has also been associated with *in vivo* myocardial injury.[37,38] Blockade of L-selectin (i.e., with DREG-200) has been shown to reduce infarct size ($14 \pm 3\%$ versus $29 \pm 3\%$ of the area at risk), reduce neutrophil adherence to postischemic coronary artery endothelium, and increase coronary artery endothelial responses to acetylcholine.[37]

The β_2-integrins (CD11/CD18) are a family of heterodimer glycoproteins that reside on neutrophils. CD11/CD18 surface expression can be stimulated by a number of mediators, including platelet activating factor. Surface expression of CD11b/CD18 specifically is triggered after the rolling phase of neutrophils on the endothelium. The involvement of CD11b/CD18 with its counterligand ICAM-1 on the endothelium results in firm adherence of PMNs. The inhibition of this interaction between CD11/CD18 and ICAM-1 with monoclonal antibodies directed at CD18 is associated with a decrease in neutrophil adherence to endothelium and a reduction in myocardial infarct size.[39]

In the immunoglobulin superfamily (ICAM-1, VCAM-1, PECAM), ICAM-1 is an important molecule constitutively expressed at a relatively low level on the surface of vascular endothelial cells. ICAM-1 is the counterligand for CD11/CD18 on neutrophils and its upregulation by cytokines 2–4 h after stimulation or after myocardial ischemia-reperfusion[40,41] coincides with the upregulation of CD11/CD18. Therefore, monoclonal antibodies to ICAM-1 inhibit cytokine-stimulated or reperfusion-stimulated neutrophil adherence to endothelium, endothelial injury, and myocardial infarction, similar to antibodies toward CD18 expressed on PMNs.[42,43]

NITRIC OXIDE ATTENUATES ACTIVATION OF THE ENDOTHELIAL ADHESION MOLECULES

Evidence has been mounting that NO may interfere with the activation of the vascular endothelium and thereby attenuate the PMN–endothelial interactions that precede the inflammatory component of reperfusion injury. Kubes and colleagues[2] reported that inhibition of NOS with the L-arginine analogue L-NAME increased PMN adherence to feline mesenteric postcapillary venules, measured by intravital microscopy, suggesting that endogenous NO modulates PMN–endothelial cell interactions. Although this important pioneering study did not implicate the endothelium as a target of NO, it posed the question of which cell type involved in the interaction between neutrophils and endothelium was directly affected by NO. Since P-selectin is upregulated during reperfusion in association with a decrease in NO production by the endothelium, a regulatory connection between NO and surface expression of P-selectin on the vascular endothelium was at least suggested. A subsequent study by Davenpeck and colleagues[44] demonstrated that superfusion of the feline mesenteric microcirculation with the NOS inhibitor L-NAME attenuated NO generation and increased PMN adherence to venular endothelial surface in conjunction with an increased surface expression of P-selectin. These physiological responses were reversed by the co-administration of L-arginine and a cGMP analog (8-bromo-cGMP), thereby implicating NO as the active molecule. The surface expression of other adhesion molecules, notably E-selectin and VCAM-1, has been found to be attenuated by NO.[45] The expression of IL-1α–stimulated VCAM-1 expression on human saphenous vein endothelial cells was reduced by 35–55%, in parallel with a decrease in monocyte adherence to the endothelial cells.

The suppression of adhesion molecule expression on endothelial cells may involve changes at the transcriptional level. Using human iliac vein endothelial cells, Armstead and colleagues[46] reported that NO (in the form of the NO donor SPM-5185) attenuated the L-NAME–stimulated increase in P-selectin protein synthesis and mRNA expression. The peak inhibitory effect was observed after 2–4 h of exposure to NO, suggesting a longer term effect rather than an acute effect relevant to the rapid surface expression response after reperfusion. DeCaterina and colleagues[45] reported that NO (S-nitroso-glutathione as an NO donor) suppressed VCAM-1 gene expression by inhibiting activation of the transcription factor NF-κB. Therefore, NO modulates the rapid surface expression of immediate response adhesion molecules, such as P-selectin, as well as attenuates the time-dependent synthesis of adhesion molecule proteins at the genetic level.

CARDIOPROTECTION FROM ISCHEMIC-REPERFUSION INJURY BY NITRIC OXIDE

TABLE 1 summarizes several NO-related therapeutic strategies for attenuating myocardial ischemic-reperfusion injury. Endogenous NO participates in the tonic modulation of various postischemic physiological variables, including electrophysiological abnormalities and myocardial injury (i.e., infarction). In view of its important regulation of infarction, modulation of endogenous NO may present an

TABLE 1. NO-related therapeutic strategies

Endogenous	Exogenous
NO˙ precursor	Authentic NO˙
L-arginine	Gas in solution
	Acidified $NaNO_2$
Agonist stimulators	NO donors
Acetylcholine	Nitroglycerin
Bradykinin	SPM-5185
	SIN-1
	Direct donors
Transfection with eNOS	

important therapeutic approach. Precursors of NO or other NOS-regulating agents can be given at concentrations sufficient to augment endogenous NO generation without the profound hypotension that may occur at higher systemic concentrations of exogenously administered authentic NO or NO donors. However, a number of studies have shown that this modulation is a negative one, that is, NO augments postischemic arrhythmias, contractile dysfunction, and infarction. This notion that NO increases postischemic injury, therefore, would suggest that blockade of NOS activity would reduce postischemic damage. Accordingly, investigating the effect of NOS blockade on *in vivo* myocardial infarction, Woolfson and colleagues[47] reported that the L-arginine analogue L-NAME reduced infarct size in an *in situ* rabbit model, which seemed to support a deleterious role for NO. Furthermore, Schultz and Wambolt[48] demonstrated that the cardioprotective effects resulting from NOS inhibition with L-NAME were abolished by co-administration of L- but not D-arginine, confirming involvement of the L-arginine–NO pathway. In contrast, Sun and Wainwright[49] reported that neither the NOS inhibitor L-NAME nor the NO donor C87-3754 altered the incidence and severity of ventricular arrhythmias during a 30-min coronary artery occlusion in anesthetized rats.

In contrast to these deleterious effects of NO, Pabla and Curtis[50] demonstrated that inhibition of NOS activity with L-NAME in isolated perfused rabbit hearts increased the incidence of reperfusion-induced ventricular fibrillation, which was reversible by co-infusion with L-arginine, thereby ascribing a beneficial electrophysiological effect to NO. Furthermore, the study by Williams and colleagues[51] using an *in vivo* rabbit model demonstrated that the systemic administration of 15 mg/kg L-NA (a non-methylated analogue of L-arginine) either before ischemia or just before reperfusion increased infarct size (51 ± 2 and $49 \pm 3\%$ of area at risk, respectively) compared to $27 \pm 2\%$ of area at risk in control (FIG. 4). In agreement with the study of Williams and colleagues,[51] other studies have reported deleterious effects of eNOS antagonists on other physiological endpoints such as a reduction in the time to ischemic contracture in globally ischemic hearts,[52] a decrease in postischemic contractile recovery,[53] and an increase in infarct size[54]; reduction in contractile recovery and increased infarction involved a concomitant increase in neutrophil accumulation. These effects on arrhythmias, contractile dysfunction, and infarction were reversed by coinfusion of L-arginine. The discrepancy in these diametrically opposed endpoints, such as infarct size by inhibition of endogenous NO formation is not fully resolved, but may relate to the choice of L-arginine

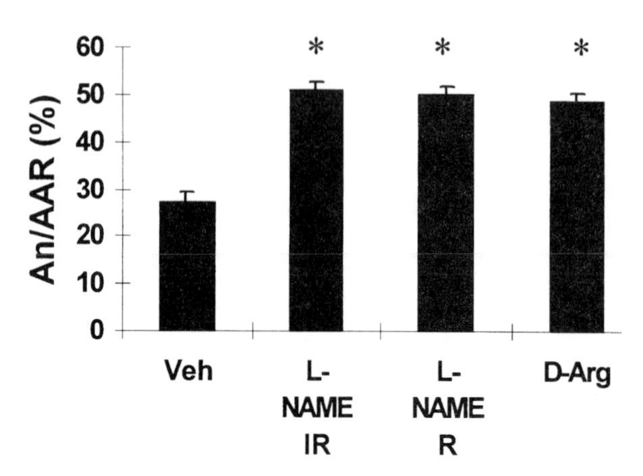

FIGURE 4. Left ventricular infarct size presented as the ratio of the area of necrosis (An) relative to the area at risk (AAR). Veh = vehicle-treated (saline) group; L-NA IR = L-nitro arginine (15 mg/kg bolus, 7.5 mg/kg/h) administered before coronary occlusion and reperfusion; L-NA R = L-NA administered before reperfusion. $*p < 0.05$ versus Veh group. Mean ± SEM.

analogue. Methylated analogues may demonstrate muscarinic-like antagonistic effects not demonstrated by non-methylated congeners. Alternatively, the reduction in postischemic damage reported with NOS inhibition may be related to a compensatory release of the cardioprotective autacoid adenosine.[47,55] In the study by Patel and colleagues[56] vasoconstriction resulting from NOS inhibition (and presumably to reduced NO release) may have resulted in ischemia as supported by an increase in lactate release.[56] This extreme vasoconstrictor-induced myocardial ischemia may have prompted the release of another cardioprotective autacoid, adenosine, with subsequent myocardial protection similar to that exerted by NO itself.

Endogenous NO can be therapeutically augmented by providing L-arginine, the precursor for NO. Although L-arginine appears in the blood and in the cytosol in sufficient concentrations to saturate NOS, supplemental L-arginine has been reported to increase NO release (directly or indirectly measured) by the coronary vascular endothelium.[15,16,57] In isolated rat aortic endothelial cells, 1 mM L-arginine increased the amperometrically measured release of NO by approximately 40% above basal levels.[15] D-arginine at the same concentration did not increase basally released NO. Hence, the provision of L-arginine favors a concentration-related production of NO.

In models of regional ischemia, intravenous[58] or intracoronary[20] supplementation with L-arginine at the time of reperfusion significantly decreased both postischemic coronary artery endothelial dysfunction and infarct size. The reduced infarct size was associated with a decrease in neutrophil adherence to endothelium and neutrophil accumulation in the area at risk. In the study by Nakanishi and colleagues[20] in which 10 mM L-arginine was infused in the LAD coronary artery at the time of reperfusion, infarct size was reduced from 35 ± 2% of the area at risk to 18 ± 3% (FIG. 5). Infarct size reduction was not observed with D-arginine (10 mM, infarct size 49 ± 5% of area at risk), confirming that an indirect (i.e., metabolic) effect of L-

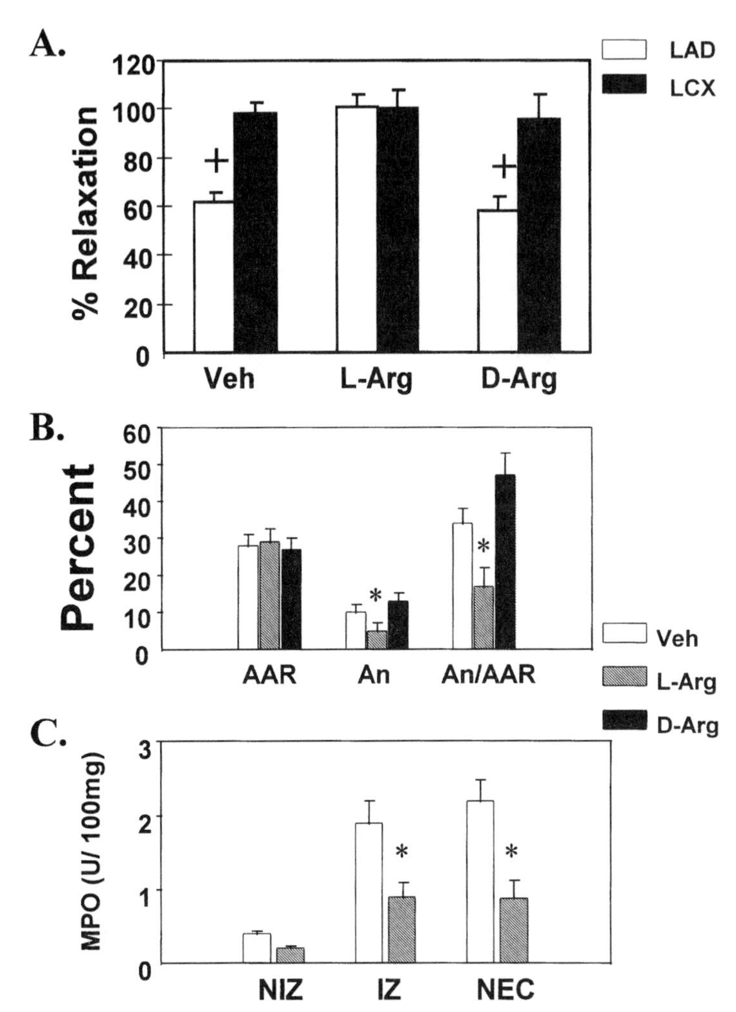

FIGURE 5. (A) Maximum endothelial relaxation responses to acetylcholine of the ischemic-reperfused left anterior descending (LAD) and nonischemic left circumflex (LCX) coronary arteries. $^{+}p < 0.05$ versus LCX responses. (B) Percent area at risk (AAR), area of necrosis (An), and necrosis/risk ratio (An/AAR) given in percentages. (C) Myeloperoxidase activity as a marker of neutrophil accumulation in myocardium from the nonischemic zone (NIZ), non-necrotic area at risk (IZ), and necrotic area at risk (NEC). $^{*}p < 0.05$ versus Veh (saline group) and D-arginine (D-Arg) if applicable. Mean ± SEM.

arginine unrelated to NO was not involved in this cardioprotective effect. Neither postischemic regional contractile function nor postischemic myocardial blood flow was improved with L-arginine treatment in this study. However, postischemic endothelial vasorelaxation responses to acetylcholine were significantly better in the L-arginine–treated group compared to both the vehicle group and the D-arginine group

(FIG. 5). Consistent with the anti-neutrophil effect of endogenously released NO, there was less neutrophil accumulation in the area at risk with L-arginine treatment at reperfusion than in vehicle or D-arginine–treated groups (FIG. 5). The mechanism of L-arginine in attenuating PMN–endothelial cell interactions is in agreement with its anti-neutrophil effect. Although L-arginine does not directly inhibit superoxide anion generation by activated PMNs, it does inhibit adherence of activated PMNs to coronary artery endothelium (FIG. 6). This inhibitory effect is reversed by L-NA; inhibition of endogenous L-arginine with L-NA also increases PMN adherence to coronary artery endothelium. Furthermore, endothelial dysfunction associated with the adherence of PMNs is attenuated by L-arginine. Therefore, the cardioprotective effects of L-arginine may involve, in large part, an attenuation of PMN-mediated actions culminating in infarction.

The study by Nakanishi and colleagues[20] raises the question of whether maximal cardioprotection was achieved with the dose of intracoronary L-arginine used. The degree of cardioprotection observed may have been truncated by (1) a submaximal dose of L-arginine, (2) a limitation in the cardioprotective capability of NO when administered only during the reperfusion period as opposed to administration before ischemia (i.e., pretreatment), or (3) a limitation in utilizing L-arginine therapy to increase NO release secondary to injury to the NO synthesis machinery, either at the

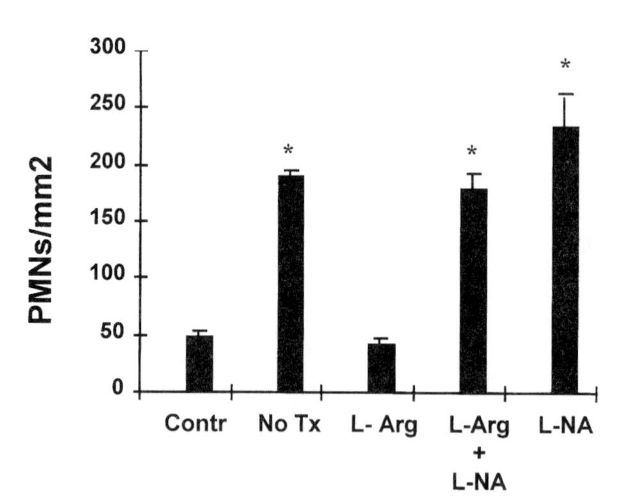

FIGURE 6. Adherence of fluorescently labeled neutrophils (PMN) to normal coronary artery segments in organ chambers in which the endothelium has been unstimulated (Contr) or stimulated with thrombin (thrombin 2 U/ml). Thrombin stimulation increased adherence (fluorescent microscopy) of PMNs to the endothelial surface by a factor of three. L-arginine (10 mM) decreased adherence to control levels, which was reversed by coincubation with the nitric oxide synthase antagonist L-nitro arginine (L-NA; L-Arg + L-NA). L-NA by itself increased PMN adherence through inhibition of endogenous NO. $^*p < 0.05$ versus unstimulated control endothelium and L-arginine. Means ± SEM.

level of the enzyme itself, its regulatory mechanisms, or at the level of the receptor or its transduction system. As described above, an injured endothelium in which the NO generation mechanisms are impaired may show attenuated responses to L-arginine, including a reduced release of NO. Further investigation is needed on the association between the dose of L-arginine used and the limitation imposed by endothelial injury on the extent of cardioprotection achieved by precursor therapy. However, any limitation in the endogenous capabilities of the heart to generate cardioprotective quantities of NO may potentially be overcome by parenteral administration of agents that donate NO *in vivo*.

The exogenous approach to NO therapy using NO donors was first reported by Johnson and colleagues in a feline model of regional myocardial ischemia-reperfusion (90 min LAD occlusion followed by 4.5 h of reperfusion) using intravenous $NaNO_2$ as an NO donor chemical[59] or authentic NO gas (approximately 10–20 nM *in vivo* concentration),[60] both at subvasodilator concentrations, administered only at the onset of reperfusion. Both forms of NO therapy decreased infarct size by about 75%, consistent with a comparable reduction in plasma creatine kinase activity, which was associated with decreased neutrophil accumulation in the area at risk (both non-necrotic and necrotic). These data suggest that NO therapy introduced at the time of reperfusion reduced infarct size possibly by inhibiting neutrophil-mediated damage. Subsequent studies have been performed using a variety of organic NO donor agents[53,61,62] and nitrosylated molecules[63] in models of *in vivo* coronary occlusion and reperfusion. The organic donors release NO either spontaneously or after bioconversion reactions. Nitroglycerin is the prototype NO donor agent, but is a poor NO donor due to its prerequisite bioconversion by a cysteine-containing enzyme that is partially depleted in the microvasculature after ischemia-reperfusion. In addition, tolerance to nitroglycerine develops over time. A cysteine-containing compound SPM-5185 (N-(3-hydroxy-pivaloyl)-S-(N′-acetylalanoyl)-L-cysteine ethyl ester (Schwarz Pharma AG, Monheim, Germany), which readily releases NO after biotransformation,[24,62] was administered by intracoronary infusion (500 nM) during reperfusion after 1 h LAD occlusion. SPM-5185 reduced infarct size from 42 ± 5% to 12 ± 3% of the area at risk (FIG. 7), in association with a 58% reduction in transmural neutrophil accumulation (tissue myeloperoxidase activity) in the area at risk.[24] The non-active form of the compound, SPM-5267, had no effect on any physiological variable measured. Untreated postischemic-reperfused LAD coronary artery segments demonstrated increased adherence of unstimulated PMNs consistent with damage to basal endothelial function. This enhanced PMN adherence was significantly attenuated by coincubation of PMN and LAD segments with SPM-5185 but not with the non-active molecule SPM-5267 (FIG. 7). Similar cardioprotection has been achieved with other intracoronary NO donors.[64] Whether the cardioprotection afforded by NO therapy is predominantly due to inhibition of neutrophil-mediated damage was studied by Pabla and colleagues.[53] Using a novel model in which isolated perfused rat hearts were perfused in the presence or absence of human neutrophils for a short period during the early moments of reperfusion, these investigators were unable to show any appreciable improvement in postischemic contractile function (left ventricular developed pressure) with an NO donor in the group perfused without neutrophils. However, a significant improvement in contractile function (postischemic) was observed in the neutrophil-supplemented hearts when an

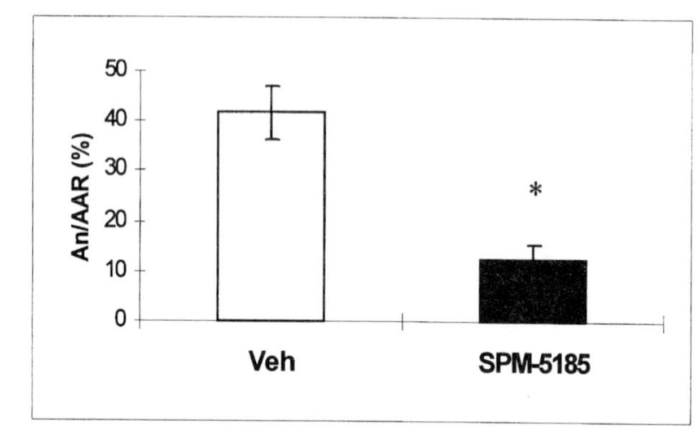

B.

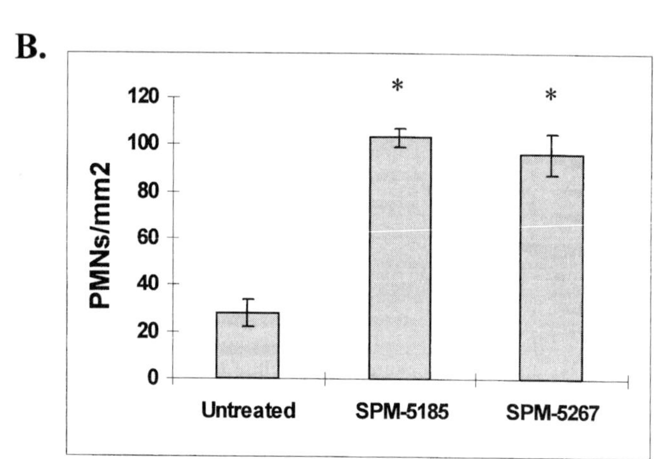

FIGURE 7. (A) Myocardial infarct size as a ratio of the area of necrosis (An) and the area at risk (AAR) after intracoronary treatment with saline (vehicle) and the NO-donor agent SPM-5185. (B) Adherence of unstimulated PMNs to endothelial surface of coronary arteries after ischemia and reperfusion as a marker of basal dysfunction. Untreated = no drugs; SPM-5185 = NO donor; SPM-5267 = non-nitrosylated parent molecule. Means ± SEM.

NO donor or L-arginine was infused at reperfusion. Therefore, whether cardioprotection with NO-donor therapy is due to a reduction in neutrophil-mediated injury predominantly may depend on the physiological variable of interest (i.e., contractile function versus infarction versus endothelial function). Hence, it is possible that NO exerts cardioprotection that is partially independent of neutrophils and neutrophil-mediated damage.

SUMMARY

NO therapy represents a potentially potent tool by which to protect the heart from ischemic-reperfusion injury. NO has an increasing number of physiological effects favorable to the protection of the heart from ischemic-reperfusion injury, among other disease processes. NO therapy attenuates endothelial injury by reducing the surface expression and upregulated synthesis of specific adhesion molecules on both the vascular endothelium and on the neutrophil. By virtue of the close association between endothelial injury and myocyte injury, with the neutrophil as central villain, preservation of the coronary vascular endothelium is most often associated with a concomitant reduction in postischemic myocardial injury as well, including attenuated contractile dysfunction, edema, enzyme release, and infarction. NO pharmacotherapy using the precursor to NO (L-arginine), various NO-donor agents, or drugs with the NO moiety "piggybacked" to the parent molecule to combine anti-inflammatory effects, will no doubt be used to reduce postischemic injury in both angioplasty procedures and surgical revascularization procedures. In the latter application, NO-related therapy may be used as adjuncts to cardioplegia solutions or can be delivered either systemically or locally during "off-pump" procedures in which extracorporeal technology is purposely avoided. The broad spectrum nature of NO therapy should find numerous targets against which to take aim. However, the potential deleterious effects of NO should be prevented or "detoxified" to more completely harness its cardioprotection.

ACKNOWLEDGMENT

The authors wish to thank Ms. Gail Nechtman for assistance in the preparation of the manuscript.

REFERENCES

1. KUBES, P., M. SUZUKI & D.N. GRANGER. 1990. Modulation of PAF-induced leukocyte adherence and increased microvascular permeability. Am. J. Physiol. **259:** G859–G864.
2. KUBES, P., M. SUZUKI & N. GRANGER. 1991. Nitric oxide: An endogenous modulator of leukocyte adhesion. Proc. Natl. Acad. Sci. USA **88:** 4651–4655.
3. MCCALL, T., B.J.R. WHITTLE, N.K. BROUGHTON-SMITH *et al.* 1988. Inhibition of FMLP-induced aggregation of rabbit neutrophils by nitric oxide. Br. J. Pharmacol. **95:** 517P.
4. DREYER, W.J., L.H. MICHAEL, M.W. WEST *et al.* 1991. Neutrophil accumulation in ischemic canine myocardium: Insights into time course, distribution, and mechanism of localization during early reperfusion. Circulation **84:** 400–411.
5. ENTMAN, M.L., L. MICHAEL, R.D. ROSSEN *et al.* 1991. Inflammation in the course of early myocardial ischemia. FASEB J. **5:** 2529–2537.
6. MULLANE, K. 1991. Neutrophil and endothelial changes in reperfusion injury. Trends Cardiovasc. Med. **1:** 282–289.
7. MULLANE, K.M., N. READ, J.A. SALMON *et al.* 1984. Role of leukocytes in acute myocardial infarction in anesthetized dogs: Relationship to myocardial salvage by anti-inflammatory drugs. J. Pharmacol. Exp. Ther. **228:** 510–522.
8. LUCCHESI, B.R. 1994. Complement, neutrophils and free radicals: mediators of reperfusion injury. [Review]. Arzneim-Forsch./Drug Res. **44:** 420–432.
9. LEFER, A.M. 1995. Role of selectins in myocardial ischemia-reperfusion injury. [Review]. Ann. Thorac. Surg. **60:** 773–777.
10. LEFER, A.M., P.S. TSAO, D.J. LEFER *et al.* 1991. Role of endothelial dysfunction in the pathogenesis of reperfusion injury after myocardial ischemia. FASEB J. **5:** 2029–2034.
11. TSAO, P.S., N. AOKI, D.J. LEFER *et al.* 1990. Time course of endothelial dysfunction

and myocardial injury during myocardial ischemia and reperfusion in the cat. Circulation **82:** 1402–1412.

12. Tsao, P.S. & A.M. Lefer. 1990. Time course and mechanism of endothelial dysfunction in isolated ischemic- and hypoxic-perfused rat hearts. Am. J. Physiol. **259:** H1660–H1666.
13. Dignan, R.J., C.M. Dyke, A.S. Abd-Elfattah *et al.* 1992. Coronary artery endothelial cell and smooth muscle dysfunction after global myocardial ischemia. Ann. Thorac. Surg. **53:** 311–317.
14. Nakanishi, K., Z.-Q. Zhao, J. Vinten-Johansen *et al.* 1994. Coronary artery endothelial dysfunction after ischemia, blood cardioplegia, and reperfusion. Ann. Thorac. Surg. **58:** 191–199.
15. Guo, J.-P., T. Murohara, M. Buerke *et al.* 1996. Direct measurement of nitric oxide release from vascular endothelial cells. J. Appl. Physiol. **81:** 774–779.
16. Engelman, D.T., M. Watanabe, R.M. Engleman *et al.* 1995. Constitutive nitric oxide release is impaired after ischemia and reperfusion. J. Thorac. Cardiovasc. Surg. **110:** 1047–1053.
17. Ma, X.-L., A.S. Weyrich, D.J. Lefer *et al.* 1993. Diminished basal nitric oxide release after myocardial ischemia and reperfusion promotes neutrophil adherence to coronary endothelium. Circ. Res. **72:** 403–412.
18. Lefer, A.M., X.-L. Ma, A. Weyrich *et al.* 1993. Endothelial dysfunction and neutrophil adherence as critical events in the development of reperfusion injury. Agents Actions Suppl **41:** 127–135.
19. VanBenthuysen, K.M., I.F. McMurtry & L.D. Horwitz. 1987. Reperfusion after acute coronary occlusion in dogs impairs endothelium-dependent relaxation to acetylcholine and augments contractile reactivity in vitro. J. Clin. Invest. **79:** 265–274.
20. Nakanishi, K., J. Vinten-Johansen, D.J. Lefer *et al.* 1992. Intracoronary L-arginine during reperfusion improves endothelial function and reduces infarct size. Am. J. Physiol. **263:** H1650–H1658.
21. Lefer, D.J., K. Nakanishi, J. Vinten-Johansen *et al.* 1992. Cardiac venous endothelial dysfunction after myocardial ischemia and reperfusion in dogs. Am. J. Physiol. **263:** H850–H856.
22. Sobey, C.G., G.J. Dusting, H.J. Grossman *et al.* 1990. Impaired vasodilation of epicardial coronary arteries and resistance vessels following myocardial ischemia and reperfusion in anesthetized dogs. Cor. Art. Dis. **1:** 363–374.
23. Kaeffer, N., V. Richard, A. Francois *et al.* 1996. Preconditioning prevents chronic reperfusion-induced coronary endothelial dysfunction in rats. Am. J. Physiol. **271:** H842–H849.
24. Lefer, D.J., K. Nakanishi, W.E. Johnston *et al.* 1993. Antineutrophil and myocardial protection actions of a novel nitric oxide donor after acute myocardial ischemia and reperfusion in dogs. Circulation **88:** 2337–2350.
25. Giraldez, R.R., A. Panda, Y. Xia *et al.* 1997. Decreased nitric-oxide synthase activity causes impaired endothelium-dependent relaxation in the postischemic heart. J. Biol. Chem. **272:** 21420–21426.
26. Lorant, D.E., K.D. Patel, T.M. McIntyre *et al.* 1991. Coexpression of GMP-140 and PAF by endothelium stimulated by histamine or thrombin: a juxtacrine system for adhesion and activation of neutrophils. J. Cell Biol. **115:** 223–234.
27. Sluiter, W., A. Pietersma, J.M.J. Lamers *et al.* 1993. Leukocyte adhesion molecules on the vascular endothelium: their role in the pathogenesis of cardiovascular disease and the mechanisms underlying their expression. J. Cardiovasc. Pharmacol. **22** (Suppl 4): S37–S44.
28. Weyrich, A.S., M. Buerke, K.H. Albertine *et al.* 1995. Time course of coronary vascular endothelial adhesion molecule expression during reperfusion of the ischemic feline myocardium. J. Leukocyte Biol. **57:** 45–55.
29. Bienvenu, K. & D.N. Granger. 1993. Molecular determinants of shear-rate dependent leukocyte adhesion in postcapillary venules. Am. J. Physiol. **264:** H1504–H1508.
30. Geng, J.-G., M.P. Bevilacqua, K.L. Moore *et al.* 1990. Rapid neutrophil adhesion to activated endothelium mediated by GMP-140. Nature **343:** 757–760.

31. DAVENPECK, K.L., T.W. GAUTHIER, K.H. ALBERTINE *et al.* 1994. Role of P-selectin in microvascular leukocyte-endothelial interaction in splanchnic ischemia-reperfusion. Am. J. Physiol. **267:** H622–630.
32. WEYRICH, A.S., X.-L. MA, D.J. LEFER *et al.* 1993. In vivo neutralization of P-selectin protects feline heart and endothelium in myocardial ischemia and reperfusion injury. J. Clin. Invest. **91:** 2620–2629.
33. JEROME, S.N., M. DORE, J.C. PAULSON *et al.* 1994. P-selectin and ICAM-1-dependent adherence reactions: role in the genesis of postischemic no-reflow. Am. J. Physiol. **266:** H1316–1321.
34. CHEN, L.Y., W.W. NICHOLS, J.B. HENDRICKS *et al.* 1994. Monoclonal antibody to P-selectin (PB1.3) protects against myocardial reperfusion injury in the dog. Cardiovasc. Res. **28:** 1414–1422.
35. KUBES, P., M. JUTILA & D. PAYNE. 1995. Therapeutic potential of inhibiting leukocyte rolling in ischemia/reperfusion. J. Clin. Invest. **95:** 2510–2519.
36. MOORE, K.L., K.D. PATEL, R.E. BRUEHL *et al.* 1995. P-selectin glycoprotein ligand-1 mediates rolling of human neutrophils on P-selectin. J. Cell Biol. **128:** 661–671.
37. BUERKE, M., A.S. WEYRICH, T. MUROHARA *et al.* 1994. Humanized monoclonal antibody DREG-200 directed against L-selectin protects in feline myocardial reperfusion injury. J. Pharmacol. Exp. Ther. **271:** 134–142.
38. MA, X.-L., A.S. WEYRICH, D.J. LEFER *et al.* 1993. Monoclonal antibody to L-selectin attenuates neutrophil accumulation and protects ischemic reperfused cat myocardium. Circulation **88:** 649–658.
39. MA, X.-L., P.S. TSAO & A.M. LEFER. 1991. Antibody to CD-18 exerts endothelial and cardiac protective effects in myocardial ischemia and reperfusion. J. Clin. Invest. **88:** 1237–1243.
40. KUKIELKA, G.L., H.K. HAWKINS, L. MICHAEL *et al.* 1993. Regulation of intercellular adhesion molecule-1 (ICAM-1) in ischemic and reperfused canine myocardium. J. Clin. Invest. **92:** 1504–1516.
41. YOUKER, K.A., H.K. HAWKINS, G.L. KUKIELKA *et al.* 1994. Molecular evidence for induction of intracellular adhesion molecule-1 in the viable border zone associated with ischemia-reperfusion injury of the dog heart. Circulation **89:** 2736–2746.
42. ZHAO, Z.-Q., D.J. LEFER, H. SATO *et al.* 1997. Monoclonal antibody to ICAM-1 preserves postischemic blood flow and reduces infarct size after ischemia-reperfusion in rabbit. J. Leukocyte Biol. **62:** 292–300.
43. IOCULANO, M., F. SQUADRITO, D. ALTAVILLA *et al.* 1994. Antibodies against intercellular adhesion molecule 1 protect against myocardial ischaemia-reperfusion injury in rat. Eur. J. Pharmacol. **264:** 143–149.
44. DAVENPECK, K.L., T.W. GAUTHIER & A.M. LEFER. 1994. Inhibition of endothelial-derived nitric oxide promotes P-selectin expression and actions in the rat microcirculation [see comments]. Gastroenterology **107:** 1050–1058.
45. DECATERINA, R., O. LIBBY, H. PENG *et al.* 1995. Nitric oxide decreases cytokine-induced endothelial activation. J. Clin. Invest. **96:** 60–68.
46. ARMSTEAD, V.E., A.G. MINCHENKO, R.A. SCHUHL *et al.* 1997. Regulation of P-selectin expression in human endothelial cells by nitric oxide. Am. J. Physiol. Heart Circ Physiol. **42:** H740–H746.
47. WOOLFSON, R.G., V.C. PATEL, G.H. NEILD *et al.* 1995. Inhibition of nitric oxide synthesis reduces infarct size by an adenosine-dependent mechanism. Circulation **91:** 1545–1551.
48. SCHULZ, R., R. WAMBOLT *et al.* 1995. Inhibition of nitric oxide synthesis protects the isolated working rabbit heart from ischaemia-reperfusion injury. Cardiovasc. Res. **30:** 432–439.
49. SUN, W. & C.L. WAINWRIGHT. 1997. The role of nitric oxide in modulating ischaemia-induced arrhythmias in rats. J. Cardiovasc. Pharmacol. **29:** 554–562.
50. PABLA, R. & M.J. CURTIS. 1996. Endogenous protection against reperfusion-induced ventricular fibrillation: role of neuronal versus non-neuronal sources of nitric oxide and species dependence in the rat versus rabbit isolated heart. J. Mol. Cell Cardiol. **28:** 2097–2110.
51. WILLIAMS, M.W., C.S. TAFT, S. RAMNAUTH *et al.* 1995. Endogenous nitric oxide (NO) protects against ischaemia- reperfusion injury in the rabbit. Cardiovasc. Res. **30:** 79–86.

52. PABLA, R. & M.J. CURTIS. 1996. Effect of endogenous nitric oxide on cardiac systolic and diastolic function during ischemia and reperfusion in the rat isolated perfused heart. J. Mol. Cell Cardiol. **28:** 2111–2121.
53. PABLA, R., A.J. BUDA, D.M. FLYNN *et al.* 1996. Nitric oxide attenuates neutrophil-mediated myocardial contractile dysfunction after ischemia and reperfusion. Circ. Res. **78:** 65–72.
54. HOSHIDA, S., N. YAMASHITA, J. IGARASHI *et al.* 1995. Nitric oxide synthase protects the heart against ischemia-reperfusion injury in rabbits. J. Pharmacol. Exp. Ther. **274:** 413–418.
55. PATEL, V.C., R.G. WOOLFSON, G.H. NEILD & D.M. YELLON. 1993. Reduction of infarct size following nitric oxide inhibition is due to compensatory adenosine release. Circulation **88:** I-330(Abstract).
56. PATEL, V.C., D.M. YELLON, K.J. SINGH *et al.* 1993. Inhibition of nitric oxide limits infarct size in the in situ rabbit heart. Biochem. Biophys. Res. Commun. **194:** 234–238.
57. PALMER, R.M.J., D.D. REES, D.S. ASHTON *et al.* 1988. L-arginine is the physiological precursor for the formation of nitric oxide in endothelium-dependent relaxation. Biochem. Biophys. Res. Commun. **153:** 1251– 1256.
58. WEYRICH, A.S., X.-L. MA & A.M. LEFER. 1992. The role of L-arginine in ameliorating reperfusion injury after myocardial ischemia in the cat. Circulation **86:** 279–288.
59. JOHNSON, G., III, P.S. TSAO, D. MULLOY *et al.* 1990. Cardioprotective effects of acidified sodium nitrite in myocardial ischemia with reperfusion. J. Pharmacol. Exp. Ther. **252:** 35–41.
60. JOHNSON, G., III, P.S. TSAO & A.M. LEFER. 1991. Cardioprotective effects of authentic nitric oxide in myocardial ischemia with reperfusion. Crit. Care Med. **19:** 244–252.
61. SIEGFRIED, M.R., J. ERHARDT, T. RIDER *et al.* 1992. Cardioprotection and attenuation of endothelial dysfunction by organic nitric oxide donors in myocardial ischemia-reperfusion. J. Pharmacol. Exp. Ther. **260:** 668–675.
62. LEFER, D.J., K. NAKANISHI & J. VINTEN-JOHANSEN. 1993. Endothelial and myocardial cell protection by a cysteine-containing nitric oxide donor after myocardial ischemia and reperfusion. J. Cardiovasc. Pharmacol. **22:** S34–S43.
63. DELYANI, J.A., T.O. NOSSULI, R. SCALIA *et al.* 1996. S-nitrosylated tissue-type plasminogen activator protects against myocardial ischemia/reperfusion injury in cats: role of the endothelium. J. Pharmacol. Exp. Ther. **279:** 1174–1180.
64. PABLA, R., A.J. BUDA, D.M. FLYNN *et al.* 1995. Intracoronary nitric oxide improves postischemic coronary blood flow and myocardial contractile function. Am. J. Physiol. **269:** H1113–H1121.

Nitric Oxide Prevents Myoglobin/*tert*-Butyl Hydroperoxide–Induced Inhibition of Ca^{2+} Transport in Skeletal and Cardiac Sarcoplasmic Reticulum

ELIZABETH V. MENSHIKOVA,[a] VLADIMIR B. RITOV,[b]
NIKOLAJ V. GORBUNOV,[b] GUY SALAMA,[a] H. GREGG CLAYCAMP,[b]
AND VALERIAN E. KAGAN[b–d]

Departments of [a]Cell Biology and Physiology, [b]Environmental and Occupational Health, and [c]Pharmacology, University of Pittsburgh, Pittsburgh, Pennsylvania 15238, USA

ABSTRACT: Interaction of hydrogen peroxide or organic hydroperoxides with hemoproteins is known to produce oxoferryl hemoprotein species that act as very potent oxidants. Since skeletal and cardiac muscle cells contain high concentrations of myoglobin this reaction may be an important mechanism of initiation or enhancement of oxidative stress, which may impair their Ca^{2+} transport systems. Using skeletal and cardiac sarcoplasmic reticulum (SR) vesicles, we demonstrated by EPR the formation of alkoxyl radicals and protein-centered peroxyl radicals in the presence of myoglobin (Mb) and *tert*-butyl hydroperoxide (t-BuOOH). The low temperature EPR signal of the radicals was characterized by a major feature at $g = 2.016$ and a shoulder at $g = 2.036$. In the presence of SR vesicles, the magnitude of the protein-centered peroxyl radical signal decreased, suggesting that the radicals were involved in oxidative modification of SR membranes. This was accompanied by SR membrane oxidative damage, as evidenced by accumulation of 2-thiobarbituric acid–reactive substances (TBARS) and the inhibition of Ca^{2+} transport. We have shown that nitric oxide (NO), reacting with redox-active heme iron, can prevent peroxyl radical formation activated by Mb/t-BuOOH. Incubation of SR membranes with an NO donor, PAPA/NO (a non-thiol compound that releases NO) at 200–500 μM completely prevented the t-BuOOH–dependent production of peroxyl radicals and formation of TBARS, and thus protected against oxidative inhibition of Ca^{2+} transport.

INTRODUCTION

Metabolic activation of molecular oxygen by hemoproteins (e.g., cytochrome P_{450}, cytochrome oxidase, peroxidases, hemoglobin, and myoglobin) produces extremely potent oxidants—oxoferryl species.[1,2] Oxoferryl hemoproteins can be detected as catalytic intermediates of enzymatic reactions[3] or found in normal human blood (oxoferryl species formed via autoxidation of hemoglobin).[4] The formation and reactivity of oxoferryl hemoglobin and myoglobin, which occur as a result of in-

[d]Address correspondence to: Dr. Valerian E. Kagan, Department of Environmental and Occupational Health, University of Pittsburgh, 260 Kappa Drive, RIDC Park, Pittsburgh, PA 15238; Telephone: (412) 967-6516; Fax: (412) 624-1020.

teraction of these hemoproteins with H_2O_2 or lipid (organic) hydroperoxides, have been proposed as contributors to the oxidative stress associated with human diseases.[5,6] In particular, formation of oxoferryl myoglobin was found in the hearts subjected to global, no-flow ischemia, followed by reperfusion under anoxic conditions.[7] It has been suggested that the peroxidative activity of oxoferryl Mb during oxygenated reperfusion may trigger accumulation of different radicals and lead to cellular damage (i.e., play a role in reperfusion injury) if this hypervalent form of myoglobin is not reduced.[8] Different physiologically relevant reductants (ascorbate, vitamin E, and its homologues, ergothioneine and other thiols, and urate) were found to reduce oxoferryl Mb[9–11] and to protect against ischemia-reperfusion injury in the myocardium.[12]

We have recently demonstrated in simple model systems that NO can reduce oxoferryl-derived radicals of Mb and hemoglobin and prevent *tert*-butyl hydroperoxide(t-BuOOH)–induced peroxidations.[13] Moreover, we found that NO protected human erythroleukemia K/VP.5 cells, which contain relatively high concentrations of endogenous hemoglobin, against oxidative stress and damage induced by organic hydroperoxides via nitrosylation of intracellular heme-iron catalytic sites.[14] Based on these findings, we hypothesized that the interaction of NO with oxoferryl hemoproteins represents an important antioxidant function of NO in hemoprotein-rich cells. Since cardiac and skeletal muscles contain high concentrations of Mb[15] it is reasonable to suggest that NO may exert its antioxidant function in these cells.

In the present work, we studied the effects of NO on Mb/t-BuOOH–dependent production of oxoferryl-derived radicals and on oxidative damage to skeletal and cardiac membranes. We chose to use isolated fractions of skeletal and cardiac sarcoplasmic reticulum as targets of oxidative attack and protection by NO because of the central roles these membrane structures play in both physiological regulation of Ca^{2+} homeostasis in muscles and its disturbances in disease.

MATERIALS AND METHODS

Membrane Preparations

The unfractionated skeletal SR vesicles were isolated from rabbit skeletal muscle as described by Abramson and colleagues.[16] The vesicle preparations were frozen at −77°C in 0.29 M sucrose, 3 mM NaN_3, and 10 mM imidazole HCl (pH 6.9 at 4°C) and kept in liquid nitrogen until their use.

The cardiac SR vesicles were isolated from canine ventricular tissue as described by Prabhu and Salama.[17] A protease inhibitor, leupeptin (1 μg/ml), was added to all of the solutions that were used to isolate SR vesicles. The vesicle preparations were frozen with liquid nitrogen in 0.29 M sucrose, 3 mM NaN_3, and 10 mM imidazole HCl (pH 6.9 at 4°C) and kept in liquid nitrogen until their use.

Antipyrylazo III–Based Measurement of Ca^{2+} Transport

Ca^{2+} uptake and efflux from SR vesicles was measured spectrophotometrically through the differential absorptional changes of the metallochromic indicator antipyrylazo III (AP III), an indicator of extravesicular free Ca^{2+}.[18] Differential absorption was measured at 720–790 nm with a time-sharing dual wavelength spectrophotometer (SDB-3A, University of Pennsylvania, Biomedical Instrumentation, Philadelphia, PA). The measurements were performed in a thermostated cuvette under continuous stirring. For skeletal SR vesicles, Ca^{2+} uptake was measured in the incubation medium containing 100 mM KCl, 0.2 mM AP III, 1 mM $MgCl_2$, 0.1 mM ATP, 2.5 U/ml creatine kinase (CK), 4 mM phosphocreatine (CP), and 20 mM HEPES, pH 7.0 (37°C). CK and CP provided an ATP-regenerating system to maintain a constant concentration of ATP and free Mg^{2+} during Ca^{2+} transport experiments. Ca^{2+} transport was initiated by adding Ca^{2+} (12 μM) and then ATP. Once Ca^{2+} sequestration was complete, the Ca^{2+} ionophore A 23187 was added to the reaction mixture to abolish any existing Ca^{2+} gradients and to determine the amount of releasable intravesicular Ca^{2+}. Calibration was performed by adding 12 nmoles of Ca^{2+} to the incubation medium.

For cardiac SR vesicles, Ca^{2+} transport was measured in a reaction medium containing 100 mM KCl, 38 mM P_i, 0.2 mM AP III, 3 mM NaN_3, 1 mM $MgCl_2$, 0.5 mM ATP, 2.5 U/ml CK, 4 mM CP, and 20 mM HEPES, pH 7.0 (37°C). A single sample of cardiac SR (0.1–0.2 mg) was added to the cuvette (1 ml) and uptake of background Ca^{2+} in the reaction medium was monitored. Two aliquots of $CaCl_2$ (12 μM) were then added to calibrate the absorption changes of AP III and to actively load the vesicles. Upon completion of Ca^{2+} uptake, the Ca^{2+} ionophore A 23187 was added to the reaction mixture to abolish any existing Ca^{2+} gradients and to determine the amount of releasable intravesicular Ca^{2+}. Calibration was performed by adding 12 nmoles of Ca^{2+} to the incubation medium.

Measurements of Ca^{2+}-ATPase Activity

Ca^{2+}-ATPase activity was measured pH-metrically by monitoring the time course of acidification of a weakly buffered incubation medium. The maximal shift of pH value of incubation medium during ATPase reaction hydrolysis did not exceed 0.025 ΔpH. The measurements were performed in a thermostated cuvette under continuous stirring. To prevent the accumulation of Ca^{2+} by SR vesicles and the inhibition of Ca^{2+}-ATPase by intravesicular Ca^{2+}, the Ca^{2+} ionophore A23187 (2 μg/ml) was added to the incubation medium. ATPase activity of SR membranes was measured in the incubation medium (2 ml) containing 100 mM KCl, 2 mM $MgCl_2$, 2 mM ATP, 3 mM NaN_3, 25–50 μg/ml of skeletal SR, and 2 mM HEPES, pH 7.0, 37°C. Mg^{2+}-dependent, Ca^{2+}-stimulated ATPase activity was determined as the difference between total (with 50 μM $CaCl_2$) and "basic" (with 1 mM EGTA) ATPase activities. Free Ca^{2+} concentrations were calculated according to a computer program of A. Fabiato.[19]

Preparation of Met-Myoglobin

All buffers were prepared free of metals with deionized H_2O double-distilled from quartz glassware. Buffers was stirred overnight in the presence of Chelex-100 ion-exchange resin (Bio-Rad, Richmond, Ca). Metmyoglobin (metMb) was prepared by oxidizing horse heart Mb in 100 mM phosphate buffer, pH 7.4, with a 5% molar excess of potassium ferricyanide in the same buffer.[20] Ferrocyanide and excess ferricyanide were removed by passing the metMb solution through a Sephadex PD-10 G-25 column (Pharmacia LKB, Uppsala, Sweden) equilibrated with 100 mM phosphate buffer, pH 7.4.

Preparation of Oxy-Myoglobin

A solution of horse heart Mb was mixed with twofold excess of $Na_2S_2O_4$, and incubated for 10 min at room temperature. The resultant solution was filtered through a Sephadex G-25 column, and the Mb solution was dialyzed against 100 mM phosphate buffer (pH 7.4 at 4°C) for 14 h.[20] This oxy-myoglobin (oxyMb) solution was divided into small aliquots and stored at –70°C until needed.

Spectrophotometric Measurement

Spectra of Mb in the range 350–700 nm were measured in a 1.0 cm pathlength and 1.4 ml volume quartz cell on Shimadzu UV160U spectrophotometer (Kyoto, Japan).

Incubation of Skeletal and Cardiac SR Vesicles with t-BuOOH, Myoglobin, and PAPA-NONOate

Skeletal or cardiac SR vesicles (2–3 mg protein/ml) were incubated for 0–40 min in the absence or presence of 500 μM PAPA-NONOate that releases NO with a half-life of 76 min, in the medium containing 100 mM KCl, 1 mM $MgCl_2$, 160 μM t-BuOOH, 100 μM oxyMb or metMb, and 20 mM HEPES (pH 7.0, 37°C).

EPR Measurement

Samples (250 μl) were placed into a Teflon tube (3.7 mm internal diameter) and frozen in liquid nitrogen, then removed from the tube to perform EPR measurements. For spectrum recording, each sample was placed in an EPR quartz tube (5 mm internal diameter) in such a way that the entire sample was within the effective microwave irradiation area. EPR measurements were performed on a JEOL-RE1X spectrometer with a variable temperature controller (Research Specialists, Chicago, IL). The spectra were recorded at −170°C, 320 mT center field, 10 mW power, 0.1 mT field modulation, 25 mT sweep width, 500 receiver gain, 0.1 sec time constant. The *g* factor values were determined relative to external standards, containing Mn^{2+} (in MgO). Analog signals were converted into digital form and imported to an IBM computer. Intensity of the signals was calculated using a program developed by David Duling.[21]

HPLC Assay of Lipid P14eroxidation

Lipid peroxidation was measured by HPLC separation and fluorescence detection of malondialdehyde-thiobarbituric acid (MDA-TBA) adduct.[22] SR membranes (0.2–0.5 mg protein/ml) were incubated for 30 min with 100 mM KCl, 1 mM $MgCl_2$, and 20 mM HEPES (pH 7.0 at 37°C) in the presence of 100 μM oxyMb and 160 μM t-BuOOH. Then 500 μM PAPA-NONOate (as NO donor) was added to some samples. The reaction was stopped by addition of 100 μM butylated hydroxytoluene (BHT) and by placing samples on ice. Aliquots of 50 μl were taken and mixed with 0.75 ml of 440 mM phosphoric acid, 0.25 ml 42 mM thiobarbituric acid (TBA), and 0.45 ml distilled water (final volume 1.5 ml). The mixture was heated at 95°C for 60 min and after cooling, the samples were extracted by 1-butanol. Aliquots of 1-butanol extracts were injected into a C-18 reverse-phase column that was eluted by mobile phase composed of 100 ml of CH_3OH, 300 ml of H_2O, and 0.17 ml H_3PO_4 (85%) at

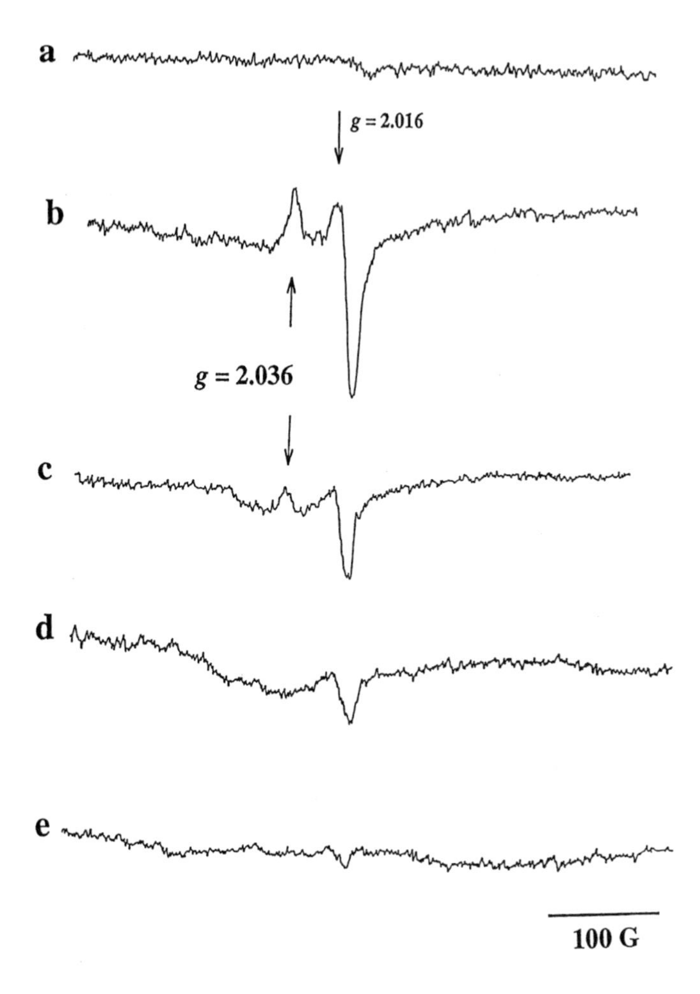

FIGURE 1. Low temperature EPR spectra obtained from solutions of oxyMb and/or t-BuOOH in the absence and presence of skeletal SR membranes. **(a)** control solution (150 μg/ml SR membranes and 150 μM t-BuOOH in HEPES buffer, pH 7.2); **(b)** 100 μM oxyMb and 150 μM t-BuOOH in HEPES buffer, pH 7.2; **(c)** same as **b**, except in the presence of 150 μg/ml SR membranes; **(d)** same as **c**, but in the presence of 1 mg/ml SR membranes; **(e)** same as **c**, except in the presence of 5 mg/ml SR membranes. Incubation conditions: SR membranes from skeletal muscles and/or oxyMb were incubated with t-BuOOH for 15 min in 20 mM HEPES (pH 7.2) containing 100 mM KCl, 1 mM $MgCl_2$, 15 μM $CaCl_2$, 1 mM ATP, 5 mM CP, 3 IU/ml CK, and 0.05 mM deferoxamine mesylate (DFO). The spectra were recorded at −170°C, 320 mT center field, 10 mW power, 0.1 mT field modulation, 500 receiver gain, 0.1 sec time constant. The *g* factor values were determined relative to external standards, containing Mn^{2+} (in MgO). Analog signals were converted into digital form and imported to an IBM computer. Intensity of the signals was calculated using a program developed by David Duling.[21] All spectra (except **c**) were recorded at scan rate 10.25 mT/min. Spectrum **c** was recorded at scan rate 6.25 mT/min.

a flow rate of 1 ml/min. A Shimadzu HPLC system (model LC-600) equipped with a fluorescence detector (model RF-551) was used. Fluorescence of MDA-TBA adduct in eluates was monitored by emission at 560 nm after excitation at 530 nm. Fluorescence data were processed and stored in digital form with Shimadzu EZChrom software.

Protein Determination

Protein concentration in SR membrane suspension was determined with the Bio-Rad Protein Assay kit with bovine serum albumin as a standard.

Statistical Analysis

Results were obtained from triplicate determinations, expressed as mean ± SD. Statistical analyses were performed using two-way analysis of variance (ANOVA). A value of $p < 0.05$ was considered significant.

Materials

Hearts from mongrel dogs (used as donor animals in liver transplantation experiments) were provided by the Department of Surgery (Pittsburgh University Medical Center) after the animals were sacrificed by lethal anesthetic injection. NOC-15 [(Z)-1-[-N-(3-ammoniopropyl)-N-(n-propyl)amino]-diazen-1-ium-1,2-diolate], PAPA-NONOate] was obtained from Cayman Chemical Co. (Ann Arbor, MI). Sephadex G-25 columns were obtained from Pharmacia-LKB (Uppsala, Sweden). Antipyrylazo III was purchased from ICN Biochemicals (Cleveland, Ohio). Other chemicals were obtained from Sigma Chemical Co. (St. Louis, MO).

RESULTS

EPR Spectra Resulting from Interaction of Myoglobin with t-BuOOH and NO

Neither t-BuOOH alone nor oxyMb alone gave any detectable signals in the low-temperature EPR spectra (FIGS. 1 and 2). Incubation of t-BuOOH with oxyMb resulted in the formation of oxoferryl-Mb–derived free radical species (FIGS. 1 and 2). When t-BuOOH (150 μM) was added to Mb-FeII(O_2) (100 μM) a broad two-line anisotropic EPR signal was observed (FIGS. 1 and 2). The g values at zero crossing point and a low-field maximum observed in the EPR spectra were 2.016 and 2.036, respectively. This EPR signal had the profile and characteristic features of protein-centered peroxyl radicals, most likely the tryptophan-centered peroxyl radical. The magnitude of the t-BuOOH/oxyMb EPR signal was less in the presence of skeletal SR membranes, than in the absence of the membranes (FIG. 1, c). The decrease of the signal was proportional to the concentration of SR membranes in the incubation system (compare FIG. 1, c–e) suggesting that the radicals were involved in oxidative modification of SR membranes. This was accompanied by SR membrane oxidative damage as evidenced by accumulation of TBARS and the inhibition of Ca^{2+} transport (*vide infra*).

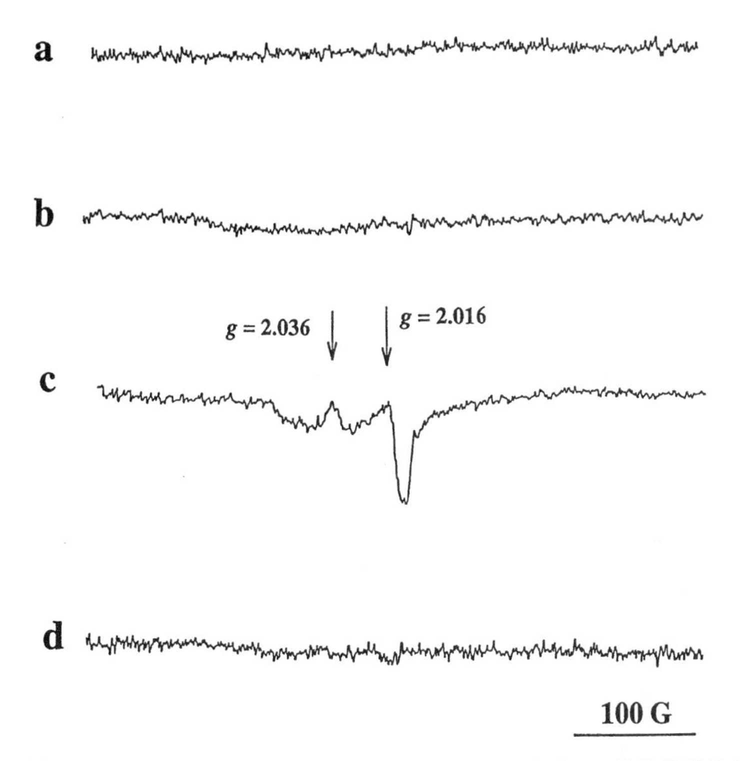

FIGURE 2. Low temperature EPR spectra obtained from solutions of Mb-FeII(O_2) and/or t-BuOOH in the absence and presence of skeletal SR membranes and NO donor PAPA-NONOate (NOC-15). SR membranes from skeletal muscles and/or oxyMb, and/or NO donor NOC-15 were incubated with t-BuOOH for 15 min (All conditions as in FIGURE 1). **(a)** control solution (150 μg/ml SR membranes and 150 μM t-BuOOH); **(b)** same as **a**, but in the absence of t-BuOOH and in the presence of 100 μM oxyMb; **(c)** same as **b**, except in the presence of 150 μM t-BuOOH; **(d)** same as **b**, but in the presence of 500 μM NOC-15.

We next studied effects of NO on oxoferryl-radicals produced by t-BuOOH/oxyMb in the presence of SR membranes. Control measurements demonstrated that neither t-BuOOH alone nor oxyMb alone causes formation of any detectable EPR signals in the presence of skeletal muscle SR membranes (FIG. 2, a,b). As was shown on FIGURE 2 (c), the combination of t-BuOOH and oxyMb gave a characteristic EPR signal of protein-centered peroxyl radical. Importantly, the generation of oxoferryl-derived radicals was completely prevented when an NO donor (PAPA-NONOate) was added to the incubation mixture containing skeletal SR membranes, t-BuOOH, and oxyMb (FIG. 2, d). In separate experiments, we demonstrated that PAPA-NONOate eliminated oxoferryl-radical EPR signals generated by t-BuOOH and oxyMb in the presence of cardiac SR membranes (data not shown). Combined, these results suggest that interaction of NO with oxyMb/t-BuOOH resulted in the reduction of oxoferryl–derived radicals similarly to that previously described for oxy-hemoglobin/t-BuOOH.[13,14] The anti-radical effect of NO was correlated with the protection

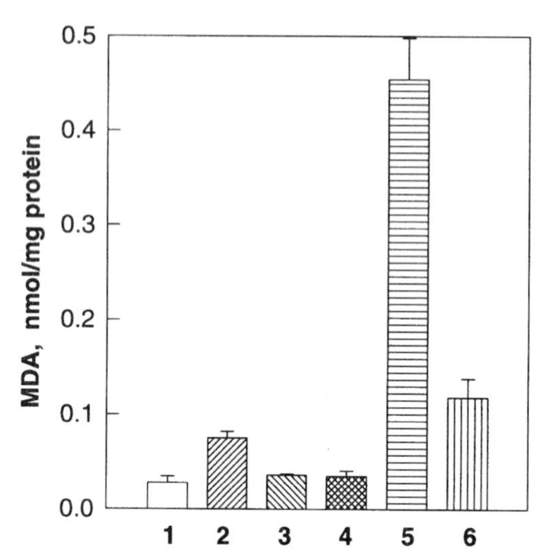

FIGURE 3. Accumulation of lipid peroxidation products in skeletal SR vesicles. Skeletal SR membranes (200 μg/ml) were incubated for 30 min at 37°C in the presence and in the absence of oxyMb (100 μM), t-BuOOH (150 μM), and PAPA-NONOate (500 μM). Lipid peroxidation was measured by HPLC separation and fluorescence detection of malondialdehyde-thiobarbituric acid (MDA-TBA) adduct (see *Materials and Methods*). (1) SR; (2) SR + oxyMb; (3) SR + PAPA-NONOate; (4) SR + t-BuOOH; (5) SR + oxyMb + t-BuOOH; (6) SR + oxyMb + t-BuOOH + PAPA-NONOate.

of SR membranes against oxidative damage induced by t-BuOOH/oxyMb (*vide infra*).

Effect of NO Donor on tert-*Butylhydroperoxide/Myoglobin–Induced Lipid Peroxidation in SR Membranes*

As shown above, the intensity of peroxyl radicals EPR signals generated in mixture of Mb-Fe(O_2)/t-BuOOH decreased in the presence of SR membranes (FIG. 1), suggesting that peroxyl radicals interacted with some components of the membranes. Therefore, we next studied lipid peroxidation in SR membranes using HPLC method with fluorescence detection of MDA-TBA adduct.[22] We found a significant accumulation of lipid peroxidation products in SR membranes incubated in the presence of Mb-Fe(O_2)/t-BuOOH. As shown in FIGURE 3, the incubation of skeletal SR membranes in presence of 160 μM t-BuOOH plus 100 μM Mb for 30 min at 37°C resulted in accumulation of approximately 0.5 nmol MDA per 1 mg SR membrane protein. The accumulation of MDA was prevented by addition of PAPA-NONOate (500 μM) to the incubation mixture.

Effect of tert-*Butylhydroperoxide/Myoglobin on Ca^{2+} Transport in Isolated SR Vesicles*

Absorptional changes of the metallochromic indicator antipyrylazo III were used to measure the effect of *tert*-BuOOH/Mb on Ca^{2+} accumulation by SR vesicles as

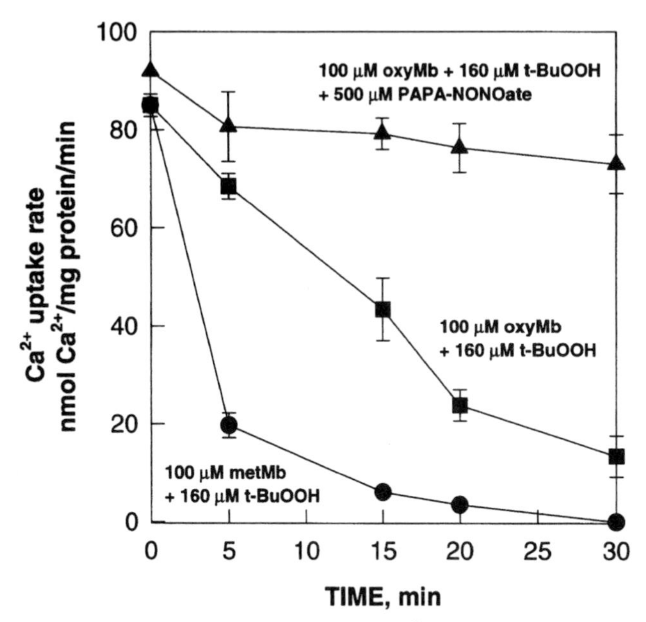

FIGURE 4. Nitric oxide prevents inhibition of Ca^{2+} transport produced by t-BuOOH/Mb in skeletal SR. Skeletal SR vesicles were pre-incubated with 100 μM oxyMb or 100 μM horse heart Mb and 160 μM t-BuOOH for 0–30 min at 37°C. Ca^{2+} transport across SR vesicles was determined by measuring extravesicular $[Ca^{2+}]_{free}$ through the differential absorption changes of AP III. Skeletal SR vesicles (0.2 mg protein) were suspended in the reaction medium containing CK, CP, and AP III. Two additions of Ca^{2+} were added to calibrate the response of AP III, then ATP was added to initiate active Ca^{2+} uptake. A23187 was added to measure the total releasable pool of Ca^{2+}. Initial Ca^{2+} uptake rates were calculated in the first two minutes.

described in *Methods*. In preliminary experiments we used the commercially available preparation of Mb from Sigma, which contains 20% of oxyMb and 80% of metMb. We found that the preincubation of SR vesicles in the presence of both Mb (100 μM) and t-BuOOH (160 μM) resulted in inhibition of skeletal SR Ca^{2+} uptake (FIG. 4). The inhibitory effect was observed when either oxy- or metMb were added to SR vesicles along with t-BuOOH (FIG. 4). Neither oxyMb or metMb alone nor t-BuOOH alone in indicated concentrations altered the rate or amounts of Ca^{2+} uptake by skeletal SR. The inhibition of skeletal SR Ca^{2+} uptake by oxoferryl-derived radicals was prevented by PAPA-NONOate (500 μM) (FIG. 4).

Qualitatively the same results were obtained with cardiac SR vesicles. t-BuOOH (160 μM) plus oxyMb (100 μM) caused a significant inhibition of Ca^{2+} uptake by CSR, most likely due to interaction of oxoferryl-derived radicals with critical components of SR membranes. Protection of protein thiols by DTT prevents inhibition of Ca^{2+} transport by t-BuOOH/Mb (FIG. 5). As shown in FIGURE 6 addition PAPA-NONOate (500 μM) to the incubation medium protected Ca^{2+} transport systems of cardiac SR membranes against free radical damage. t-BuOOH/Mb has been demonstrated to inhibit SR Ca^{2+}-ATPase in skeletal SR.[23] In line with these data, we also

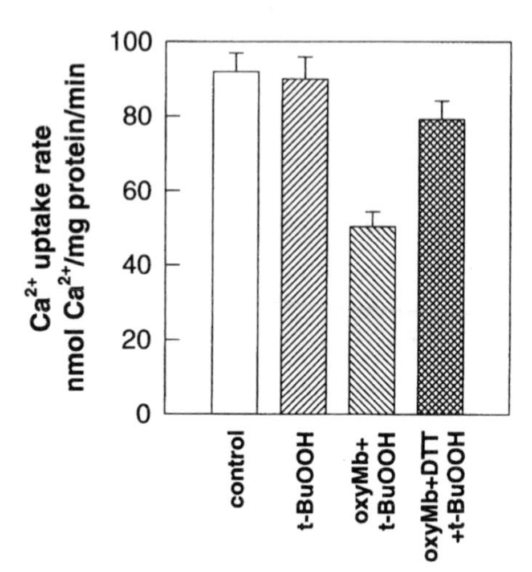

FIGURE 5. Dithiothreitol (DTT) prevents inhibition of Ca^{2+} transport produced by t-BuOOH/Mb in skeletal SR. Skeletal SR vesicles were pre-incubated with 100 μM oxyMb and/or 160 μM t-BuOOH in the presence and in the absence of 1 mM DTT for 15 min at 37°C. Ca^{2+} uptake was measured as in FIGURE 4. Initial Ca^{2+} uptake rates were calculated in the first two minutes.

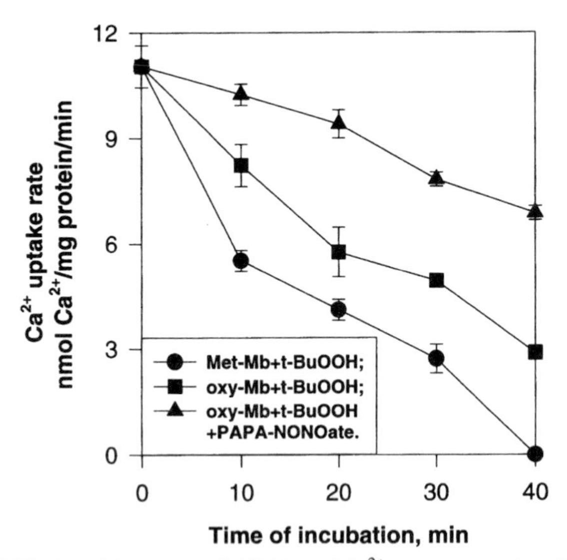

FIGURE 6. Nitric oxide prevents inhibition of Ca^{2+} transport produced by t-BuOOH/Mb in cardiac SR. Cardiac SR vesicles were pre-incubated with 100 μM oxyMb or 100 μM horse heart Mb and 160 μM t-BuOOH for 0–40 min at 37°C. Ca^{2+} uptake was measured as in *Materials and Methods*. Initial Ca^{2+} uptake rates were calculated in the first two minutes.

observed the inhibition of SR Ca^{2+}-ATPase by 40% of control when SR vesicles were incubated with t-BuOOH/Mb (FIG. 7). The inhibition of SR Ca^{2+} uptake by t-

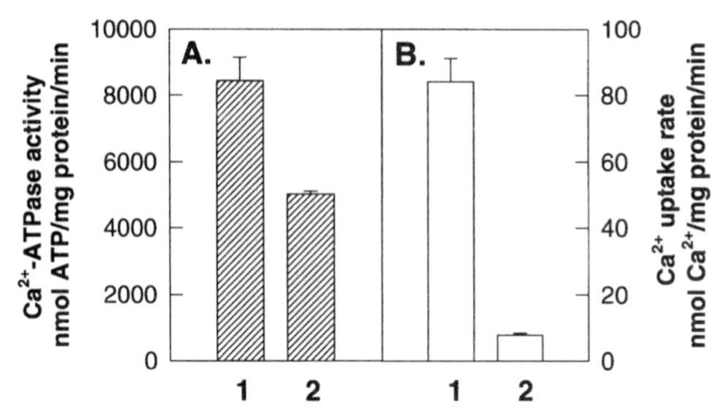

FIGURE 7. Effect of t-BuOOH/Mb on Ca^{2+}-ATPase activity and Ca^{2+} transport in skeletal SR vesicles. Skeletal SR vesicles were pre-incubated with 100 µM horse heart Mb and 160 µM t-BuOOH for 5 min at 37°C. Ca^{2+}-ATPase activity was measured pH-metrically by monitoring the time course of acidification of a weakly buffered incubation medium in the presence of Ca^{2+} ionophore A23187 (see *Materials and Methods*) (**A**). Ca^{2+} uptake was measured as in FIGURE 4 (**B**). Initial Ca^{2+} uptake rates were calculated in the first two minutes. (1) control; (2) Mb + t-BuOOH.

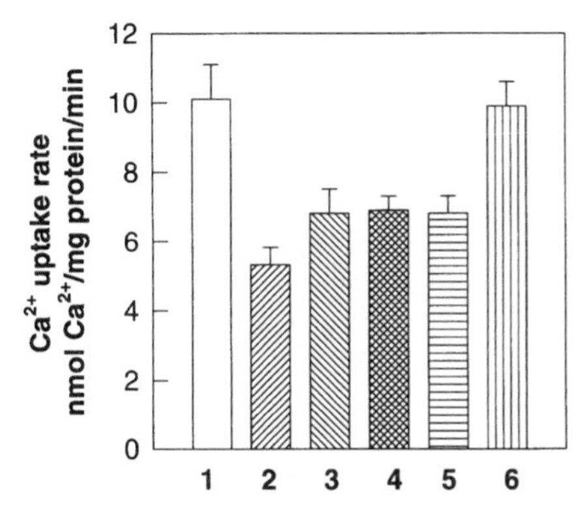

FIGURE 8. Effects of tetracaine, ruthenium red, and ryanodine on inhibition of Ca^{2+} transport produced by t-BuOOH/Mb in cardiac SR vesicles. Cardiac SR vesicles (0.2–0.4 mg/ml) were pre-incubated with 100 µM oxyMb and 160 µM t-BuOOH for 20 min at 37°C in the absence (2) and in the presence of 0.2 mM tetracaine (3), 10 µM ruthenium red (4), and 100 µM ryanodine (5). Ca^{2+} uptake was measured as in FIGURE 4. Initial Ca^{2+} uptake rates were calculated in the first two minutes. (1) SR; (2–5) SR + oxyMb + t-BuOOH; (6) 160 µM t-BuOOH.

BuOOH/Mb, however, can not be explained solely by the inhibition of Ca^{2+}-ATPase. Indeed, the same concentrations of t-BuOOH and Mb (500 µM t-BuOOH and 100 µM Mb, incubation 5 min at 37°C) caused 90% inhibition of Ca^{2+} uptake (FIG. 7).

The t-BuOOH/Mb-induced inhibition of cardiac SR Ca^{2+} uptake could be reversed to some extent by Ca^{2+} channel blockers—ruthenium red, tetracaine, and a high concentration of ryanodine (FIG. 8). This suggests that the t-BuOOH/Mb–induced inhibition of Ca^{2+} uptake was due at least in part to the activation of ryanodine-sensitive Ca^{2+} channels. The other cause of the t-BuOOH/Mb–induced inhibition of SR Ca^{2+} uptake could originate from peroxidation of SR membrane phospholipids. We found that incubation of SR membranes with t-BuOOH/Mb yielded approximately 0.5 nmol MDA per 1 mg membrane protein (FIG. 9). This level of MDA in the SR membranes is not sufficient to induce Ca^{2+} release from SR vesicles.[24]

DISCUSSION

Nitric oxide has been implicated in a number of diverse physiological processes, including smooth muscle relaxation, platelet inhibition, neurotransmission, and immunoregulation.[25–29] NO forms complexes with transition metals, binding in a linear or a bent mode depending on the metal complex. It binds readily to heme-containing proteins, such as hemoglobin, Mb, cytochrome *c*, and guanylyl cyclase. NO also interacts with iron in the iron-sulfur centers of various enzymes.[30] Among the important physiological reactions of NO is its interaction with oxyhemoglobin to produce the ferric form of hemoglobin, methemoglobin, and nitrate.[30] Another aspect of NO metabolism *in vivo* is the formation of a variety of high and low molecular weight nitrosothiols.[29,30]

Attention now focuses on the role of NO in free radical cytotoxic events. The ability of NO to interact with various oxygen radical species, iron-heme proteins, and thiols, assures that NO might play a role in the regulation of intracellular free radical reactions. There are, however, contradictions as to whether NO mediates or limits free radical–mediated tissue injury. Nitric oxide can act as both prooxidant, causing cytotoxic effects through oxidative damage of critical biomolecules, and as an antioxidant, protecting cells against oxidative damage. The antioxidant effect of NO was associated with its ability to scavenge lipid alkoxyl and peroxyl radicals.[31–34] Interaction of NO with hemoglobin and Mb may prevent hydroperoxide-induced formation of oxoferryl-hemoproteins, thus blocking subsequent generation of oxygen-derived reactive species and oxidative damage.[13,32,35] It has recently been demonstrated that NO was capable of inhibiting oxoferryl-induced oxidation in simple model systems, such as t-BuOOH/hemoglobin or t-BuOOH/Mb[13] as well as in erythroleukemia cells via nitrosylation of heme and non-heme iron.[14]

Nitric oxide is essential for maintenance of vascular tone.[36] Contradictory results were obtained during studies of NO effects in postischemic reperfusion injury. Ischemia increases the amount of NO in myocardium,[28] but the consequences of this increase for the postischemic restoration of heart contractility still remain undiscovered. Generation of superoxide during postischemic reperfusion opens the possibility for the formation of potent oxidant, peroxynitrite, in the reaction of superoxide with NO.[37] Modification of proteins and membrane phospholipids by peroxynitrite can aggravate the reperfusion injury. It has been suggested that concentration of NO is a crucial factor in tissue injury induced by ischemia and reperfusion.[38] High concentrations of oxyMb in myocardium probably prevent the buildup of peroxynitrite because practically all free NO in myocardium cells should be trapped by oxyMb.

It is also well documented that NO provides protection of cells against Fenton-type–mediated toxicity.[14,33,35] Our experiments in a model system including SR vesicles, Mb, and t-BuOOH confirm these observations. We found that interaction of Mb with t-BuOOH induced generation of reactive protein-centered peroxyl radicals that induced peroxidation of membrane phospholipids and thiols in Ca^{2+} dependent ATPase and in ryanodine receptors. The NO donor PAPA-NONOate was able to protect significantly against free radical damage of sarcoplasmic reticulum. Our results suggest that exogenous NO donors may represent a group of promising compounds for protecting the heart against damaging free radical events during postischemic reperfusion of the myocardium.

REFERENCES

1. Newmyer, S.L. & P.R. Ortiz de Montellano. 1995. Horseradish peroxidase His-42 → Ala, His-42 → Val, and Phe-41 → Ala mutants. Histidine catalysis and control of substrate access to the heme iron. J. Biol. Chem. **270**(33): 19430–19438.
2. Gunther, M.R., D.J. Kelman, J.T. Corbett & R.P. Mason. 1995. Self-peroxidation of metmyoglobin results in formation of an oxygen-reactive tryptophan-centered radical. J. Biol. Chem. **270**(27): 16075–16081.
3. Sucheta, A., K.E. Georgiadis & O. Einarsdottir. 1997. Mechanism of cytochrome c oxidase-catalyzed reduction of dioxygen to water: evidence for peroxy and ferryl intermediates at room temperature. Biochemistry **36**(3): 554–565.
4. Svistunenko D.A., R.P. Patel, S.V. Voloshchenko & M.T. Wilson. 1997. The globin-based free radical of ferryl hemoglobin is detected in normal human blood. J. Biol. Chem. **272**(11): 7114–7121.
5. Patel R.P., D.A. Svistunenko, V.M. Darley-Usmar & M.C. Symons. 1996. Redox cycling of human methaemoglobin by H_2O_2 yields persistent ferryl iron and protein based radicals. Free Radical Res. **25**(2): 117–123.
6. Giulivi, C. & K.J. Davies. 1994. Hydrogen peroxide-mediated ferrylhemoglobin generation *in vitro* and in red blood cells. Methods Enzymol. **231**: 490–496.
7. Arduini, A., L. Eddy & P. Hochstein. 1990. Detection of ferryl myoglobin in the isolated ischemic rat heart. Free Radical Biol. Med. **9**(6): 511–513.
8. Prasad, M.R., X. Liu, J.A. Rousou, R.M. Engelman, R. Jones, A. George & D.K. Das. 1992. Reduced free radical generation during reperfusion of hypothermically arrested hearts. Molec. Cell. Biochem. **111**(1-2): 97–102.
9. Arduini, A., G. Mancinelli, G.L. Radatti, W. Damonti, P. Hochstein & E. Cadenas. 1992. Reduction of sperm whale ferrylmyoglobin by endogenous reducing agents: potential reducible loci of ferrylmyoglobin. Free Radical Biol. Med. **13**(4): 449–454.
10. Giulivi, C. & E. Cadenas. 1993. Inhibition of protein radical reactions of ferrylmyoglobin by the water-soluble analog of vitamin E, Trolox C. Arch. Biochem. Biophys. **303**(1): 152–158.
11. Giulivi, C. & E. Cadenas. 1993. The reaction of ascorbic acid with different heme iron redox states of myoglobin. Antioxidant and prooxidant aspects. FEBS Lett. **332**(3): 287–290.
12. Arduini, A., L. Eddy & P. Hochstein. 1990. The reduction of ferryl myoglobin by ergothioneine: a novel function for ergothioneine. Arch. Biochem. Biophys. **281**(1): 41–43.
13. Gorbunov, N.V., A.N. Osipov, B.W. Day, B. Zayas-Rivera, V.E. Kagan & N.M. Elsayed. 1995. Reduction of ferrylmyoglobin and ferrylhemoglobin by nitric oxide: a protective mechanism against ferryl hemoprotein-induced oxidations. Biochemistry **34**: 6689–6699.
14. Gorbunov, N. V., J.C. Yalowich, A. Gaddam, P. Thampatty, V.B. Ritov, E.R. Kisin, N.M. Elsayed & V.E. Kagan. 1997. Nitric oxide prevents oxidative damage produced by *tert*-butyl hydroperoxide in erythroleukemia cells via nitrosylation of heme and non-heme iron. Electron paramagnetic resonance evidence. J. Biol. Chem. **272**(19): 12328–12341.

15. TAGGART, D.P., L. HADJINIKOLAS, J. HOOPER, J. ALBERT, M. KEMP, D. HUE, M. YACOUB & J.C. LINCOLN. 1997. Effects of age and ischemic times on biochemical evidence of myocardial injury after pediatric cardiac operations. J. Thorac. Cardiovasc. Surgery **113**(4)**:** 728–735.
16. ABRAMSON, J., J.L. TRIMM, L. WEDEN & G. SALAMA. 1983. Heavy metals induce rapid calcium release from sarcoplasmic reticulum vesicles isolated from skeletal muscle. Proc. Natl. Acad. Sci. USA **80:** 1526–1530.
17. PRABHU, S. & G. SALAMA. 1990. Reactive disulfide compounds induce Ca^{2+} release from cardiac sarcoplasmic reticulum. Arch. Biochem. Biophys. **28:** 275–283.
18. PRABHU, S. & G. SALAMA. 1990. The heavy metals Ag^{+} and Hg^{2+} trigger Ca^{2+} release from cardiac sarcoplasmic reticulum vesicles. Arch. Biochem. Biophys. **277:** 47–55.
19. FABIATO, A. 1979. Calculator programs for computing the composition of the solutions containing multiple metals and ligands used for experiments in skinned muscle cells. J. Physiol. (Paris) **75:** 463–505.
20. ARNELLE, D.R. & J.S. STAMLER. 1995. NO^{+}, $NO^{\cdot}$, and NO^{-} donation by S-nitrosothiols: Implications for regulation of physiological functions by S-nitrosylation and acceleration of disulfide formation. Arch. Biochem. Biophys. **318**(2)**:** 279–285.
21. DULING, D.R. 1994. Simulation of multiple isotropic spin-trap EPR spectra. J. Mag. Reson. B **104:** 105–110.
22. WONG, S.H.Y., J.A. KNIGHT, S.M. HOPFER, O. ZAHARIA, C.N. LEACH, JR. & F.W. SUNDERMAN. 1987. Lipoperoxides in plasma as measured by liquid-chromatographic separation of malondialdehyde-thiobarbituric acid adduct. Clin. Chem. **33:** 214–220.
23. COAN, C., J. Y., K. HIDEG & R.J. MEHLHORN. 1992. Protein sulfhydryls are protected from irreversible oxidation by conversion to mixed disulfides. Arch. Biochem. Biophys. **295:** 369–378.
24. KAGAN, V. E. 1983. Lipid Peroxidation in Biomembranes. CRC Press. Boca Raton, FL.
25. GARTHWAITE, J., S.L. CHARLES & R. CHESS-WILLIAMS. 1988. Endothelium-derived relaxing factor release on activation of NMDA receptors suggests role as intercellular messenger in the brain. Nature **336:** 385–388.
26. PALMER, R.M.J., A.G. FERRIGE & S. MONCADA. 1987. Nitric oxide release accounts for the biological activity of endothelium-derived relaxing factor. Nature **327:** 524–526.
27. VALLANCE, P., A. LEONE, A. CALVER, J. GOLLIER & S. MONCADA. 1992. Accumulation of an endogenous inhibitor of nitric oxide synthesis in chronic renal failure. Lancet **339:** 572–575.
28. DRAPIER, J.C., C. PELLAT & Y. HENRY. 1991. Generation of EPR-detectable nitrosyl-iron complexes in tumor target cells cocultured with activated macrophages. J. Biol. Chem. **266:** 10162–10167.
29. STAMLER, J.S., D.J. SINGEL & J. LOSCALZO. 1992. Biochemistry of nitric oxide and its redox-activated forms. Science **258:** 1898–1902.
30. FELDMAN, P.L., O.W. GRIFFITH & D.J. STUEHR. 1993. The surprising life of nitric oxide. CAEN **12:** 26–38.
31. WINK, D.A., J.A. COOK, M.C. KRISHNA, J. HANBAYER, W. DEGRAFF, J. GAMSON & J.B. MITCHELL. 1995. Nitric oxide protects against alkyl peroxide-mediated cytotoxicity: further insights into the role nitric oxide plays in oxidative stress. Arch. Biochem. Biophys. **319:** 402–407.
32. KERWIN, J.F., JR., J.R. LANCASTER, JR. & P.L. FELDMAN. 1995. Nitric oxide: a new paradigm for second messengers. J. Med. Chem. **38:** 4343–4362.
33. KANNER, J., S. HAREL & R. GRANIT. 1991. Nitric oxide as an antioxidant. Arch. Biochem. Biophys. **289:** 130–136.
34. CHAMULITRAT, W. 1998. Nitric oxide inhibited peroxyl and alkoxyl radical formation with concomitant protection against oxidant injury in intestinal epithelial cells. Arch. Biochem. Biophys. **355:** 206–214.
35. WINK, D.A., I. HANBAYER, M.C. KRISHNA, W. DEGRAFF, J. GAMSON & J.B. MITCHELL. 1993. Nitric oxide protects against cellular damage and cytotoxicity from reactive oxygen species. Proc. Natl. Acad. Sci. USA **90:** 9813–9817.
36. MONCADA, S., R.M.J. PALMER & E.A. HIGGS. 1991. Nitric oxide: physiology, pathophysiology, and pharmacology. Pharmacol. Rev. **43:** 109–142.

37. BECKMAN, J. S., T.W. BECKMAN, J. CHEN, P.A. MARSHALL & B.A. FREEMAN. 1990. Apparent hydroxyl radical production by peroxynitrite: implications for endothelial injury from nitric oxide and superoxide. Proc. Natl. Acad. Sci. USA **87:** 1620–1624.
38. MATHEIS, G., M.P. SHERMAN, G.D. BUCKBERG, D.M. HAYBRON, H.H. YOUNG & L.J. IGNARRO. 1992. Role of L-arginine–nitric oxide pathway in myocardial reoxygenation injury. Am. J. Physiol. **262:** H616–H620.
39. ZWEIER, J. L., P. WANG & P. KUPPUSAMY. 1995. Direct measurements of nitric oxide generation in the ischemic heart using electron paramagnetic resonance spectroscopy. J. Biol. Chem. **270:** 304–307.

Role for NADPH/NADH Oxidase in the Modulation of Vascular Tone[a]

THOMAS MÜNZEL,[b] ULRICH HINK, THOMAS HEITZER, AND THOMAS MEINERTZ

The University Hospital Eppendorf, Division of Cardiology, 20246 Hamburg, Germany

ABSTRACT: The endothelium modulates vascular tone by producing vasodilator andvasoconstrictor substances. Of these, the best characterized and potentially most important are nitric oxide (NO•) and $O_2^{-\bullet}$. These small molecules exhibit opposing effects on vascular tone and chemically react with each other in a fashion that negates their individual effects and leads to the production of potentially toxic substances, such as peroxynitrite ($ONOO^-$). These dynamic interactions may likely have important implications, altering not only tissue perfusion but also contributing to the process of atherosclerosis. The precise $O_2^{-\bullet}$ source within vascular tissue remains to be determined. Recent work demonstrated that in endothelial cells as well as in vascular smooth muscle cells, a membrane-associated NAD(P)H-dependent oxidase represents the most significant $O_2^{-\bullet}$ source. Interestingly, this oxidase is activated upon stimulation with angiotensin II, suggesting that under all conditions of an activated circulating and/or local renin-angiotensin system endothelial dysfunction secondary to increased vascular $O_2^{-\bullet}$ production is expected.

INTRODUCTION

Traditionally, the role of the vascular endothelium was thought primarily to be that of a semiselective barrier to the diffusion of macromolecules from the blood lumen to the interstitial space. During the past decade, numerous additional roles of the endothelium have been defined, such as modulation of inflammation,[1] regulation of vasomotor tone via producing endothelium-derived relaxing (EDRF) and constricting factors (EDCF), promotion and inhibition of vascular growth, and modulation of coagulation. More recent research identified EDRF as the radical nitric oxide (NO) or a closely related compound.[2,3] It is proposed that NO rapidly reacts with reactive oxygen species such as superoxide ($O_2^{-\cdot}$)[4] to form short-lived reaction products, such as peroxynitrite ($ONOO^-$),[5] which in turn may imitate an endogenous second messenger and result in changes in the metabolic responses of cells and tissues. *In vivo* therapy with NO, e.g., via treatment with organic nitrates, has been shown to stimulate rather than inhibit vascular $O_2^{-\cdot}$ production,[6,7] which may be interpreted as a biochemical baroreflex to limit vascular conseqences of "NO intoxication." Experimental data suggest that traditional $O_2^{-\cdot}$ sources, such as xanthine oxidase, arachidonic acid, and the mitochondria, play a minor role in the production

[a]This work was supported by the Deutsche Forschungsgemeinschaft Mu 1079-2/1.

[b]Address correspondence to: Thomas Münzel M.D., Universitätskrankenhaus Eppendorf, Abteilung für Kardiologie, Martinistrasse 52, 20246 Hamburg; Telephone: 49-40-4717-3988; Fax: 49-40-4717-5862; E-mail: muenzel@uke.uni-hamburg.de

of oxygen-derived free radicals in vascular tissue.[8,9] With this review we want to focus on the recently described membrane-associated NAD(P)H oxidase, which has been demonstrated to represent the most significant $O_2^{-\cdot}$–producing enzyme in endothelial cells, smooth muscle cells, and/or the vascular adventitia and which is activated *in vitro* and *in vivo* upon stimulation with angiotensin II.[10]

THE INTERPLAY BETWEEN NITRIC OXIDE AND SUPEROXIDE

Before 1980, it was generally thought that the major *in vivo* mechanism whereby vessels constricted and dilated was via an action of neurohumoral substances on the vascular smooth muscle. It is now clear that the action of almost every vasoactive agent is either directly caused by or indirectly modified by release of vasoactive factors from the endothelium. Evidence that a diffusible endothelium-derived factor was released from endothelial cells was derived from bioassay studies in which the substance could be transferred from a vessel with intact endothelium to a vessel with denuded endothelium.[11] Estimates of its half-life varied from a few seconds to 1.5 min, depending on the experimental techniques used. Yet before EDRF was identified as NO, it was demonstrated that EDRF could be degraded by superoxide anions and protected by superoxide dismutase (SOD).[4] In 1987, Palmer and colleagues first reported detecting (after reduction pre-processing) an NO-like compound released from cultured endothelial cells upon stimulation with bradykinin.[12] In addition to its role as a vasodilating agent, NO has several other important biological effects. Nitric oxide released from endothelial cells works in concert with prostacyclin to inhibit platelet aggregation.[13] In higher concentrations, NO inhibits vascular smooth muscle proliferation.[14] The half-life, and therefore biological activity, of NO is decisively determined by reactive oxygen species such as $O_2^{-\cdot}$.[4] Superoxide rapidly reacts with NO to form the highly reactive intermediate $ONOO^-$ at a rate close to that limited by simple diffusion and exceeds that for most targets in the cell.[5] The rapid bimolecular reaction between of NO with $O_2^{-\cdot}$ to yield $ONOO^-$ is more than three times faster than the enzymatic dismutation of $O_2^{-\cdot}$ catalyzed by SOD.[5] Thus, $ONOO^-$ formation represents a major potential pathway of NO reactivity that depends on rates of tissue $O_2^{-\cdot}$ production. $ONOO^-$ will protonate to peroxynitrous acid (ONOOH) to yield an oxidant with the reactivity of hydroxyl radical ($OH^\cdot$) via metal-independent mechanisms. At low concentrations, $ONOO^-$ has been shown to be beneficial while at high concentrations it will cause oxidative damage to protein, lipid, carbohydrate, DNA, subcellular organelles, and cell systems groups.[5,15–18]

SOURCES OF SUPEROXIDE IN VASCULAR TISSUE

Superoxide is membrane impermeant and therefore restricted to reaction in the compartment where it is generated. One potentially important extracellular $O_2^{-\cdot}$ source represents the circulating xanthine oxidase, which may bind to glycosaminoglycan binding sites in vascular endothelial cells. For example, xanthine oxidase binding has been reported in the blood vessels of hypercholesterolemic animals.[19] Other sources of vascular $O_2^{-\cdot}$ production include NO synthase (in the presence of L-arginine or BH_4 deficiency), mitochondrial enzymes, cytochrome P_{450}, cyclooxygenases, and lipoxygenases.

More recently Griendling and colleagues demonstrated that in vascular smooth muscle cells the most significant $O_2^{-\cdot}$ source represents a NAD(P)H-dependent oxidase and that the activity of this oxidase is increased upon stimulation with angiotensin II.[9] Initially it was unclear whether this activity represents a single oxidase using NADH in preference to NADPH or multiple enzymes with different specific activities and substrate or cofactor specificities. Using a stable transfection approach with the antisense to p22phox, Ushui-Fukai showed an inhibition of the expression of the p22phox subunit together with a significant inhibition of the NADPH- and NADH-dependent superoxide production, suggesting that this oxidase uses NADH as well as NADPH as substrates to produce $O_2^{-\cdot}$.[20] In addition, the antisense approach also markedly inhibited angiotensin II–stimulated leucine incorporation, providing the first evidence that vascular NADPH oxidase plays an important role in regulating vascular hypertrophy.

Vascular endothelial cells have also been shown to generate $O_2^{-\cdot}$ and hydrogen peroxide (H_2O_2) under basal and stimulated conditions. More recently, Mohazzab and colleagues described an NADH oxidoreductase (similar to smooth muscle cells) as a significant source of $O_2^{-\cdot}$ in endothelial cells.[21] They demonstrated that the lucigenin-enhanced chemiluminescence signal of cultured bovine coronary artery endothelial cells was increased markedly in response to NADH while only minor changes were observed upon stimulation of the xanthine oxidase and mitochondrial $O_2^{-\cdot}$-producing enzymes. The signal was inhibited with the radical scavenger tiron and by the inhibitor of neutrophil NADPH oxidase diphenylene iodonium. Recent preliminary studies also demonstrate that similar to smooth muscle cells, the activity of this oxidase is increased in endothelial cells in response to stimulation with angiotensin II.[22]

Hemodynamic stress has been shown to have a potent effect on NADPH/NADH oxidase activity. Howard and colleagues demonstrated that cyclic strain caused an early, transient increase in NADH/NADPH oxidase activity and a sustained increase in H_2O_2 in cultured porcine aortic endothelial cells.[23] This increase in oxidative stress was reflected in an increase in lipid peroxidation products released from these cells, suggesting that reactive oxygen species may serve to transduce mechanical signals into biochemical events. Interestingly, oscillatory and laminar shear stress seems to affect differentially human endothelial redox state. Oscillatory shear, used at an amplitude modeled *in vivo* at vascular bifurcations, progressively enhanced the activity of $O_2^{-\cdot}$-producing NADH oxidase and expression of redox-sensitive genes, such as HO-1, whereas levels of $O_2^{-\cdot}$ scavenger Cu/Zn SOD remained unchanged. In contrast, steady laminar shear initially increased NADH oxidase activity and HO-1 mRNA expression, but these responses seem to be transient and returned to baseline within 24 hours. Moreover, Cu/Zn SOD mRNA and protein expression were increased after 24 h, suggesting that mechanisms able to compensate for the oxidative stress are induced.

SIMILARITIES AND DISCREPANCIES OF NEUTROPHIL NADPH AND VASCULAR NAD(P)H OXIDASE STRUCTURE

Neutrophil NADPH oxidase has been shown to consist of membrane and cytoplasmic structural units (FIG. 1). At least five protein components are required for

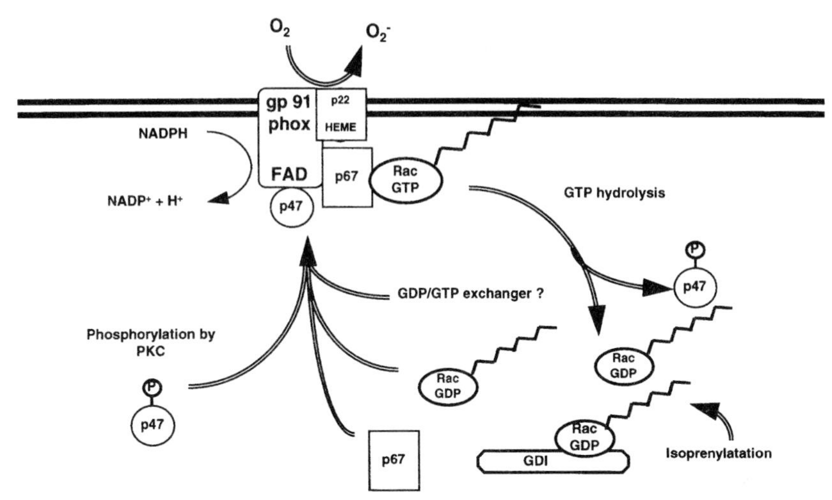

FIGURE 1. Structural features of the neutrophil NADPH oxidase. NADPH oxidase consists of the cytochrome b558 with two subunits, gp22phox and gp 91phox. Upon activation of the NADPH oxidase (e.g., by phorbolesters), cytosolic components of the enzyme are translocated to the membrane (p47phox and p67phox), assembly with the cytochrome, and subsequently the initiation of superoxide synthesis. Translocation of the p47 subunit has been demonstrated following phosphorylation by PKC and recent studies have shown that increased PKC activity within vascular tissue is associated with increased NADPH oxidase activity.[31] (Adapted from Bastian and Hibbs.[24])

NADPH oxidase function. The membrane unit is a cytochrome b558 consisting of two subunits, the p22phox and the gp91phox. Cytoplasmic components include a 47 kD (p47phox) and a 67 kD (p67phox) protein and a small molecular weight G protein, either rac-1 or rac-2.[24] Activation of the NADPH oxidase involves phosphorylation of the p47phox, e.g., by protein kinase C (PKC). On activation, the cytosolic constituents are translocated to the plasma membrane where they bind to the cytochrome (membrane assembly) and initiate $O_2^{-\cdot}$ synthesis.[25]

Studies with cultured endothelial cells using RT-PCR identified the expression of gp91phox, p22phox, p47phox, and 67phox.[26] Expression of p22phox was also confirmed by Northern blot analysis. Immunoperoxidase staining showed expression of the 47 and 67 phox proteins. Using heme spectroscopy, however, they failed to demonstrate the presence of the low potential cytochrome b558, which led the authors to conclude that a contribution of the endothelial NADPH oxidase to endothelial $O_2^{-\cdot}$ formation is not very likely. In vascular smooth muscle cells, the p22phox subunit has been cloned.[27] Stable transfection with antisense p22phox prevented angiotensin II–induced increases in the expression of the p22phox and markedly reduced NADPH- as well as NADPH-induced $O_2^{-\cdot}$ generation.[20] With these studies they were also able to demonstrate a spectophotometric peak at 553 nm and not at 558 nm, suggesting that the cytochrome associated with the vascular enzyme may be different from the neutrophil cytochrome. The same group was unable to detect the other cytochrome subunit gp91phox, suggesting that the other subunit of the NAD(P)H oxidase may be structurally distinct from that in phagocytes.

In neutrophil NADPH oxidase, the large subunit of cytochrome b558 (gp91phox) functions as the substrate recognition site, the FAD binding site, and most likely binds heme. Thus the unknown large subunit of the vascular NADH/NADPH oxidase may be the component that confers on smooth muscle its unique kinetics, substrate specificity, and activation requirements.

An interesting new aspect was recently presented from Wang and colleagues.[28] They demonstrated heavy immunohistochemical staining for NADPH oxidase proteins, such as gp91phox, p22phox, p47phox, and 67phox, almost exclusively in the adventitia of the rat aorta while no substantial staining was detected in the media. Using organ chamber experiments, they were able to demonstrate that superoxide released from the adventitia is able to induce endothelial dysfunction.

ROLE FOR SUPEROXIDE AND NADPH OXIDASE IN ANGIOTENSIN II HYPERTENSION

Recent *in vivo* studies confirmed the observations made *in vitro*. Infusion of angiotensin II for a 5-day period resulted in a marked degree of hypertension, endothelial dysfunction, increased vascular $O_2^{-\cdot}$ production,[10] and a fourfold increase in the expression of the NADPH oxidase subunit p22 phox[29] (FIG. 2). These changes do not seem to be secondary to the hypertensive stimulus of angiotensin II, since infusion of noradrenaline as a reference constrictor and a comparable degree of hypertension did not change endothelial function and vascular $O_2^{-\cdot}$ production at all.[10] The angiotensin II–induced effects were completely inhibited using losartan (FIG. 3), an angiotensin II receptor blocker suggesting that all these changes are mediated through stimulation of the angiotensin II receptor subtype AT-1. Treatment with losartan prevented the angiotensin II–induced $O_2^{-\cdot}$ production, the development of endothelial dysfunction, and even improved endothelial function and decreased vascular $O_2^{-\cdot}$ production in control animals. These observations suggest that physiolog-

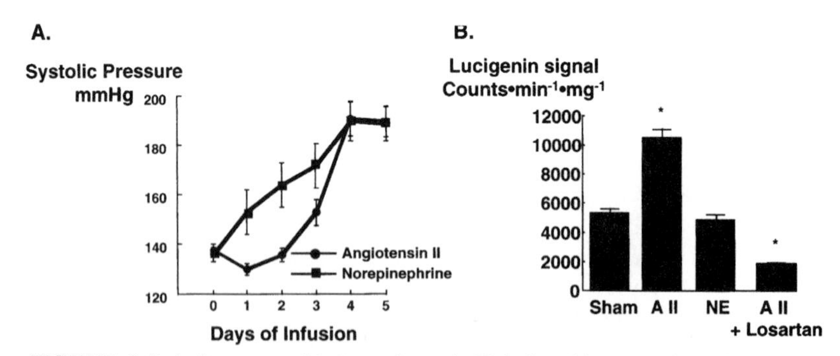

FIGURE 2. Role for superoxide in angiotensin II–induced hypertension. (**A**) Effects of angiotensin II (AII) and norepinephrine (NE) infusion on systolic blood pressure in rats. Within 4–5 days of chronic infusion, AII and NE caused a similar degree of hypertension. (**B**) Despite a similar hypertensive stimulus, vascular superoxide production was increased in AII-infused rats only. AII-induced increases in vascular superoxide were markedly inhibited by the AT1 receptor antagonist losartan, identifying AT1 receptor blockers as potent antioxidants. (Adapted from Rajagopalan and colleagues.[10])

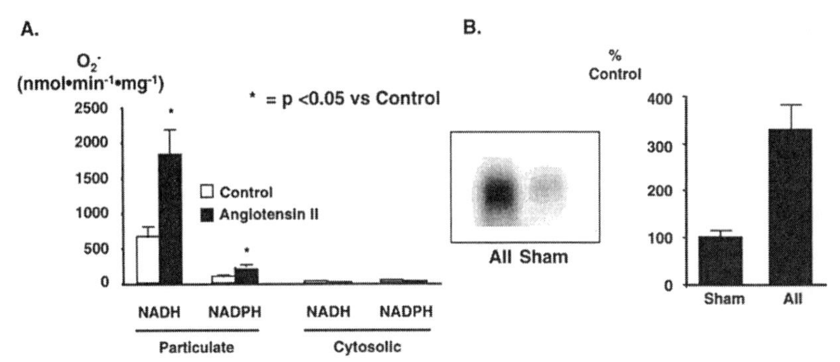

FIGURE 3. Role for NADPH oxidase in angiotensin II–induced hypertension. (**A**) NADPH oxidase activity in vascular homogenates from sham-operated and angiotensin II–infused rats. Superoxide production was markedly increased in angiotensin II–infused rats and the activity of the enzyme was almost exclusively in the particulate fraction, indicating the membrane association of the enzyme. (Adapted from Rajagopalan and colleagues.[10]) (**B**) Effects of angiotensin II infusion on p22phox expression. Within 5 days of continuous angiotensin II treatment, p22phox mRNA levels were increased 338 ± 41% of control levels. (Adapted from Fukui and colleagues.[29])

ically circulating angiotensin II may already stimulate vascular $O_2^{-\cdot}$ production and may influence endothelial function and that AT-1 receptor blocker and angiotensin-converting enzyme inhibitors behave like potent antioxidants.

In vitro, endothelial dysfunction in aortas from angiotensin II–infused animals was completely reversed using a liposome-encapsulated SOD preparation suggesting that angiotensin II–induced $O_2^{-\cdot}$ production and subsequently increased NO degradation mainly accounts for endothelial dysfunction in this particular animals model (FIG. 4). More recent experimental work provided evidence that angiotensin II–induced reactive oxygen species production may be at least in part responsible for the angiotensin II–induced hypertension.[30] With their studies, Laursen and colleagues showed *in vivo* treatment with liposomal SOD markedly corrected hypertension induced by angiotensin II, while having no effect on hypertension induced by the reference constrictor noradrenaline[30] (FIG. 5). These data suggest that hypertension induced by elevated circulating levels of angiotensin II is mediated at least in part by $O_2^{-\cdot}$-mediated degradation of the endothelium-derived relaxant factor NO. These findings may also imply that under all conditions where one has an activated renin-angiotensin system, endothelial dysfunction and hypertension may be secondary to increased angiotensin II–induced vascular $O_2^{-\cdot}$ production. Increased activation of the vascular NADPH oxidase is also observed upon endogenous activation of the renin-angiotensin system. Using 2K1C hypertension, we were able to demonstrate that hypertension was associated with endothelial dysfunction and increased vascular NADPH oxidase activity. Interestingly, $O_2^{-\cdot}$ production was normalized using calphostin C, suggesting that part of NADPH oxidase activation in this particular animal model is PKC dependent.[31]

Recent experimental work from the Griendlings' group addressed the effects of chronic angiotensin II infusion on the expression of the cytochrome b558 subunit, p22phox.[29] During angiotensin II infusion, the blood pressure began to rise within 3

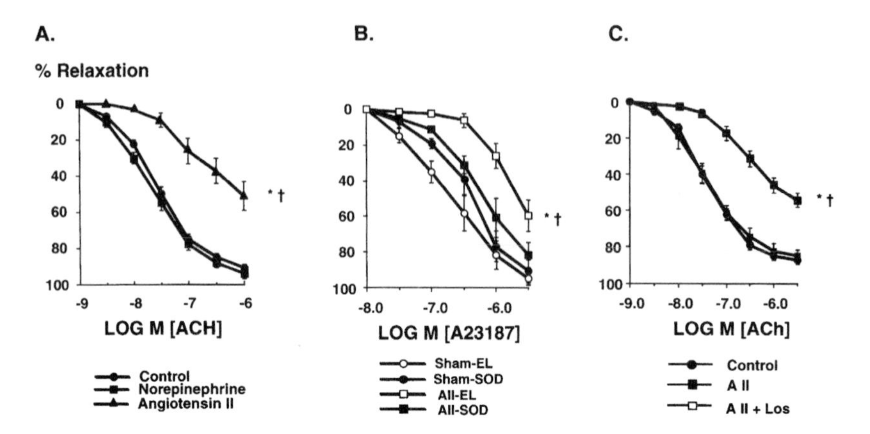

FIGURE 4. Angiotensin II infusion causes endothelial dysfunction. (**A**) Effects of angiotensin II and norepinephrine on endothelial function in rat aorta. Despite similar degrees of hypertension, angiotensin II infusion (but not norepinephrine infusion) was associated with endothelial dysfunction. (**B**) Endothelial dysfunction was almost completely reversed *in vitro* using liposome-encapsulated SOD, indicating increased vascular superoxide. (**C**) Most angiotensin II–induced endothelial dysfunction is mediated via AT1 receptor stimulation, since concomitant treatment with the AT1 receptor blocker losartan completely prevented angiotensin II–induced endothelial dysfunction. (Adapted from Rajagopalan and colleagues.[10])

days and remained elevated for up to 14 days. Expression of the p22phox subunit was increased within 3 days and peaked within 5 days. The increase in expression was accompanied by an increase in the content of the corresponding cytochrome (twofold) and NAD(P)H oxidase activity. In this particular study the authors observed a close correlation between the upregulation of the p22phox mRNA expression and the increases in NAD(P)H oxidase activity.[29] Two weeks later, however, blood pressure was still elevated, although the p22phox expression had returned to baseline. The authors postulated that increased oxidative stress within the vasculature may activate redox-sensitive genes or increased wall thickness may be responsible for sustaining hypertension. Interestingly, treatment with liposomal SOD *in vivo* blocked the angiotensin II–induced hypertension and markedly attenuated the increase in p22phox expression. This observation suggests that $O_2^{-\cdot}$ itself may regulate p22phox expression via a positive feedback.

In contrast to these observations, Pagano and colleagues showed that constitutive $O_2^{-\cdot}$-generating activity was localized to aortic adventitial fibroblasts rather than to smooth muscle cells and was enhanced by vasoconstrictor angiotensin II. Immunohistochemistry of aortic sections demonstrated the presence of p22phox, gp91phox, p47phox, and p67phox localized exclusively in rabbit aortic adventitia, coincident with the site of staining for superoxide production. Furthermore, immunodepletion of p67(phox) from adventitial fibroblast particulates resulted in the loss of NADPH oxidase activity, which could be restored by the addition of recombinant p67(phox).[32] It remains therefore to be established whether or not smooth muscle cells and/or the adventitia is the major localization of the vascular NADPH oxidase.

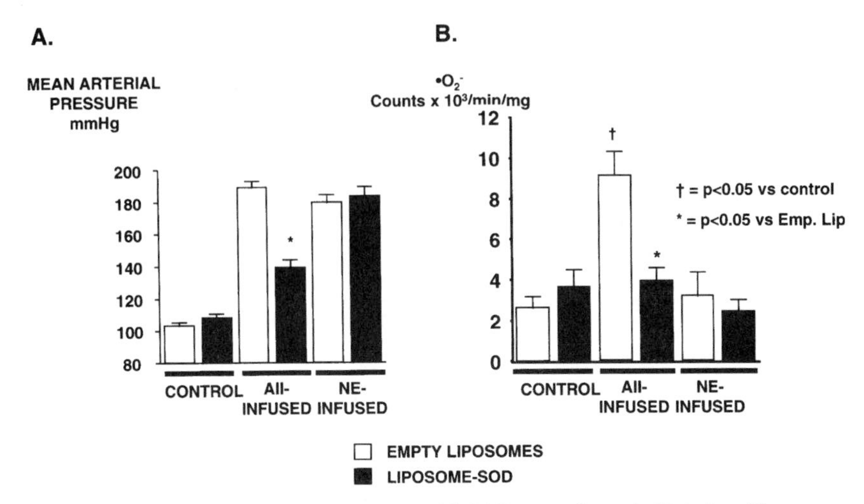

FIGURE 5. Effects of *in vivo* treatment with SOD on angiotensin II–induced hypertension and vascular superoxide production. (**A**) Effects of *in vivo* treatment with liposomal SOD on mean arterial pressure in chronically instrumented rats. In rats infused with angiotensin II, SOD treatment markedly reduced mean arterial pressure while catecholamine induced hypertension was not changed at all by SOD. This indicates that hypertension induced by angiotensin II is likely secondary to increased vascular superoxide production. (**B**) SOD treatment normalizes vascular superoxide production in vessels from angiotensin II–infused rats while having no effect on superoxide production in norepinephrine (NE)-treated animals. (Adapted from Larsen and colleagues.[30])

A p22phox polymorphism has been recently demonstrated to influence significantly the susceptibility to develop coronary artery disease. Using restriction fragment length polymorphism Inoue and colleagues found that the TC + TT genotype of the C242T polymorphism was significantly more frequent in control subjects than in patients with coronary artery disease. The association of the C242T polymorphism of the p22phox gene with coronary artery disease was statistically significant and independent of other risk factors. The authors concluded that a mutation of the potential heme binding site of the p22phox gene may reduce susceptibility to coronary artery disease.[33]

SUPEROXIDE AND NADH OXIDASE IN NITRATE TOLERANCE: EVIDENCE FOR A BIOCHEMICAL BAROREFLEX

Nitroglycerin (NTG) is one of the foremost drugs in the treatment of acute and chronic ischemic episodes in patients with coronary artery disease.[34] Its long-term efficacy is blunted, however, due to the development of nitrate tolerance.[35,36] Recently, we demonstrated a new mechanism of how the vasculature may adapt to long-term therapy with organic nitrates. With these studies we showed that chronic treatment with NO (via organic nitrates) leads to tolerance and cross-tolerance to other endothelium-dependent and -independent vasodilators.[37] Aortic segments from rab-

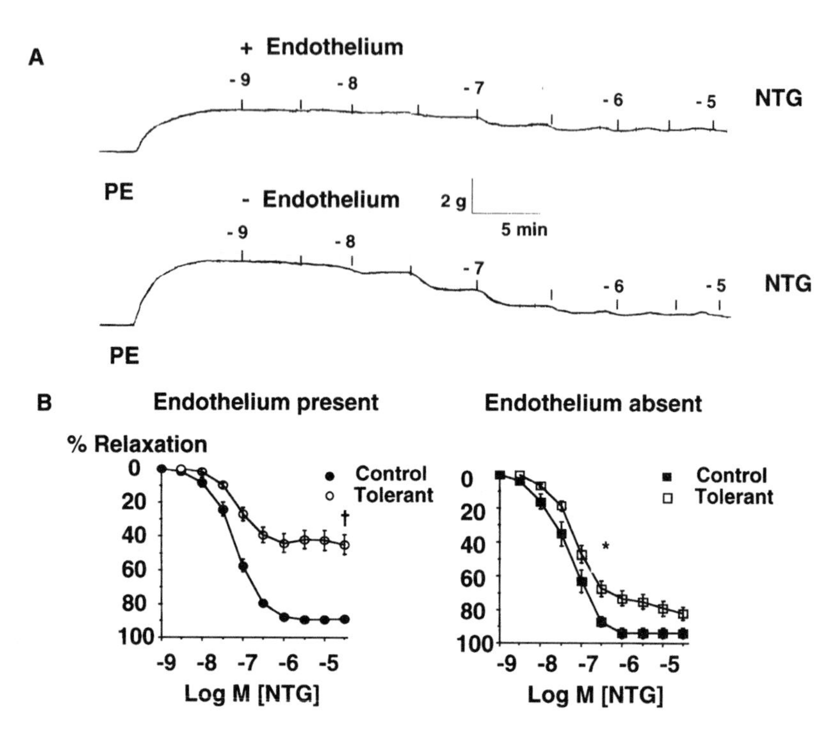

FIGURE 6. (**A**) Experimental record demonstrating the effect of endothelial removal on the relaxations to NTG in tolerant rabbit aortic rings. Segments were preconstricted with phenylephrine. Relaxations to cumulative concentrations of NTG are recorded. In the presence of the endothelium, the relaxation of vessels is maximally 37% and in the absence of the endothelium relaxation is 78%. (**B**) Mean data demonstrating NTG-induced relaxations in control and NTG-tolerant vessels with and without endothelium. (Adapted from Münzel and colleagues.[37])

bits treated for 3 days with NTG demonstrated a greater degree of tolerance to NTG if the endothelium is present than if it is removed (FIG. 6). Similarly, removal of the endothelium markedly attenuated cross-tolerance to the nitrovasodilator SIN-1. This observation lead us to hypothesize that NO released from NTG is getting chemically inactivated before stimulating the vascular smooth muscle guanylyl cyclase. In support of the latter hypothesis we found that the superoxide levels in tolerant vessels were about twice that of control vessels. Interestingly, removal of the endothelium increased $O_2^{-\cdot}$ production in control vessels but paradoxically decreased it in tolerant vessels (FIG. 7). This observation led us to conclude that the endothelium indeed represents the major source of $O_2^{-\cdot}$ in nitrate tolerance. This hypothesis that $O_2^{-\cdot}$ plays in important role in tolerance was further strengthened by our observations that attenuated NTG responses in the setting of nitrate tolerance could be almost completely corrected by preincubation of vessels with a liposomal SOD preparation.[37]

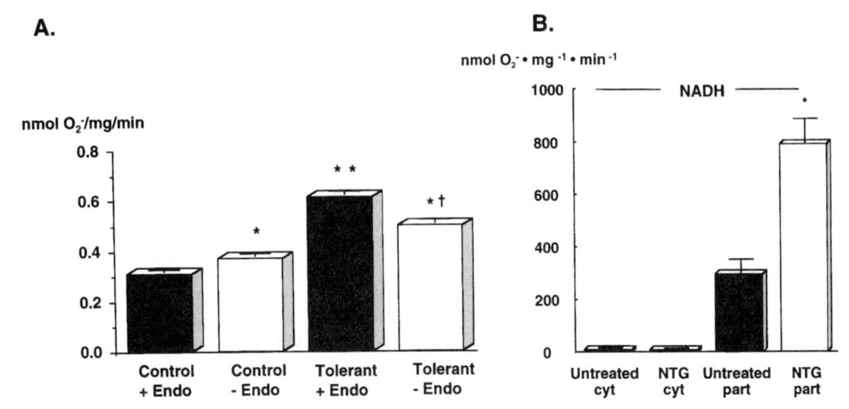

FIGURE 7. (**A**) Effects of 3-day NTG treatment on vascular superoxide production. In control aorta, endothelial removal slightly but significantly increases lucigenin-derived chemiluminescence signals indicating that under control conditions the endothelium might have some free radical scavenging properties. In the setting of tolerance, vascular superoxide production is doubled. Removal of the endothelium in tolerant tissue decreases rather than increases superoxide levels, identifying the endothelium as a major superoxide source. (Adapted from Münzel and colleagues.[37]) (**B**) Effect of 3-day NTG treatment on the NADH-driven enzyme activity in cellular subfractions. Almost 100% of the NADH oxidase activity was present in the particulate (membrane) fraction. The activity of the membrane-associated enzyme was increased almost threefold in NTG-treated animals. (Adapted from Münzel and colleagues.[7])

NAD(P)H-DEPENDENT OXIDASE REPRESENTS THE MAJOR SUPEROXIDE SOURCE IN NITRATE TOLERANCE

These studies also provided some insight into the potential sources of superoxide in nitrate tolerance. Superoxide production of tolerant rabbit aorta was completely normalized by adding diphenylene iodonium, a potent inhibitor of flavoprotein-containing oxidases. These include mitochondrial oxidases, NO synthase, xanthine oxidase, and plasmalemmal NADH- and NADPH-dependent oxidases. By using specific inhibitors we could exclude mitochondrial enzymes, NO synthase, or the xanthine oxidase as major superoxide sources, indicating a potential role for NAD(P)H-driven oxidases. To address an involvement of this oxidase in tolerance, we examined $O_2^{-\cdot}$ production by homogenates of aortas from normal and nitrate-tolerant animals. The use of homogenates allowed us to add various substrates to characterize the oxidases involved. As previously reported, the $O_2^{-\cdot}$ production evoked by addition of NADH was substantially (approximately threefold) greater than that observed upon addition of NADPH.[6,7] Also consistent with previous reports, the oxidase activity was predominantly in the particulate fraction, indicating that this is a membrane-associated enzyme. NTG treatment for 3 days caused an almost threefold increase in activity of the NADH oxidase in the nitrate-tolerant vessel homogenates. Likewise, the activity of the membrane fractions of tolerant vessels was substantially increased compared to control membranes (FIG. 7). The mechanism whereby NTG

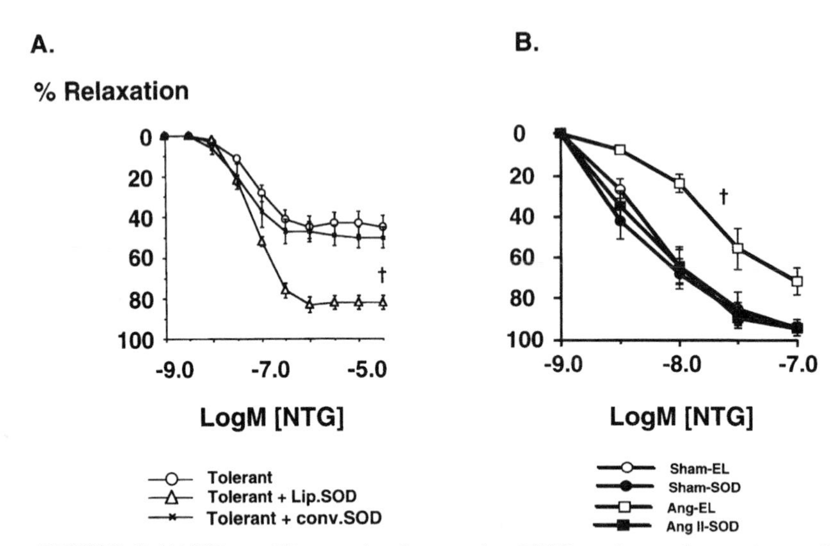

FIGURE 8. (**A**) Effects of liposomal and conventional SOD on nitrate tolerance in vessels with endothelium. Convential SOD, which can not cross endothelial membranes due to its negative charge failed to modify the attenuated NTG dose-response relationship in nitrate-tolerant aorta. In contrast, liposome-encapsulated SOD markedly improved NTG-induced relaxation. (**B**) Effects of angiotensin II infusion on NTG dose-response relationship. Angiotensin II treatment markedly decreased sensitivity to NTG due to increasing vascular superoxide production. Similar to aortas from NTG-treated animals, liposomal SOD restored nitrate sensitivity. (Adapted from Münzel and colleagues[37]and from Rajagopalan and colleagues.[10])

treatment increases the activity of these oxidases remains unclear, but may involve activation of this oxidase by neurohumoral stimuli such as angiotensin II.[36] Preliminary experiments demonstrate that in nitrate-tolerant tissue, the expression of the gp91phox subunit (using RT-PCR with an internal standard) was increased more than twofold in tolerant vessels as compared to controls.[38] We were able to demonstrate that removal of the endothelium did not change the gp91phox expression signal in control vessels, but significantly reduced the expression signal in tolerant tissue. These findings indicate increased expression of an NADPH oxidase subunit in nitrate tolerance and point to its predominant location within endothelial cells.[38]

REGULATION OF NAD(P)H OXIDASE ACTIVITY BY MEMBRANE POTENTIAL

In a recent study we tested to what extent tolerance and vascular $O_2^{-\cdot}$ production is modified by hydralazine, a compound shown to cause vasodilation via hyperpolarization secondary to stimulation of endothelial and/or smooth muscle potassium channels. We found that hydralazine potently inhibits the development of nitrate tolerance and in parallel prevents the NTG-induced activation of vascular NAD(P)H oxidase.[7] Interestingly, hydralazine was only effective as an antioxidant when administered *in vivo* or in intact rings, but had no effect when administered to vascular homogenates. One explanation may be that hydralazine prevents assembly of the oxidase rather than directly inhibiting the enzyme. Another possibility is that the effect of hydralazine requires the intact cell to exert its effect, possibly via its known hyperpolarizing effects. This concept was strengthened by the observation that hyperpolarizing agents, such as pinacidil, inhibit (similar to neutrophils[39]) vascular $O_2^{-\cdot}$ production and that the antioxidant effect of hydralazine is inhibited by pretreating rings with depolarizing potassium chloride concentrations. This would imply that the activity of this membrane-associated oxidase is regulated by potassium channels[40] and by the membrane potential. This concept was strengthened recently by preliminary reports, where Sohn and colleagues showed that $O_2^{-\cdot}$ production in endothelial cells is modulated by membrane potential.[41] They could demonstrate that HUVECS-mediated production of $O_2^{-\cdot}$ was increased following membrane depolarization and that hyperpolarization via K_{ATP} channel opening decreased superoxide. Pretreatment with the tyrosine kinase inhibitor genestein completely abolished the depolarization-induced increases in $O_2^{-\cdot}$, suggesting an involvement of tyrosine phosphorylation in this phenomenon.[41]

ROLE FOR PROTEIN KINASE C IN NADPH OXIDASE ACTIVATION

Recent reports demonstrated that nitrate tolerance is associated with increased sensitivity to vasoconstrictors secondary to an activation of protein kinase C (PKC)[42] (an important second messenger for vascular smooth muscle contraction) and that *in vivo* treatment with PKC inhibitors not only inhibited the development of a NTG-induced hypersensitivity to vasoconstrictors but also prevented the development of nitrate tolerance.[43] What is the link between PKC and increased vascular (endothelial) $O_2^{-\cdot}$ production? The demonstration that *in vivo* PKC inhibition prevented the development of nitrate tolerance may suggest that activation of one or more PKC subtypes in the endothelium may be involved in the reversible inactivation of NTG-metabolizing enzymes. Interestingly, PKC has been shown to activate NAD(P)H-dependent $O_2^{-\cdot}$-producing oxidases in phagocytes.[44] Preliminary data indicate that $O_2^{-\cdot}$ production in the setting of nitrate tolerance can be inhibited by the PKC inhibitor chelerythrine (unpublished observation). It is tempting to speculate that PKC activation during NTG therapy may in turn activate oxidases in the vascular endothelial cells resulting in increased $O_2^{-\cdot}$ production and consequently enhanced NO degradation and/or decreased NTG biotransformation.

The concept that nitrate tolerance is at least in part mediated by increasing vascular $O_2^{-\cdot}$ production was recently confirmed by clinical studies. Treating patients with heart failure or coronary artery disease with nitrates and concomitantly with antioxidants such as vitamin C and vitamin E almost completely prevented tolerance development.

SUMMARY

The review focused on the importance of NAD(P)H-driven oxidases in the regulation of vascular tone. The activity of this recently discovered oxidase is modulated by physicochemical forces (oscillatory shear stress) and neurohormonal stimuli, such as angiotensin II. So far it remains to be elucidated whether the enzyme is predominantly located in endothelial and/or smooth muscle cells or in the vascular adventitia and whether it uses NADH[9] or NADPH preferentially as a substrate to produce superoxide.[32,47] Despite favorable *in vitro* results showing substantial anti-atherosclerotic properties of NO, *in vivo* treatment with NO (via organic nitrates) markedly activates $O_2^{-\cdot}$-producing enzymes, which in turn when given continuously, may accelerate rather than inhibit the atherosclerotic process.

REFERENCES

1. Bevilacqua, M.P. 1993. Endothelial-leucocyte adhesion molecules. Annu. Rev. Immunol. **11:** 767–804.
2. Myers, P.R., R.L. Minor, Jr., R. Guerra, Jr., J.N. Bates & D.G. Harrison. 1990. Vasorelaxant properties of the endothelium-derived relaxing factor more closely resemble S-nitrosocysteine than nitric oxide. Nature **345:** 161–163.
3. Palmer, R.M. J., D.S. Ashton & S. Moncada. 1988. Vascular endothelial cells synthesize nitric oxide from L-arginine. Nature **333:** 664–666.
4. Gryglewski, R.J., R.M.J. Palmer & S. Moncada. 1986. Superoxide anion is involved in the breakdown of endothelium-derived vascular relaxing factor. Nature **320:** 454–456.
5. Beckman, J.S., T.W. Beckman, J. Chen, P.A. Marshall & B.A. Freeman. 1990. Apparent hydroxyl radical production by peroxynitrite: implications for endothelial injury from nitric oxide and superoxide. Proc. Natl. Acad. Sci. USA **87:** 1620–1624.
6. Munzel, T., S. Kurz, S. Rajagopalan, M. Tarpey, B. Freeman & D.G. Harrison. 1995. Identification of the membrane bound NADH oxidase as the major source of superoxide anion in nitrate tolerance. Endothelium **3**(Suppl)**:** s14(abstract).
7. Munzel, T., S. Kurz, S. Rajagopalan, M. Thoenes, W.R. Berrington, J.A. Thompson, B.A. Freeman & D.G. Harrison. 1996. Hydralazine prevents nitroglycerin tolerance by inhibiting activation of a membrane-bound NADH oxidase: a new action for an old drug. J. Clin. Invest. **98:** 1465–1470.
8. Mohazzab, H.K.M., P.M. Kaminski & M.S. Wolin. 1994. NADH oxidoreductase is a major source of superoxide anion in bovine coronary endothelium. Am. J. Physiol. **266:** H2568–H2572.
9. Griendling, K.K., C.A. Minieri, J.D. Ollerenshaw & R.W. Alexander. 1994. Angiotensin II stimulates NADH and NADPH oxidase activity in cultured vascular smooth muscle cells. Circ. Res. **74:** 1141–1148.
10. Rajagopalan, S., S. Kurz, T. Munzel, M. Tarpey, B.A. Freeman, K.K. Griendling & D.G. Harrison. 1996. Angiotensin II–mediated hypertension in the rat increases vascular superoxide production via membrane NADH/NADPH oxidase activation. Contribution to alterations of vasomotor tone. J. Clin. Invest. **97:** 1916–1923.
11. Furchgott, R.F. & J.V. Zawadzki. 1980. The obligatory role of endothelial cells in the relaxation of arterial smooth muscle by acetylcholine. Nature **228:** 373–376.
12. Palmer, R.M., A.G. Ferrige & S. Moncada. 1987. Nitric oxide release accounts for the biological activity of endothelium-derived relaxing factor. Nature **327:** 524–526.
13. Radomski, M.W., R.M. Palmer & S. Moncada. 1987. The anti-aggregating properties of vascular endothelium: interactions between prostacyclin and nitric oxide. Br. J. Pharmacol. **92:** 639–646.
14. Garg, U.C. & A. Hassid. 1989. Nitric oxide–generating vasodilators and 8-bromo-cyclic guanosine monophosphate inhibit mitogenesis and proliferation of cultured rat vascular smooth muscle cells. J. Clin. Invest. **83:** 1774–1777.
15. Liu, S., J.S. Beckman & D.D. Ku. 1994. Peroxynitrite, a product of superoxide and nitric oxide, produces coronary vasorelaxation in dogs. J. Pharmacol. Exp. Ther. **268:** 1114–11121.

16. RUBBO, H., R. RADI, M. TRUJILLO, R. TELLERI, B. KALYANARAMAN, S. BARNES, M. KIRK & B.A. FREEMAN. 1994. Nitric oxide regulation of superoxide and peroxynitrite-dependent lipid peroxidation. Formation of novel nitrogen-containing oxidized lipid derivatives. J. Biol. Chem. **269:** 26066–26075.
17. RADI, R., J.S. BECKMAN, K.M. BUSH & B.A. FREEMAN. 1991. Peroxynitrite-induced membrane lipid peroxidation: the cytotoxic potential of superoxide and nitric oxide. Arch. Biochem. Biophys. **288:** 481–487.
18. RADI, R., J.S. BECKMAN, K.M. BUSH & B.A. FREEMAN. 1991. Peroxynitrite oxidation of sulfhydryls. The cytotoxic potential of superoxide and nitric oxide. J. Biol. Chem. **266:** 4244–4250.
19. WHITE, C.R., V. DARLEY-USMAR, W.R. BERRINGTON, M. MCADAMS, J.Z. GORE, J.A. THOMPSON, D.A. PARKS, M.M. TARPEY & B.A. FREEMAN. 1996. Circulating plasma xanthine oxidase contributes to vascular dysfunction in hypercholesterolemic rabbits. Proc. Natl. Acad. Sci. USA **93:** 8745–8749.
20. USHIO-FUKAI, M., A.M. ZAFARI, T. FUKUI, N. ISHIZAKA & K.K. GRIENDLING. 1996. p22phox is a critical component of the superoxide generating NADH/NADPH oxidase system and regulates angiotensin II-induced hypertrophy in vascular smooth muscle cells. J. Biol. Chem. **271:** 23317–23321.
21. MOHAZZAB, K.M., P.M. KAMINSKI & M.S. WOLIN. 1994. NADH oxidoreductase is a major source of superoxide anion in bovine coronary artery endothelium. Am. J. Physiol. **266:** H2568–H2572.
22. LANG, D., A.C. SHAKESBY, S. MOSFER & M.J. LEWIS. 1997. Angiotensin II upregulates NADH/NADPH oxidase mediated superoxide anion production by guinea pig coronary mircovascular endothelial cells. Circulation **96:** I-44.
23. HOWARD, A.B., R.W. ALEXANDER, R.M. NEREM, K.K. GRIENDLING & W.R. TAYLOR. 1997. Cyclic strain induces an oxidative stress in endothelial cells. Am. J. Physiol. **272:** C421–427.
24. BASTIAN, N.R. & J. HIBBS, JR. 1994. Assembly and regulation of NADPH oxidase and nitric oxide synthase. [Review]. Curr. Opinion Immunol. **6:** 131–139.
25. DUSI, S., V. DELLA-BIANCA, M. GRZESKOWIAK & F. ROSSI. 1993. Relationship between phosphorylation and translocation to the plasma membrane of p47phox and p67phox and activation of the NADPH oxidase in normal and Ca(2+)-depleted human neutrophils. Biochem. J. **290:** 173–178.
26. JONES, S.A., V.B. O'DONNELL, J.D. WOOD, J.P. BROUGHTON, E.J. HUGHES & O.T.G. JONES. 1996. Expression of phagocyte NADPH oxidase components in human endothelial cells. Am. J. Physiol. **271:** H1626–H1634.
27. FUKUI, T., B. LASSEGUE, H. KAI, R.W. ALEXANDER & K.K. GRIENDLING. 1995. Cytochrome b-558 alpha-subunit cloning and expression in rat aortic smooth muscle cells. Biochim. Biophys. Acta **1231:** 215–219.
28. WANG, H.D., J. PAGANO, Y. DU, A.J. CAYATTE, M.T. QUINN, P. BRECHER & R.A. COHEN. 1998. Superoxide anion from the adventitia of the rat thoracic aorta inactivates nitric oxide. Circ. Res. **82:** 810–818.
29. FUKUI, T., N. ISHIZAKA, S. RAJAGOPALAN, J.B. LAURSEN, Q. CAPERS IV, W.R. TAYLER, D.G. HARRISON, H. DE LEON, J.N. WILCOX & K.K. GRIENDLING. 1997. p22phox mRNA expression and NADPH oxidase activity are increased in aortas from hypertensive rats. Circ. Res. **80:** 45–51.
30. LAURSEN, J.B., S. RAJAGOPALAN, Z. GALIS, M. TARPEY, B.A. FREEMAN & D.G. HARRISON. 1997. Role of superoxide in angiotensin II-induced but not catecholamine-induced hypertension [see comments]. Circulation **95:** 588–593.
31. HEITZER, T., U. WENZEL, U. HINK, D. KROLLNER, M. SKATCHKOV, R.A.K. STAHL, R. MACHARZINA, T. MEINERTZ & T. MÜNZEL. 1999. Increased NAD(P)H oxidase mediated superoxide production in renovascular hypertension: evidence for an involvement of protein kinase C. Kidney International. **55:** 252–260.
32. PAGANO, P.J., J.K. CLARK, M.E. CIFUENTES-PAGANO, S.M. CLARK, G.M. CALLIS & M.T. QUINN. 1997. Localization of a constitutively active, phagocyte-like NADPH oxidase in rabbit aortic adventitia: enhancement by angiotensin II. Proc. Natl. Acad. Sci. USA **94:** 14483–14488.

33. Inoue, N., S. Kawashima, K. Kanazawa, S. Yamada, H. Akita & M. Yokoyama. 1998. Polymorphism of the NADH/NADPH oxidase p22 phox gene in patients with coronary artery disease. Circulation **97:** 135–137.
34. Abrams, J. 1988. A reappraisal of nitrate therapy. [Review]. J. Am. Med. Assoc. **259:** 396–401.
35. Roth, A., D. Kulick, L. Freidenberger, R. Hong, S.H. Rahimtoola & U. Elkayam. 1987. Early tolerance to hemodynamic effects of high dose transdermal nitroglycerin in responders with severe chronic heart failure. J. Am. Coll. Cardiol. **9:** 858–864.
36. Munzel, T., T. Heitzer, S. Kurz, D.G. Harrison, C. Luhman, L. Pape, M. Olschewski & H. Just. 1996. Dissociation of coronary vascular tolerance and neurohormonal adjustments during long-term nitroglycerin therapy in patients with stable coronary artery disease. J. Am. Coll. Cardiol. **27:** 297–303.
37. Munzel, T., H. Sayegh, B.A. Freeman, M M. Tarpey & D.G. Harrison. 1995. Evidence for enhanced vascular superoxide anion production in nitrate tolerance. A novel mechanism underlying tolerance and cross-tolerance. J. Clin. Invest. **95:** 187–194.
38. Munzel, T., T. Heitzer, R. Macharzina, U. Rückschloss, H. Morawetz, D. Darmer & J. Holtz. 1997. Nitrat-Toleranz durch chronische Nitroglyzeringabe führt zu veränderter Expression der NAD(P)H-Oxidase Untereinheiten und zu vermehrter Superoxidanionen-Bildung im Endothel von Kaninchen. Z. Kardiol. **86:** 197 (abstract).
39. Pieper, G.M. & G.J. Gross. 1992. Anti-free-radical and neutrophil-modulating properties of the nitrovasodilator, nicorandil. Cardiovasc. Drugs Ther. **6:** 225–232.
40. Pieper, G.M. & G.J. Gross. 1992. EMD 52692 (bimakalim), a new potassium channel opener, attenuates luminol-enhanced chemiluminescence and superoxide anion radical formation by zymosan-activated polymorphonuclear leukocytes. Immunopharmacology **23:** 191–197.
41. Sohn, H.Y., M. Keller, T. Gloe & U. Pohl. 1998. Kalium-induzierte Membrandepolarisation steigert die Superoxidanionen-Produktion in humanen Endothelzellen. Z. Kardiol. **87:** 105(abstract).
42. Munzel, T., A. Giaid, S. Kurz, D.J. Stewart & D.G. Harrison. 1995. Evidence for a role of endothelin 1 and protein kinase C in nitroglycerin tolerance. Proc. Natl. Acad. Sci. USA **92:** 5244–5248.
43. Zierhut, W. & H.A. Ball. 1996. Prevention of vascular nitroglycerin tolerance by inhibition of protein kinase C. Br. J. Pharmacol. **119:** 3–5.
44. Majumadar, S., L.H. Kane, M.W. Rossi, B.D. Volpp, W.M. Nauseef & H.M. Korhak. 1993. Protein kinase C isotypes and signal-transduction in human neutrophils: selective substrate specificity of calcium-dependent β-PKC and novel calcium independent nPKC. Biochim. Biophys. Acta **1176:** 276–286.
45. Bassenge, E., N. Fink, M. Skatchkov & B. Fink. 1998. Dietary supplement with vitamin C prevents nitrate tolerance. J. Clin. Invest. **102:** 67–71.
46. Watanabe, H., M. Kakihana, S. Ohtsuka & Y. Sugishita. 1997. Randomized, double-blind, placebo-controlled study of supplemental vitamin E on attenuation of the development of nitrate tolerance. Circulation **96:** 2545–2550.
47. Pagano, P.J., Y. Ito, K. Tornheim, P.M. Gallop, A.I. Tauber & R.A. Cohen. 1995. An NADPH oxidase superoxide-generating system in the rabbit aorta. Am. J. Physiol. **268:** H2274–2280.

Differential Regulation of Apoptosis by Ischemia-Reperfusion and Ischemic Adaptation[a]

NILANJANA MAULIK,[b] HIROAKI SASAKI, AND NATHANIEL GALANG

Department of Surgery, University of Connecticut School of Medicine, Farmington, Connecticut 06030-1110, USA

ABSTRACT: Ischemia and reperfusion injure the heart, as manifested by myocardial infarction, postischemic ventricular functional dysfunctions, arrhythmias, and cardiomyocyte apoptosis. Hearts can be adapted to ischemic-reperfusion injury by subjecting them to non-lethal cyclic episodes of short-term ischemia and reperfusion. The adapted myocardium becomes resistant to subsequent lethal ischemic injury. Reactive oxygen species and oxidative stress play crucial roles in the pathophysiology of ischemic-reperfusion injury. The adapted hearts, when subjected to subsequent ischemia and reperfusion, generate a reduced amount of oxygen free radicals compared to the nonadapted hearts. The number of cardiomyocytes undergoing apoptotic cell death is reduced in the adapted hearts subjected to ischemia and reperfusion. In concert, the adapted myocardium is associated with increased antioxidant gene Bcl-2, increased binding activity of the nuclear transcription factor NFκB, and reduced binding activity of AP-1 compared to nonadapted hearts. Yet when nonadapted hearts are subjected to ischemia and reperfusion, Bcl-2 is downregulated while NFκB is moderately upregulated and AP-1 is significantly upregulated.

INTRODUCTION

Apoptosis is a unique process of physiological cell deletion. It can be induced in susceptible cells by a wide variety of normal physiological stimuli as well as by deleterious environmental conditions and cytotoxic agents.[1] Apoptosis is an active process of gene-directed cellular self-destruction.[2,3]

Myocardial ischemia and reperfusion result in apoptotic cell death in addition to tissue necrosis.[4,5] Prolonged reperfusion after ischemia in rat myocardium caused downregulation of the antioxidant gene Bcl-2 in concert with enhanced DNA fragmentation.[6] Bcl-2 is also known as an oncogene that inversely regulates apoptosis. Recent studies have established apoptotic cell death in ischemic brain[7] and ischemic liver.[8] Reperfusion of ischemic renal tissues was found to be associated with apoptotic cell death.[9,10] Extensive evidence exists to indicate that reperfusion of ischem-

[a]This study was supported by grant HL 56803 from the National Institutes of Health and by a Grant-in-Aid from the American Heart Association.

[b]Address correspondence to: Nilanjana Maulik, Ph.D., Department of Surgery, University of Connecticut Medical Center, 263 Farmington Avenue, Farmington, CT 06030-1110; Telephone: (860) 679-2857; Fax: (860) 679-4606; E-mail: nmaulik@panda.uchc.edu

ic myocardium leads to the generation of free radicals, intracellular Ca^{2+} overload, and loss of membrane phospholipids.[11] Reactive oxygen species serve as triggers for apoptosis in a variety of cell types.[12,13] Both apoptotic cell death and DNA fragmentation occurred after prolonged ischemia or acute ischemia followed by reperfusion. The redistribution of cardiomyocyte phospholipids occurred during ischemia. Externalization of both phosphatidylserine and phosphatidylethanolamine occurred after 20 min of ischemia and the extent of translocation remained the same during reperfusion.[14] Several studies demonstrated that inhibition of aminophospholipid translocase and activation of scramblase are characteristic features of apoptosis.[15,16] Apoptosis seems to be induced by oxidative stress developed during the reperfusion of ischemic myocardium because ebselen, an antioxidant and glutathione peroxidase mimic, reduces apoptotic cell death and DNA laddering.[17] Ischemic preconditioning mediated by cyclic episodes of short-term ischemia and reperfusion reduces apoptotic cell death.[18] Two redox-regulated proteins, NFκB and AP-1, participate in the regulation of apoptosis in some cell types.[19,20] The transcription factor NFκB is a nuclear protein of the Rel oncogene family and is involved in the regulation of numerous genes.[21] It exists in the cytoplasm as an inactive form and is stabilized by an inhibitory subunit, IκB, which inhibits its DNA binding activity. The transcriptional factors c-Jun and c-Fos form heterodimers or homodimers that bind to DNA. The complex formed by these proteins is AP-1.[22] Recent discoveries have revealed that AP1 and NFκB stimulate or inhibit oxidative stress–induced apoptosis in a trigger-dependent or a cell type–specific manner.[23–26] To explore molecular mechanisms involved in apoptosis during ishemia-reperfusion as well as during ischemic preconditioning, we have studied two important transcription factors, NFκB and AP-1, along with the anti-death gene Bcl-2. The extent of apoptosis and DNA laddering was also evaluated.

MATERIALS AND METHODS

Isolated Perfused Heart Preparation

Sprague Dawley rats weighing about 300 g were anesthetized with pentobarbital (80 mg/kg, i.p.). After intravenous administration of heparin (500 IU/kg), the chests were opened, and the hearts were rapidly excised and mounted on a non-recirculating Langendorff perfusion apparatus.[27] The perfusion buffer used in this study consisted of a modified Krebs-Henseleit bicarbonate buffer (KHB) (in mM: 118 NaCl, 4.7 KCl, 1.2 $MgSO_4$, 1.2 KH_2PO_4, 25 $NaHCO_3$, 10 glucose, and 1.7 $CaCl_2$, gassed with 95% O_2–5% CO_2 and filtered through a 5 mm filter to remove any particulate contaminants, pH 7.4) maintained at a constant 37°C and gassed continuously for the duration of the experiment. Left atrial cannulation was then carried out and after allowing for a stabilization period of 10 min in the retrograde perfusion mode, the circuit was switched to the antegrade working mode, which allows for the measurement of myocardial contractility as well as aortic and coronary flows, as described in detail in a previous paper.[27] Essentially, it is a left heart preparation in which the heart is perfused with a constant preload of 17 cm H_2O (being maintained by means of a Masterflex variable speed modular pump, Cole Parmer Instrument Company, Vernon Hills, IL) and pumps against an afterload of 100 cm H_2O.

At the end of 10 min, after the attainment of steady-state cardiac function, baseline functional parameters were recorded as usual. The circuit was then switched back to the retrograde mode. The hearts were divided into three groups. In Group I hearts were perfused with KHB buffer for 210 min. Group II hearts were perfused 1 h with KHB. In Group III, the hearts were subjected to ischemic stress adaptation by repeated ischemia-reperfusion: inducing global ischemia for 5 min followed by 10 min of reperfusion and repeating the process four times as described previously.[27] At the end of this period all hearts (except for those in Group I) were subjected to global ischemia for 15 min followed by 2 h of reperfusion. The first 10 min of reperfusion was in the retrograde mode to allow for post-ischemic stabilization and thereafter in the antegrade working mode to allow for assessment of functional parameters.

For NFκB and AP-1 binding activity studies and Northern blot analysis, left ventricles from the control and experimental hearts were kept frozen in liquid nitrogen. The extent of myocardial apoptosis was evaluated in the heart after each experiment.

Electrophoretic Mobility Assay

Nuclear proteins were isolated from the heart to estimate NFκB translocation according to described previously methods. The nuclear extracts were stored at –70°C. Protein concentration was estimated by using Pierce protein assay kit (Pierce Chemical Company, Rockford, IL). NFκB oligonucleotide (AGTTGAGGGGACTTTC-CCAGG) (2.5 μl [20 ng/μl]) was labeled using T4 polynucleotide kinase as previously described.[25] The binding reaction mixture contained (in a total volume of 20.2 μl) 0.2 μl DTT (0.2 M), 1 μl BSA (20 mg/ml), 4 μl poly dI-dC (0.5 μg/μl), 2 μl Buffer D^+, 4 μl Buffer F, 2 μl ^{32}P-oligo (0.5 ng/μl), and 7 μl extract containing 10 μg protein. Composition of Buffer D^+ was 20 mM HEPES, pH 7.9, 20% glycerol, 100 mM KCl, 0.5 mM EDTA, 0.25% NP 40. Buffer F contained 20% Ficoll 400, 100 mM HEPES, pH 7.9, and 300 mM KCl. Incubation was carried out for 20 min at room temperature. Ten μl of the solution was loaded onto a 4% acrylamide gel and separated at 80 V until the dye reached the bottom. After electrophoresis, gels were dried and exposed to Kodak X-ray film at –70°C.

AP-1

The oligonucleotide used for AP-1 consisted of the following sequence: 5′-CGCTTGATGAGTCAGCCGAA-3′. Gel shift assay was performed according to the manufacturer's (Promega) protocol with slight modification. ^{32}P end–labeled oligonucleotide was incubated in a 10 ml reaction mixture containing 10 mmol/l Tris-HCl, pH 7.5, 0.5 mmol/l EDTA, 0.5 mmol/l DTT, 4% glycerol, 50 mmol/l NaCl, 1 mmol/l $MgCl_2$, 0.5 μg Poly(dI-dC), and 4.5 μg of nuclear extracts for 30 min at room temperature. Parallel competition experiments were also performed using unlabeled oligonucleotide (10–100 molar) added to the binding reaction mixture. After incubation, dye was added to the reaction mixture and the complex formed was separated in 4% polyacrylamide gel (acrylamide:bisacrylamide 30:1) by electrophoresis. The gel was subsequently dried and exposed to Kodak film at –70°C.

Bcl-2

Total RNA was extracted from the heart tissues by the acid-guanidinium thiocyanate-phenol-chloroform method. For Northern blot analysis, total RNA was electrophoresed in 1% agarose formaldehyde-formamide gel and transferred to Gene Screen Plus hybridization transfer membrane (Biotech Systems, NEN Research products, Boston, MA). The membrane was then baked for 1 h under vacuum at 80°C. Each hybridization was repeated at least three times using different membranes. After each hybridization the residual cDNA was removed and rehybridized with GAPDH cDNA probe, the results of which served as a loading control. The autoradiograms were quantitatively evaluated by computerized β scanner. The results of densitometric scanning were normalized relative to the signal obtained for GAPDH cDNA.

Evaluation of Apoptosis

DNA Fragmentation

To examine DNA laddering, cellular DNA were isolated from the control perfused, ischemic-reperfused, and preconditioned myocardium. From 0.5–1.0 μg cellular DNA was isolated from each group and treated with 5 U of Klenow polymerase using 0.5 μCi of ^{32}P-labeled dCTP in the presence of 10 mM Tris-HCl, pH 7.5, and 5 mM $MgCl_2$. The reaction was incubated for 10 min at room temperature and terminated by adding 10 mM EDTA. The unincorporated nucleotides were removed

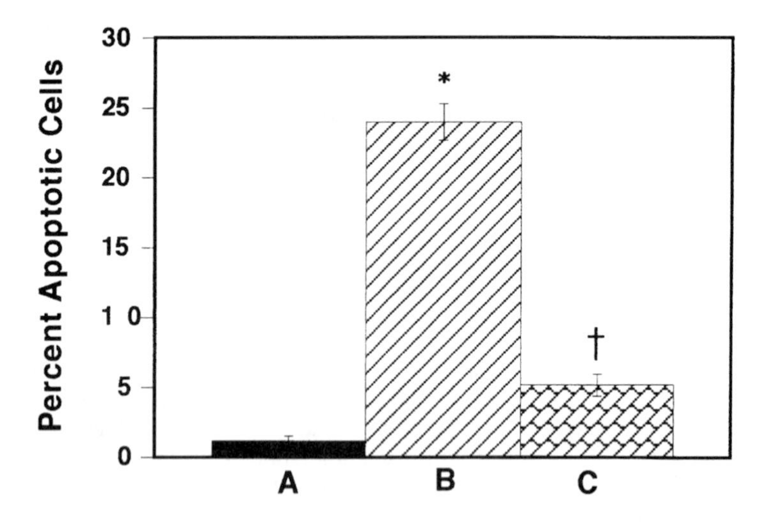

FIGURE 1. Evaluation of apoptosis by tunnel staining. Evaluation of apoptosis reveals increased number of apoptotic cells in the ischemic-reperfused myocardium. Sections of control and experimental heart tissues were analyzed for apoptosis using APOPTAG^R kit as described in *Methods*. Percent apoptotic cells are shown. Results are expressed as means ± S.E.M of six different rats per group. *$p < 0.05$ compared to the perfused control. A, Perfused control; B, ischemia-reperfusion; C, ischemic precondition.

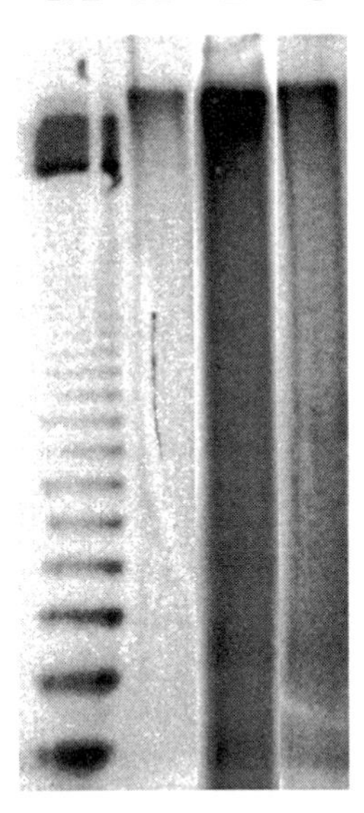

FIGURE 2. DNA fragmentation. DNA extracted from control perfused (lane A), ischemia-reperfused (lane B), preconditioned (lane C) rat myocardium, labeled with ^{32}P-dCTP, and electrophoresed for 3 h at 60 V. After drying the gel on 3MM Whatman paper, the filter was exposed for autoradiography. Lane M represents the 123 bp ladder with ^{32}P-dCTP. Lane A and lane C show no sign of DNA fragmentation, whereas DNA fragmentation is very obvious in lane B.

and the labeled DNA was electrophoresed on a 1.8% agarose gel for 3 h at 60 V. After drying, the gel was placed on 3MM Whatman paper filter and exposed for autoradiography.

Visualization of Apoptotic Cells

Apoptotic cells were visualized by labeling the 3′ OH ends of DNA by utilizing digoxigenin incorporation by TDT enzymes. In brief, paraffinized sections were deparaffinized with xylene and washed in succession with different concentrations of ethanol. Sections were treated with proteinase K followed by TDT for 1 h at 37°C. After applying stop-wash solution to the sections, anti-digoxigenin-fluorescein was added to the slides, incubated for 30 min, washed, and counterstained with propidium iodide/antifade directly on the slides. Apoptotic cells were visualized by direct fluorescein detection of digoxigenin-labeled genomic DNA by epifluorescence using standard fluorescein excitation and emission filters with an Axiovert 100 TV microscope.

Statistical Analysis

For statistical analysis, a two-way analysis of variance (ANOVA) followed by Scheffe's test was first carried out using Primer Computer Program (McGraw-Hill, 1988) to test for any differences between groups. If differences were established, the values were compared using Student's t test for paired data. The values were expressed as mean ± SEM. The results were considered significant if $p < 0.05$.

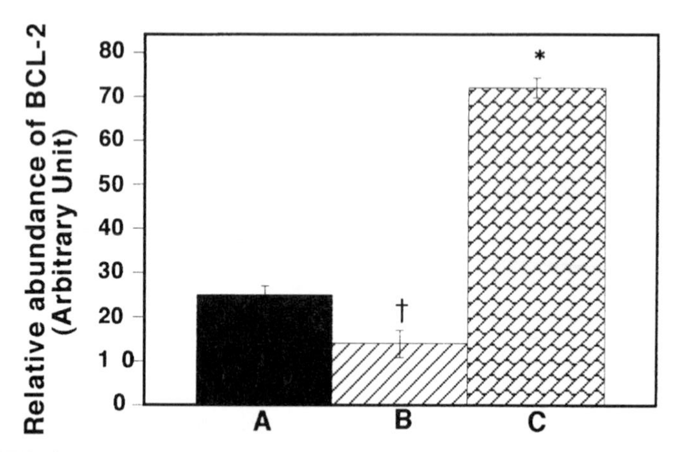

FIGURE 3. Northern blot analysis for BCl-2. Total RNA was isolated and Northern hybridization was performed as described in *Methods*. The results of densitometric scanning (mean ± S.E.M) for four different experiments at each time point are shown for each blot. $^*p < 0.05$ compared to the perfused control.

RESULTS AND DISCUSSION

Preconditioning of the heart by repeated ischemia and reperfusion can delay the onset of further irreversible injury[28] or even reduce subsequent postischemic ventricular dysfunction[29,30] and incidence of arrhythmias.[31] Such myocardial preservation by repeated short-term reversible ischemia followed by short duration of reperfusion (ischemic-reperfusion) led to the development of the concept of stress adaptation. Consequently, a number of investigators developed new ideas of preconditioning, which include adenosine, potassium channel opening, hypoxia, heat shock, and oxidative stress.[31,32] Reactive oxygen species and oxidative stress play crucial roles in the pathophysiology of ischemic-reperfusion injury. The adapted hearts, when subjected to subsequent ischemia and reperfusion, generate reduced amount of oxygen free radicals compared to the nonadapted hearts.

The common inducers of apoptosis include oxygen free radicals, oxidative stress, and Ca^{2+}, which are also implicated in the pathogenesis of myocardial ischemic-reperfusion injury. Although cardiomyocyte death and infarction associated with ischemia-reperfusion injury are traditionally believed to be induced via necrosis, a clearcut mechanism of accidental cell death, its precise mechanism remains unclear. Recent studies implicated apoptotic cell death in ischemic brain and ischemic liver as well as in the ischemic-reperfused rat myocardium.[33] Reperfusion of ischemic renal tissues was found to be associated with apoptopic cell death.[10] Cardiomyocytes exposed to hypoxia revealed apoptotic cell death as evidenced by DNA fragmentation in conjunction with the expression of Fas mRNA. More recently, evidence was furnished in support of reperfusion injury–mediated apoptosis in cardiomyocytes. Based on pathological evaluation, these investigators concluded that apoptosis might be a specific feature of reperfusion injury in cardiac myocytes. Apoptotic and necrotic myocyte cell deaths associated with ischemia-reperfusion were shown to be inde-

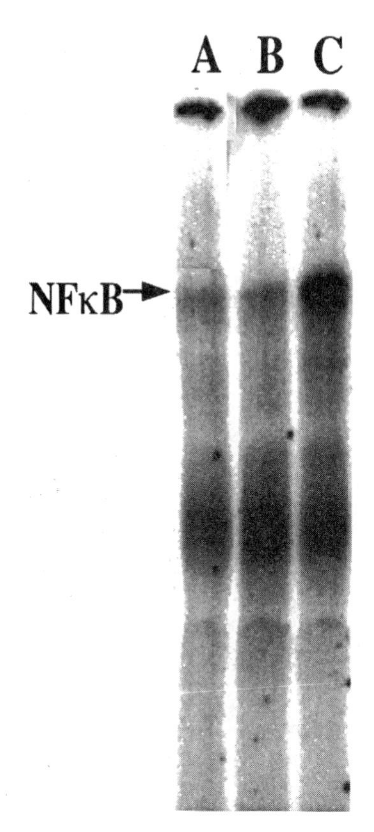

FIGURE 4. Electrophoretic mobility assay for NFκB. Nuclear proteins were isolated as described in *Methods*. Lane A, perfused control; lane B, ischemia-reperfusion; lane C, preconditioned group. Lane A represents basal NFκB binding activity. In the preconditioned group, lane C, the NFκB binding activity is fivefold higher compared to the ischemic-reperfused group, lane B.

pendent contributing variables of infarct size in rats. A separate study has shown apoptosis to be a feature of human vascular pathology, including restenotic lesions and, to a lesser extent, atherosclerotic lesions, suggesting that apoptosis may modulate the cellularity of lesions that produce human vascular obstruction.[34]

In this study the number of cardiomyocytes undergoing apoptotic cell death is reduced in the adapted hearts subjected to ischemia-reperfusion (FIG. 1). In our study DNA fragmentation was not apparent in the control perfused hearts (FIG. 2, lane A). Ischemic adaptation was associated with a significant decrease in DNA fragmentation (FIG. 2, lane C) when compared with the ischemic-reperfused group (FIG. 2, lane B). In concert, the adapted myocardium is associated with increased expression of the anti-apoptotic gene Bcl-2 (FIG. 3), increased induction of the expression of the nuclear transcription factor NFκB (FIG. 4), and downregulation of AP-1 (FIG. 5) compared to nonadapted hearts. In contrast, when nonadapted hearts are subjected to ischemia-reperfusion, Bcl-2 is downregulated (FIG. 3) while NFκB is moderately upregulated and AP-1 is significantly upregulated. To confirm NFκB binding activity with p65, we performed super-shift assays with polyclonal antibody recognizing NFκB p65 subunit. We have also shown that ebselen, a glutathione peroxidase mimic, can preserve Bcl-2 by reducing oxidative stress in the postischemic-reperfused

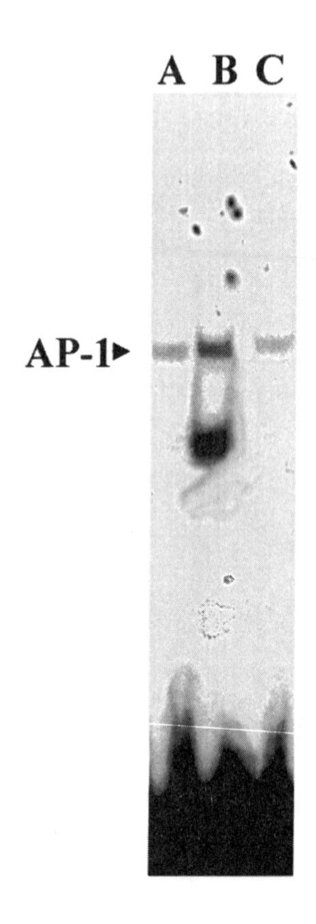

FIGURE 5. Electrophoretic mobility assay for AP-1. Nuclear proteins were isolated as described in *Methods*. Lane A, perfused control; lane B, ischemia-reperfusion; lane C, preconditioned group. AP-1 activity was significantly higher in the ischemic-reperfused group, lane B. In the preconditioned group, the activity remained the same as in the control perfused group.

myocardium.[17] The cardioprotective effects of adaptation can be blocked by pretreating the hearts with a hydroxyl radical scavenger dimethyl thiourea, which also blocks the induction of the transcription factors and HSP 27 gene expression. Taken together, it appears that myocardial adaptation to ischemia is precisely controlled by a redox switch and oxygen free radicals appear to function as a signaling molecule in this process. NFκB is a critical regulator for gene expression induced by diverse stress signals including mutagenic, oxidative and hypoxic stresses. Activation of NFκB is likely to be involved in the induction of gene expression associated with the ischemic adaptation. AP-1 is a redox-sensitive signaling molecule that plays an important regulatory role in cellular responses to stress induced by external factors. The AP-1 transcription factor complex is composed of a group of proteins encoded by the Jun and Fos families which bind to the AP-1 consensus sequences. Regulation of AP-1 in response to external stimuli is mediated by members of the MAPK family.[35] AP-1 regulates the activation of transcription of a variety of genes, some of them may be involved in apoptosis. The exact mechanism by which AP-1 and NFκB modulate apoptosis is not clear. We have shown moderate binding activity of NFκB in the ischemic-reperfused rat heart, whereas significant binding activity was observed in the preconditioned heart by electrophoretic mobility assay. Therefore, there must be a certain extent of binding activity of NFκB necessary to reduce apoptosis in the rat myocardium. Whereas AP-1 binding activity is only observed in the ischemic-reperfused myocardium, AP-1 activity in the ischemic preconditioned group remains the same as in the control perfused group

The Bcl-2 family proteins are known as the suppressors of caspase-activating proteins, e.g, CED-4 family members. Bcl-2 family proteins are also involved in the regulation of a variety of mitochondrial events. This anti-apoptotic gene is involved in reducing oxidant- and hypoxia-induced necrosis as well.[36] In our study the significant induction of the expression of Bcl-2 in the ischemic preconditioned myocardium as compared to the nonadapted myocardium indicates the anti-apoptotic activity of Bcl-2, which correlates with the reduction in the extent of DNA fragmentation and the number of apoptotic cells.

SUMMARY

Ischemic preconditioning leads to the activation of the nuclear transcription factor NFκB, the downregulation of the activator protein AP-1, and the upregulation of the anti-apoptotic gene Bcl-2. Such contributions by ischemic adaptation result in the reduction of apoptosis. Taken together, it appears that myocardial adaptation to ischemia is precisely controlled by a redox switch and oxygen free radicals appear to function as a signaling molecule in this process.

REFERENCES

1. McConkey, D.J., S. Orrenius & M. Jondal. 1990. Cellular signaling in programmed cell death (apoptosis). Immunol Today **11:** 120–121.
2. Lockshine, R.A. & Z. Zakeri. 1991. Programmed cell death and apoptosis. Curr. Comm. Cell Molec. Biol. **3:** 47–60.
3. Bredesen, D.E. 1994. Neuronal apoptosis: genetic and biochemical modulation. Curr. Comm. Cell Molec. Biol. **3:** 397–421.
4. Gottlieb, R.A., K.O. Burleson, R.A. Kloner, B.M. Babior & R.L. Engler. 1994. Reperfusion injury induces apoptosis in rabbit cardiomyocytes. J. Clin. Invest. **94:** 1621–1628.
5. James, T.N. 1994. Normal and abnormal consequences of apoptosis in the human heart from postnatal morphogenesis to paroxysmal arrhythmias. Circulation **90:** 556–573.
6. Maulik, N., T. Yoshida, R.M. Engelman, J.A. Rousou, J.E. Flack, D. Deaton & D.K. Das. 1997. Oxidative stress developed during reperfusion of ischemic myocardium downregulates the BCL-2 gene and induces apoptosis and DNA laddering. Surgical Forum **XL:** VIII.
7. Tominaga, T., S. Kure, K. Narisawa & T. Yoshimoto. 1993. Endonuclease activation after focal ischemic injury in the rat brain. Brain Res. **608:** 21–26.
8. Fukuda, K., M. Kojiro & J.F. Chiu. 1993. Demonstration of extensive chromatin cleavage in transplanted Morris hepatoma 7777 tissue: apoptosis or necrosis. Am. J. Pathol. **142:** 935–946.
9. Gobe, G.C., R.A. Alexsen & J.W. Searle. 1990. Cellular events in experimental unilateral ischemic renal atrophy and in regeneration after contralateral nephrectomy. Lab. Invest. **63:** 770–779.
10. Schumer, M., M.C. Colombel, I.S. Sawczuk, J. Connor, K.M. O'Toole, G.J. Wise & R. Buttyan. 1992. Morphologic, biochemical and molecular evidence of apoptosis during the reperfusion phase after brief periods of renal ischemia. Am. J. Pathol. **140:** 830–838.

11. Das, D.K., R.M. Engelman, M.R. Prasad, J.A. Rousou, R.H. Breyer, R. Jones, H. Young & G.A. Cordis. 1989. Improvement of ischemia reperfusion induced myocardial dysfunction by modulating calcium-overload using a novel specific calmodulin antagonist, CGC 9343B. Biochem. Pharmacol. **38:** 465–471.
12. Greenlund, L.J.S., T.L. Deckwerth & E.M. Johnson, Jr. 1995. Superoxide dismutase delays neuronal apoptosis: a role for reactive oxygen species in programmed neuronal death. Neuron **14:** 303–315.
13. Verity, M.A., D.E. Bredesen & T. Sarafian. 1995. Role of reactive oxygen species in neuronal degeneration. Ann. N.Y. Acad. Sci. **765:** 340.
14. Maulik, N., V.E. Kagan, V.A. Tyurin & D.K. Das. 1998. Redistribution of phosphatidylethylethanol amine and phosphatidylserine precedes reperfusion-induced apoptosis. Am. J. Physiol. **274:** H242–H248.
15. Wyllie, A.H. 1980. Glucocorticoid-induced thymocyte apoptosis is associated with endogenous endonuclease activation. Nature **284:** 555–556.
16. Wyllie, A.H., J.F.R. Kerr & A.R. Currie. 1980. Cell death: the significance of apoptosis. Int. Rev. Cytol. **68:** 251–306.
17. Maulik, N., T. Yoshida & D.K. Das. 1998. Oxidative stress developed during the reperfusion of ischemic myocardium induces apioptosis. Free Rad. Biol. Med. **24:** 869–875.
18. Maulik, N., T. Yoshida, R.M. Engelman, D. Deaton, J. Flack, J.A. Rousou & D. K. Das. 1998. Ischemic preconditioning attenuates apoptotic cell death associated with ischemia/reperfusion. Mol. Cell. Biochem. **186:** 139–145.
19. Ishikawa, Y., T. Yokoo & M. Kitamura. 1997. Biochem. Biophys. Res. Commun. **240:** 496–501.
20. Sun, Y. & L.W. Oberley. 1998. Redox regulation of transcriptional activators. Free Rad. Biol. Med. **21:** 335–348.
21. Yamazaki, T., Y. Seko, T. Tamatani, M. Miyasaka, H. Yagita, K. Okumura, R. Nagai & Y. Yazaki. 1993. Expression of intercellular adhesion molecule-1 in rat heart with ischemia/reperfusion and limitation of infarct size by treatment with antibodies against cell adhesion molecules. Am. J. Pathol. **143:** 410–418.
22. Diamond, M.I., J.N. Miner, S.K. Yoshinaga & K.R. Yamamoto. 1990. Transcription factor interactions: selection of positive or negative regulation from a single DNA element. Science **249:** 1266–1272.
23. Lin, K.I., S.H. Lee, R. Narayanan, J.M. Barbaran, J.M. Hardwick & R.R. Ratan. 1995. Thiol agents and BCl-2 identify an alphavirus induced apoptotic pathway that requires activation of the transcription factor NF-kB. J. Cell Biol. **131:** 1149–1161.
24. Ghosh, S., A.M. Gifford, L.R. Riviere, P. Tempst, G.P. Nolan & D. Baltimore. 1990. Cloning of the p50 DNA binding subunit of NFκB: Homology to rel and dorsal. Cell **62:** 1019–1029.
25. Angel, P. & M. Karin. 1991. The role of Jun, Fos and the AP-1 complex in cell proliferation and transformation. Biochim. Biophy. Acta **1072:** 129–157.
26. Beg, A.A. & D. Baltimore. 1996. An essential role for NF-kappaB in preventing TNF-alpha induced cell death. Science **274:** 782–784.
27. Maulik, N., S. Motoaki, D.P. Brendan & D.K. Das. 1998.An essential role of NF-kB in tyrosine kinase signaling of P38 MAP kinase regulation of myocardial adaptation to ischemia. FEBS Lett. **429:** 365–369.
28. Murry, C.E., R.B. Jennings & K.A. Reimer. 1986. Preconditioning with ischemia: a delay of lethal cell injury in ischemic myocardium. Circulation **74:** 1124–1136.
29. Flack, J.E., Y. Kimura, R.M. Engelman, J.A. Rousou, J. Iyengar, R. Jones & D.K. Das. 1991. Preconditioning the heart by repeated stuuning improves myocardial salvage. Circulation **84:** III-369–III-374.
30. Schott, R.J., S. Rohmann, E.R. Braun & W. Schaper. 1990. Ischemic preconditioning reduces infarct size in swine myocardium. Circ. Res. **66:** 1133–1142.
31. Tosaki, A. G.A. Cordis, P. Szerdahelvi, R.M. Engelman & D.K. Das. 1994. Effects of preconditioning on reperfusion arrhythmias, myocardial functions, formation of free radicals, and ion shifts in isolated ischemic/reperfused rat hearts. J. Cardiovasc. Pharmacol. **23:** 365–373.
32. Gross, G.J. & J.A. Auchampach. 1992. Blocked of ATP-sensitive potassium channels protects myocardial preconditioning in dogs. Circ. Res. 70: 223–233.

33. TANAKA, M., H. ITO, S. ADACHI, H. AKIMOTO, T. NISHIKAWA, T. KASAJIMA, F. MARUMO & H. HIROE. 1994. Hypoxia induces apoptosis with enhanced expression of Fas antigene messenger RNA in cultured neonatal rat cardiomyocytes. Circ. Res. **75:** 426–433.
34. KAJSTURA, J., W. CHENG, K. REISS, W.A. CLARK, E.H. SONNENBLICK, S. KRAJEWSKI, J.C. REED, G. OLIVETTI & P. ANVERSA. 1996. Apoptotic and necrotic myocyte cell deaths are independent contributing variables of infarct size in rats. Lab. Invest. **74:** 86–107.
35. MACHO, A., M.V. BLAZQUEZ, P. NAVAS & E. MUNOZ. 1998. Induction of apoptosis by vanilloid compounds does not require de novo gene transcription and activator protein 1 activity. Cell Growth Diff. **9:** 277–286.
36. GREEN, D.R. & J.C. REED. 1998. Mitochondria and apoptosis. Science **281:** 1309–1312.

Apoptosis in Myocardial Ischemia-Reperfusion

ROBERTA A. GOTTLIEB[a] AND ROBERT L. ENGLER[b]

Division of Biochemistry, Department of Molecular & Experimental Medicine, The Scripps Research Institute, La Jolla, California 92037 USA
[b]*Research Service, Veterans Affairs San Diego Healthcare System, San Diego, California 92093 USA*

ABSTRACT: The signal transduction pathways by which ischemia-reperfusion leads to apoptosis may involve the JNK pathway, ceramide generation, and inhibition of protective PKC pathways. The biochemical events associated with apoptosis include mitochondrial inactivation, cytochrome *c* dislocation, caspase activation, and cytoplasmic acidification. Through the concerted efforts of multiple classes of enzymes, apoptosis is accomplished, resulting in the death of a cell in which potentially transforming oncogenes have been degraded and inflammatory contents are contained within the plasma membrane until the fragments can be ingested by phagocytes. This non-inflammatory mode of cell death permits tissue remodeling with minimal scar formation, and so is preferable to necrotic cell death. The distinction between apoptosis and necrosis, which implies different mechanisms of cell death, is blurred in the case of a pathologic insult such as ischemia-reperfusion. It is suggested that it is more useful to view cell death in the context of whether or not it can be prevented

Heart failure arises from diverse causes, including cumulative injury from ischemic episodes. Indeed, this is one of the most common causes of subsequent heart failure. In this review, I focus on what is known about apoptosis in ischemia-reperfusion.

Myocardial ischemia and reperfusion leads to cell death,[1] much of which is accomplished through apoptosis.[2] Apoptosis is a cell-autonomous mechanism (suicide) to eliminate injured or unwanted cells without inducing an inflammatory response. In contrast, necrosis, which commonly arises from an externally derived insult (death by murder), results in spillage of cellular DNA and actin and provokes inflammation. Because apoptosis is a complex series of ordered biochemical events, it may be possible to interfere in any one of these biochemical events, perhaps resulting in survival of the cell, but also possibly converting apoptosis to necrosis. We will consider some of the biochemical events that characterize myocardial injury during ischemia and reperfusion and relate them to apoptosis.

One of the most potent means to protect myocardium from ischemia-reperfusion injury is preconditioning. Preconditioning is operationally defined as a brief period of cellular stress that activates a protective response in the cell that minimizes injury

[a]Address correspondence to: Roberta A. Gottlieb, M.D., Division of Biochemistry, Department of Molecular & Experimental Medicine, The Scripps Research Institute, 10550 North Torrey Pines Road, La Jolla, California 92037; Telephone: 619/784-7929; Fax: 619/784-7981.

upon exposure to a second, more sustained insult, such as ischemia-reperfusion. Preconditioning, accomplished by brief ischemia, exposure to phorbol esters, or adenosine, has been shown to protect myocardium. Apoptotic cell death after prolonged ischemia and reperfusion was reduced by preconditioning.[3] We will consider whether preconditioning interferes with one or more events required for the initiation and execution of the apoptotic program.

WHAT ARE THE EVENTS ASSOCIATED WITH APOPTOSIS, AND WHICH OF THESE HAVE BEEN IDENTIFIED IN THE HEART?

It has been shown that p53, which is involved in response to DNA-damaging agents and oxidative stressors, is also activated by hypoxia[4] to cause the induction of apoptosis. Although a host of genes induced by p53 have been identified,[5,6] it is still not clear how the expression of these genes serve to initiate apoptosis. Moreover, it was recently shown in the p53 (–/–) mouse that infarct size was not reduced relative to heterozygous littermates, suggesting that ischemia-reperfusion injury does not lead to apoptotic cell death through a p53-dependent pathway.[7] However, p73, a recently identified homolog of p53,[8] may play a role in the hypoxic heart.

Ultraviolet light, DNA-damaging agents, and oxidative stressors have been shown to activate a kinase pathway leading to phosphorylation of c-jun.[9] This pathway, known as the Jun-N-terminal kinase (JNK) pathway or stress-activated protein kinase pathway (SAPK), has been shown to participate in the activation of programmed cell death in a variety of systems.[10] Since the JNK pathway and caspase activation have been shown to be linked,[11] various pathways are available to the cell that lead to caspase activation and apoptosis. Many cellular stressors, such as DNA-damaging agents, gamma irradiation, and pro-apoptotic cytokines such as tumor necrosis factor α (TNFα), also activate acidic and or neutral sphingomyelinases to generate ceramide. Ceramide acts as an intracellular signaling molecule to activate a kinase pathway that leads to apoptosis in some settings and proliferation in others.[12] Ceramide has been shown to play a role in TNFα-mediated apoptosis in cultured cardiomyocytes.[13] Most recently the p38/MAP kinase pathway was shown to be involved in the hypertrophic response as well as apoptosis.[14] Such diametrically opposed responses suggest that cells utilize additional information to reach a divide-or-die decision. c-Myc has been implicated in this antipodean response.[15]

As cells enter apoptosis, dramatic morphologic alterations ensue. There is profound shrinkage and membrane blebbing, which is associated with externalization of phosphatidylserine. Cytoskeletal architecture is altered by the proteolytic cleavage of fodrin, actin, and of one or more G-proteins that regulate the state of assembly of the cytoskeleton.[16,17] Related plasma membrane events include expression of cell surface markers for ingestion. One of the most important aspects of apoptosis is the preservation of an intact plasma membrane until the cell can be ingested by a neighboring cell or professional phagocyte. This serves to limit inflammation. Aided in the process of maintaining the integrity of the dying cell is the enzyme tissue transglutaminase, which crosslinks proteins together through the *de novo* formation of gamma-glutamyl dipeptide bonds. This serves to crosslink actin and a variety of other skeletal proteins to form a cornified outer envelope.[18]

Changes in membrane potential, ion fluxes, and possibly also water loss accompany the death process as well. These alterations result in cytoplasmic acidification. In some cell types, changes are also associated with an increase in intracellular calcium. It should be noted that these features are particularly distinct from the changes seen in necrosis, in which the plasma membrane ruptures, either due to external damage or through a swelling process that arises after loss of ATP and failure of the sodium-potassium ATPase.

One of the most widely recognized biochemical features of apoptosis is the activation of a class of cysteine proteases known as caspases, which have the unique property of cleaving proteins on the carboxyl side of aspartic acid. Cells possess multiple caspases, which may work in a cascade fashion. The redundancy may serve to amplify and accelerate the response, as well as to provide multiple mechanisms to get the job done. Indeed this redundancy is apparent in the phenotypes of knockout mice in which the deletion of a single caspase is associated with a relatively unimpressive phenotype. Deletion of caspase-3 results in a failure of neuronal apoptosis, and the mice are born with overlarge brains and die soon after birth.[19] However, deletion of caspase-1 or caspase-11 does not result in dramatic phenotypic changes; thus the roles for these caspases are less clear.[20,21] However, in many cases of knockouts, organismic homeostasis is maintained until the system is stressed. We may learn more from assessing whether these knockouts will have an alteration of cell death in response to ischemia-reperfusion, for instance. Such studies are underway and may provide insight into the role for one or more of these caspases in myocardial cell death. Caspases have a common structure, in which there is a prodomain of variable length, followed by a region of ~20 kD that contains the QACRG active site and a carboxy terminal region of ~10 kD. The three domains are separated by consensus caspase cleavage sites, and the inactive procaspase must be cleaved between the 20 and 10 kD regions to become active. The two fragments associate and form a heterotetramer that represents the fully active enzyme. Mutation of the cleavage site between the p20 and p10 domains greatly reduces activity of the enzyme. Additional information about the consensus sequences for proteolytic cleavage is rapidly evolving, and has been reviewed recently.[22] It has been noted that the general classes of substrates (in addition to other caspases) represent cytoskeletal proteins and signaling enzymes that would favor cellular proliferation. Much interest has been directed to the question of caspase activation: how does the first proenzyme get processed to become active?

CASPASE ACTIVATION PATHWAYS

Two pathways have been identified: one activated through a cell surface signal leading directly to caspase activation, and another more complicated pathway involving the mitochondria. These are outlined in FIGURE 1.

By analogy to the cascade of proteolytic clotting enzymes, caspases may be initiated by an initial aggregation event at the plasma membrane in which the cell surface receptor Fas is aggregated upon binding its ligand. This leads to the intracellular association of proteins that interact through a conserved region known as the death domain, one example of which is FADD (Fas-associated death domain). FADD then

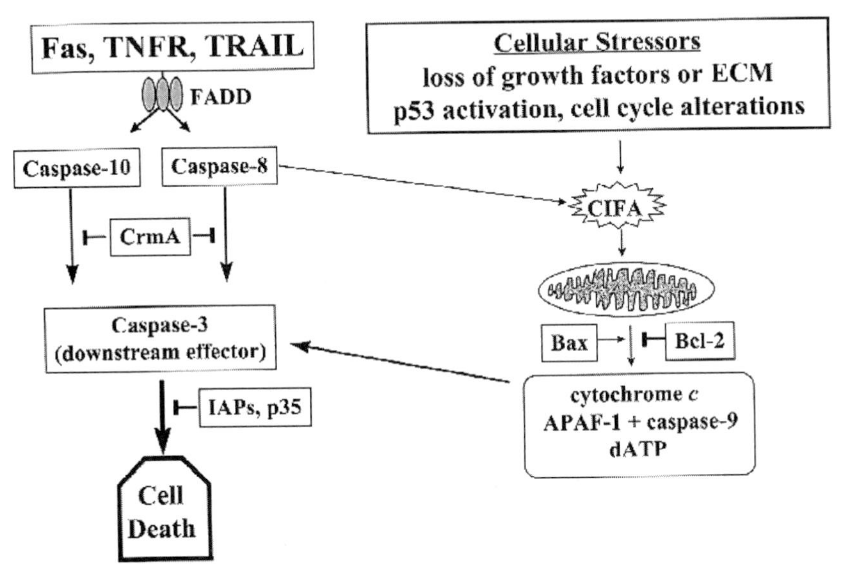

FIGURE 1. Pathways of caspase activation. Ligation of a cell surface receptor, such as Fas, tumor necrosis factor α, or TRAIL, results in association with additional intracellular molecules (FADD) through self-association domains. Caspase-8 or caspase-10 is recruited to the complex (known as a death-inducing signal complex), where it undergoes autoprocessing. The activated caspase is then free to act on downstream effector caspases, such as caspase-3. Cowpox response modifier protein, CrmA, inhibits caspase-8 but not caspase-3. Inhibitor of apoptosis proteins (IAPs) interact with downstream caspases. Other cellular stressors, including agents that activate p53, act through a mitochondrial-dependent pathway, in which CIFA causes the dissociation of cytochrome *c*, thereby enabling it to interact with Apaf-1 and dATP to promote the processing of procaspase-9. The activated caspase-9 then processes caspase-3. Caspase-8 also leads to the activation of CIFA.

recruits a specialized caspase (caspase-8, also known as FLICE) through a second domain (the death effector domain), and the aggregated complex results in autoprocessing of caspase-8 molecules. The fully processed caspase-8 is then free to interact with downstream caspases such as caspase-3, as well as other targets such as mitochondria.[23] Recently it was shown that ultraviolet light exposure resulted in membrane changes that led to aggregation of Fas and downstream activation of caspase-8. It is possible that other oxidative stresses may provoke a similar aggregation. It has been shown that hypoxia in neonatal myocytes results in upregulation of Fas, although it was not shown that this transcriptional response was required for apoptosis to ensue.

The other well-characterized pathway to caspase activation involves participation of the mitochondria. In 1997 it was shown that cytochrome *c* participated in caspase activation, in concert with other proteins that were subsequently identified as caspase-9 and Apaf-1. Apaf-1 contains a region shared with other caspases and may be required for protein-protein interaction. In addition, it has a binding site for ATP (or dATP), and a series of 12 WD-40 repeats, which may be involved in binding cytochrome *c*.[24] In addition, Apaf-1 has a region of homology to the *Caenorhabditis*

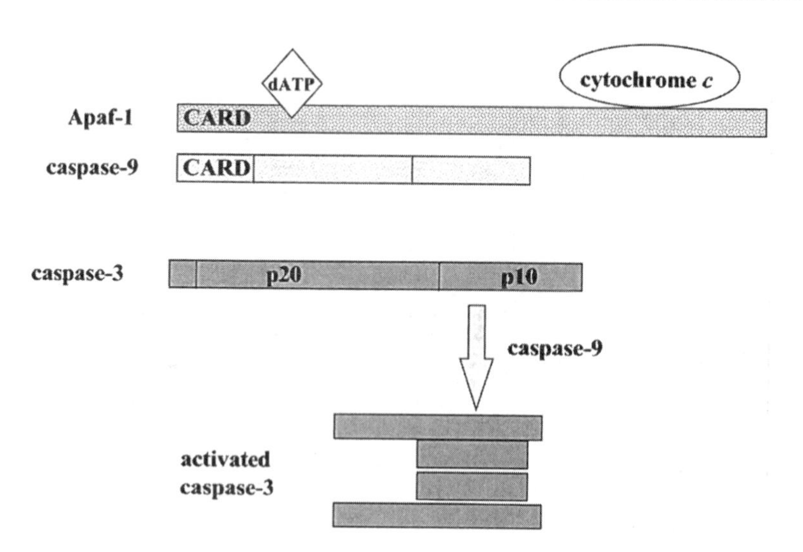

FIGURE 2. Formation of the caspase activation complex. Apaf-1 binds cytochrome *c* and dATP, then recruits caspase-9 through homologous caspase activation recruitment domains (CARD), resulting in autoprocessing of caspase-9. The activated caspase-9 then processes caspase-3, removing the short amino-terminal prodomain and clipping between the p20 and p10 regions to give rise to the fully active heterotetramer.

elegans death gene 4 (Ced-4), one of three genes controlling developmental programmed cell death in the nematode. It is now thought that Apaf-1 represents the mammalian homolog of Ced-4 and interacts with cytochrome *c* and dATP to activate caspase-9.[25] The activated and processed caspase-9 then cleaves caspase-3 to generate the active enzyme, which is the effector protease that proceeds to degrade most of the cellular targets (FIG. 2). One problem with this model is that it depends upon cytochrome *c* being released from the mitochondria, where it is normally sequestered in the intermembrane space. Recent studies have indicated that Bcl-2 prevents the release of cytochrome *c*, while bax promotes its release, leading to apoptosis. Thus, agents affecting mitochondrial integrity may lead to cytochrome *c* release and activation of caspases. Little information is available explaining how cytochrome *c* release is controlled, or even if this is a nonspecific event accompanying general loss of mitochondrial integrity or a regulated release of a single protein. It appears to occur before loss of mitochondrial membrane potential,[26] but may represent generalized leakage of intermembrane space constituents. We have shown that loss of outer membrane integrity is a rather late event, but far earlier, cytochrome *c* has become unavailable for electron transport, although still present in the intermembrane space.[27] This suggests its interaction with other protein(s) that eventually may all be released from the mitochondria when the outer membrane ruptures.

One postulated mechanism for the rupture of the outer mitochondrial membrane to occur is swelling of the matrix.[28] Since the inner membrane is heavily infolded, it can tolerate swelling in response to ion fluxes and will not rupture; however, as it swells, it will stretch and eventually rupture the outer membrane. Since Bcl-2 and bax are postulated to function as ion channels, this explanation is attractive. However, Bcl-2 and bax are located in the outer mitochondrial membrane, rather than the inner membrane, so it is unclear how ion flux through the (already ion-permeable) outer membrane would lead to matrix swelling. There is not enough information yet to fully establish the concept. Disruption of mitochondrial calcium homeostasis, leading to the formation of the permeability transition pore, may also result in mitochondrial matrix swelling and rupture.[29]

It is important to note that there is another important aspect of the mitochondrial dysfunction that accompanies the onset of apoptosis. Our lab has shown that one of the earliest events is the production of a cytosolic factor (designated CIFA, for cytochrome *c*–interacting factor of apoptosis) that penetrates the outer mitochondrial membrane to cause dissociation of cytochrome *c* from its normal resting place in the electron transport chain.[30] If the mitochondrial outer membrane is breached, as occurs with homogenization of the cells, the dissociated cytochrome diffuses out of the mitochondria and can be detected in the cytosol,[27] where it is hypothesized to interact with Apaf-1 and dATP to promote activation of caspase-9.[25] However, it is possible that the caspase activation actually occurs in the mitochondrial intermembrane space. We and others have detected mitochondrial caspases[31] (unpublished data, R.A. Gottlieb). Overexpression of Bcl-2 has been observed to prevent cytochrome *c* release from mitochondria, while overexpression of bax promotes release of cytochrome *c*.[26,32,33] Bcl-2 opposes the action of CIFA,[34] and would thereby limit the dissociation of cytochrome *c* and its potential to interact with the mitochondrial caspase activation complex. These interactions are depicted in FIGURE 3. Recently it was shown that loss of cytochrome *c* from the electron transport chain resulted in increased superoxide production,[35] presumably through ubiquinone. If these findings are supported by additional studies, it could explain the basis of free radical production observed in many instances of apoptosis and would explain how Bcl-2 indirectly serves to prevent free radical generation.

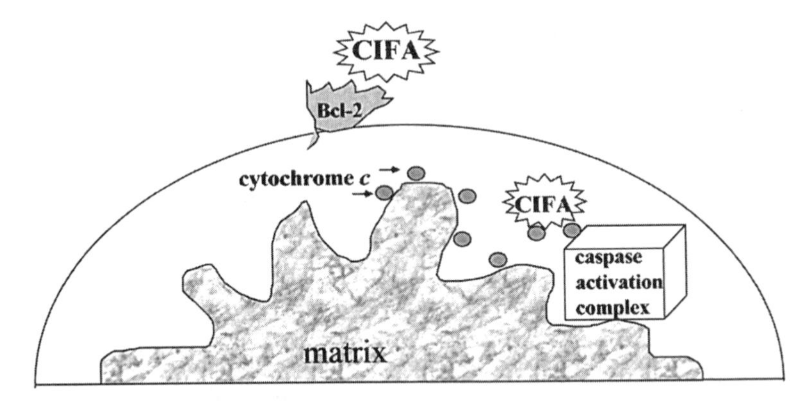

FIGURE 3. Model for the role of cytochrome *c* interacting factor of apoptosis (CIFA). CIFA is generated in the cytosol by an apoptotic stimulus, then translocates to the mitochondria, where it causes the dissociation of cytochrome *c* from the electron transport chain, thereby making it possible to interact with the caspase activation complex in the mitochondrial intermembrane space. Bcl-2 opposes the action of CIFA, possibly through a direct association.

A widely recognized target of caspases is the enzyme poly(ADP-ribose) polymerase (PARP). This enzyme recognizes single-strand DNA breaks and serves to activate repair enzymes by poly-ADP-ribosylating them. However, in the face of extensive DNA damage, this enzyme can consume all available nicotinamide adenine dinucleotide (NAD), which will lead to depletion of cellular energy currency. It has been suggested that inactivation of PARP through proteolytic cleavage is essential for the cell to retain enough energy to complete the apoptotic process. Apoptosis has been shown to require ATP.[36] However, the process of apoptosis also results in inactivation of mitochondrial electron transport, forcing the cell to rely on less efficient means of generating ATP. An increased demand on glycolysis may also contribute to cytoplasmic acidification through the production of lactic acid.

Once activated, caspase cleaves multiple targets. One such target is DNA fragmentation factor (DFF), which is one endonuclease responsible for degradation of the genome during apoptosis.[37] Other endonucleases have been implicated, including both DNase I and II. DNase I is a calcium- and magnesium-dependent endonuclease that has been shown to cleave DNA into oligonucleosomal multiples as are seen in apoptosis.[38] This has been shown to occur in settings where intracellular calcium rises sufficiently. However, it is not clear that such drastic elevations of calcium occur in most settings of apoptosis. DNase II is constitutively expressed in a wide variety of cell types, and can be extracted from the nucleus, where it presumably exists as a latent enzyme. However, as the intracellular pH drops below 6.8, the enzyme becomes active and can generate oligonucleosomal fragments. Since this is the only endonuclease detected in some cell types (such as neutrophils[39]), it is believed to play a role in some settings. Most, if not all, cell types acidify during apoptosis.[40] However, DNA degradation by an endonuclease is not essential for apoptosis to be accomplished. Indeed, in developmentally regulated programmed cell death in *C. elegans* the apoptotic cells do not express an endonuclease. Instead, the endonuclease is expressed by the phagocytic cells that remove the corpse.

It can be seen, then, that apoptosis serves to activate a variety of enzymatic processes that serve to degrade the genomic DNA (this also serves to degrade viral DNA in the event of viral invasion of a cell), inactivate cellular enzymes that might facilitate survival of the cell, rundown the remaining energy of the cell (much as one might empty the fuel tanks of an airplane before an anticipated crash-landing), and to fragment the cell into bite-size pieces to facilitate its removal.

APOPTOSIS IN CARDIOMYOCYTES

Apoptosis in the heart was first recognized in 1994,[1] in the setting of ischemia-reperfusion injury. Most work has relied upon the use of the TUNEL assay to detect DNA strand breaks in tissue sections.[41,42] Apoptosis has been recognized in a wide variety of pathological conditions, including arrhythmogenic right ventricular dysplasia,[43] as a feature of overstretch,[44] and in heart failure.[45] However, beyond the detection of DNA fragmentation and subtle chromatin condensation (apparent only at the EM level), little is known about the biochemical alterations in apoptosis. Recently it was shown that caspases were activated in apoptosis,[46] and we have shown that inhibition of caspases protects against cell death in cardiomyocytes subjected to metabolic inhibition and recovery to simulate ischemia-reperfusion.[47] Little is known about the specific caspases present or activated in the myocardium—to date there are more than ten members of the caspase family and their tissue distribution overlaps widely. Detection of specific caspase substrates has also not been examined in detail, although it is widely presumed that the targets will be similar in different cell types.

Probably the best information about apoptosis in the heart has been derived from studies of experimental ischemia-reperfusion. Anversa has shown that apoptosis is the predominant mode of cell death in ischemic-reperfused tissue.[2] With that in mind, it is possible to reconsider a great deal of literature relating to metabolic alterations during ischemia-reperfusion, dating from a time when apoptosis was not considered. These findings are nonetheless important and quite informative. Additional insights are gained from studies of preconditioning. Preconditioning is a brief period of cellular stress that induces a protective response that reduces tissue death when subjected to an ischemic stress that would ordinarily result in extensive tissue damage. Preconditioning does not appear to ameliorate injury associated with permanent ischemia, although there are experimental difficulties in answering this directly. However, our best understanding is that preconditioning is protective against the cell death associated with reperfusion injury. Wolfe[3] has shown that preconditioning decreases the extent of apoptosis in the heart. What are the metabolic parameters altered by preconditioning that influence apoptosis? Activation of protein kinase C (PKC) has been shown to be essential for preconditioning, although the specific isoform remains to be determined.[48] Mitochondrial K_{ATP} channels have also been implicated,[49,50] although the mechanism by which they confer protection is unclear. However, since mitochondria appear to be key to the initiation of apoptosis, any mitochondrial event may be important. Many investigators have shown that preservation of energy stores and maintenance of pH and calcium homeostasis are important features of preconditioning.[51]

We have investigated the subject of pH and calcium homeostasis in the model system of isolated adult rabbit cardiomyocytes subjected to metabolic inhibition with deoxyglucose and cyanide to simulate ischemia-reperfusion. In this cell culture model we can demonstrate preconditioning, which is dependent upon PKC. The preconditioning response can be simulated by the addition of phorbol myristate acetate (PMA) and inhibited by chelerythrine. Protection by preconditioning was reflected in preservation of cell viability and rod-shaped morphology as well as a decrease in the incidence of apoptosis measured by DNA nick-end labeling.[47] Using pH-sensitive fluorescent probe BCECF-AM and ratiometric fluorescence imaging, we measured alterations in intracellular pH during metabolic inhibition in naïve and preconditioned cardiomyocytes. We found that metabolic inhibition resulted in a drop in intracellular pH to a mean value of 6.85. However, preconditioning attenuated this pH drop to a mean value of 7.00. We investigated the basis for this difference in proton elimination and found that it was due, at least in part, to the activity of the vacuolar proton ATPase (VPATPase). Inhibition of the VPATPase with the macrolide antibiotic bafilomycin A_1 resulted in loss of preconditioning, reflected in a loss of viability, an increase in DNA nick-end labeling (apoptosis), and increased cytoplasmic acidification to a mean pH value of 6.63. These findings led us to conclude that preconditioning activated the vacuolar proton ATPase through a PKC-dependent pathway.

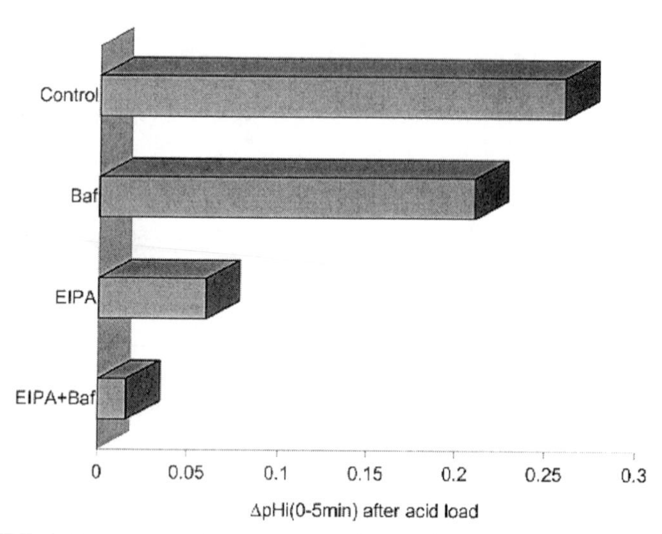

FIGURE 4. Relative contribution of the sodium-hydrogen exchanger and the vacuolar proton ATPase (VPATPase) to proton efflux. Neonatal rat cardiomyocytes were loaded with a fluorescent pH indicator and subjected to proton loading with propionic acid. Before acid challenge, cardiomyocytes were treated with bafilomycin (Baf) to inhibit the VPATPase, ethylisopropylamiloride (EIPA) to inhibit the sodium-hydrogen exchanger, or with both Baf and EIPA. The recovery of pH was monitored for 5 min, and the results are reported in pH units. Although the sodium-hydrogen exchanger plays a major role in proton efflux, the VPATPase also plays a role.

However, one puzzling finding was that although the sodium-hydrogen exchanger is the primary mechanism by which cells eliminate protons, its inhibition improved cell survival. However, the inhibition of both sodium-hydrogen exchange and VPATPase resulted in loss of preconditioning protection. To examine this in greater detail, we switched to studies in the neonatal rat cardiomyocyte system. Although we could not demonstrate preconditioning in these cells, we were able to investigate intrinsic modes of ion homeostasis during metabolic inhibition and recovery, utilizing pH, calcium-sensitive fluorescent probes, and flow cytometry. We also examined the activity of these systems in response to an acute proton load (accomplished by the addition of propionic acid to the medium). We found that the sodium-hydrogen exchanger is the major route of proton elimination during metabolic inhibition and recovery, as well as in response to acid loading. The VPATPase contribution to proton extrusion is not apparent until the sodium-hydrogen exchanger is inhibited (FIG. 4). The importance of the VPATPase, however, becomes much more apparent when intracellular calcium is measured. Inhibition of the VPATPase results in increased activity of the sodium-hydrogen exchanger, resulting in increased sodium accumulation. This sodium is then eliminated via the sodium-calcium exchanger operating in reverse. Therefore inhibition of the VPATPase results in increased calcium influx (FIG. 5). Inhibition of the sodium-hydrogen exchanger results in less calcium accumulation, as does inhibition of the NCX reverse mode using the compound KB-R7943 from Kanebo.[52] By scoring cells whose calcium content exceeded the upper

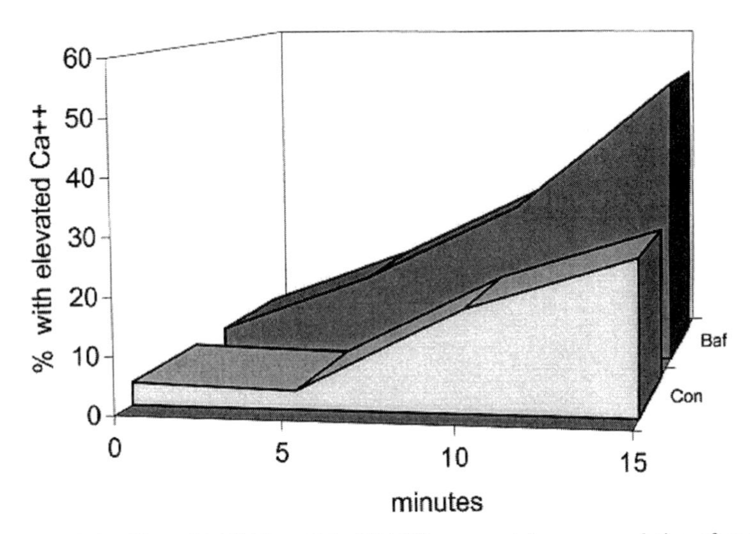

FIGURE 5. Effect of inhibition of the VPATPase on calcium accumulation after metabolic inhibition (MI). Neonatal rat cardiomyocytes were loaded with a fluorescent calcium indicator and subjected to metabolic inhibition, while calcium accumulation was monitored by flow cytometry. The *y* axis reflects the number of cells (as a percentage) whose calcium values exceeded the upper limit of normal. Before MI, cells were treated with DMSO vehicle (Con) or with bafilomycin (Baf) to inhibit proton efflux via the VPATPase. Increased calcium accumulation is seen with Baf treatment.

limits of normal (using flow cytometry and indo-1), we found that 67% of cells subjected to MI/R had elevated calcium levels by 45 min, versus 54% of cells treated with KB-R7943 ($p < 0.05$). Prevention of calcium influx preserves cell viability and reduces apoptosis, as measured by propidium iodide uptake (51.5% versus 29.3% for the KB-R7943–treated group, $p = 0.001$).[53]

These findings led us to propose the following model (FIG. 6), in which proton elimination is accomplished through both the exchanger and the VPATPase. Sodium accumulation through the exchanger is handled by reverse sodium-calcium exchange through another membrane transporter, the sodium-calcium exchanger (NCX). Inhibition of the sodium-hydrogen exchanger prevents sodium influx and secondary calcium influx. The protons are eliminated through increased compensatory activity of the vacuolar proton ATPase. However, inhibition of both mechanisms of proton extrusion results in acidosis and cell death. The mechanism by which calcium overload activates cell death is unclear, but may relate to activation of the calcium-dependent protease, calpain. A number of investigators have demonstrated a role for calpain in apoptosis.[54] Calcium overload is handled in part by mitochondrial sequestration via calcium ATPase. The metabolic consequences of sustained calcium overload may lead to mitochondrial depolarization, formation of the permeability transition pore, inhibition of ATP synthesis, and cell death.[55]

Caspase activation is also believed to occur in cardiomyocytes subjected to ischemia-reperfusion *in vivo* or metabolic inhibition *in vitro*. This has been documented using an antibody that recognizes only the fully processed, active caspase-3.[46] A

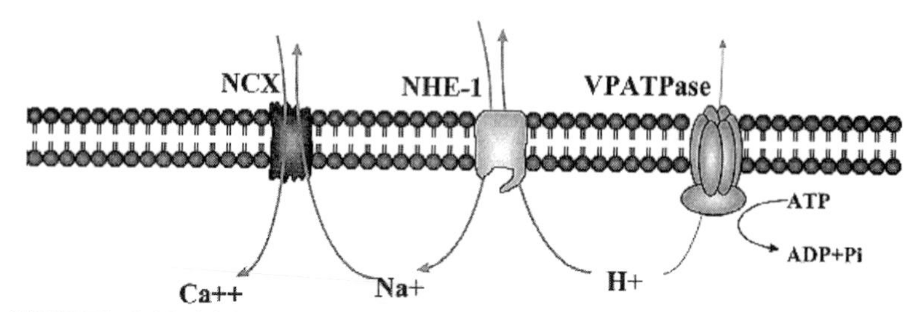

FIGURE 6. Model for interactions between ion transport systems. The sodium-hydrogen exchanger (NHE-1) plays a major role in proton efflux, but results in sodium influx. The elevated intracellular sodium drives the sodium-calcium exchanger (NCX) in reverse, leading to calcium influx. Participation of the VPATPase in proton efflux reduces the activity of NHE-1 and limits sodium accumulation and secondary calcium influx.

requirement for caspase activation has been demonstrated in our own studies in which the addition of a peptide fluoromethylketone inhibitor prevents apoptosis in response to metabolic inhibition and recovery.[47] Additional work is needed to determine if inhibition of caspase activation will result in long-term tissue salvage in the heart. In a study of isolated fibroblasts,[15] inhibition of caspases prevented features of apoptosis, but did not prevent the ultimate death of the cell through a necrotic pathway.

Myocardial tissue is exquisitely dependent upon mitochondrial oxidative phosphorylation to generate sufficient ATP to support contractile function. Therefore, even if downstream events of caspase activation are prevented, it will be important to preserve or restore mitochondrial function. It has been shown that cytochrome *c* is lost from the mitochondria during ischemia and reperfusion.[56] This is significant not only because of the potential for cytochrome *c* to interact with the caspase activation complex, but also because of the block to electron transport. If CIFA is generated in response to a variety of insults, it may explain the inactivation of electron transport in cardiomyocytes recovering from ischemia-reperfusion, and may represent an important therapeutic target.

SUMMARY

Myocardial ischemia-reperfusion results in cell loss through apoptosis. The signal transduction pathways by which ischemia-reperfusion lead to apoptosis may involve the JNK pathway, ceramide generation, and inhibition of protective PKC pathways. The biochemical events associated with apoptosis include mitochondrial inactivation, cytochrome *c* dislocation, caspase activation, and cytoplasmic acidification. These events lead to morphologic changes in the cytoskeletal architecture, culminating in cell shrinkage and rounding-up. Disruption of ion homeostasis results in cytoplasmic acidification and calcium accumulation, which in turn further disturb mitochondrial function and permit the activation of one or more endonucleases that degrade nuclear DNA. Through the concerted efforts of multiple classes of enzymes, apoptosis is accomplished, resulting in the death of a cell in which potentially transforming oncogenes have been degraded and in which inflammatory contents are contained within the plasma membrane until the fragments can be ingested by phagocytes. This non-inflammatory mode of cell death permits tissue remodeling with minimal scar formation and so is preferable to necrotic cell death.

Ischemia-reperfusion injury leads to cell death through an apoptotic pathway. However, in cells excessively energy-starved, plasma membrane integrity may be lost before the process of apoptosis is complete, resulting in a necrotic cell. The distinction between apoptosis and necrosis, which implies different mechanisms of cell death, is blurred in the case of a pathologic insult such as ischemia-reperfusion. I suggest that it is more useful to view cell death in the context of whether or not it can be prevented. It may be possible to greatly reduce cell death if key steps in the pathway can be blocked. Intensive efforts are directed at identifying the required steps, so as to develop novel therapeutic agents.

REFERENCES

1. Gottlieb, R.A., K.O. Burleson, R.A. Kloner, B.M. Babior & R. L. Engler. 1994. Reperfusion injury induces apoptosis in rabbit cardiomyocytes. J. Clin. Invest. **94:** 1621–1628.
2. Kajstura, J., W. Cheng, K. Reiss, W.A. Clark, E.H. Sonnenblick, S. Krajewski, J.C. Reed, G. Olivetti & P. Anversa. 1996. Apoptotic and necrotic myocyte cell deaths are independent contributing variables of infarct size in rats. Lab. Invest. **74:** 86–107.
3. Piot, C.A., D. Padmanaban, P.C. Ursell, R.E. Sievers & C.L. Wolfe. 1997. Ischemic preconditioning decreases apoptosis in rat hearts in vivo. Circulation **96:** 1598–1604.
4. Long, X., M.O. Boluyt, M.L. Hipolito, M.S. Lundberg, J.S. Zheng, L. O'Neill, C. Cirielli, E.G. Lakatta & M.T. Crow. 1997. p53 and the hypoxia-induced apoptosis of cultured neonatal rat cardiac myocytes. J. Clin. Invest. **99:** 2635–2643.
5. Polyak, K., Y. Xia, J.L. Zweier, K.W. Kinzler & B. Vogelstein. 1997. A model for p53-induced apoptosis. Nature **389:** 300.
6. Miyashita, T. & J.C. Reed. 1995. Tumor suppressor p53 is a direct transcriptional activator of the human *bax* gene. Cell **80:** 293–299.
7. Bialik, S., D.L. Geenen, I.E. Sasson, R. Cheng, J.W. Horner, S.M. Evans, E.M. Lord, C.J. Koch & R.N. Kitsis. 1997. Myocyte apoptosis during acute myocardial infarction in the mouse localizes to hypoxic regions but occurs independently of p53. J. Clin. Invest. **100:** 1363–1372.
8. Jost, C.A., M.C. Marin & W.G. Kaelin, Jr. 1997. p73 is a human p53-related protein that can induce apoptosis [see comments]. Nature **389:** 191–194.
9. Devary, Y., R.A. Gottlieb, L.F. Lau & M. Karin. 1991. Rapid and preferential activation of the c-*jun* gene during the mammalian UV response. Molec. Cell. Biol. **11:** 2804–2811.
10. Johnson, L.N., A.M. Gardner, K.M. Diener, C.A. Lange-Carter, J. Gleavy, M.B. Jarpe, A. Minden, M. Karin, L.I. Zon & G.L. Johnson. 1996. Signal transduction pathways regulated by mitogen-activate/extracellular response kinase kinase kinase induce cell death. J. Biol. Chem. **271:** 3229–3237.
11. Cardone, M.H., G.S. Salvesen, C. Widmann, G. Johnson & S. M. Frisch. 1997. The regulation of anoikis: MEKK-1 activation requires cleavage by caspases. Cell **90:** 315–323.
12. Obeid, L.M., C.M. Linardic, L.A. Karolak & Y.A. Hannun. 1993. Programmed cell death induced by ceramide. Science **259:** 1769–1771.
13. Krown, K.A., M.T. Page, C. Nguyen, D. Zechner, V. Gutierrez, K.L. Comstock, C.C. Glembotski, P.J. Quintana & R.A. Sabbadini. 1996. Tumor necrosis factor

alpha-induced apoptosis in cardiac myocytes. Involvement of the sphingolipid signaling cascade in cardiac cell death. J. Clin. Invest. **98:** 2854–2865.
14. WANG, Y., B. SU, V. P. SAH, J.H. BROWN, J. HAN & K.R. CHIEN. 1998. Cardiac hypertrophy induced by mitogen-activated protein kinase kinase 7, a specific activator for c-Jun NH_2-terminal kinase in ventricular muscle cells. J. Biol. Chem. **273:** 5423–5426.
15. EVAN, G.I., A.H. WYLLIE, C.S. GILBERT, T.D. LITTLEWOOD, H. LAND, M. BROOKS, C.M. WATERS, L.Z. PENN & D.C. HANCOCK. 1992. Induction of apoptosis in fibroblasts by c-myc protein. Cell **69:** 119–128.
16. RUDEL, T. & G.M. BOKOCH. 1997. Membrane and morphological changes in apoptotic cells regulated by caspase-mediated activation of PAK2. Science **276:** 1571–1574.
17. LEE, N., H. MACDONALD, C. REINHARD, R. HALENBECK, A. ROULSTON, T. SHI & L.T. WILLIAMS. 1997. Activation of hPAK65 by caspase cleavage induces some of the morphological and biochemical changes of apoptosis. Proc. Natl. Acad. Sci. USA **94:** 13642–13647.
18. RICE, R.H. & H. GREEN. 1977. The cornified envelope of terminally differentiated human epidermal keratinocytes consists of cross-linked protein. Cell **11:** 417–422.
19. KUIDA, K., T.S. ZHENG, S. NA, C. KUAN, D. YANG, H. KARASUYAMA, P. RAKIC & R.A. FLAVELL. 1996. Decreased apoptosis in the brain and premature lethality in CPP32-deficient mice. Nature **384:** 368–372.
20. LI, P., H. ALLEN, S. BANERJEE & T. SESHADRI. 1997. Characterization of mice deficient in interleukin-1 beta converting enzyme. J. Cell Biochem. **64:** 27–32.
21. WANG, S., M. MIURA, Y.K. JUNG, H. ZHU, E. LI & J. YUAN. 1998. Murine caspase-11, an ICE-interacting protease, is essential for the activation of ICE. Cell **92:** 501–509.
22. VILLA, P., S.H. KAUFMANN & W.C. EARNSHAW. 1997. Caspases and caspase inhibitors. Trends Biochem. Sci. **22:** 388–393.
23. KUWANA, T., J.J. SMITH, M. MUZIO, V. DIXIT, D.D. NEWMYER & S. KORNBLUTH. 1998. Apoptosis induction by caspase-8 is amplified through the mitochondrial release of cytochrome c. J. Biol. Chem. **273:** 16589–16594.
24. ZOU, H., W.J. HENZEL, X. LIU, A. LUTSCHG & X. WANG. 1997. Apaf-1, a human protein homologous to *C. elegans* CED-4, participates in cytochrome c-dependent activation of caspase-3. Cell **90:** 405–413.
25. LI, P., D. NIJHAWAN, I. BUDIHARDJO, S.M. SRINIVASULA, M. AHMAD, E.S. ALNEMRI & X. WANG. 1997. Cytochrome *c* and dATP-dependent formation of Apaf-1/Caspase-9 complex initiates an apoptotic protease cascade. Cell **91:** 479–489.
26. KLUCK, R.M., E. BOSSY-WETZEL, D.R. GREEN & D.D. NEWMEYER. 1997. The release of cytochrome c from mitochondria: a primary site for Bcl-2 regulation of apoptosis. Science **275:** 1132–1136.
27. ADACHI, S., R. A. GOTTLIEB & B.M. BABIOR. 1998. Lack of release of cytochrome c from mitochondria into cytosol early in the course of Fas-mediated apoptosis of Jurkat cells. J. Biol. Chem. **273:** 19892–19894.
28. VANDER HEIDEN, M.G., N.S. CHANDEL, E.K. WILLIAMSON, P.T. SCHUMACKER & C.B. THOMPSON. 1997. Bcl-xL regulates the membrane potential and volume homeostasis of mitochondria [see comments]. Cell **91:** 627–637.
29. FONTAINE, E., O. ERIKSSON, F. ICHAS & P. BERNARDI. 1998. Regulation of the permeability transition pore in skeletal muscle mitochondria. Modulation by electron flow through the respiratory chain complex [In Process Citation]. J. Biol. Chem. **273:** 12662–12668.
30. KRIPPNER, A., A. YAGI, R.A. GOTTLIEB & B.M. BABIOR. 1996. Loss of function of cytochrome *c* in Jurkat cells undergoing Fas-mediated apoptosis. J. Biol. Chem. **271:** 21629–21636.
31. MANCINI, M., D.W. NICHOLSON, S. ROY, N.A. THORNBERRY, E.P. PETERSON, L.A. CASCIOLA-ROSEN & A. ROSEN. 1998. The caspase-3 precursor has a cytosolic and mitochondrial distribution: implications for apoptotic signaling. J. Cell Biol. **140:** 1485–1495.
32. YANG, J., X. LIU, K. BHALLA, C.N. KIM, A.M. IBRADO, J. CAI, T.I. PENG, D.P. JONES & X. WANG. 1997. Prevention of apoptosis by Bcl-2: release of cytochrome c from mitochondria blocked. Science **275:** 1129–1132.
33. ROSSE, T., R. OLIVIER, L. MONNEY, M. RAGER, S. CONUS, I. FELLAY, B. JANSEN & C. BORNER. 1998. Bcl-2 prolongs cell survival after Bax-induced release of cytochrome *c*. Nature **391:** 496–499.

34. ADACHI, S.A.R. CROSS, B.M. BABIOR & R.A. GOTTLIEB. 1997. Bcl-2 and the outer mitochondrial membrane in the inactivation of cytochrome c during Fas-mediated apoptosis. J. Biol. Chem. **272:** 21878–21882.
35. CAI, J. & D.P. JONES. 1998. Superoxide in apoptosis. Mitochondrial generation triggered by cytochrome c loss. J. Biol. Chem. **273:** 11401–11404.
36. EGUCHI, Y., S. SHIMIZU & Y. TSUJIMOTO. 1997. Intracellular ATP levels determine cell death fate by apoptosis or necrosis. Cancer Res. **57:** 1835–1840.
37. LIU, X., H. ZOU, C. SLAUGHTER & X. WANG. 1997. DFF, a heterodimeric protein that functions downstream of caspase-3 to trigger DNA fragmentation during apoptosis. Cell **89:** 175–184.
38. PEITSCH, M.C., B. POLZAR, H. STEPHAN, T. CROMPTON, H.R. MACDONALD, H.G. MANNHERZ & J. TSCHOPP. 1993. Characterization of the endogenous deoxyribonuclease involved in nuclear DNA degradation during apoptosis (programmed cell death). EMBO J. **12:** 371–377.
39. GOTTLIEB, R.A., H. GIESING, R.L. ENGLER & B.M. BABIOR. 1995. The acid deoxyribonuclease of neutrophils: A possible participant in apoptosis-associated genome destruction. Blood **86:** 2414–2418.
40. GOTTLIEB, R.A. 1996. Cell acidification in apoptosis (Review). Apoptosis **1:** 40–48.
41. GAVRIELI, Y., Y. SHERMAN & S.A. BEN-SASSON. 1992. Identification of programmed cell death *in situ* via specific labeling of nuclear DNA fragmentation. J. Cell Biol. **119:** 493–501.
42. WIJSMAN, J.H., R.R. JONKER, R. KEIJZER, C.J.H. VAN DER VELDE, C.J. CORNELISSE & J. H. VAN DIERENDONCK. 1993. A new method to detect apoptosis in paraffin sections. *In situ* end-labeling of fragmented DNA. J. Histochem. Cytochem. **41:** 7–12.
43. MALLAT, Z., A. TEDGUI, F. FONTALIRAN, R. FRANK, M. DURIGON & G. FONTAINE. 1996. Evidence of apoptosis in arrhythmogenic right ventricular dysplasia. N. Engl. J. Med. **335:** 1190–1196.
44. CHENG, W., B. LI, P. LI, M.S. WOLIN, E.H. SONNENBLICK, T.H. HINTZE, G. OLIVETTI & P. ANVERSA. 1995. Stretch-induced programmed myocyte cell death. J. Clin. Invest. **96:** 2247–2259.
45. NARULA, J., N. HAIDER, R. VIRMANI, T.G. DISALVO, F.D. KOLODGIE, R.J. HAJJAR, U. SCHMIDT, M.J. SEMIGRAN, G.W. DEC & B.-A. KHAW. 1996. Apoptosis in myocytes in end-stage heart failure. N. Engl. J. Med. **335:** 1182–1189.
46. BLACK, S.C., J. Q. HUANG, P. REZAIEFAR, S. RADINOVIC, A. EBERHART, D.W. NICHOLSON & I.W. RODGER. 1998. Co-localization of the cysteine protease caspase-3 with apoptotic myocytes after *in vivo* myocardial ischemia and reperfusion in the rat. J. Mol. Cell Cardiol. **30:** 733–742.
47. GOTTLIEB, R.A., D.L. GRUOL, J.Y. ZHU & R.L. ENGLER. 1996. Preconditioning in rabbit cardiomyocytes: Role of pH, vacuolar proton ATPase, and apoptosis. J. Clin. Invest. **97:** 2391–2398.
48. PUCEAT, M., R. HILAL-DANDAN, B. STRULOVICI, L.L. BRUNTON & J.H. BROWN. 1994. Differential regulation of protein kinase C isoforms in isolated neonatal and adult rat cardiomyocytes. J. Biol. Chem. **269:** 16938–16944.
49. FRYER, R.M., A.K. HSU, J.T. EELLS, H. NAGASE & G.J. GROSS. 1999. Opioid-induced second window of cardioprotection: Potential role of mitochondrial KATP channels. Circ. Res. **84:** 846–851.
50. GARLID, K.D., P. PAUCEK, V. YAROV-YAROVOY, H.N. MURRAY, R.B. DARBENZIO, A.J. D'ALONZO, N.J. LODGE, M.A. SMITH & G.J. GROVER. 1997. Cardioprotective effect of diazoxide and its interaction with mitochondrial ATP-sensitive K^+ channels. Possible mechanism of cardioprotection. Circ. Res. **81:** 1072–1082.
51. STEENBERGEN, C., M. E. PERLMAN, R. E. LONDON & E. MURPHY. 1993. Mechanism of preconditioning: Ionic alterations. Circ. Res. **72:** 112–125.
52. IWAMOTO, T., T. WATANO & M. SHIGEKAWA. 1996. A novel isothiourea derivative selectively inhibits the reverse mode of Na^+/Ca^{2+} exchange in cells expressing NCX1. J. Biol. Chem. **271:** 22391–22397.
53. KARWATOWSKA-PROKOPCZUK, E., J. NORDBERG, H.L. LI, R.L. ENGLER & R.A. GOTTLIEB. 1998. Effect of the vacuolar proton ATPase on intracellular pH, calcium, and on

apoptosis in neonatal cardiomyocytes during metabolic inhibition and recovery. Circ. Res. **82:** 1139–1144.
54. SQUIER, M.K. & J.J. COHEN. 1997. Calpain, an upstream regulator of thymocyte apoptosis. J. Immunol. **158:** 3690–3697.
55. RICHTER, C. 1997. Reactive oxygen and nitrogen species regulate mitochondrial Ca^{2+} homeostasis and respiration. Biosci. Rep. **17:** 53–66.
56. PIPER, H.M., O. SEZER, M. SCHLEYER, J.F. HUTTER & P.G. SPIECKERMANN. 1985. Development of ischemia-induced damage in defined mitochondrial subpopulations. J. Mol. Cell Cardiol. **17:** 885–896.

Stress Signal to Survival and Apoptosis[a]

ATSUSHI TAKEDA[b] AND NOBUAKIRA TAKEDA

Department of Internal Medicine, Aoto Hospital, Jikei University School of Medicine, 6-41-2 Aoto, Katsushika-ku, 125 Tokyo, Japan

ABSTRACT: This investigation focused on whether apoptosis can be observed in some heart diseases. Apoptosis was examined immunochemically using monoclonal antibodies such as p53, Bcl-2 and cyclin E, A, and B1 in parallel with flow cytometry. Left ventricular myocardium was obtained at autopsy from 40 patients with acute myocarditis (AM; N = 10, 6 males, 4 females, mean age 56 ± 13 years), chronic myocarditis (CM; N = 10, 5 males, 5 females, mean age 48 ± 16 years), dilated cardiomyopathy (DCM; N = 10, 7 males, 3 females, mean age 60 ± 11 years), and no heart disease (Cont; N = 10, 5 males, 5 females, mean age 63 ± 14 years). Cell cycle analysis of myocytes by flow cytometry revealed that the relative content of G2M phase in acute myocarditis was far higher than those in other heart diseases (AM, 12.3 ± 3.7%; CM, 5.2 ± 4.5%; DCM, 6.3 ± 4.0%; Cont, 3.4 ± 1.8%; Mean ± SD). Expression of p53 was observed mainly in myocytes from chronic myocarditis. Expression of Bcl-2, on the other hand, was detected in myocytes from acute myocarditis. Results suggest that apoptosis may play some role in the repairing process of myocardial inflammation.

INTRODUCTION

Inflammation is a dynamic process by which living tissues react to injury. It is defined as a focal defensive response with circulation disturbance, exudation, and inflammatory cell infiltration and proliferation in the tissue. It is still unknown whether regressive and regenerative changes occur at the same time in this inflammatory lesion. Apoptosis, in contrast to inflammation, is a natural phenomenon and has been thought to be an active as well as reactive process.

Using immunohistochemical and flow cytometrical analysis, we examined whether apoptosis and cell cycle disturbances can be observed in some heart diseases.

MATERIALS AND METHODS

Materials

At autopsies performed in our hospital, hearts were sampled for this study. Left ventricular myocardium was obtained at autopsy from 40 patients: 10 with acute my-

[a]This study was partly supported by the Research Committee for Epidemiology and Etiology of Idiopathic Cardiomyopathy of the Ministry of Health and Welfare of Japan, and a research grant from the Vehicle Racing Commemorative Foundation.

[b]Address correspondence to: Atsushi Takeda, M.D., Ph.D., Department of Internal Medicine, Aoto Hospital, Jikei University, 6-41-2 Aoto, Katsushika-ku, 125 Tokyo, Japan; Telephone: 81-3-3603-2111, Fax: 81-3-3602-2839; E-mail: Shingen@bea.hi-ho.me.jp.

ocarditis (AM; 6 males, 4 females, mean age 56 ± 13 years), 10 with chronic (persistent) myocarditis (CM; 5 males, 5 females, mean age 48 ± 16 years), 10 with dilated cardiomyopathy (DCM; 7 males, 3 females, mean age 60 ± 11 years), and 10 with no heart disease (Cont; 5 males, 5 females, mean age 63 ± 14 years).

Methods

Pathological Study

Myocardium was stained with hematoxylin-eosin stain, Masson-trichrome stain periodic acid-Schiff stain, Elastica von Gieson stain, and phosphotungstic acid hematoxylin stain after routine 10% formalin fixation, paraffin embedding, and sectioning.

Immunohistochemical Study

These sections were also investigated immunohistochemically with anti-cyclin E, A, and B1 (Pharmingen Co.) and anti-p53, Bcl-2 monoclonal antibodies (DAKO Co.) by the streptavidin-biotin complex (SAB) method (FIG. 1).[10]

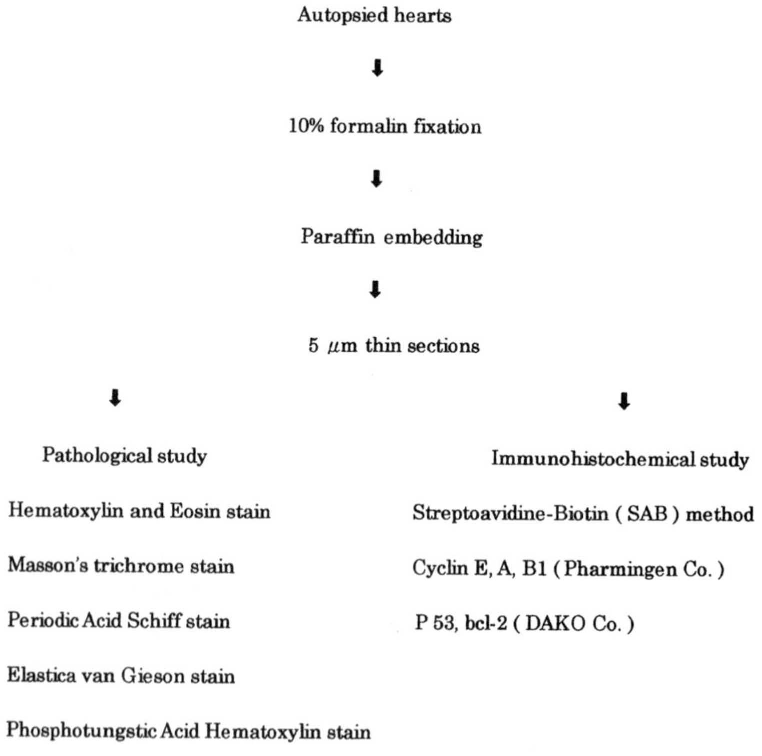

Autopsied hearts

↓

10% formalin fixation

↓

Paraffin embedding

↓

5 μm thin sections

↓ ↓

Pathological study	Immunohistochemical study
Hematoxylin and Eosin stain	Streptoavidine-Biotin (SAB) method
Masson's trichrome stain	Cyclin E, A, B1 (Pharmingen Co.)
Periodic Acid Schiff stain	P 53, bcl-2 (DAKO Co.)
Elastica van Gieson stain	
Phosphotungstic Acid Hematoxylin stain	

FIGURE 1. Pathological and immunohistological methods.

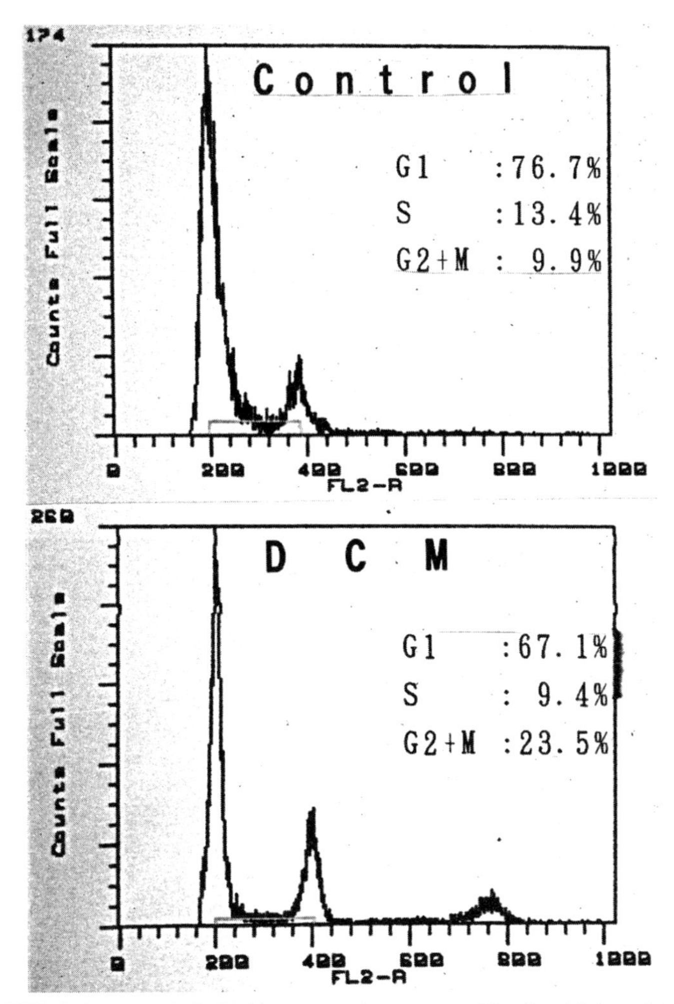

FIGURE 2. Fluorescein DNA histogram of a myocyte. The first high peak is the $G_{0\text{-}1}$ phase and the second one is the G2M phase.

Cell Cycle Analysis with Flow Cytometry

The percent ratios of each phase were calculated automatically with the integral calculus by the FACS flow cytometry (Becton Dickinson Co.)[1–3] The cell cycles were measured by flow cytometry and statistical analysis were perfomed in comparison with normal control hearts. Several 60-μm sections were cut from each paraffin block of tissue.[4] These sections were placed in tubes with xylene for 20 min and then gradually rehydrated with distilled water. Then the sample tubes were incubated for 1 h at 37°C in a water bath after adding 1 ml of 0.5% pepsin solution (pH 1.5) in 0.9% NaCl. After pipetting off this solution, target nuclei were purified by filtering

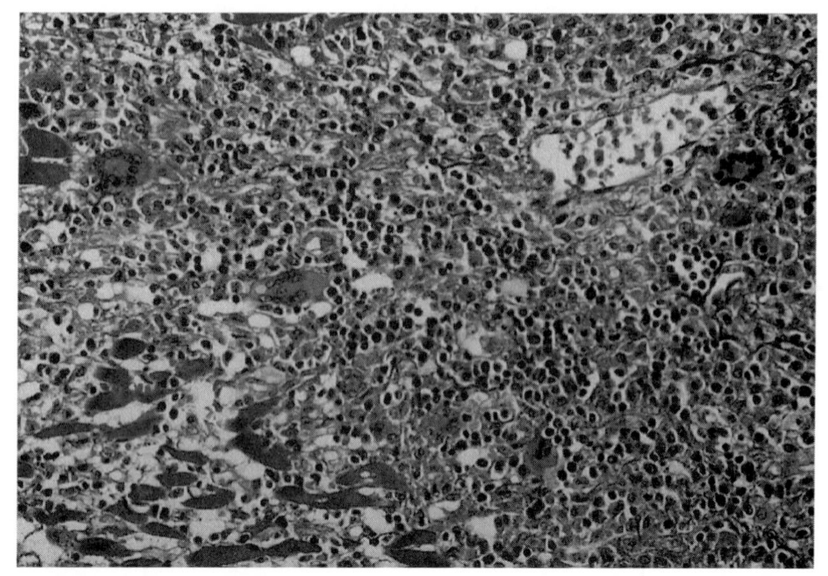

FIGURE 3. Myocardial tissue (left ventricle) of acute myocarditis (Masson-trichrome stain, original magnification ×400).

through a 30–60 μm Teflon mesh to remove debris (modified Hedley method).[5,6] Then the nuclei were stained with 50 μg/ml propidium iodide (PI) and 0.1% Triton X-100 in 4 mM sodium citrate (Vindelov method). This solution was centrifuged (4°C, 400×*g*, 10 min), the supernatant was discarded, 0.5 ml PI solution was discarded, 0.5 ml PI solution was added, and then a FACScan (Becton Dickinson Co.) was used for flow cytometry.[1,2,7–9]

In the fluorescein DNA histogram, the first peak indicates the $G_{0\text{-}1}$ phase of cell cycle and the second peak is the G2M phase of cell cycle. The valley between $G_{0\text{-}1}$ and G2M shows the S phase (FIG. 2).[1,2]

The DNA frequency histogram was deconvoluted and results were computer analyzed using the Multicycle software (Phoenix Flow System, San Diego, CA).[1,2] Results are presented as means ± SD. Comparisons between values were performed using a Student's *t* test. A value of $p < 0.05$ was considered statistically significant.

RESULTS

Histopathological and Immunohistochemical Study

There was extensive lymphocyte infiltrate in the acute myocarditis samples (FIG. 3) and focal lymphocyte infiltrate in the interstitium in chronic (persistent) myocarditis samples (FIG. 4). Interstitial fibrosis is perinuclear in distribution and the interstitium is involved by patchy fibrosis in dilated cardiomyopathy (FIG. 5).

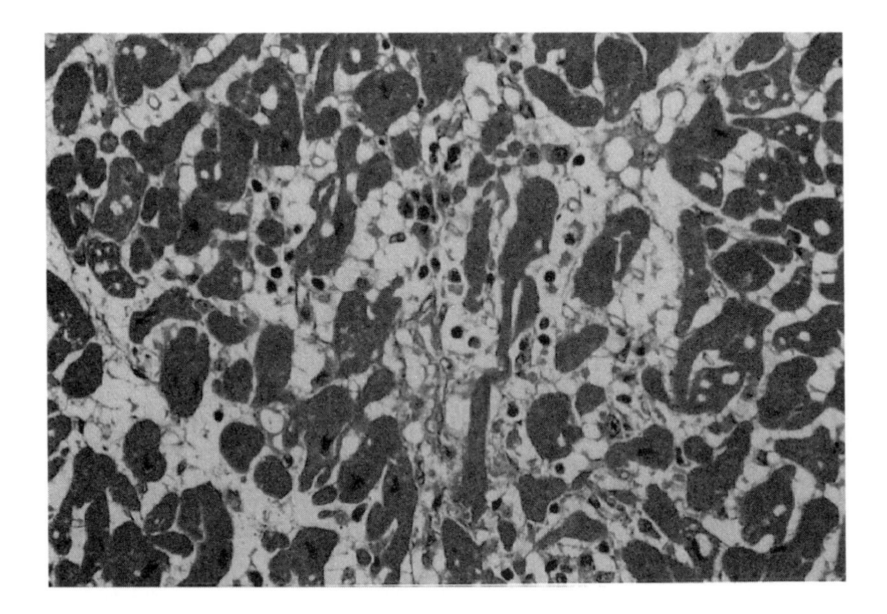

FIGURE 4. Myocardial tissue (left ventricle) of persistent (chronic) myocarditis (Masson-trichrome stain, original magnification ×400).

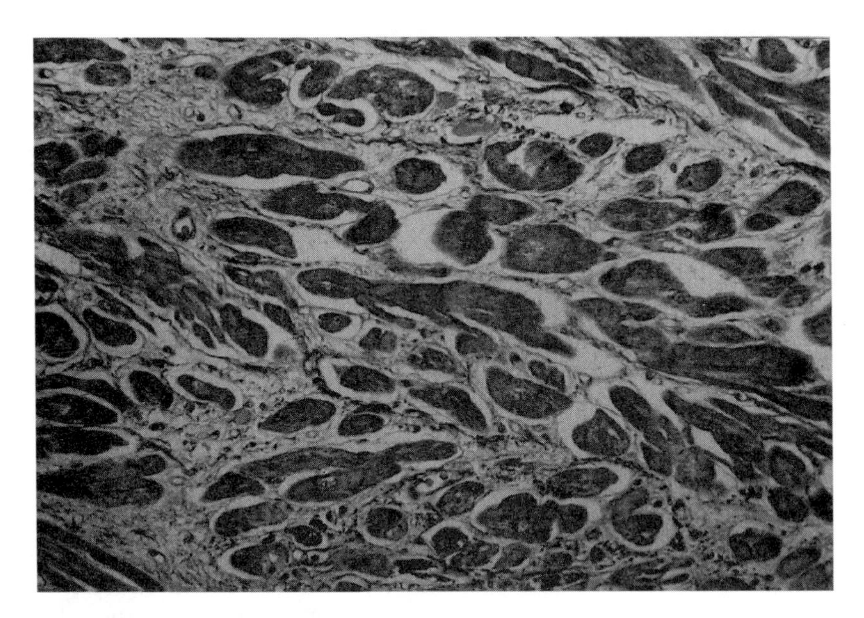

FIGURE 5. Myocardial tissue (left ventricle) of dilated cardiomyopathy (Masson-trichrome stain, original magnification ×200).

TABLE 1. Cell cycle of myocytes in myocarditis, dilated cardiomyopathy, and control[a]

	Acute Myocarditis	Chronic Myocarditis	Dilated Cardiomyopathy	Control
$G_{0\text{-}1}$ phase (%)	77.4 ± 4.6	87.1 ± 5.5	86.0 ± 2.8	90.1 ± 1.6
S phase (%)	10.4 ± 2.5	7.7 ± 2.1	8.1 ± 2.9	6.5 ± 2.0
G2M phase (%)	12.3 ± 3.7	5.2 ± 4.5	6.2 ± 4.0	3.4 ± 1.8

(Brackets in the printed table: $G_{0\text{-}1}$: Acute vs Control * *; Acute vs Chronic * *; Dilated vs Control *. S phase: Acute vs Control * *; Acute vs Chronic *. G2M phase: Acute vs Control * *; Acute vs Chronic *.)

[a]$N = 10$, mean ± S.D., $*p < 0.05$, $**p < 0.01$.

In case of acute myocarditis, scattered Bcl-2–positive myocytes were detected in the myocardial tissues of patients (5/10 cases) (FIG. 6), but no (0/10 cases) p53-positive myocytes were found immunohistochemically in the tissue. In case of chronic myocarditis on the other hand, no Bcl-2–positive myocytes were detected in the tissue, but p53-positive myocytes were found in the tissue (4/10 cases) (FIG. 7).

Cell Cycle Analysis with Flow Cytometry

According to the cell cycle analysis, the G2M phase was more prominent in myocytes of acute myocarditis than in control (acute myocarditis, 12.3 ± 3.7% versus Control, 3.4 ± 1.8%; $p < 0.01$) or chronic myocarditis (acute myocarditis, 12.3 ± 3.7% versus chronic myocarditis, 5.2 ± 4.5%; $p < 0.05$). However, there was no significant increase of the G2M phase in chronic myocarditic and dilated cardiomyopathic myocytes compared to Control.

In the same manner, the extent of the $G_{0\text{-}1}$ phase was significantly less in acute myocarditis and dilated cardiomyopathy than in controls (acute myocarditis, 77.4 ± 4.6% versus Control, 90.1 ± 1.6%; $p < 0.01$. Dilated cardiomyopathy, 86.0 ± 2.8% versus Control, 90.1 ± 1.6%; $p < 0.05$). However, there was no significant difference in the $G_{0\text{-}1}$ phase of chronic myocarditis than that of control. The S phase was also more prominent in myocytes of acute myocarditis than in Control (acute myocarditis, 12.3 ± 3.7% versus Control, 5.2 ± 4.5%; $p < 0.05$) (TABLE 1).

With regard to the selection of nuclei, the average size of nuclei in the myocardium was measured in hematoxylin-eosin–stained tissue using the light microscope. Only myocardial nuclei were filtrated through the optimum Teflon mesh, whose hole size was a little smaller than size of the nuclear myocytes, and almost all the nuclei of the interstitial cells were taken out (FIG. 8). However, the mixing ratio (percentage) of interstitial cell nuclei was technically between about 2–8% (somewhere around 6%) after the measurement.

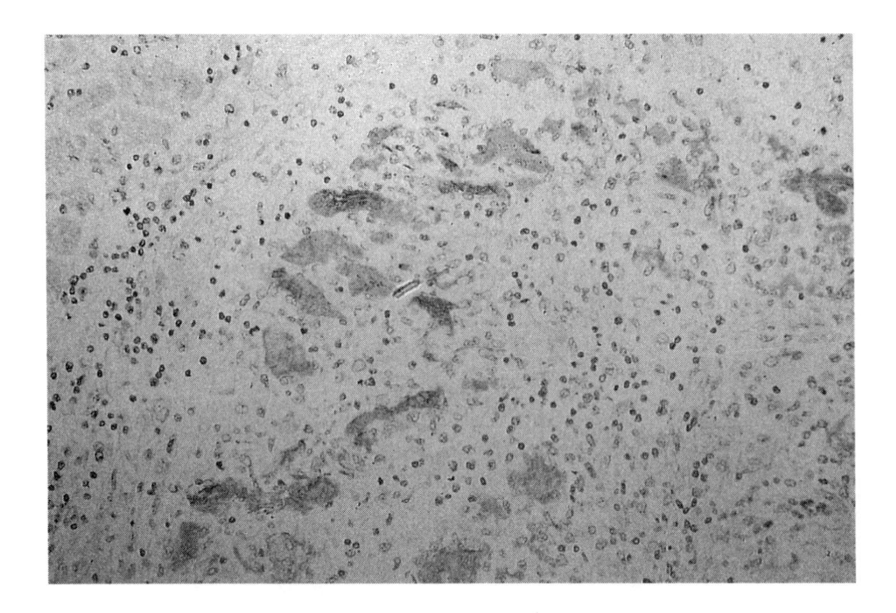

FIGURE 6. Bcl-2–positive myocyte in myocardial tissue (left ventricle) of acute myocarditis (Masson-trichrome stain, original magnification ×200).

FIGURE 7. p53-positive myocytes in myocardial tissue (left ventricle) of chronic myocarditis (Masson-trichrome stain, original magnification ×400).

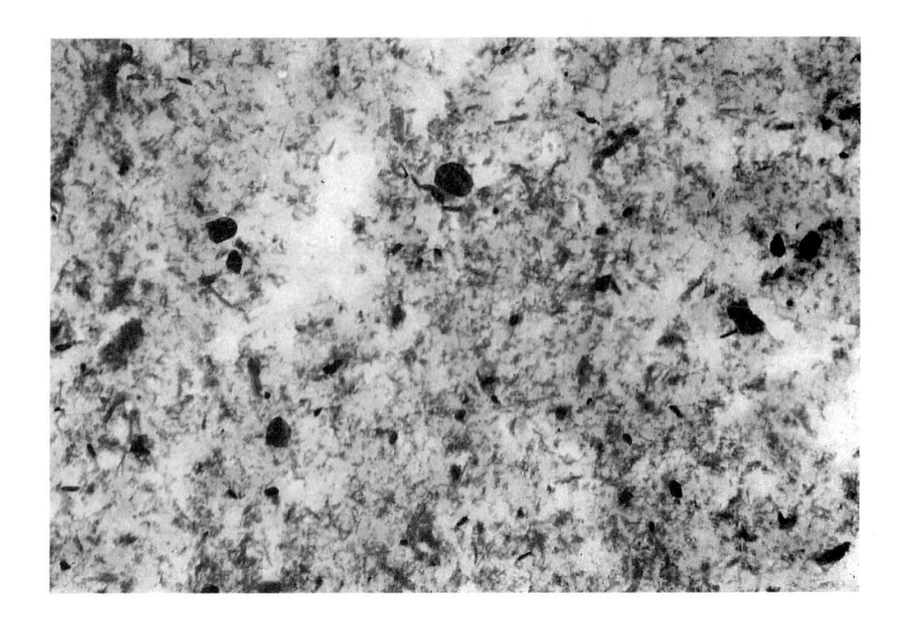

FIGURE 8. The naked nucleus after nuclear DNA analysis (hematoxylin-eosin stain, original magnification ×600).

DISCUSSION

In the case of acute myocarditis, a scattering of Bcl-2–positive myocytes could be detected in myocardial tissues of patients (5/10 cases) (FIG. 6), but no p53-positive myocytes could be found immunohistochemically in the tissue. This suggests that the Bcl-2 expression in myocytes could protect the myocardial damage from the several kind of cytokines induced by inflammatory cell infiltration against the viral infection. In the case of chronic myocarditis on the other hand, p53 expression in myocytes could be thought of as a repairing process for remodeling damaged tissue. In DCM cases, there were few p53 and Bcl-2–positive cells in the myocardial tissue. According to the cell cycle analysis, the G2M and S phases were more prominent in myocytes of acute myocarditis than other cases. It could be that the myocytes of acute myocarditis were strongly influenced on the cell cycle compared to the stable phase of control myocytes. And also, there was no correlation in S and G2M phase between DCM and Control. It shows that the myocytes of DCM are little influenced and some myocytes are stable in a polyploidy state. These results suggest that apoptosis may play some role in the repairing process of myocardial inflammation.

REFERENCES

1. FRIED, J. 1976. Method for the quantitative evaluation of data from microfluorometry. Comp. Biomed. Res. **9:** 263.

2. DEAN, P. N. & J.H. JETT. 1974. Mathematical analysis of DNA distributions derived from microfluorometry. J. Cell Biol. **60:** 523.
3. BABA, H.A., A. TAKEDA, C. SCHMID & M. NAGANO. 1996. Early proliferative changes in hearts of hypertensive Goldblatt ratio: an immunohistochemical and flow-cytometrical study. Basic. Res. Cardiol. **91:** 275–282.
4. STEPHENSON, R.A., H. GAY & W.R. FAIR. 1986. Effect of section thickness on quality of flow cytometric DNA content determinations in paraffin-embedded tissue. Cytometry **7:** 41–44.
5. HEDLEY, D.W., M.L. FRIEDLANDER & I.W. TAYLOR. 1983. Method for analysis of cellular DNA content of paraffin-embedded pathological materials using flow cytometry. J. Histochem. Cytochem. **31:** 1333–1335.
6. HEDLEY, D.W., M.L. FRIEDLANDER & I.W. TAYLOR. 1985. Application of DNA flow cytometry to paraffin-embedded archival material for the study of aneuploid and clinical significance. Cytometry **6:** 327–333.
7. REYNDER, S.B. & M.J. BOSMAN. 1985. Flow cytometric determination of DNA ploidy level in nuclei isolated from paraffin-embedded tissue. Cytometry **6:** 26–30.
8. VINDELOVE, L.L., I.J. CHRISTENSEN & N.I. NISSEN 1983. A detergent-trypsin method for the preparation of nuclei for flow-cytometric DNA analysis. Cytometry **3:** 323–327.
9. TAKEDA, A., S. CHIBA, T. IWAI, A. TANAMURA, Y. YAMAGUCHI & N. TAKEDA. 1999. Cell cycle of myocytes of cardiac and skeletal muscle in mitochondrial myopathy. Jpn. Circ. J. In press.
10. TAKEDA, A., N. TAKEDA, A. SAKATA, Y. ENDO, S. CHIBA, Y. TAKEUCHI, Y. HAYASHI, T. IWAI, A. TAMANURA & H. SUZUKI. 1997. What is the nature of multinucleated giant cells in giant cell myocarditis? Cardiovasc. Pathobiol. **2:** 119–125.

Index of Contributors